CATALYSIS AND INHIBITION OF
CHEMICAL REACTIONS

ENGLAND: BUTTERWORTH & CO. (PUBLISHERS) LTD.
                    LONDON: 88 Kingsway, W.C.2

AFRICA: BUTTERWORTH & CO. (AFRICA) LTD.
                    DURBAN: 33/35 Beach Grove

AUSTRALIA: BUTTERWORTH & CO. (AUSTRALIA) LTD.
                    SYDNEY: 6–8 O'Connell Street
                    MELBOURNE: 473 Bourke Street
                    BRISBANE: 240 Queen Street

CANADA: BUTTERWORTH & CO. (CANADA) LTD.
                    TORONTO: 1367 Danforth Avenue, 6

NEW ZEALAND: BUTTERWORTH & CO. (NEW ZEALAND) LTD.
                    WELLINGTON: 49/51 Ballance Street
                    AUCKLAND: 35 High Street

U.S.A.:   BUTTERWORTH INC.
                    WASHINGTON, D.C.: 7235 Wisconsin Avenue, 14

CATALYSIS AND INHIBITION
OF
CHEMICAL REACTIONS

P. G. ASHMORE, M.A., Ph.D.

Lecturer in Physical Chemistry, University of Cambridge
Fellow and Tutor of Churchill College

LONDON
BUTTERWORTHS
1963

Suggested U.D.C. number : 541·128

Printed in Great Britain by
William Clowes & Sons, Limited, London and Beccles

CONTENTS

PART III HETEROGENEOUS CATALYSIS

PART IV   CATALYSIS AND INHIBITION OF CHAIN REACTIONS

PREFACE

CATALYSED REACTIONS are immensely important in both spontaneous and controlled chemical processes, and there is an abundant output of original papers on all aspects of theory and practice. Many advanced monographs and detailed reference books have appeared recently, and the series *Advances in Catalysis* regularly provides excellent reviews of progress in various specialized fields. However, few general descriptions of current ideas on the catalysis and inhibition of chemical reactions have appeared since the translation in 1937, by H. S. Taylor and R. Spence, of G. M. Schwab's *Katalyse vom Standpunkt der chemischen Kinetik*. I hope my book will provide a similar introduction to our present ideas that will be useful to students of all branches of chemistry.

I have chosen as wide a definition of 'catalysts' as allowed by current use in order to compare and contrast the mechanisms of their action in processes as diverse as enzyme reactions, surface catalyses and polymerizations. In attempting this, I have been sadly aware of a saying attributed to Berzelius, the 'father' of catalysis: 'The Devil may write chemical text-books, for every year the whole thing changes.' It would be folly to pretend that I have extracted the last word from the voluminous literature, but I have attempted to emphasize the points where our ideas are changing. Inevitably, this treatment gives the impression in some sections of uncertainty and even confusion, but I believe this situation to be real. In heterogeneous catalysis, for example, it is hard to find one reaction with a mechanism that is accepted by all who are working on it. Possibly the nearest is the synthesis of ammonia over promoted iron catalysts, but it is significant that the most acceptable mechanism does not follow the schemes, discussed so widely in text-books, which assume that the rate is controlled by a reaction of chemisorbed species on the surface of the catalyst; instead, the *rate of adsorption* of nitrogen controls the rate of synthesis. Again, it has proved extremely difficult to identify the precise sites of reaction on metal surfaces, on enzyme molecules or on stereo-specific Ziegler catalysts, and this has severely handicapped attempts to explain the relative effectiveness of catalysts. Nevertheless, these difficulties and uncertainties provide a challenge and a spur to all investigators.

I have been saved from many errors by the kindness of friends who have read various chapters, and in particular I warmly thank Drs. G. C. Bond, K. McQuillen, V. M. Clark, B. J. Tyler and R. D. A. Lipman. I wish to thank Mr. E. Smith for help in preparing the figures, and the staff of Messrs. Butterworths who have gently impressed upon me a more uniform presentation of the various Sections. I acknowledge with thanks permission from the authors and publishers to reproduce figures and tables from previous publications. I also pay an affectionate tribute to my wife and family who have helped me considerably with references and with the Index, and without whose urging 'that book' would never have been finished.

PART I

INTRODUCTION

CATALYSTS AND CATALYSED REACTIONS

1.1. INTRODUCTION

WHEN Berzelius[1] first put forward the suggestion that some reactions should be classified together as 'catalysed', the emphasis was placed almost entirely upon the nature and amount of the products rather than upon the rate of their formation. It appeared that much more reaction occurred in the presence of the catalysts, which could often be recovered easily from the products and used again. Berzelius thought there was a special force, 'a catalytic force of bodies', which caused this increased yield.

It is still found useful to class some reactions together as catalysed, and to speak of 'catalysts for a reaction'. However, a catalyst does not increase the yield of a reaction but it increases the rate of approach to an equilibrium position which is thermodynamically possible, although difficult of realization, in the absence of the catalyst. This it does by providing 'an alternative and more speedy reaction route', to quote Hinshelwood's definition[2] of a catalysed reaction, which can usually be explained in terms of normal chemical reactions between catalyst and substrate to give intermediates, these eventually yielding the products and regenerating the catalyst. This behaviour is clearly shown in the catalysis of many decompositions in the gas phase by iodine vapour. For example, acetaldehyde decomposes thermally at a rate which can be measured easily at about 450°C. The reaction is probably a chain reaction, although there have been reports of a molecular mechanism. The net reaction is

$$CH_3 \cdot CHO \rightarrow CH_4 + CO$$

The order varies from 2 to $\frac{3}{2}$, and the activation energy from 46 to 50 kcal, depending upon the pressure. The addition of a small proportion of iodine vapour will increase the rate several thousandfold; the catalysed rate is proportional to the concentrations of iodine and of acetaldehyde, and has an activation energy of about 32 kcal. At the start of the catalysed reaction, almost all the iodine disappears, and its concentration remains low until near the end of the reaction, when it is reformed[3]. It seems that a series of fast reactions produces some relatively stable intermediates, probably by a chain mechanism involving iodine atoms. These stable intermediates then slowly yield the products and regenerate the iodine. The catalysed reaction can be represented by the successive reactions:

$$CH_3 \cdot CHO + I_2 \rightarrow CH_3I + HI + CO \qquad \text{(fast reaction)}$$

$$CH_3 + HI \rightarrow CH_4 + I_2 \qquad \text{(slow reaction)}$$

It is rare, however, for the intermediates to be as stable and as obvious as in this example. More often the intermediates are very reactive species, present in low concentrations even relative to the catalyst. They may be saturated compounds or ions or free radicals or atoms, and they may exist in the gas or liquid phase or be bound to a surface. However, it is certain that their behaviour can be explained by their unusual reactivity, and this, in turn, by their structure rather than by any special power peculiar to catalysed reactions. Thus the theory of catalysis deals, firstly, with the identification of the intermediates, the reactions in which they are produced and those they undergo in yielding the products and the catalyst, and, secondly, with the reasons why the kinetic mechanism introduced by the catalyst gives a faster rate than is possible in its absence.

Although this pattern of formation and reaction of intermediates can be discerned in all reactions which would, by common agreement, be classed as catalysed, there is a great diversity of kinetic mechanisms. It is helpful in any systematic study which seeks to explain the faster rates, to consider catalysed reactions in various groups, the mechanisms of all the reactions in one group being alike in kind, even if there is variety in detail. There is much more hope of finding general principles governing catalytic activity in each group than in arriving at any one 'explanation' of catalytic behaviour. With this aim, in this book catalysts and catalysed reactions are examined and discussed in three main groups. The first group contains reactions which proceed in a few simple homogeneous steps involving molecules, ions or free radicals as intermediates. The second contains reactions proceeding in an interfacial layer between two discrete phases, that is, heterogeneously catalysed reactions. The third group contains catalysed chain reactions and, besides its own special features, incorporates some of the phenomena found in the first two groups.

Group I. Catalysed reactions which proceed in a few simple homogeneous steps involving molecules, ions or free radicals as intermediates

Reactions in solution which are catalysed by acids and bases form one large subdivision of this group. These reactions include the hydrolyses, condensations, decompositions and addition reactions important in simple organic preparations. The intermediates have been identified as ionic species usually formed by the extraction of a proton from, or the addition of a proton to, the reactant or 'substrate' molecule, although occasionally a larger charged group is added or removed. The study of these reactions has a long history. Acid-catalysed reactions in aqueous solution were often used in the early attempts to measure systematically the velocities of chemical reactions. Later, there was a close link between these studies of reaction velocity and the embryonic theories of the behaviour of electrolytes in solution; still later, the theory of general acids and bases gained much from the investigations of the catalysis of simple reactions. The mechanisms of catalysis by general acids and bases in aqueous solutions are now well understood and, therefore, introduced early in this book. In other solvents, such as strong acids or organic solvents of low dielectric constant, the pattern of behaviour is not so clear, but the ideas being developed are essentially those encountered in the theories of the mechanisms of heterolytic organic reactions in general.

Another smaller subdivision of this group contains those reactions which involve electron transfer, such as many of the oxidation–reduction reactions of inorganic chemistry which are catalysed by ions capable of existence in several oxidation states. Here the intermediates are usually unstable ions, often of a complex nature, formed by reaction between catalyst, reactant and solvent.

A subdivision of the group, of great extent and importance, consists of enzyme-catalysed reactions. In the past, there has often been conflict between chemist and biologist over the interpretation of these reactions. Thanks to the strenuous efforts of biochemists over the last thirty years, however, the mysterious influence of 'ferments' has been replaced by recognized chemical reactions of enzymes which have been identified as largely, sometimes entirely, protein in character. Here is the story of the 'catalytic force' over again. Nevertheless, a full understanding of the behaviour of enzymes *in vivo* is a distant objective still. Even the simpler task of isolating each of the important enzymes and studying *in vitro* the kinetics of its reaction with appropriate substrates is very complicated. On the one hand, the activity of an enzyme—which on a molecular basis is extremely high—is very sensitive to conditions of temperature, to the pH of the solution and to the addition of traces of 'inhibitors' which seem to block the catalysed reaction path. On the other hand, the enzyme under normal conditions reacts in a series of linked reactions and quasi-equilibria involving many intermediates. Some enzymes are highly specific (for example urease, which will hydrolyse only urea and not substituted ureas), while others will react with only one stereochemical form of optically active substrates; others will react with a range of substrates of similar structure[4].

Group II.   Heterogeneously catalysed reactions

Heterogeneous catalysis occurs whenever the rate of a chemical reaction is enhanced by the presence of an interface between two phases. The surfaces of solids are particularly important as heterogeneous catalysts for reactions between gases or between a gas and a liquid. The problems that have arisen from attempts to use these surfaces to prepare chemicals more speedily and selectively have proved fascinating to chemists and physicists. It is no exaggeration to say that the majority of improvements in utilizing these catalysts for large-scale preparations have come from carefully designed and extensive experiments rather than from the application of chemical theory. The scope of heterogeneous catalysis shows the magnitude of this effort. As indicated in *Table 5.1*, page 107, the catalyses include the synthesis of ammonia from its elements, and its oxidation to nitric oxide and nitric acid; the oxidation of sulphur dioxide to trioxide and the oxidation of hydrocarbons to useful oxygenated products; the various rearrangements, cyclizations and decompositions and polymerizations that occur in the cracking of petroleums; the synthesis of hydrocarbons, alcohols and aldehydes from carbon monoxide and hydrogen; and innumerable hydrogenations and dehydrogenations.

For many years, the theoretical treatment of these catalysed reactions lagged behind the practice, and the practice in turn added little to our theoretical knowledge. The change came with Langmuir's recognition[5] that the intermediates in these reactions are surface compounds formed by the chemisorption of the reactants as ions, radicals or atoms, on the surface of the solid. The precise identification of these intermediates has proved difficult in all cases, and in many heterogeneous reactions the rate-determining step has not been identified with certainty. Quantitative studies of the extent, rate and energies of the chemisorption of gases have helped, and so have measurements of the dipole moment of the adsorbed layer (measured through changes in the work function of the solid) or its electrical conductivity. More recently, infrared absorption studies have been helpful in identifying the type of bond in adsorbed molecules, while field emission and electron microscope techniques have helped to locate the adsorbed fragments in relation to the crystal faces and edges. In the absence of certainty about the mechanisms, it has been impossible to explain in any quantitative manner the catalytic activity of even pure solids, although there are many promising approaches to the problem; it will be some time before the behaviour of the complex surfaces of industrial catalysts is fully understood.

Group III. Catalysed chain reactions

This group of reactions includes thermal decompositions, oxidations and auto-oxidations, halogenations and polymerizations which can proceed by free-radical or ionic mechanisms. Generally the function of the catalyst is to increase the rate of initiation of the chains, for although the catalyst could in principle introduce chain-branching by reacting with one chain centre to give two centres, this behaviour seems rare. In some cases of polymerization, notably with Ziegler catalysts, the catalyst also affects the propagation step to produce a stereoregulated polymer. In some of these catalysed chain reactions the catalyst becomes incorporated in the product, although only in minute proportions. Later in this chapter, some consideration will be given to the propriety of calling this type of mechanism catalysis as is done very commonly. An important feature of all chain reactions is that the rate can be decreased by the addition of inhibitors. These can function as the poisons for heterogeneous catalysts or enzymes, by inactivating the catalyst; but, more often, they act by removing the chain centres themselves. Inhibitors can be useful in slowing unwanted reactions such as the auto-oxidation of oils, the decomposition of substances such as hydrogen peroxide, or the fast reactions leading to knock in petrol engines; and they have also been useful in showing whether a reaction proceeds by a chain mechanism. In many cases, the reactions introduced by the catalysts or inhibitors are heterogeneous, as for the cracking reactions, the polymerizations with some Friedel–Crafts or Ziegler catalysts, or for the termination of chains on the walls of the vessel.

1.2. DEFINITIONS OF CATALYSTS AND CATALYSED REACTIONS

This short survey of the main groups of catalysed reactions has served to indicate the scope of the following chapters and also to emphasize the diversity of catalysts. In view of this diversity, it seems appropriate to examine the definitions of catalysts which have been proposed at various times. The first systematic definitions of catalysts in modern terminology were rather more precise than the definition[2] referred to at the beginning of this chapter. In 1895 Ostwald[6] defined a catalyst as 'any substance which alters the velocity of a chemical reaction without modification of the energy factors of the reaction'. Seven years later he proposed[7] an alternative definition which became widely adopted: 'A catalyst is any substance which alters the velocity of a chemical reaction without appearing in the end product of the reaction.'

These definitions were meant to exclude from the category of catalysts substances which accelerated the rate of a reaction by producing an entirely fresh equilibrium position which could not be attained in the absence of the added substance. A very good example of this behaviour is provided by the action of nitric oxide on the decomposition of nitrogen pentoxide[8]. Nitrogen pentoxide decomposes slowly at room temperature by a complex mechanism involving the unstable intermediate nitrogen trioxide; the slow step is the formation of nitric oxide and oxygen from this nitrogen trioxide, a reaction in which nitrogen dioxide plays some part.

$$N_2O_5 \rightleftharpoons NO_2 + NO_3 \qquad \text{('fast' equilibrium)}$$
$$NO_2 + NO_3 \rightarrow NO + NO_2 + O_2 \qquad \text{(slow step)}$$
$$NO + NO_3 \rightarrow 2NO_2 \qquad \text{(fast reaction)}$$

The nitric oxide is removed rapidly by reaction with nitrogen trioxide, so that neither accumulate. If nitric oxide is added, however, the slow step is not necessary—but then no oxygen will be formed. Thus the decomposition of nitrogen pentoxide is accelerated, but really by reaction with nitric oxide to give only one product, nitrogen dioxide, instead of nitrogen dioxide and oxygen.

$$N_2O_5 \rightarrow N_2O_4 + \tfrac{1}{2}O_2$$
$$N_2O_5 + NO \rightarrow 3NO_2$$

This would not normally be considered as catalysis of the decomposition but as a separate reaction. If one were to include such reactions, catalysis would be equivalent to reactivity, and would cease to have any meaning as a sub-division of reaction kinetics.

Another example of this behaviour is provided by the possibility of preparing benzaldehyde from benzene and carbon monoxide in the presence of aluminium chloride (the Gattermann–Koch reaction). Benzene and carbon monoxide alone will not react to give benzaldehyde, for at room temperatures and above there is an increase of free energy in this reaction[9]. Thus the free energy change at room temperature (ΔG°_{298}) is 2,060 cal and at 100°C, 4,350 cal for the reaction

$$C_6H_{6(l)} + CO_{(g)} \rightleftharpoons C_6H_5 \cdot CHO_{(l)} \qquad (1.1)$$

In the presence of aluminium chloride, however, the benzaldehyde forms a complex with sufficient decrease in the free energy to make feasible the reaction

$$C_6H_{6(l)} + CO_{(g)} + AlCl_{3(s)} \rightarrow C_6H_5 \cdot CHO \cdot AlCl_{3(s)} \qquad (1.2)$$

The value[9] of ΔG°_{298} for this reaction is about -400 cal. However, it would not be useful to class this as an example of catalysis even if the aluminium chloride can be recovered from the complex and used again: the recovery is not a spontaneous process. In contrast, it is proper to speak of the catalysis of the alkylation or acylation of benzene by aluminium chloride. Alkylations generally proceed rapidly in the presence of small proportions of aluminium chloride:

$$C_6H_6 + RCl + AlCl_3 \rightarrow C_6H_5R + HCl + AlCl_3 \qquad (1.3)$$

The function of the aluminium chloride is not the same as in (1.2), as the basic reaction is accompanied by a decrease of free energy and the catalyst is spontaneously regenerated. With acylations, however, a complication arises which,

7

strictly maintained in the literature of chemical kinetics. The distinction will be made for free-radical polymerizations in Chapter 10, but it will not be insisted upon rigorously.

The properties of a catalyst may be summarized as follows. The catalyst increases the rate of approach to an equilibrium position which is chemically and thermodynamically possible in its absence. It must not alter the free energy change of progress from reactants to the equilibrium position by more than a very small proportion of the original value. It should be effective when present in small proportions relative to the reactants. It functions by reacting chemically with one or more of the reactants, and it often exchanges atoms with them. A catalyst or initiator of free-radical polymerizations is often bound in whole or in part into the polymer molecules although in small proportions by weight.

A definition which is in keeping with current use of the term catalyst is: 'A catalyst is a substance which speeds the approach to equilibrium of a given chemical change with only a slight modification of the free energy change of this process.'

1.3. CATALYSTS AND REVERSIBLE REACTIONS

The discussion of catalysts and the definition of catalysts given above lead to an important deduction about their effect on the velocities of the component reactions of a reversible reaction. This deduction was first tested by Van't Hoff[19]. The uncatalysed and the catalysed reactions can be represented as follows:

$$R \underset{k_b}{\overset{k_f}{\rightleftharpoons}} P$$

$$R + C \underset{k_b'}{\overset{k_f'}{\rightleftharpoons}} P + C$$

The ratio of the velocity constants for each reversible reaction is related to the free energy change ΔG° for the reaction, giving the equations:

$$-(\Delta G^\circ) = RT \ln \frac{k_f}{k_b}$$

$$-(\Delta G^\circ)' = RT \ln \frac{k_f'}{k_b'}$$

From the definition of a catalyst, it follows that $(\Delta G^\circ) = (\Delta G^\circ)'$ and so

$$k_f/k_b = k_f'/k_b' \quad \text{or} \quad k_f/k_f' = k_b/k_b' \tag{1.5}$$

Thus any change which the catalyst brings about in the velocity constant of the forward reaction is accompanied by a corresponding change in the velocity constant of the back reaction. It is plain that the factor will not, in general, be a dimensionless number, because it is very unlikely that k_f and k_f' will have the same dimensions.

There is plenty of qualitative evidence that catalysts have similar effects on the forward and backward reactions. For example, good hydrogenation catalysts are known to be good dehydrogenation catalysts. It is less easy to produce quantitative evidence for the relationships (1.5). An indirect test is to show that the equilibrium is independent of the amount or type of catalyst present; this was done by Koelichen[20] for the base-catalysed reaction

$$2CH_3 \cdot CO \cdot CH_3 \rightleftharpoons (CH_3)_2 \cdot C(OH) \cdot CH_2 \cdot CO \cdot CH_3$$

and by Bodenstein and Pohl[21] for the oxidation of sulphur dioxide in the presence of various solid catalysts. A more direct test is to evaluate the velocity constants k_f' and k_b' separately from measurements of the initial velocities of the catalysed reaction starting from each side of the reaction. Thus Van't Hoff[22] examined Knoblauch's results[23] on the formation and hydrolysis of ethyl acetate in the presence of hydrochloric acid, and found k_f'/k_b' equal to 2·94 at a temperature where the equilibrium constant was measured as 2·84. Maron and La Mer[24] examined the catalysis by acids and bases of the reversible reaction (see Chapter 2)

$$\underset{R'}{\overset{R}{\diagdown}}CHNO_2 + base \underset{k_b}{\overset{k_f}{\rightleftharpoons}} \underset{R'}{\overset{R}{\diagdown}}C\!:\!NOO^- + \text{conjugate acid}$$

They compared the measured values of k_f with those calculated from the measured values of k_b and the value of the equilibrium constant of the reaction; the equilibrium constant was in turn calculated from the measured ionization constant of the nitroparaffin and the dissociation constant of the conjugate acid catalyst. Some results at $0°C$ show the extent of agreement:

Conjugate acid	$k_{f\text{calc}}$	$k_{f\text{meas}}$
H_3O	$2{\cdot}24 \times 10^{-9}$	$1{\cdot}4 \times 10^{-9}$
$CH_2Cl \cdot COOH$	$1{\cdot}36 \times 10^{-5}$	$1{\cdot}1 \times 10^{-5}$
$CH_3 \cdot COOH$	$2{\cdot}3 \times 10^{-4}$	$2{\cdot}1 \times 10^{-4}$

However, the kinetics of reactions under 'initial' conditions, i.e. those far from equilibrium, are not always the same as the kinetics of the same reactions near equilibrium. As explained in more detail later, most catalysed reactions proceed by a number of steps involving the formation and reaction of intermediates, and it is quite possible for one step to be rate-determining under equilibrium conditions and another step to be so in the initial stages of reaction[25-27]. Consequently it is not surprising that there are relatively few accurate tests of the relationships. In fact, the relationships can be looked upon as based securely on the principle of microscopic reversibility. If the mechanism chosen for the reversible reaction holds under the conditions of the kinetic measurements, and the velocity constants are correctly evaluated from the kinetic data, then the relationships should hold; if they do not do so within the accuracy expected of the measurements, then the chosen mechanism may be wrong. It is interesting to note, therefore, that the comparison of kinetic and equilibrium data forms an important part of the tests of the validity of mechanisms proposed for various complex reactions. This can be illustrated by two examples, one taken from enzyme kinetics and one from the reversible dissociation of gaseous nitrosyl chloride.

11

The reversible reaction

$$\text{Fumarate ion} + H_2O \rightleftharpoons \text{malate ion}$$

is catalysed by the enzyme fumarase. The equilibrium constant of the reaction can be determined from spectrophotometric measurements of the concentration of the fumarate ion. In the presence of the enzyme (E) an intermediate (X) is formed:

$$H_2O + F^{2-} + E \underset{k_2}{\overset{k_1}{\rightleftharpoons}} X \underset{k_4}{\overset{k_3}{\rightleftharpoons}} M^{2-} + E$$

In spite of the complexity of this set of reversible reactions, the equilibrium constant can be calculated (as explained in Chapter 3) from measurements of: (i) the initial velocities of the forward reaction with different initial concentrations of fumarate ions, and (ii) the initial velocities of the reverse reaction with different initial concentrations of malate ions. In this way Alberty[28, 29] has shown that the spectrophotometric equilibrium constant is equal to 4·45 and the kinetic equilibrium constant is $4·2 \pm 0·4$, in very satisfactory agreement. However, it is necessary to point out that the same results would be obtained with any number of intermediates in equilibrium with X.

The reversible dissociation of nitrosyl chloride can be represented by the equation

$$2NOCl \underset{2}{\overset{1}{\rightleftharpoons}} 2NO + Cl_2$$

and until recently it was thought that the reactions concerned were the homogeneous reactions 1 and 2. A detailed analysis[30] of the effects of inert gases has shown that a free-atom mechanism also operates and becomes more important at higher temperatures. It can be summarized by the homogeneous reaction steps:

$$NOCl + M \underset{4}{\overset{3}{\rightleftharpoons}} NO + Cl + M$$

$$NOCl + Cl \underset{6}{\overset{5}{\rightleftharpoons}} NO + Cl_2$$

together with a heterogeneous contribution which does not concern this discussion. Thus the formation of the intermediate chloride is catalysed by inert gases. The velocity constants k_3 and k_4 have been evaluated independently from the kinetic data, and the equilibrium constant for reactions 3, 4 can be computed from other known equilibrium constants (those of the over-all reaction 1, 2 and of the dissociation $Cl_2 \rightleftharpoons 2Cl$), with the following results:

Temperature °C	$K_{3,4}$	k_3/k_4 with $M = CO_2$ $\times 10^{16}$ mole cm^{-3}	k_3/k_4 with $M = Cl_2$
250	24	40	30
300	560	910	700

For this type of catalysis, too, the agreement between the kinetic and the equilibrium determinations is reasonably satisfactory and provides support for the chosen mechanism.

1.4. SIMPLE GENERAL MECHANISMS FOR CATALYSED REACTIONS

Although there is great diversity of reaction mechanisms among catalysed reactions, as emphasized earlier in this chapter, the common pattern of formation of reactive intermediates suggests that there may be certain simple reaction schemes which can explain many of the features of catalysed reactions, and which can be elaborated to explain the detailed behaviour of particular catalysts and substrates. Indeed, some very useful conclusions emerge from an examination of two simple mechanisms of wide applicability. One mechanism is particularly suited to catalysed reactions in groups I and II, and the other to reactions in group III. In order to present these mechanisms in the simplest way, it is convenient to consider the catalysis of a reaction

$$R+R' \rightarrow P$$

which eventually proceeds almost to completion, so that the reverse reaction can be ignored.

Mechanism I

In this mechanism, the reaction proceeds in a few steps in which the intermediate is formed and reacts. A very common pattern is:

$$R+C \underset{k_2}{\overset{k_1}{\rightleftharpoons}} X$$

$$X+R' \overset{k_3}{\longrightarrow} P+C$$

Here, X represents one or two intermediates which can revert to reactant and catalyst by reaction 2 or be converted to product and catalyst by reaction 3. As explained earlier, it is unusual for X to be a stable substance or stable substances, and usually reaction 2 or reaction 3 or both are fast compared with reaction 1. If reaction 2 is fast, but reaction 3 is slow, the first pair of reactions establish a concentration of X very near the equilibrium concentration expected for this pair of reversible reactions, the slow formation of the product having little effect. Such an intermediate is known as an *Arrhenius intermediate*, because it resembles the activated intermediate which Arrhenius suggested is formed from the reactants in all reactions. It is perhaps helpful to point out that R and C first form a transition state or activated complex which then forms X; X is *not* the activated complex itself. A different situation, and different kinetics, result if both reactions 2 and 3 are fast, for the reaction tends to 'run through' to the products; the intermediate is then called a *Van't Hoff intermediate*. The kinetics appropriate to each of these situations turn out to be particular cases of a common rate equation which can be derived for the set of reactions 1 to 3. In this derivation, it is assumed that the concentration of the intermediate X rapidly reaches a low, stationary value so that the net rate of formation of X can be set equal to zero; the conditions under which this holds have been examined by Benson[31]. Thus

$$\frac{d[X]}{dt} = k_1[C][R] - k_2[X] - k_3[X][R'] = 0$$

Therefore

$$[X] = \frac{k_1[C][R]}{k_2+k_3[R']}$$

13

and

$$\frac{d[P]}{dt} = k_3[X][R'] = \frac{k_1 k_3[C][R][R']}{k_2 + k_3[R']} \tag{1.6}$$

Equation (1.6) gives the rate, at any time, in terms of the 'local' concentrations. It is not easy to test the observed rates against such an equation unless the individual concentrations have been separately determined experimentally. The only time when these concentrations are known may be very early in the reaction, i.e. under 'initial' conditions. With complicated reactions, such as those which include reversible reactions, it is essential to use these initial rate methods, especially in the early stages of an investigation.

An equation of slightly different form is used for the initial rates. This equation allows for the fact that the initial combination of C and R may remove an appreciable amount of C and R. If so, it is better[32] to put $[C] = [C]_0 - [X]$ and $R = [R]_0 - [X]$ *before* solving for [X]. Then, neglecting terms involving $[X]^2$, it can readily be shown that

$$V_0 = \left(\frac{d[P]}{dt}\right)_{t=0} = \frac{k_1 k_3[R]_0[R']_0[C]_0}{k_2 + k_1[C]_0 + k_1[R]_0 + k_3[R']_0} \tag{1.7}$$

Now in all important catalysed reactions, $[C]_0 \ll [R]_0 \sim [R']_0$ so that the second term in the denominator can be neglected in comparison with the third and the equation reduces to

$$V_0 = \frac{k_1 k_3[R]_0[R']_0[C]_0}{k_2 + k_1[R]_0 + k_3[R']_0} \tag{1.8}$$

The concentration of the intermediate X cannot be greater than $[C]_0$, no matter how large $[R]_0$ is made. Consequently it is always possible, in principle, to make $k_1[R]_0$ comparable with k_2. However, the relative magnitude of $k_3[R']_0$ determines whether the intermediate is of the Arrhenius or of the Van't Hoff type, and considerably alters the kinetics.

If $k_3[R']_0 \ll k_2 \sim k_1[R]_0$, X is an Arrhenius intermediate and the rate equation becomes

$$V_0 = \frac{k_1 k_3[R]_0[R']_0[C]_0}{k_2 + k_1[R]_0} \tag{1.9}$$

The rate will be proportional to $[C]_0$ and to $[R']_0$ but of variable order in $[R]_0$. The rate must be less than the rate of reaction 1, because the factor $k_1[R]_0/k_2 + k_1[R]_0$ must be less than unity.

If $k_3[R']_0 \gg k_2 \sim k_1[R]_0$, and X is a Van't Hoff intermediate, the rate of reaction becomes

$$V_0 = k_1[C]_0[R]_0 \tag{1.10}$$

and is equal to the rate of the first reaction of the sequence.

Equation (1.8) is of the same form as the expression derived by Briggs and Haldane[33] for enzyme-catalysed reactions, and equation (1.9) is the simpler form derived earlier by Michaelis and Menten[34].

Equation (1.8) predicts that when all the concentrations are low, the reaction may well be first order in each of the concentrations $[C]_0$, $[R]_0$ and $[R']_0$. If then any one of these concentrations is increased in successive experiments in which the initial rates are measured, the initial rates will tend to a maximum value, as shown for a reactant S in *Figure 4.1*. This means that the order with respect to $[R]_0$ will change slowly from one to zero. Similar behaviour could happen with $[R']_0$; but it is unlikely to happen with $[C]_0$, for this will generally be much less than the other concentrations, and the order in catalyst concentration is usually one.

Very valuable information about the individual velocity constants k_1, k_2 and k_3 has been obtained for various reactions from a study of the way the initial rate changes as the concentration of each reactant is changed. Thus, if $[R]_0$ is increased, the maximum initial rate is equal to $k_3[R']_0[C]_0$, while if $[R']_0$ is increased the maximum initial rate is then $k_1[R]_0[C]_0$. Thus k_1 and k_3 can be determined. Moreover, if the variation of the initial rate V_0 with the change of $[R]_0$ (when $[R']_0$ and $[C]_0$ are kept constant) is considered in more detail, equation (1.7) can be rewritten as

$$\frac{1}{V_0} = \frac{k_2 + k_1[C]_0 + k_3[R']_0}{k_1 k_3 [R']_0 [C]_0 [R]_0} + \frac{1}{k_3 [R']_0 [C]_0} \tag{1.11}$$

Now $k_3[R']_0[C]_0$ is the *maximum* initial rate V_{max}, and so

$$\frac{1}{V_0} = \frac{k_2 + k_1[C]_0 + k_3[R']_0}{k_1 V_{max} [R]_0} + \frac{1}{V_{max}} \tag{1.12}$$

Thus a plot of $1/V_0$ against $1/[R]_0$ should give a straight line, with intercept $1/V_{max}$ on the $1/V_0$ axis. This allows the determination of V_{max} without using extremely high values of $[R]_0$. The slope of the plot, with the values of k_1, k_3 and the initial fixed concentrations $[R']_0$ and $[C]_0$, allows the determination of k_2. These useful plots are called Lineweaver–Burk plots[35] and have been widely used in studies of enzyme kinetics (see Chapter 4).

Many examples of catalysed reactions which follow the rate laws (1.6) or (1.8), or their simplified forms, are known among acid–base reactions, enzyme reactions and heterogeneous reactions. Extensions of the simple treatment outlined here can be made to allow for the presence of inhibitors or poisons, for inhibition by one of the reactants or by the products, or for further activation of the catalyst by the product or the similar effect of extra catalysis by the product (autocatalysis). It is not profitable to discuss these extensions in any more detail here; they will be considered in later chapters when individual reactions are discussed.

Before leaving the simple mechanism I, however, one point which has been mentioned deserves further emphasis. It is that the rate of the catalysed reaction proceeding in a few steps cannot exceed the rate of the initial reaction between reactant and catalyst and will usually be lower than it. It follows that for catalysis to occur, the catalyst must react with one reactant more rapidly than that reactant normally decomposes or reacts with the other reactant. The first step of the mechanism holds the key to the behaviour of the catalyst and is the one to be compared with the uncatalysed reaction. This may seem a trivial conclusion, but it is actually the reason for the importance of several 'laws' of catalytic behaviour such as the Brönsted relationship between the velocity constant of the reaction catalysed by an acid and the dissociation constant of that acid, and it is also the reason for the need to study carefully the rate of chemisorption in heterogeneous catalysis where in the limit, the rate

Ia. Arrhenius intermediate:

$$\text{Rate} = \frac{k_1 k_3}{k_2}[C]_0[R]_0[R']_0 \tag{1.21}$$

Ib. Van't Hoff intermediate:

$$\text{Rate} = k_1[C]_0[R]_0 \tag{1.22}$$

The chain carriers of mechanism II lead to the cases IIa and IIb.

IIa. Linear termination:

$$\text{Rate} = \frac{k_p k_i[C]_0[R]_0[R']_0}{k_t[I]_0} \tag{1.23}$$

IIb. Mutual termination:

$$\text{Rate} = \frac{k_p[R]_0[R']_0 \sqrt{(k_1[C]_0)}}{\sqrt{k_m}} \tag{1.24}$$

Assuming that each of the rate constants of the individual steps can be represented by the usual Arrhenius expression $k = A \exp(-E/RT)$, the over-all activation energies of the catalysed reactions would be expected to be:

Ia: $E_1 + E_3 - E_2$ Ib: E_1

IIa: $E_p + E_i - E_t$ IIb: $E_p + \frac{1}{2}(E_i - E_m)$

Thus the measured activation energy of the catalysed reaction is equal to that of the rate-determining step only in case Ib. In case Ia, the activation energy of the rate-determining step E_3 is increased by the difference between the activation energies of the reactions 1 and 2, that is, by the heat absorbed (ΔE) in the forward reaction, as can be seen from the energy diagram for the reaction path (*Figure 1.1*). Incidentally, from the diagram alone it might be

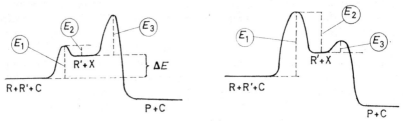

Figure 1.1

anticipated that the effective activation energy would be E_3 in case Ia, by analogy with case Ib where the higher activation energy is the only one to count. An example of behaviour like Ia which is perhaps reasonably familiar, is the decomposition of a gas such as nitrous oxide over a gold surface; the apparent activation energy is equal to that of the surface reaction *plus* the heat *absorbed* in the adsorption of the gas—or, as it is more usually expressed, that of the surface reaction *less* the heat *evolved* upon adsorption. In cases IIa and IIb it generally happens that E_i is fairly large (although usually smaller than E_i for the *uncatalysed* reaction), E_p is fairly small, and E_t and E_m are very small. In IIa, therefore, the apparent activation energy will be rather greater than that of the step involving the catalyst, while in case IIb it may be considerably less.

It often happens that the activation energy of a catalysed reaction is less than that of the uncatalysed reaction. Some examples for various types of catalyst are included in *Table 1.1*. However, it is not correct to assume that the relative rates of reaction are given by the simple ratio $\exp (E_u - E_c)/RT$. In the first place, the concentration of catalyst in a homogeneously catalysed reaction, or the extent of the surface in a heterogeneously catalysed reaction, will affect the rate; in fact, it is difficult to find a logical basis for comparing a homogeneous and a heterogeneous rate. In the second place, if reactions in

Table 1.1.   The activation energies of uncatalysed and catalysed reactions

Reaction	Catalyst	Temperature °C	Activation energy (E) kcal	Reference
Decomposition of acetaldehyde	None	450	46–50	37
	Iodine vapour	320	32·5	37
Decomposition of nitrous oxide	None	900	58·5	38
	Iodine vapour	900	49·0	38
	Platinum surface	700	32·5	39
	Gold surface	900	29·0	40
Decomposition of hydrogen peroxide in aqueous solutions	None	0–50	17–18	41
	Iodide ion	0–50	13–14	41
	Ferric ion	0–50	10	41
	Platinum surface	0–50	11–12	41
	Enzyme catalase	0–50	1–2	41
$H_2 + D_2 \rightleftharpoons 2HD$	None	600–750	60	42
	Copper foil	310–350	23	43
	Silver foil	400–460	16	43
	Gold foil	330–750	14	43
ortho-$H_2 \rightleftharpoons$ para-H_2	None	700–800	60	42
	Gold foil	above 300	17·5	44
		50–230	5·2	44
	Copper	100–300	10–12	44
	Palladium	−100–60	4	45
Inversion of sucrose	Hydrogen ion	25	25	46
	Invertase (malt)	25	13	46

the same phase are compared, it will still be found that the pre-exponential factors of the catalysed and uncatalysed reactions are of different dimensions. For these reasons, it is better to examine the velocities of a particular reaction in the presence of various catalysts of a similar type, and to see whether these velocities are controlled by changes in the activation energy alone. When this is done, it is immediately apparent that changes in the activation energy are not the only causes of changed rates.

Table 1.2 gives some examples of large changes in the velocities of reactions catalysed by different acids or bases or solid surfaces without much change in the activation energy from catalyst to catalyst. The data for the acid-catalysed

19

REFERENCES

[1] BERZELIUS, J. J. *Jber. chem. UntersuchAmt. Hannover* 1836, **15**, 237

[2] HINSHELWOOD, C. N. *The Structure of Physical Chemistry*: Oxford University Press, London, 1951, p. 398

[3] FAULL, R. F. and ROLLEFSON, G. K. *J. Amer. chem. Soc.* 1936, **58**, 1755

[4] DIXON, M. and WEBB, E. C. *Enzymes*: Longmans Green, London, 1955, Ch. VI

[5] LANGMUIR, I. *Phys. Rev.* 1916, **8**, 149; *J. Amer. chem. Soc.* 1916, **38**, 2221

[6] OSTWALD, W. *Chemische Betrachtungen, Aula* 1895, No. 1

[7] OSTWALD, W. *Phys. Z.* 1902, **3**, 313

[8] FROST, A. A. and PEARSON, R. G. *Kinetics and Mechanism*: Wiley, New York, 1953, chapter 11H

[9] DILKE, M. H. and ELEY, D. D. *J. chem. Soc.* 1949, p. 2601

[10] ROBERTS, I. and HAMMETT, L. P. *J. Amer. chem. Soc.* 1937, **59**, 1063

[11] BENFRY, O. T. *J. Amer. chem. Soc.* 1948, **70**, 2163

[12] BELL, R. P. *Acid–Base Catalysis*: Oxford University Press, London, 1941

[13] FAIRBROTHER, F. *J. chem. Soc.* 1937, p. 503

[14] GOULD, E. S. *Mechanism and Structure in Organic Chemistry*: Holt, New York, 1959, p. 447

[15] WINTER, E. R. S. *Chemisorption* (Ed. W. E. Garner): Butterworth, London, 1957, p. 189

[16] DAINTON, F. S. and SUTHERLAND, G. B. B. M. *J. Amer. chem. Soc.* 1952, **74**, 2027

[17] ARNETT, L. M. and PETERSON, J. H. *J. Amer. chem. Soc.* 1952, **74**, 203

[18] FLORY, P. J. *Principles of Polymer Chemistry*: Cornell University Press, Ithaca, N.Y., 1953, p. 108

[19] VAN'T HOFF, J. H. *Lectures on Theoretical and Physical Chemistry* (Trans. R. A. Lehfeldt) Vol. I: Arnold, London, pp. 204, 214

[20] KOELICHEN, K. *Z. phys. Chem. (Leipzig)* 1900, **33**, 129

[21] BODENSTEIN, M. and POHL, W. *Z. Elektrochem.* 1905, **11**, 373

[22] VAN'T HOFF, J. H. *Lectures on Theoretical and Physical Chemistry* (Trans. R. A. Lehfeldt) Vol. I: Arnold, London, p. 204

[23] KNOBLAUCH, O. *Z. phys. Chem. (Leipzig)* 1897, **22**, 268

[24] MARON, S. H. and LA MER, V. K. *J. Amer. chem. Soc.* 1939, **61**, 2018

[25] SCHWAB, G. M. *Catalysis* (Trans. H. S. Taylor and R. Spence): Macmillan, London, 1937, p. 15

[26] FROST, A. A. *J. chem. Educ.* 1941, **18**, 272

[27] MANES, M., HOFER, L. J. E. and WELLER, S. *J. chem. Phys.* 1950, **18**, 1355

[28] ALBERTY, R. A. *Advanc. Enzymol.* 1955, **17**, 1

[29] ALBERTY, R. A. and BOCK, R. M. *J. Amer. chem. Soc.* 1953, **75**, 1921

[30] ASHMORE, P. G. and SPENCER, M. *Trans. Faraday Soc.* 1959, **55**, 1868

[31] BENSON, S. W. *J. chem. Phys.* 1952, **20**, 1605; *Foundations of Chemical Kinetics*: McGraw-Hill, New York, 1960

[32] LAIDLER, K. J. and SOCQUET, I. M. *J. phys. Chem.* 1950, **54**, 519
LAIDLER, K. J. *Chemical Kinetics*: McGraw-Hill, New York, 1950, p. 278

[33] BRIGGS, G. E. and HALDANE, J. B. S. *Biochem. J.* 1925, **19**, 338

[34] MICHAELIS, L. and MENTEN, M. L. *Biochem. Z.* 1913, **49**, 333

[35] LINEWEAVER, H. and BURK, D. *J. Amer. chem. Soc.* 1934, **56**, 658

[36] ASHMORE, P. G. and CHANMUGAM, J. *Trans. Faraday Soc.* 1953, **49**, 254

[37] HINSHELWOOD, C. N. *The Kinetics of Chemical Change*: Clarendon Press, Oxford, 1940, p. 244

[38] MUSGRAVE, F. F. and HINSHELWOOD, C. N. *Proc. R. Soc. A* 1932, **137**, 25

[39] HINSHELWOOD, C. N. and PRICHARD, C. R. *J. chem. Soc.* 1925, p. 327

[40] HINSHELWOOD, C. N. and PRICHARD, C. R. *Proc. R. Soc. A* 1925, **108**, 211

[41] LAIDLER, K. J. *The Chemical Kinetics of Enzyme Action*: Oxford University Press, London, 1958, p. 199

REFERENCES

[42] FARKAS, A. and FARKAS, L. *Proc. R. Soc. A* 1935, **152**, 124

[43] MIKOVSKY, R. J., BOUDART, M. and TAYLOR, H. S. *J. Amer. chem. Soc.* 1954, **76**, 3814

[44] ELEY, D. D. and ROSSINGTON, D. R. *Chemisorption* (Ed. W. E. Garner): Butterworth, London, 1957, p. 137

[45] COUPER, A. and ELEY, D. D. *Disc. Faraday Soc.* 1950, **8**, 172

[46] LAIDLER, K. J. *Chemical Kinetics*: McGraw-Hill, New York, 1950, p. 310

[47] BELL, R. P. *Acid–Base Catalysis*: Oxford University Press, London, 1941, p. 176

[48] FRIESS, S. L. *J. Amer. chem. Soc.* 1953, **75**, 323

[49] OUELLET, L., LAIDLER, K. and MORALES, M. F. *Arch. Biochem. Biophys.* 1952, **39**, 37

[50] HINSHELWOOD, C. N. and TOPLEY, B. *J. chem. Soc.* 1923, p. 1014

[51] BEECK, O. *Rev. mod. Phys.* 1945, **17**, 61

[52] HINSHELWOOD, C. N. *The Kinetics of Chemical Change*: Clarendon Press, Oxford, 1940, pp. 257 *et seq.*

[53] CREMER, E. *Advanc. Catalys.* 1955, **7**, 75

[54] SCHWAB, G. M. *Advanc. Catalys.* 1950, **2**, 251

HOMOGENEOUS CATALYSIS BY
PROTON TRANSFER

2.1. INTRODUCTION

A WIDE variety of reactions is catalysed by substances which are now classed as acids or bases. The most familiar of these reactions take place in aqueous solution, where the acid HA and its conjugate base A^- are in reversible equilibrium with the solvent according to the equation

$$HA + H_2O \rightleftharpoons H_3O^+ + A^-$$

The reactions include hydrolyses, decompositions and molecular rearrangements. Some typical examples are assembled in *Table 2.1* under headings that are explained later in this chapter.

The investigation of the kinetics of these reactions is complicated by the behaviour of the solvent as both an acid and a base. Although some of these reactions were studied in the earliest systematic work on reaction velocities, detailed interpretations of the mechanisms have changed with advancing knowledge. An extensive body of information about the velocity constants of the steps in many of these kinetic mechanisms is available[1-4], and some of it will be mentioned in the discussion of the more important mechanisms later in this chapter.

Less is known about reactions in other solvents[2,3], but they are very important in preparative chemistry and much work is in progress to elucidate their mechanisms. Some solvents, like the alcohols, resemble water in behaving as an acid and a base, but have lower dielectric constants which may complicate the kinetics by favouring association complexes. Other solvents, like the hydrocarbons, are unable to gain or lose a proton; in these *aprotic* solvents, there are fewer molecular and ionic species to act as catalysts, but this advantage is usually offset by the complications due to their low dielectric constants. An interesting group of these reactions are the alkylations, isomerizations and related reactions catalysed by the Friedel–Crafts catalysts. It appears that these reactions depend upon proton transfers and are best interpreted as examples of acid–base catalysis. In many respects, the very similar catalysts used to initiate ionic polymerizations behave as acid–base catalysts, but as the polymerizations involve chain reactions, they are considered in Part IV of this book. The reactions called 'cracking' reactions, which include decompositions, isomerizations, alkylations and hydrogenation–dehydrogenation reactions, also occur over acid catalysts and are certainly initiated by acid–base reactions, but the subsequent steps as well as the initiation reaction are surface reactions, and so these 'cracking' reactions are considered in Part III.

2.2.   EARLY WORK ON ACID–BASE REACTIONS AND CATALYSES

The hydrolysis or inversion of cane sugar and the hydrolysis of esters were among the first acid-catalysed reactions to be studied. Ostwald[5] collected together data on the velocity of hydrolysis of methyl acetate and of cane sugar in normal solutions of acids, and showed that the velocity relative to that in normal hydrochloric acid (with the same concentration of reactant) closely paralleled the relative conductivity of the acids. Ostwald and Arrhenius considered that the conductivities changed with the extent of dissociation of the acid, according to the dissociation constant, and that the parallel behaviour showed that the rates probably changed with the concentration of the hydrogen ion common to the solutions. The velocity of reaction was therefore set proportional to the concentrations of reactant and of hydrogen ion:

$$\text{velocity of reaction} = k[\text{H}^+][\text{reactant}]$$

When the reactant concentration is held constant, it follows that the logarithm

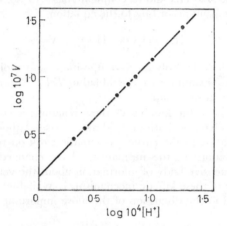

Figure 2.1.   Velocity of hydrolysis V of
ethyl acetate[6] as a function of $[\text{H}^+]$
The line has unit slope

of the velocity should be a linear function of the logarithm of the hydrogen ion concentration or the pH:

$$\log(\text{velocity}) = \log[\text{H}^+] + \text{constant} \tag{2.1}$$

Later work confirmed this equation, as can be seen from *Figure 2.1* where some of Dawson and Lowson's results[6] on the acid-catalysed hydrolysis of ethyl acetate are plotted.

Further detailed investigations showed that some reactions were catalysed to a significant extent by hydrogen ions only, some by hydroxyl ions only and some by both. When hydrogen ion is the only effective catalyst, the reaction is said to be an example of *specific acid catalysis*, while catalysis by hydroxyl ion only is classed as *specific base catalysis*. Strictly speaking, the active acid species in water is not the hydrogen ion but the acid H_3O^+, and the reaction should be called *specific hydronium ion catalysis*. In other solvents that ionize to give a proton, *specific lyonium ion catalysis* takes place. However, the first terms mentioned are common and have been used to classify the catalysed reactions shown in *Table 2.1*. The hydrolyses of carboxylic esters, of amides and of

28

γ-lactones are catalysed by both hydrogen ion and hydroxyl ion, and the velocity of reaction for esters can be expressed as:

$$\text{velocity of reaction} = k_{\text{cat}}[\text{reactant}]$$

where:

$$k_{\text{cat}} = k_0 + k_{\text{H}_3\text{O}^+}[\text{H}_3\text{O}^+] + k_{\text{OH}^-}[\text{OH}^-] \qquad (2.2)$$

The values of the velocity constants k_0, $k_{\text{H}_3\text{O}^+}$ and k_{OH^-} vary with the temperature and the nature of the reactant, of course. The value of $k_0[\text{reactant}]$ represents the *spontaneous* velocity and will be discussed later; it is small compared with the other terms. Dawson[7] correlated several investigations of the hydrolysis of ethyl acetate at $25\,^\circ\text{C}$, and found $k_{\text{OH}^-} = 6\cdot5$ l. mole^{-1} min^{-1}, $k_{\text{H}_3\text{O}^+} = 6\cdot45 \times 10^{-3}$ l. mole^{-1} min^{-1} and $k_0 = 10^{-8}$ min^{-1}. In the mutarotation of glucose, Hudson[8] found $k_{\text{OH}^-} = 9\cdot750$, $k_{\text{H}_3\text{O}^+} = 0\cdot258$ and $k_0 = 0\cdot0096$ (units as before); for the depolymerization of the dimer of dihydroxyacetone, Bell and Baughan[9] found $k_{\text{OH}^-} = 4\cdot03 \times 10^7$, $k_{\text{H}_3\text{O}^+} = 1\cdot72$ and $k_0 = 0\cdot00255$ (units as before). The last two investigations were carried out in the absence of acids other than hydrogen ion and bases other than hydroxyl ion, although both showed general acid–base catalysis.

The hydrogen and the hydroxyl ion concentrations are related by the expression

$$[\text{H}_3\text{O}^+][\text{OH}^-] = K_w$$

where K_w, the *ionic product* for water, can be taken as constant at a constant temperature. (It does vary with the ionic strength, but this variation can be ignored for the present.) By substituting $[\text{OH}^-] = K_w/[\text{H}_3\text{O}^+]$ in the expression for k_{cat}, it can be readily shown that k_{cat} passes through a minimum value as $[\text{H}_3\text{O}^+]$ increases, such that $[\text{H}_3\text{O}^+]_{\min} = (k_{\text{OH}^-}K_w k_{\text{H}_3\text{O}^+})^{1/2}$. By measuring $k_{\text{H}_3\text{O}^+}$ from the velocities in strongly acid solutions and k_{OH^-} from those in alkaline solutions, and determining $[\text{H}_3\text{O}^+]_{\min}$, the ionic product K_w could be calculated. This was an important link between the theories of the mechanism of reactions and of conductivity when the measurements were first made; later and more accurate determinations of K_w by this method agree well with values obtained from conductivity measurements[7].

As more work was done on these catalysed reactions, difficulties arose with the simple interpretation in terms of catalysis by hydrogen and hydroxyl ions alone. It was eventually found that some reactions were catalysed by undissociated molecules of substances capable of yielding protons, and this was called *general acid catalysis*. However, this was not established until the rather puzzling effects on the rate of changing the ionic strength of the reacting mixture had been elucidated. There are now known to be two main effects:

(*i*) If the hydrogen ions are formed by the dissociation of a weak acid, as in a buffer solution, changes in the concentration of the buffer mixture or the addition of a neutral salt will alter the activities a of the species present, and a change in the degree of dissociation will result. The activities of the acid HA, its anion A$^-$ and the hydrogen ion must obey the relationship

$$a_{\text{H}_3\text{O}^+}\, a_{\text{A}^-}/a_{\text{HA}} = K_{\text{Th}} = \text{constant}$$

Therefore

$$\frac{c_{\text{H}_3\text{O}^+}\, c_{\text{A}^-}\, \gamma_{\text{H}_3\text{O}^+}\, \gamma_{\text{A}^-}}{c_{\text{HA}}\gamma_{\text{HA}}} = \text{constant}$$

Table 2.1. Examples of acid and base catalysis in aqueous solution

Type of catalysis	Brief title of reaction	Equation of reaction	Reaction number
Specific acid	Inversion of cane sugar	$C_{12}H_{22}O_{11} + H_2O = C_6H_{12}O_6 + C_6H_{12}O_6$	1
	Decomposition of diazoacetic ester	$N_2{:}CH{\cdot}COOC_2H_5 + H_2O = CH_2OH{\cdot}COOC_2H_5 + N_2$	2
	Hydrolysis of acetals	$R_1CH(OR_2)_2 + H_2O = R_1{\cdot}CHO + 2R_2OH$	3
	Hydration of unsaturated aldehydes	$CH_2{:}CH{\cdot}CHO + H_2O = CH_2OH{\cdot}CH_2{\cdot}CHO$	4
Specific base	Cleavage diacetone–alcohol	$CH_3{\cdot}CO{\cdot}CH_2{\cdot}C(OH)(CH_3)_2 = 2(CH_3)_2{\cdot}CO$	5
	Decomposition of nitrosoacetoneamine	$\begin{array}{c} CH_2{\cdot}C(CH_3)_2 \\ CO \quad\quad N{\cdot}NO \\ CH_2{\cdot}C(CH_3)_2 \end{array} \longrightarrow \begin{array}{c} CH{\cdot}C(CH_3)_2 \\ CO \\ CH{\cdot}C(CH_3)_2 \end{array} + N_2 + H_2O$	6
	Claisen condensation	$C_6H_5{\cdot}CHO + CH_3{\cdot}CHO = C_6H_5{\cdot}CH{:}CHO + H_2O$	7
	Michael condensation	$R_1R_2C{:}CH{\cdot}CO{\cdot}R_3 + CH_2(COOC_2H_5)_2 = R_1R_2C\!\!\begin{array}{l} CH(COOC_2H_5)_2 \\ CH_2{\cdot}CO{\cdot}R_3 \end{array}$	8
	Aldol condensation	$2R{\cdot}CH_2{\cdot}CHO = R{\cdot}CH_2{\cdot}CH(OH){\cdot}CHR{\cdot}CHO$	9
Specific acid and base	Hydrolysis of γ-lactones	$\underset{\underline{\qquad\; O \;\qquad}}{CH_2{\cdot}CH_2{\cdot}CH_2{\cdot}C}{:}O + H_2O = CH_2OH{\cdot}CH_2{\cdot}CH_2{\cdot}COOH$	10
	Hydrolysis of amides	$R{\cdot}CO{\cdot}NH_2 + H_2O = R{\cdot}COONH_4$	11
	Hydrolysis of esters	$R_1{\cdot}COOR_2 + H_2O = R_1{\cdot}COOH + R_2OH$	12

Table 2.1—continued

General acid	Decomposition of acetaldehyde hydrate	$CH_3 \cdot CH(OH)_2 = CH_3 \cdot CHO + H_2O$	13
	Hydrolysis of *o*-esters	$HC \cdot (OC_2H_5)_3 + H_2O = H \cdot COOC_2H_5 + 2C_2H_5OH$	14
	Formation of nitro-compound	$CH_2{:}NO_2{}^- + acid = CH_3 \cdot NO_2 + base^-$	15
	Decomposition of diazoacetate ion	$N_2{:}CH \cdot COO^- + H_2O = CH_2OH \cdot COO^- + N_2$	16
General base	Decomposition of nitramide	$NH_2NO_2 = N_2O + H_2O$	17
	Bromination of nitromethane	$CH_3 \cdot NO_2 + Br_2 = CH_2BrNO_2 + HBr$	18
	Ionization of nitromethane	$CH_3 \cdot NO_2 + base = CH_2{:}NO_2{}^- + acid^+$	19
	Aldol with acetaldehyde	$2CH_3 \cdot CHO = CH_3 \cdot CH(OH) \cdot CH_2 \cdot CHO$	20
General acid and base	Mutarotation of glucose	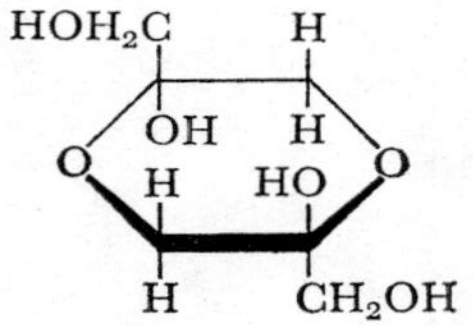 (glucose ring structure) ⇌ (glucose ring structure)	21
	Halogenation, exchange, racemization of ketones	$R \cdot CO \cdot CH_3 + X_2 = R \cdot CO \cdot CH_2X + XH$	22
	Addition to carbonyl	$R_1 \cdot CO \cdot R_2 + NH_2OH = R_1R_2 \cdot COH \cdot NHOH$	23
	Depolymerization of di-dihydroxy-acetone	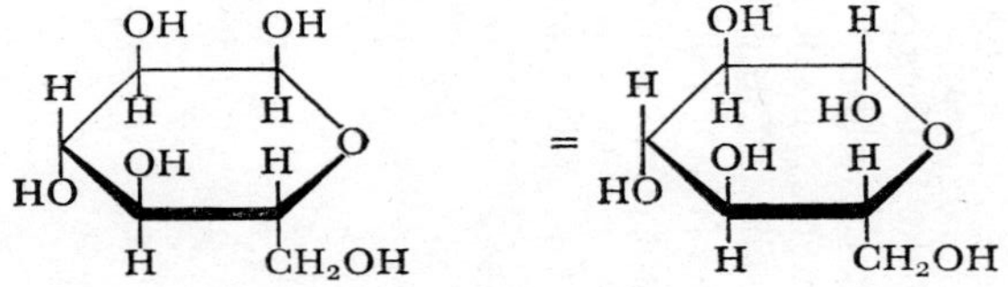 (ring structure) $= 2(CH_2OH)_2CO$	24

31

Whenever the activity coefficients γ of the ions are increased by some change in the ionic strength μ of the solution ($\mu = \frac{1}{2}\sum_i c_i z_i^2$) it follows that the concentrations of H_3O^+ and A^- must *decrease*; the effect on the species HA is small. A good example of this secondary salt effect is provided by the results of a study[10] of the hydrolysis of acetal in the presence of formate buffer:

$$CH_3 \cdot CH(OC_2H_5)_2 + H_2O \rightarrow CH_3 \cdot CHO + 2C_2H_5OH$$

If the buffer concentration is lowered but the ionic strength is kept constant by the addition of the correct amount of sodium chloride, the catalytic constant k_{cat} is not altered (first three lines of *Table 2.2*). But if the ionic strength is allowed to fall, the activity coefficients rise in these dilute solutions and so the $[H_3O^+]$ falls, with a marked effect on k_{cat}. The value of $[H \cdot COO^-]$ is kept equal to $[H \cdot COOH]/2 \cdot 96$.

Table 2.2. Secondary salt effect[10] on k_{cat}

$[H \cdot COO^-]$	μ	k_{cat} min^{-1}
0·100	0·100	0·0410
0·060	0·100	0·0405
0·033	0·100	0·0407
0·075	0·075	0·0378
0·050	0·050	0·0348
0·020	0·020	0·0309
0·010	0·011	0·0288

In another investigation of the hydrolysis of diazoacetic ester, catalysed by hydrogen ions from acetic acid, the rate of reaction changed by about 30 per cent when potassium nitrate was added to a 0·1M solution.

$$N_2:CH \cdot COOC_2H_5 + H_2O \rightarrow CH_2(OH) \cdot COOC_2H_5 + N_2$$

In general, if the acid has charge z positive units, and ionizes

$$H_2O + HA^{z+} \rightleftharpoons H_3O^+ + A^{(z-1)+}$$

the thermodynamic dissociation constant K_{Th} is given by the expression

$$K_{Th} = \frac{[H_3O^+][A^{(z-1)+}]}{[HA^{z+}]} \cdot \frac{\gamma_{H_3O^+} \gamma_{A^{(z-1)+}}}{\gamma_{HA^{z+}}}$$

By using the appropriate Debye–Hückel expression for each activity coefficient γ, it follows that

$$\log \frac{[H_3O^+][A^{(z-1)+}]}{HA^{z+}} = \text{constant} - \frac{2\alpha(z-1)\sqrt{\mu}}{1+\sqrt{\mu}}$$

where α is close to 0·5 for aqueous solutions near 25°C and μ is the ionic strength. There is thus no effect if the acid has charge +1, e.g. with the ammonium ion, NH_4^+. With other acids, this secondary salt effect occurs even if the catalysed reaction takes place between hydrogen ion and an uncharged molecule.

(*ii*) Changes in the ionic strength can also alter the velocity constant of any reaction between ions. A successful theoretical treatment of this effect was first suggested by Brönsted[11]; a later treatment by Bjerrum[12] can be looked upon as a particular case of the more general treatment by the transition state theory. The ions are in equilibrium with a transition complex X which carries the sum of the charges of the ions (z_1, z_2 represent the charges):

$$R_1^{z_1} + R_2^{z_2} \rightleftharpoons X^{z_1 + z_2}$$

Thus

$$K_{eq} = \frac{a_X}{a_{R_1} a_{R_2}} = \frac{[X]}{[R_1][R_2]} \cdot \frac{\gamma_X}{\gamma_{R_1} \gamma_{R_2}}$$

The rate of reaction is supposed to be proportional to the concentration of X with a velocity constant k_X. Hence the conventional rate constant k_{vel} and k_X are related through the equations

$$\text{rate} = k_{vel}[R_1][R_2] = k_X[X] = k_X K_{eq}[R_1][R_2] \frac{\gamma_{R_1} \gamma_{R_2}}{\gamma_X}$$

Therefore

$$k_{vel} = k_X K_{eq} \frac{\gamma_{R_1} \gamma_{R_2}}{\gamma_X}$$

If k_X and K_{eq} are independent of the ionic strength, k_{vel} will vary as the activity coefficients change with the ionic strength μ. In general, in dilute solution with reaction between ions of *like* charge, it is found that k_{vel} increases as μ increases, but it decreases for reactions between ions of opposite charge. This is in agreement (quantitative in very dilute solution) with predictions made from the equation of Debye and Hückel connecting γ and μ. In more concentrated solutions, however, no useful theoretical treatment can be given.

This *primary salt effect* is more direct, but smaller, than the secondary salt effect. Thus, the changes in the catalytic velocity constants are usually less than 5 per cent when salts are added to 0·1M concentrations, increasing for hydrogen ion catalysis, sometimes increasing and sometimes decreasing for hydroxyl ion catalysis.

The theoretical treatment of rates where the ionic strength is allowed to vary is obviously very complex. The procedure adopted in the earlier work was to keep the ionic strength constant by the judicious addition of salts, and to work in as dilute solutions as possible. In recent years, interest has turned to rates in solutions of higher ionic strength. It will be convenient to deal separately with the two ranges of ionic strength.

2.3. GENERAL ACID–BASE CATALYSIS IN DILUTE AQUEOUS SOLUTION

By conducting experiments in which these effects of ionic strength were eliminated, it became clear that species other than hydrogen ion and hydroxyl ion can catalyse some reactions. This shows up on plots like those in *Figure 2.2* as a prolonged flat portion, cutting short the lines of slope ± 1 (top curve). Such species are the *general acids and bases*[2] originally defined by Lowry and Brönsted. An acid is defined as a species that can give up a proton to another species: the remaining anion of the acid is a base, termed the conjugate base

3—c.   33

of the acid, for it can accept a proton to re-form the acid. Often the solvent is the acceptor of the proton from the acid, thus:

$$HSO_4^- + H_2O \rightleftharpoons H_3O^+ + SO_4^{2-}$$

The species HSO_4^- and SO_4^{2-} are thus conjugate acid and base. Other examples are:

acid: H_3O^+, H_2O, $CH_3 \cdot COOH$, NH_4^+, $[Fe(H_2O)_6]^{3+}$, $H_2PO_4^{2-}$

base: H_2O, OH^-, $CH_3 \cdot COO^-$, NH_3, $[Fe(OH)(H_2O)_5]^{2+}$, HPO_4^{3-}

In general acid catalysis, a species such as $CH_3 \cdot COOH$ behaves as the hydronium ion in specific acid catalysis, by providing a proton for the reactant

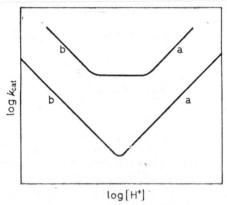

Figure 2.2. Schematic plots of log k_{cat} for specific acid catalysis (branches a), specific base catalysis (branches b) and general catalysis (flat portions) as log [H⁺] changes

molecule to form the intermediate ion. Similarly, in general base catalysis, a species such as $CH_3 \cdot COO^-$ accepts a proton from a reactant molecule. It would appear that the catalytic constant for a reaction showing general acid and general base catalysis with an acid HA and its conjugate base A^- should be expressed as the sum of appropriate terms, e.g. in aqueous solution:

$$k_{cat} = k_0 + k_1[H_3O^+] + k_2[OH^-] + k_3[HAc] + k_4[Ac^-] \tag{2.3}$$

and it appears that k_0 may include the solvent concentration, the solvent acting as a weak acid or base. An example will illustrate the general procedure for determining the separate velocity constants.

A reaction which shows general acid–base catalysis is the mutarotation of glucose (*Table 2.1*). The velocity of mutarotation has been studied by a variety of experimental methods. The change in specific rotation, from $[\alpha]_D = 113°$ for fresh solutions of α-glucose to $52°$ for the equilibrium mixture

$$\alpha\text{-glucose} \underset{k_b}{\overset{k_f}{\rightleftharpoons}} \beta\text{-glucose}$$

makes polarimetric methods[13,14] suitable; volume changes[15] and refractive index changes have also been used. The net rate of change from the α-form to the β-form is given by

$$- \frac{d[\alpha]}{dt} = k_f[\alpha] - k_b[\beta] = k_f[\alpha] - k_b([\alpha_0] - [\alpha])$$

The equilibrium concentration of the α-form, $[\alpha_{eq}]$, is also given by

$$k_f[\alpha_{eq}] = k_b([\alpha_0] - [\alpha_{eq}])$$

Therefore

$$- \frac{d([\alpha] - [\alpha_{eq}])}{dt} = (k_f + k_b)([\alpha_0] - [\alpha_{eq}])$$

and so

$$- \ln ([\alpha] - [\alpha_{eq}]) = (k_f + k_b)t + \text{constant}$$

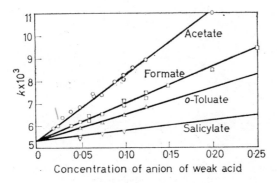

Figure 2.3. Catalysis by basic anions in the muta-rotation of glucose[15]

Thus $k_f + k_b$ can be determined from the velocity experiments and k_f/k_b from the equilibrium measurements, and so k_f and k_b can be calculated. Each of these velocity constants is composite, of the form shown above for k_{cat}. The next step is to determine the separate catalytic constants k_0, k_1 and so on. k_1 can readily be determined by working in solutions of pH less than 4, k_0 by working with solutions of pH between 4 and 6. The determination of k_2 is difficult because it is so great, but dilute solutions of hydroxides and ammonium buffers have been used. The relative values of $k_0 : k_1 : k_2$ are about $1 : 26 : 10^6$ at 25°C. In order to evaluate k_3 and k_4, measurements are made in buffer solutions of pH 4 to 6, in which [HAc] and [Ac$^-$] are varied but the ratio [HAc]/[Ac$^-$], r, is kept constant, and the ionic strength is kept constant by adding a neutral salt. The value of k_{cat} is then given by

$$k_{cat} = \text{constant} + (rk_3 + k_4)[\text{Ac}^-] \tag{2.4}$$

That plots of k against anion concentration are linear is shown for several buffers in *Figure 2.3*, taken from the work of Brönsted and Guggenheim[15]. From the slopes S, S' of two lines with different buffer ratios r, r', the equations

$$rk_3 + k_4 = S$$
$$r'k_3 + k_4 = S'$$

allow the calculation of k_3 and k_4.

The methods used to evaluate the separate catalytic coefficients for the mutarotation can be applied, with suitable modifications, to other reactions. Some of these show general acid and base catalysis, while others show only general acid or general base catalysis; a few examples are given in *Table 2.1*.

Examination of the catalytic constants led to a general relationship of considerable interest and utility. This connects the catalytic constant (k_{cat}) for an acid-catalysed reaction with the dissociation constant (K_A) of the acid, and the

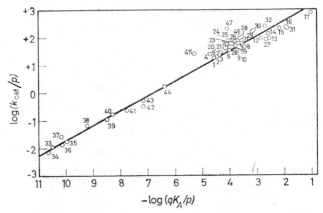

Figure 2.4. Brönsted plot for the general acid-catalysed dehydration of acetaldehyde hydrate[18]

catalytic constant for a base-catalysed reaction with the dissociation constant of the acid conjugate to the base. For catalyses by monobasic acids such as ammonium, anilinium and phenol (and substituted aniliniums and phenols) the relationship is

$$\log k_{cat} = \alpha \log K_A + \beta \tag{2.5}$$

α and β are constants for the particular reaction studied, and are both positive and less than unity. This relationship may be compared with the expression for *specific* acid catalysis (2.1)

$$\log k_{cat} = \log [H^+] + \text{constant}$$

Brönsted and Pedersen suggested[16,17] that for polyfunctional acids and bases, the relationship should compare k_{cat} and K_A per functional group. If the number of *separate* groups in the acid which can yield a proton is p, and the number of different atoms in the conjugate base which can accept a proton is q, then the appropriate relationships are

For general acid catalysis:

$$\log \frac{k_{cat}}{p} = \alpha' \log \frac{qK_A}{p} + \beta' \qquad (2.6)$$

For general basic catalysis:

$$\log \frac{k_{cat}}{q} = \alpha'' \log \frac{p}{qK_{Aconj}} + \beta'' \qquad (2.7)$$

These 'Brönsted relationships' hold over wide ranges of k_{cat} and K_A with very fair accuracy, and have been tested by many investigations. The results of a recent investigation[18] into the acid-catalysed dehydration of acetaldehyde hydrate, followed with a dilatometer, are shown in *Figure 2.4*.

There is some arbitrariness about the values chosen for p and q. For example, the acid NH_4 could conceivably have $p=1$ or $p=4$; it is found that $p=1$ gives better agreement with the relationship, as well as appearing more realistic, and the general rule is to ignore multiple proton sites on the *same* central atom. For the carboxylate ion $R \cdot COO^-$, the values 1 or 2 could be chosen for q, according to the choice of structure (*I*) or the mesomeric formulation (*II*)

(I)   *(II)*

Here the value 2 gives better results and fits present ideas upon the structure of the ion. Two other examples may be given; for the ion, $H_2PO_4^-$ with conjugate base, HPO_4^{2-}, $p=2$ and $q=3$; for the ion $HOOC \cdot COO^-$, $p=1$ and $q=4$.

Table 2.3. Brönsted relationships in the base-catalysed decomposition of nitramide[2]

Catalyst	p	q	K_A	$k_{cat(obs)}$	$k_{cat(calc)}$
Bases with two negative charges: $k_{cat}/q = 2 \cdot 07 \times 10^{-5} (p/qK_A)^{0 \cdot 87}$					
Secondary phosphate ion	2	3	$5 \cdot 8 \times 10^{-8}$	86	85
Succinate ion	1	4	$2 \cdot 4 \times 10^{-6}$	$1 \cdot 8$	$2 \cdot 0$
Malate ion	1	4	$7 \cdot 8 \times 10^{-6}$	$0 \cdot 72$	$0 \cdot 68$
Tartrate ion	1	4	$4 \cdot 1 \times 10^{-5}$	$0 \cdot 165$	$0 \cdot 163$
Oxalate ion	1	4	$6 \cdot 8 \times 10^{-5}$	$0 \cdot 104$	$0 \cdot 100$
Bases with one negative charge: $k_{cat}/q = 7 \cdot 2 \times 10^{-4} (p/qK_A)^{0 \cdot 80}$					
Trimethylacetate ion	1	2	$9 \cdot 4 \times 10^{-6}$	$0 \cdot 83$	$0 \cdot 90$
Acetate ion	1	2	$1 \cdot 8 \times 10^{-5}$	$0 \cdot 50$	$0 \cdot 51$
Benzoate ion	1	2	$6 \cdot 5 \times 10^{-5}$	$0 \cdot 19$	$0 \cdot 19$
Salycilate ion	1	2	$1 \cdot 0 \times 10^{-3}$	$0 \cdot 021$	$0 \cdot 021$
Monochloroacetate ion	1	2	$1 \cdot 4 \times 10^{-3}$	$0 \cdot 016$	$0 \cdot 017$
Bases with no charge: $k_{cat}/q = 1 \cdot 70 \times 10^{-4} (p/qK_A)^{0 \cdot 75}$					
p-Toluidine	1	1	$7 \cdot 0 \times 10^{-6}$	$1 \cdot 16$	$1 \cdot 24$
m-Toluidine	1	1	$1 \cdot 5 \times 10^{-5}$	$0 \cdot 64$	$0 \cdot 70$
p-Chloraniline	1	1	$9 \cdot 1 \times 10^{-5}$	$0 \cdot 21$	$0 \cdot 18$
m-Chloraniline	1	1	$3 \cdot 0 \times 10^{-4}$	$0 \cdot 081$	$0 \cdot 074$
o-Chloraniline	1	1	$2 \cdot 1 \times 10^{-3}$	$0 \cdot 018$	$0 \cdot 017$

Table 2.3 shows some extracts from the extensive tables of kinetic data given by Bell[2]. For a given reaction, α' (or α'') changes slightly with the charge type of the catalyst, while β' (or β'') varies more widely. Bell has also given[19] an interesting table in which he estimates the relative contributions made by H_3O^+, H_2O and $CH_3 \cdot COOH$ to an acid-catalysed reaction; he shows that the main catalysis is due to the solvent when α is near zero, to the hydrogen ion when α is near one, and to general acids when α takes intermediate values. It appears from this analysis that specific catalysis is not a unique phenomenon, but that specific catalysis and the absence of catalysis are the two extremes of general acid–base catalysis. The same conclusion will emerge from a study of the mechanisms of various reactions.

2.4. PROTON TRANSFER REACTIONS

It is clear from the previous sections that acid–base catalysis in aqueous solution consists of transfers of a proton between reactants and the conjugate acids

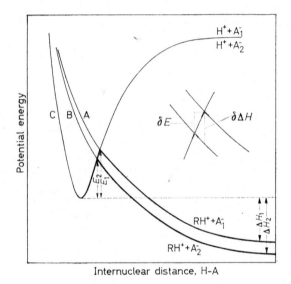

Internuclear distance, H-A

Figure 2.5. Potential energy changes during proton transfer from two acids HA_1 and HA_2 to reactant R

and bases formed by the solvent and the catalysts. For the catalyst to be regenerated, there must be at least two such transfers, but only one of these will usually control the rate of the catalysed reaction. In studies of the reaction mechanism of a catalysed reaction, attempts are made to formulate the transfer reactions and any labile intermediates, and to select the rate-determining step to account for the observed reaction kinetics.

The relative rates of proton transfers from a series of acids HA_1, HA_2, . . . to the reactant R can be examined on the basis of the transition state theory if it is assumed that an elementary transfer can be regarded as a three-centre reaction; that is, any effect of the solvent on this reaction is ignored. If the acids are all of similar type, for example a series of monobasic carboxylic acids, then their potential energy curves for the dissociation into H^+ and A^- can be superposed at their minima, and can be represented by the single curve C in *Figure 2.5*. This is crossed by the repulsion curve of the species RH^+ and A_1^- (A) and that of the species RH^+ and A_2^- (B). The thicker lines then represent the reaction paths for the changes

$$(1) \ R + HA_1 \rightarrow RH^+ + A_1^- \quad \text{and} \quad (2) \ R + HA_2 \rightarrow RH^+ + A_2^-$$

and the difference in activation energy is δE and the difference in heats of reaction, $\delta\Delta H$. If the repulsion curves are nearly parallel for the series of acids, then δE will always be proportional to $\delta\Delta H$. However, if the reactions (1) and (2) are compared with the dissociation reactions of the acids in the solvent S, which are

$$S + HA_1 \rightarrow SH^+ + A_1^- \quad \text{and} \quad S + HA_2 \rightarrow SH^+ + A_2^-$$

it seems likely that ΔH will change in the same way for the transfers and for the dissociations and that $\Delta H \propto \Delta H_{\text{Diss}}$. Thus

$$\delta E \propto \delta\Delta H \propto \delta\Delta H_{\text{Diss}}$$

Now the activation energy can be linked to the velocity constant by the Arrhenius equation (see p. 18 where k, A and E are defined), which in its simplest integrated form is

$$\ln k = \text{constant} - E/RT$$

If changes in k when going from one acid catalyst to another are due solely to changes in E, then $\delta E = -RT\delta \ln k$. With similar assumptions about K_A, the acid dissociation constant and ΔH_{Diss} it can be shown that

$$\delta\Delta H_{\text{Diss}} = -RT\delta \ln K_A$$

Combination of the relationships then gives

$$\frac{\delta \ln k}{\delta \ln K_A} = \frac{\delta E}{\delta\Delta H_{\text{Diss}}} = \alpha, \quad \text{where } \alpha < 1$$

Hence $\ln k = \alpha \ln K_A + \text{constant}$, which is the Brönsted relationship. With the drastic assumptions made, this derivation cannot be regarded as a proof of its validity. The treatment emphasizes that the catalysts should be of similar structure and charge type, for otherwise their potential energy curves will not be similar.

The assumption that changes in k are due solely to changes in the activation energy can, of course, be checked experimentally. It turns out to be true for a series of very closely related compounds. In the alkaline hydrolysis of esters of type $C_6H_4X \cdot COOC_2H_5$, in 85 per cent aqueous alcohol, *meta-* and *para-* substituted X groups do give linear relationships between $\log k$ and E of the correct slope $(-2 \cdot 303RT)$, but *ortho-*derivatives fall off the line[20,21].

Similarly, there is a fair fit to the line of slope $-2 \cdot 303RT$ between $\log k_{\text{cat}}$ and E for the base-catalysed decomposition of nitramide, as shown in *Figure 2.6*, and the Brönsted relationship holds for the catalysed reactions, as would be expected from the theoretical treatment just developed. It is perhaps significant that the mechanism of the catalysed decomposition is particularly simple, as

The rapid reversible reaction $B+H_2O \rightleftharpoons BH^+ +OH^-$ means that $[B]$ and $[BH^+]$ are always related by the equation $[BH^+][OH^-]=K_B[B]$. The rate of the slow step is $k_{slow}[R^-][R_1]$ and the first equilibrium gives $[R^-][BH^+]=K_{eq}[RH][B]$. Hence the rate of the catalysed reaction is

$$\text{rate} = k_{slow}K_{eq}\frac{[RH][B][R_1]}{[BH^+]} = k_{slow}\frac{K_{eq}}{K_B}[RH][OH^-][R_1] \qquad (2.8)$$

The reaction thus shows a specific base catalysis. This appears to happen for the cleavage of diacetone alcohol (*Table 2.1*, reaction 5), the aldol condensation for higher aldehydes (reaction 9) and the Claisen (7), Michael (8) and Perkin reactions. (The Perkin reaction resembles the Claisen, but uses acetic anhydride with potassium acetate as the source of the catalyst.)

The alkaline hydrolysis of esters, which is sometimes referred to as a specific base-catalysed reaction, is really a displacement reaction (see section 2.6).

The two patterns which have just been discussed are really limiting cases of the mechanism I discussed in Chapter 1 (see p. 13).

$$RH+B \underset{k_2}{\overset{k_1}{\rightleftharpoons}} R^- +BH^+$$

$$R^- +R_1 \overset{k_3}{\longrightarrow} \text{products}$$

If $k_3[R_1]>k_2[BH^+]$, then k_1 becomes rate determining and we have the first pattern; if the reverse holds, then the second pattern follows.

In many acid-catalysed reactions, the reactant and an acid (which could, of course, be hydronium ion) come rapidly to an equilibrium and there follows a slow proton transfer from the products of this equilibrium. With this pattern, the reaction shows general acid catalysis:

$$R+HA \overset{\text{rapid}}{\underset{\text{rapid}}{\rightleftharpoons}} RH^+ +A^-$$

$$RH^+ +B \overset{\text{slow}}{\longrightarrow} \text{product}+BH^+$$

The base B could be identical with A^-, and the concentrations of acids and bases remain virtually constant because of rapid equilibria like

$$A^- +BH^+ = AH+B$$

If K_1 is the equilibrium constant for the first equilibrium, and K_2 for the second, the rate of reaction is $k_{slow}[RH^+][B]$ which gives

$$\text{rate} = k_{slow}K_1K_2[R][BH^+] = K[R][A] \qquad (2.9)$$

A similar result follows if the initial equilibrium involves hydrogen ion as the acid; K_2 is then the dissociation constant of the acid BH^+. The reaction is thus classed as general acid catalysis, although it can be looked upon as a disguised base catalysis. A base and an acid are both required, although in aqueous solution this will be automatically ensured. A well-known example of this requirement is furnished by the work of Lowry and Faulkner[23] upon the mutarotation of tetramethylglucose. This is catalysed in aqueous solution by pyridine and also by *m*-cresol, but in pure dry pyridine, which is a moderately strong base giving a very weak acid (the pyridinium ion) rotation does not occur, nor does it in pure dry *m*-cresol which is a moderately strong acid whose anion is a very weak base. In a mixture of the solvents, however, rotation occurred readily, showing the requirement of both an acid and a base in keeping with the above mechanism. Similarly, in aqueous solutions of pyridine or cresol, water molecules can supply the acid or base missing in the pure solvents.

Another very interesting observation on the catalysis of mutarotation reactions has been described by Swain and Brown[24]. They examined the effectiveness of various catalysts on the mutarotation of tetramethylglucose in benzene. In agreement with the work of Lowry and Faulkner, Swain and Brown found that neither pyridine nor phenol alone was very effective, but a mixture of the two was a powerful catalyst. The rate of reaction was proportional to the concentrations of the sugar, the pyridine and the phenol. In addi-

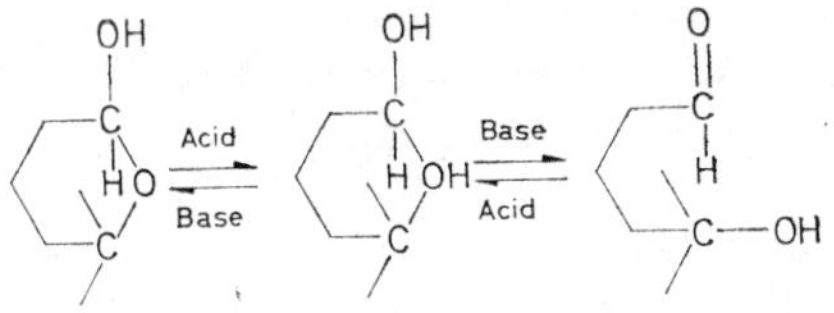

(III)

tion, they made the significant discovery that 2-hydroxypyridine was a better catalyst than an equivalent mixture of the pyridine and the phenol. This was not due to increase in the base or acid strength, relative to the separate catalysts, for the 2-hydroxypyridine is a weaker base than pyridine and a weaker acid than phenol. It seems very likely that the groups in the substituted pyridine are in some spatial relationship that favours the reaction, perhaps by allowing simultaneous attack of acid and base groups. With separate acid and base, the reactions can be depicted as *(III)*. After formation of the open-chain aldehyde, the reverse reactions lead to mutarotation. With the bifunctional

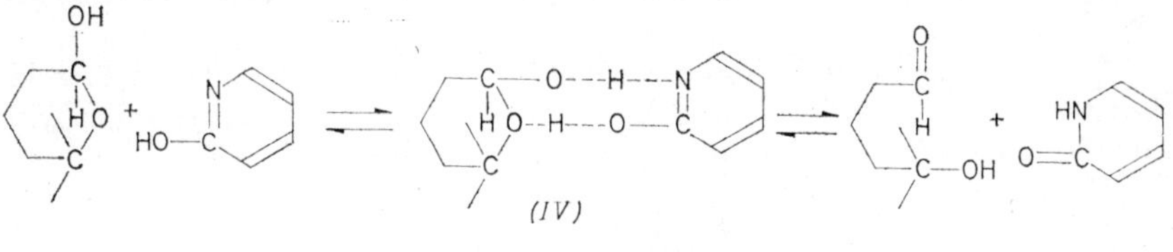

(IV)

catalyst, the first two steps may be occurring simultaneously through a complex *(IV)*. This idea of bifunctional catalysts, or of the simultaneous action of several 'catalytic points', is extremely important. As will be seen in Chapter 4, it forms the basis of current ideas about the function of 'active sites' in enzymes. In the hydrolysis of esters it has been emphasized by Laidler[25], who envisages the simultaneous attack of an acid species and a water molecule. In modified form, it appears in heterogeneous catalysis in the VCI mechanism (see page 175), and also in current views of many hydrogenation or exchange reactions.

In the acid-catalysed halogenation of ketones, it is thought[21] that the enol form of the ketone is formed by two equilibria:

$$R_1COCH_3 + HA \underset{}{\overset{k_1}{\rightleftharpoons}} \left[\begin{array}{c} OH \\ | \\ R_1C \\ | \\ CH_3 \end{array} \right]^+ + A^-$$

$$\left[\begin{array}{c} OH \\ | \\ R_1C \\ | \\ CH_3 \end{array} \right]^+ + A^- \overset{k_2}{\rightleftharpoons} R_1C(OH){:}CH_2 + HA_2$$

followed by rapid reaction of the enol form with halogens. The halogen is very unlikely to react rapidly with the positive ion which results from the step k_1. However, either step k_1 or step k_2 in the formation of the enol form could be rate-determining. The experimental evidence is in favour of k_2 being the slow step. Thus, with optically active ketone there is a rapid initial change of rotation followed by a slow racemization; the initial rapid change could be due to the change in reaction k_1 being rapid. Also, if k_1 is the rate-determining step in the halogenation, then there should be a Brönsted relationship between the velocity constant for the halogenation and the base-constant of the ketone (or the acid dissociation constant of its anion), for the ketone is acting as a weak base. This was tested with several ketones and the same acid catalyst, and a very poor fit was found; it was concluded that k_1 is not the rate-determining step. It would also be expected from knowledge of rate-determining steps that the rearrangement of bonds of the keto-structure in reaction k_2 would make it slower than the reaction in k_1. We can thus consider the mechanism of enolization as a slightly more complicated variation of the general mechanism.

Besides accounting for observations of the acid-catalysed mutarotation of glucose and substituted glucoses (*Table 2.1*, reaction 21) and the acid-catalysed enolization and subsequent halogenation, racemization or exchange of ketones (reaction 22), this mechanism appears to be successful for the acid-catalysed dehydration of acetaldehyde hydrate (reaction 13), the depolymerization of the dimer of dihydroxyacetone (reaction 24) and the acid-catalysed addition of hydrazine, hydroxylamine and semicarbazides to the carbonyl group (reaction 23).

When the prior equilibrium mechanism involves the reactant and an acid, but the rate-determining step is not a proton transfer but is a reaction with another molecule such as water, the scheme becomes:

$$R + HA \overset{rapid}{\rightleftharpoons} RH^+ + A^-$$

$$RH^+ + H_2O \overset{slow}{\longrightarrow} products$$

In addition, there is the dissociation of the acid which rapidly reaches equilibrium $HA + H_2O \rightleftharpoons H_3O^+ + A^-$ with a dissociation constant given by $K_A = [H_3O^*][A^-]/[HA]$. Thus:

$$\begin{aligned} rate &= k_{slow}[RH^+][H_2O] \\ &= k_{slow}K_{eq}[H_2O][R][HA]/[A^-] \\ &= k_{slow}K_{eq}[H_2O][R][H_3O^+]/K_A \end{aligned} \quad (2.10)$$

Thus the reaction shows specific acid catalysis. This mechanism applies to the inversion of cane sugar (*Table 2.1*, reaction 1), the hydrolysis of diazoacetic ester (reaction 2), the hydrolysis of acetals (reaction 3) and the hydrolysis or alcoholysis of esters, although additional equilibria may be involved in some examples. The hydrolysis of esters deserves further mention.

2.6. HYDROLYSIS OF ESTERS[21]

The heterolytic cleavage of an ester could occur at either of two bonds, at the acyl–oxygen bond or the alkyl–oxygen bond; the cleavage could be unimolecular, or bimolecular with the help of a base such as hydroxyl ion acting on the ester itself (under basic conditions) or on its conjugate acid (in acid solution). There are thus eight possible mechanisms! Of these, the two bimolecular, acyl–oxygen fission mechanisms are by far the most common. Unimolecular acyl fissions and bimolecular alkyl fissions are rare. The two unimolecular mechanisms involving alkyl–oxygen fission occur with the esters of certain alcohols which readily form carbonium ions. Davies and Kenyon[26] have recently reviewed the conditions under which the alkyl–oxygen heterolysis occurs. They suggest it is favoured if: (*i*) any possible (nucleophilic) attaching species is weak, that is, if no strong bases are present; (*ii*) the alcohol group readily releases electrons to the alkyl oxygen atom, and (*iii*) the acyl group strongly attracts electrons. Consequently A_{Al^1} and B_{Al^1} mechanisms occur in weakly basic or acidic solutions with esters of alcohols such as benzhydrol and α-methylallyl alcohol. With the substituted allyl alcohols, under mild alkaline conditions, partial rearrangement occurs; with the ester of an optically active alcohol, under similar conditions, racemization occurs. These and other observations confirm that the step controlling the rate of reaction is

$$R \cdot CO \cdot OR' \rightarrow R \cdot CO_2^- + R'^+$$

Again, in weakly acid solutions in $H_2^{18}O$, t-butyl acetate yields labelled t-butyl alcohol, showing alkyl–oxygen cleavage; rearrangements and racemizations can occur as in weakly basic solutions.

That acyl–oxygen heterolysis is usual in the basic hydrolysis of esters was shown by Polanyi and Szabo[27] by using water enriched in ^{18}O. The result was a labelled carboxylate ion and an unlabelled alcohol. The kinetics were of the second order. The reaction is probably:

$$^{18}OH^- + \overset{\displaystyle O}{\overset{\|}{\underset{\underset{\displaystyle CH_3}{|}}{C}}} - OC_5 - H_{11} \xrightarrow{\text{slow}} H^{18}O - \overset{\displaystyle O}{\overset{\|}{\underset{\underset{\displaystyle CH_3}{|}}{C}}} + OC_5H_{11}^-$$

$$\xrightarrow{\text{fast}} {}^{18}O \cdot CO \cdot CH_3^- + C_5H_{11}OH$$

Older evidence that the alkyl–oxygen bond remained intact was provided by the absence of racemization in the products of the basic hydrolysis of secondary-alcohol esters; if the bond broke, the absence of racemization could only be explained by the unlikely event of two configurational inversions.

Later it was shown that acyl–oxygen fission occurred in the acid-catalysed reaction, as demonstrated by the reactions with methyl hydrogen succinate[28]

$$HOOC \cdot CH_2 \cdot CH_2 \cdot CO \cdot OC_3H_5 + H^{18}OH$$

$$\xrightarrow{H^+} HOOC \cdot CH_2 \cdot CH_2 \cdot CO^{18}OH + CH_3OH$$

and with butyrolactone

$$\underset{\displaystyle H_2C\!\!-\!\!-\!\!-\!\!C\!\!=\!\!O}{\overset{\displaystyle \overset{H_2}{\underset{\displaystyle H_2C}{C}}\diagdown}{O}} + H^{18}OH \xrightarrow{H^+} HO \cdot CH_2 \cdot CH_2 \cdot CH_2 \cdot CO^{18}OH$$

These two principal mechanisms are termed B_{Ac^2} and A_{Ac^2}, respectively, showing in the first the basic conditions, the fission of acyl–oxygen and the second-order reaction with a bimolecular mechanism; in the acid conditions, with acyl fission, the slow step is seen, by inspection of the mechanism (see page 50), to involve water. It is not easy to demonstrate the participation of water as proposed, in aqueous solution; for example, solutions of esters in acetone, on the addition of water in small amounts, do show rates of hydrolysis proportional to the water concentration, but this may be due to an effect of the water on the dielectric constant of the mixed solvent, with a consequent effect on the rate. A better test is provided by studying the reaction in fairly strong acid media and seeing whether the rate remains proportional to the hydrogen ion concentration or to a different quantity, the Hammett h_0 function[29-31] (see section 2.9).

2.7. SUMMARY OF SIMPLE MECHANISMS

The various simple reaction mechanisms which have been discussed in the last section can be collected together to give some idea of the principal mechanisms which lead to the categories of acid–base catalysis summarized in *Table 2.4*:

Specific acid

$$AH+R \underset{slow}{\overset{fast}{\rightleftharpoons}} A^- + RH^+ \xrightarrow{R'} products$$

Specific base

$$HR+B \underset{slow}{\overset{fast}{\rightleftharpoons}} R^- + BH^+ \xrightarrow{R'} products$$

General acid

$$AH+R \underset{fast}{\overset{slow}{\rightleftharpoons}} A^- + RH^+ \xrightarrow{R'} products$$

General base

$$HR+B \underset{fast}{\overset{slow}{\rightleftharpoons}} R^- + BH^+ \xrightarrow{R'} products$$

General acid and base

$$AH+R \underset{fast}{\overset{fast}{\rightleftharpoons}} A^- + RH^+ \xrightarrow{B} products$$

In addition, Frost and Pearson[32] mention that a mechanism not included above can lead to general catalysis as follows, the addition compound sometimes involving hydrogen bonds:

General acid

$$AH+R \underset{fast}{\overset{fast}{\rightleftharpoons}} R \cdot HA \xrightarrow{R'} products$$

General base

$$HR+B \underset{fast}{\overset{fast}{\rightleftharpoons}} HR \cdot B \xrightarrow{R'} products$$

46

2.8. METAL IONS AS ACID CATALYSTS

Metal ions can be considered as Lewis acids, and they can catalyse many of the reactions that are catalysed by Brönsted acids[33]. A few years ago, Pedersen[34] discovered that small concentrations of cupric ion strongly catalysed the bromination of acetoacetic ester. It is now known that some keto-acids decarboxylate readily in the presence of a variety of metal ions[35, 36], especially those of iron, copper and nickel, and that the esters and amides of amino acids can be hydrolysed in the presence of cupric ions at a far greater rate than in the presence of the same concentration of hydrogen ions[37]. In all these examples, it appears essential for the substrate to be able to complex with the metal ion, although not too strongly. The complexing usually takes place at the carbonyl or carboxyl oxygen, in a manner similar to the attachment of

(V)

hydrogen ion in the acid catalysis of the enolization of ketones (page 44); in the enolizations, a base then extracts a different proton, and it seems reasonable that the complexing of a positive ion produces the same effect. Thus the catalysis of the bromination of acetoacetic ester could be written[33] as forming the complex intermediate (V) which reacts with base B.

In the decarboxylation of keto-acids, the activity of various ions shows that the formation of a complex is essential, and the influence of pH shows that the complex is formed with the di-anion. Oxaloacetic, oxalosuccinic and acetone-dicarboxylic acids can also be decarboxylated rapidly with metal ions, but acetoacetic acid cannot. It appears that the metal complexes with the keto group and one of the carboxyl groups, the other losing carbon dioxide. A suggested mechanism is through the intermediate (VI) (for oxaloacetic acid)[34,35]. As with all complexes that act as intermediates, it is essential that

(VI)

the complexing is not too strong. Ions that form very strong complexes may not even be catalytically active: this seems to happen for aluminium and beryllium ions which are active complexing agents but do not catalyse the bromination of acetoacetic ester.

2.9. CATALYTIC ACTIVITY OF CONCENTRATED ACIDS

In dilute aqueous solution, as explained, molecules of acids donate protons to the water to varying extents depending on the strength of the acid, so that the effective species in dilute solutions of strong acids is the hydronium ion, H_3O^+. The 'acidity', or tendency of such solutions to donate a proton to any base, is measured as the concentration of hydronium ion and is usually reported as the pH of the solution. In these dilute solutions, there is little difficulty in calculating or measuring hydronium ion concentration, but in more concentrated solutions great difficulties arise; the quantities calculated from acid

47

dissociation constants, and measured often from the e.m.f. of suitable concentration cells, are *activities* and there is no known way of calculating the hydronium ion concentration from the activity except in dilute solution. The difficulties of defining and measuring pH in concentrated solutions have been set out very clearly by Bates[38].

A way of avoiding this difficulty was suggested by Hammett and Deyrup[29], and their proposal has led to a new scale of acidity which is equal to the pH scale in dilute solution but generally, and correctly, indicates a greater acidity than does the pH scale in concentrated solutions. To see how the new scale arises, consider an uncharged base B in aqueous solution. The equilibrium

$$B + H_3O^+ \rightleftharpoons BH^+ + H_2O$$

leads to a dissociation constant K_{BH^+} for the acid BH^+ conjugate to the base.

$$K_{BH^+} = \frac{a_{H_3O^+} a_B}{a_{BH^+}}$$

and hence:

$$K_{BH^+} = \frac{a_{H_3O^+} \gamma_B}{\gamma_{BH^+}} \cdot \frac{[B]}{[BH^+]} \tag{2.11}$$

Now if B is a basic indicator, the ratio $[B]/[BH^+]$ can be determined colorimetrically. If K_{BH^+} is known (and it can be measured easily in dilute solutions) then it is possible to evaluate the quantity $h_0 = a_{H_3O^+} \gamma_B / \gamma_{BH^+}$. In very dilute solutions, $h_0 = [H_3O^+]$, as may be inferred from its definition; in more concentrated solutions, it has been found experimentally that h_0 is independent of the base used, so long as it is uncharged (similar functions can be defined for bases with single positive or negative charges, but their behaviour has not been investigated in detail). From the definition of h_0 and equation (2.11) it follows that

$$h_0 = K_{BH}[BH^+]/[B] \tag{2.12}$$

and so h_0 measures the tendency of the solution to transfer a proton to the base B and hence to *any* base of the same type. Thus h_0 is a suitable measure of the acidities of concentrated solutions as well as those of dilute solutions. In parallel with the pH scale $(pH = -\log [H_3O^+])$ there is a new scale for concentrated solutions $(H_0 = -\log h_0)$. It follows that

$$H_0 = -\log (K_{BH^+} [BH^+]/[B]) \tag{2.13}$$

and

$$H_0 = -\log K_{BH^+} - \log [BH^+]/[B]$$

$$= pK_{BH^+} + \log [B]/[BH^+] \tag{2.14}$$

Thus the H_0 value of a solution can be measured if a basic indicator can be selected which gives a suitable ratio of $[BH^+]/[B]$ for colorimetric determination. Enough such indicators are known to allow a wide range of H_0 values to be measured.

Like pH, H_0 becomes more negative the greater the acidity of the solution, and may reach -10 or less in very concentrated acids. As catalysis by acids in concentrated solutions involves the transfer of a proton to the reactant via the hydronium ion, it might be expected that k_{cat} would depend on h_0 rather than the hydronium ion concentration so that $\log k_{cat}$ becomes a linear function of H_0 instead of a linear function of pH as shown for specific acid catalysis in dilute solution (*Figure 2.3*). This behaviour was found in the inversion of sucrose in concentrated acids[39] (*Figure 2.7*). The anomalous behaviour of trichloracetic acid, probably connected with its comparative weakness as an acid, occurs with other reactions. Long and Paul[39] have recently surveyed the reactions which have been found to show this linear connection between $\log k_{cat}$ and H_0, and have examined a suggestion put forward by Hammett and Zucker[40] that the dependence of $\log k_{cat}$ on H_0, or on pH, can be used to discriminate between certain mechanisms thought possible for the rate-determining step.

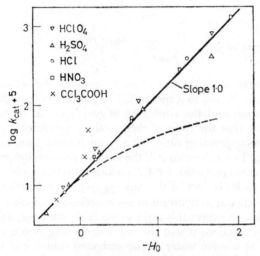

Figure 2.7. Relationship between $\log k_{cat}$ and H_0
for the inversion of sucrose at $25°C$[39]
Dotted line shows the expected values of $\log k_{cat}$ if
the rate were proportional to $[H_3O^+]$

This suggestion is best explained in more detail by considering a definite type of reaction such as the hydrolysis of an ester, or of sucrose, in which there are two possible mechanisms for catalysis in acid solution. In each, an intermediate is formed in a preliminary equilibrium rapidly established; in mechanism A1 this is followed by a slow unimolecular decomposition of the intermediate, followed in turn by a rapid reaction with water; in mechanism A2, the intermediate reacts with water in a bimolecular reaction as the rate-determining step.

Mechanism A1:

$$R + H_3O^+ \rightleftharpoons RH^+ + H_2O \qquad \text{(equilibrium established)}$$

$$RH^+ \rightleftharpoons \text{(activated complex } C_1^+) \rightarrow X^+ \qquad \text{(slow reaction)}$$

$$X^+ + H_2O \rightarrow \text{product} \qquad \text{(fast reaction)}$$

Mechanism A2:

$$R + H_3O^+ \rightleftharpoons RH^+ + H_2O \qquad \text{(equilibrium established)}$$

$$RH^+ + H_2O \rightleftharpoons \text{(activated complex } C_2^+) \rightarrow \text{product}$$
$$\text{(slow reaction)}$$

As the solutions are concentrated, the equilibria must be expressed in activities and the Brönsted treatment must be followed for the slow steps. The rates can then be derived as:

Mechanism A1:

$$\text{rate} = k_{\text{slow}} \cdot \frac{[R] a_{H_3O^+} \gamma_R}{K_{RH^+} \gamma_{C_1^+}} = k_{\text{slow}} \cdot \frac{[R]}{K_{RH^+}} \cdot h_0 \qquad (2.15)$$

Mechanism A2:

$$\text{rate} = k_{\text{slow}} \cdot \frac{[R] a_{H_2O}}{K_{RH^+}} \cdot \frac{a_{H_3O^+} \gamma_R}{\gamma_{C_2^+}} \qquad (2.16)$$

In the first expression for the rate in mechanism A1, the activity coefficients refer to the reactant R and to a species C_1^+ which differs from R only by the addition of a proton and the stretching of one bond. It seems reasonable, therefore, to think that the ratio of these activity coefficients will not differ much from the corresponding ratio for any uncharged base, and hence the introduction of h_0. In mechanism A2, the activity ratio no longer refers to the 'base' R and its conjugate acid, for C_2^+ contains a water molecule, as well as a proton, added to R. In fact, if the ratio $\gamma_{H_3O^+} \gamma_R / \gamma_{C_2^+}$ remains constant, the rate will be proportional to hydronium ion concentration rather than to h_0. It is not unreasonable to expect this ratio to be fairly constant, and it is surely significant that in reactions where the rate-determining step is believed to be bimolecular and to involve water in the activated complex of that step (the hydrolysis of simple carboxylic esters), the rate (or k_{cat}) is proportional to the hydronium ion concentration rather than to h_0[41,42]. On the other hand, the inversion of sucrose in concentrated acids seems to proceed by an A1 mechanism, for there is good proportionality between k_{cat} and h_0, as shown in *Figure 2.7*[43].

Long and Paul[39] have given many examples of reactions where the rate is proportional to h_0, i.e. of mechanism A1. These include the hydrolyses of β-lactones, of epoxides, of acetic anhydride and of acetals; the depolymerization of trioxane, $(CH_2O)_3$, and of paraldehyde, $(CH_3 \cdot CHO)_3$; the formation of γ-butyrolactone; and several decompositions of carboxylic acids in concentrated sulphuric acid.

In contrast to these reactions, in the enolization of acetophenone and in the hydrolyses of most carboxylic esters and of γ-lactones the rate remains proportional to the hydronium ion concentration and not to h_0. The hydrolysis and the formation of γ-butyrolactone form an interesting contrast in view of Hammett and Zucker's proposal. The results[44] are shown in *Figures 2.8* and *2.9*. The analysis just carried out would suggest that where the rate is proportional to h_0 the activated complex for the rate-determining step does not include a water molecule; this would be entirely appropriate for the formation of the γ-butyrolactone (*Figure 2.9*). On the other hand, in the hydrolysis of the lactone, the bond which is opened is the acyl–oxygen (see page 46) as in the common hydrolysis of simple esters; hence the mechanism is likely to be of

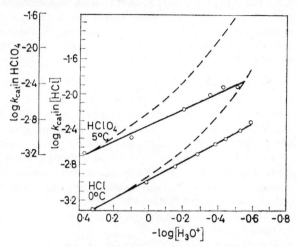

Figure 2.8. Relationship between log k_{cat} and log $[H_3O^+]$ for the acid-catalysed hydrolysis of γ-butyrolactone[44]
Dotted lines are predicted curves for dependence of rate on h_0

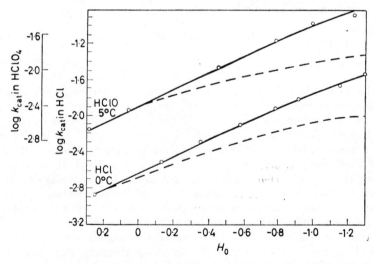

Figure 2.9. Relationship between log k_{cat} and H_0 for the acid-catalysed lactonization of γ-hydroxybutyric acid[44]
Dotted lines are predicted curves for dependence of rate on $[H_3O^+]$

the A2 type, and in keeping with the analysis for this mechanism, the rate is proportional to the hydronium ion concentration (*Figure 2.8*).

This brief introduction to the use of the H_0 and h_0 functions has of necessity omitted the more complex and puzzling features of the investigations to date.

It is important, therefore, to repeat the warning given by Long and Paul that although the A1 and A2 mechanisms should give the effects described, it is not safe to assume that the effects are always indicative of those mechanisms. It is possible, for example, for a slow proton transfer to the reactant to make k_{cat} depend on h_0. However, until more direct information about activity coefficients in concentrated solutions becomes available, it is certain that the correlation of rates with hydronium ion concentration or h_0 will be helpful in selecting mechanisms.

2.10. CATALYSIS IN NON-AQUEOUS SOLVENTS

It has been found that the relative strengths of acids are approximately constant in solvents as different as water, the alcohols, m-cresol, formamide, acetic acid, chloroform and benzene. The comparison of strengths in a variety of solvents is conveniently made by reacting the acid with a basic indicator. As a consequence of the proportionality of acid strengths, when testing the Brönsted relationship for catalysed reactions in non-aqueous solvents the dissociation constants for the acids in water can be used without much error[2,3]. Some of the solvents investigated behave like water, in acting themselves as an acid and a base, and the mechanisms given for aqueous solutions can often be applied to reactions in them.

In aprotic solvents there can be no question of specific catalysis. In these solvents, the concentrations of acid and conjugate base are no longer maintained by rapidly established equilibria between acid and solvent, but depend upon the extent of the catalysed reaction. If the reaction involves only one proton exchange, as in the scheme

$$R + HA \underset{k_2}{\overset{k_1}{\rightleftharpoons}} RH^+ + A^-$$

$$RH^+ \overset{k_3}{\longrightarrow} products$$

the kinetics will be of integral order if k_1 is the rate-determining step and the reaction shows general acid catalysis. If, however, k_3 is the rate-determining step, the rate will be proportional to $([R][HA])^{1/2}$, and the order will be fractional with respect to both catalyst and reactant. If the reaction involves two proton transfers, however, as in the enolization of a ketone, kinetics will again be of simple integral order and show general acid catalysis. However, complexing of the intermediate RH^+ with the anion A^-, in media of low dielectric constant, may leave the configuration of the intermediate unsuitable for proton transfer, unless this occurs in collision with another complex or acid molecule. This can lead to higher-order kinetics. Another complication may arise from the well-known dimerization of certain acids in these solvents, due to hydrogen bonding. It is hardly surprising, therefore, that many of the reactions studied, such as the reaction of diazoacetic ester with formic or picric acids in benzene, or the rearrangement of N-bromoacetalilide in chlorobenzene, do not show simple kinetics[22]. The catalytic constant often appears to involve several reactions and to depend upon the acid catalyst concentration c and the (aqueous) dissociation constant K_A of the acid by equations such as

$$k_{cat} = K_A c + \alpha\sqrt{c}$$
$$k_{cat} = K_A c + \beta c^2$$

At present, our knowledge of the kinetics of acid- and base-catalysed reactions in non-aqueous solvents is in much the same condition as was information upon catalysed reactions in aqueous solution during the period 1920–1935. With the amount of work going on, doubtlessly some unifying principles and reaction mechanisms similar to those discovered for aqueous solutions will emerge before long.

2.11.   FRIEDEL–CRAFTS SYNTHESES AND RELATED REACTIONS

The basic Friedel–Crafts reaction[45] consists of the alkylation or acylation of an aromatic ring in the presence of Lewis acids such as aluminium chloride. The reaction can also be extended to the alkylation and acylation of aliphatic hydrocarbons, saturated or unsaturated[46,47]. The basic reaction is often accompanied by secondary reactions such as polymerizations or isomerizations of the substrate or of the alkylating group. It is further complicated by the formation of complexes between the reactants, catalysts and products, as mentioned in Chapter 1, and some of these complexes can form separate phases[48]. Although the main pattern of the mechanisms has been firmly established, quantitative treatment of the kinetics is not easy and has only been carried out for a few reactions and under favourable conditions.

The useful catalysts include the halides of boron, aluminium, gallium, iron, zirconium, titanium, tin, zinc, niobium and tantalum. These substances are all electron acceptors and general acids in the Lewis definition. Their function appears to be to facilitate the formation of carbonium ions from olefins, from alkyl halides or alcohols, or from alkyl or aryl acid chlorides, acid anhydrides or esters[49]. The carbonium ions react readily with aromatic hydrocarbons and these reactions form valuable synthetic paths for the derivatives of aromatic hydrocarbons. Some examples are:

$$C_6H_5R' + RCl \rightarrow C_6H_5R'R + HCl$$

$$C_6H_5COCl + C_6H_6 \rightarrow C_6H_5COC_6H_5 + HCl$$

Alkylations can also be catalysed by strong acids such as hydrogen fluoride, sulphuric acid, sulphonic acids and phosphoric acids. With these obviously acid catalysts, much isomerization occurs, and they are extensively used in the petroleum industry to bring about rearrangements. With the metal chlorides as catalysts, isomerization occurs more readily with aluminium halides than with those of iron or gallium, and so the latter are preferred for mechanism studies.

The alkylations are reversible, and there have been difficulties in distinguishing the initial reaction because of later rearrangements among the ring positions and within aliphatic or side chains. Thus, the proportion of *ortho-*, *meta-* and *para*-substituted products will alter with the first example temperature and also with the catalyst; generally, the higher the temperature or the more effective the catalyst (as indicated below) the greater the proportion of *meta*-derivative. However, there are clear indications from careful comparisons of the rate of substitution, under uniform conditions, about the nature of the unit which enters the aromatic ring. The rate of reaction appears to be controlled by a reaction between the aromatic substance and an intermediate which is strongly electrophilic. Thus the rate is *increased* when the aromatic nucleus contains —OR, —OH or alkyl, so that in alkylation the substitution tends to run on. On the other hand, groups such as —NO_2, —CHO and —CN *decrease* the rate of alkylation so markedly that nitrobenzene (for example) can be used as a solvent for these alkylations. When substituted benzenes are alkylated, the alkyl group is oriented as in nitration or sulphonation. Examination of the effect of changing the alkyl group in the halide shows that the rate is increased if the electron-releasing properties of R in the halide RX are increased; thus rates are faster with tertiary alkyl groups than with secondary, and are still slower with primary groups. Lastly, the rates are greater with the catalysts which are known to have better electron-accepting properties; thus aluminium chloride is more effective than tin or zinc chlorides, while silicon chloride and sodium chloride are ineffective.

All this evidence suggests the following sequence of reactions:

(*i*) A rapidly reached equilibrium to give an ion pair which will not readily dissociate in the solvents usually employed, but which will confer conductivity on the solutions:

$$RX + AlCl_3 \rightleftharpoons \overset{+}{R} \cdot Al\overset{-}{Cl_3}X$$

(*ii*) The carbonium ion (with the gegen-ion in close attendance) attacks the aromatic nucleus, in a slow reaction:

$$C_6H_6 + \overset{+}{R} \cdot AlC\overset{-}{l_3}X \rightarrow C_6H_5 \cdot R + AlCl_3 + HX$$
$$\rightarrow C_6H_5 \cdot R + AlCl_2X + HCl$$

In support of these ideas, the kinetics are first-order in the aromatic and in the catalyst complex for aluminium chloride and aluminium bromide in the slightly polar solvents nitrobenzene and 1,2,4-trichlorobenzene[50,51]. The kinetics do not distinguish between attack on the aromatic by a complex RX.AlCl3 and the ion-pair shown in (*ii*); they do exclude[52] attack by free R$^+$ ions, as their concentration would be proportional to the square root of the product [RX].[AlCl3]. In non-polar solvents the kinetics appear to be more complex and reactions that are second order in the catalyst have been reported[53].

There is separate evidence for the ionization represented by (*i*), in that alkyl halides and aluminium halides give conducting solutions in which the aluminium migrates to the anode[54-56]. Weak complexes are also formed between aromatic hydrocarbons and the metal halides, but much stronger complexes which can give solutions with quite marked conductivity are formed if hydrogen halides are also present[46,47]. These complexes from the three constituents have been studied by cryoscopic means, by transport properties under an electrical potential, and by absorption spectroscopy; a great many formulae have been proposed, for example $C_6H_7^+.Al_2X_6Y^-$ and $C_6H_7^+.AlX_3Y^-$. The evidence for these and other complexes has been extensively discussed[48].

Another important series of complexes is formed between the metal halides and the ketonic products of acylation reactions. These ketonic complexes appear to have little catalytic activity; they form fairly stable crystalline solids, of composition one halide: one ketone with aluminium halides, or one halide: two ketones with the halides of tin, titanium and zirconium. These ketonic complexes are too stable to act as catalysts, so that as the product is formed, the effective catalyst is removed; consequently, high proportions of catalyst must be used in the original mixtures. However, the formation of the ketonic derivatives proceeds smoothly to a single product.

In contrast to this, in reactions between alkyl halides and aromatic substances, only a very small proportion of catalyst is required, and several products result. Not only can multiple alkylation occur, but a rearrangement of the side chain often occurs; thus primary alkyl halides almost always yield secondary side chains. This may occur in the carbonium ion intermediate R^+ or in the transition complex (VII). In either case, the result is in agreement

(VII)

with Whitmore's rule[57] (see also section 8.7) that the most stable rearrangement is that which gives most radicals (alkyl or aryl) on the carbonium carbon. It seems unlikely that an olefin is formed as another intermediate from the primary carbonium ion.

The catalytic alkylation of olefins and of saturated hydrocarbons has become an important process in petroleum chemistry, for it can provide a motor or aviation fuel of high quality from light hydrocarbons. Ipatieff and Pines in 1932 used aluminium chloride as a catalyst for the alkylation, and in 1936 Dunstan and Birch used sulphuric acid as the catalyst. The hydrocarbons most used are C_4 olefins and isobutane, with acid catalysts; propylenes and anylenes can also be alkylated. The catalysts most used are phosphoric acid adsorbed on kieselguhr or quartz, and hot or cold sulphuric acid in an emulsion with the oil. By analogy with the aromatic alkylations and the formation of carbonium ions in acid–base catalysis, it is assumed that the catalyst donates a proton to the olefin to form a carbonium ion:

$$CH_3 \cdot CH_2CH:CH_2 + HA \rightleftharpoons CH_3 \cdot CH_2 \cdot \overset{+}{C}H \cdot CH_3 + A^-$$

This carbonium ion can react with an isobutane molecule:

$$CH_3 \cdot CH_2 \cdot \overset{+}{C}H \cdot CH_3 + \underset{\underset{CH_3}{|}}{\overset{\overset{CH_3}{|}}{C}H \cdot CH_3} \rightarrow CH_3 \cdot CH_2 \cdot CH_2 \cdot CH_3 + (CH_3)_3C^+$$

The tertiary butyl carbonium ion can combine with another molecule of olefin to give an octane ion which can rearrange or lose a proton or gain a hydride ion in further reactions.

$$(CH_3)_3C^+ + CH_2=CH \cdot CH_2CH_3 \rightarrow (CH_3)_3C \cdot CH_2 \cdot \overset{+}{C}H \cdot CH_2 \cdot CH_3$$

There is a great deal of technical knowledge about the conditions which favour the production of fuels of high octane numbers, but little certainty about the mechanisms concerned. The carbonium ion formed in the above reaction can add to another olefin molecule. With many olefins, such as isobutylene, this ionic reaction can lead to high polymers. The ionic polymerizations catalysed by acids and by Friedel–Crafts catalysts are discussed in section 10.3.

The reverse of the Friedel–Crafts alkylation and polymerization reactions are represented by the decompositions which occur, accompanied by many rearrangement reactions, in the 'cracking' of petroleums over acid catalysts. These are usually heterogeneous reactions, and are discussed in section 8.7.

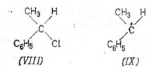

(VIII) (IX)

There are several other reactions which are catalysed by Friedel–Crafts catalysts, and which probably proceed by mechanisms similar to those discussed. In the racemization of optically active halides such as (VIII) the same order of effectiveness of metal halides is observed as for alkylations. The racemization is readily pictured if the planar carbonium ion (IX) is formed as as an intermediate.

REFERENCES

[1] MOELWYN-HUGHES, E. A. *Kinetics of Reactions in Solution*: Oxford University Press, London, 1947

[2] BELL, R. P. *Acid–Base Catalysis*: Oxford University Press, London, 1941

[3] BELL, R. P. *Advanc. Catalys.* 1952, **4**, 151

[4] KILPATRICK, M. *Advanc. Catalys.* 1954, **6**, 241

[5] OSTWALD, W. *J. prakt. Chem.* 1884, **30**, 39

[6] DAWSON, H. M. and LOWSON, W. *J. chem. Soc.* 1928, p. 2146

[7] DAWSON, H. M. *J. chem. Soc.* 1927, p. 1290

[8] HUDSON, C. S. *J. Amer. chem. Soc.* 1907, **29**, 1571

[9] BELL, R. P. and BAUGHAN, E. C. *J. chem. Soc.* 1937, p. 1947

[10] BRÖNSTED, J. N. and WYNNE-JONES, W. F. K. *Trans. Faraday Soc.* 1929, **25**, 59

[11] BRÖNSTED, J. N. *Z. phys. Chem. (Leipzig)* 1922, **102**, 169; 1925, **115**, 337

[12] BJERRUM, N. *Z. phys. Chem. (Leipzig)* 1924, **108**, 82

[13] LOWRY, T. M. and SMITH, G. F. *J. chem. Soc.* 1927, p. 2539

[14] MOELWYN-HUGHES, E. A. and KENDREW, J. C. *Proc. R. Soc. A* 1940, **176**, 352

[15] BRÖNSTED, J. N. and GUGGENHEIM, E. A. *J. Amer. chem. Soc.* 1927, **49**, 2554

[16] BRÖNSTED, J. N. and PEDERSEN, K. *Z. phys. Chem. (Leipzig)* 1924, **108**, 185

[17] BRÖNSTED, J. N. *Chem. Rev.* 1928, **5**, 231 (see p. 322)

[18] BELL, R. P. and HIGGINSON, W. C. E. *Proc. R. Soc. A* 1949, **197**, 141

[19] BELL, R. P. *Advanc. Catalys.* 1952, **4**, 163

[20] EVANS, D. P., GORDON, J. J. and WATSON, H. B. *J. chem. Soc.* 1937, p. 1430

REFERENCES

[21] INGOLD, C. K. *Structure and Mechanism in Organic Chemistry*: Bell, London, 1953, Chapter XIV

[22] HAMMETT, L. P. *Physical Organic Chemistry*: McGraw-Hill, New York, 1940

[23] LOWRY, T. M. and FAULKNER, I. J. *J. chem. Soc.* 1925, p. 2883

[24] SWAIN, C. G. and BROWN, J. F., Jr. *J. Amer. chem. Soc.* 1952, **74**, 2534, 2538

[25] LAIDLER, K. J. and LANDSKROENER, P. A. *Trans. Faraday Soc.* 1956, **52**, 200

[26] DAVIES, A. G. and KENYON, J. *Quart. Rev. (Lond.)* 1955, **9**, 203

[27] POLANYI, M. and SZABO, A. L. *Trans. Faraday Soc.* 1934, **30**, 508

[28] DATTA, S. C., DAY, J. N. E. and INGOLD, C. K. *J. chem. Soc.* 1939, p. 838

[29] HAMMETT, L. P. and DEYRUP, A. J. *J. Amer. chem. Soc.* 1932, **54**, 2721

[30] HAMMETT, L. P. and PAUL, M. A. *J. Amer. chem. Soc.* 1934, **56**, 827

[31] PAUL, M. A. and LONG, F. A. *Chem. Rev.* 1957, **57**, 1

[32] FROST, A. A. and PEARSON, R. G. *Kinetics and Mechanism*: Wiley, New York, 1953, Chapter 9

[33] BASOLO, F. and PEARSON, R. G. *Mechanisms of Inorganic Reactions*: Wiley, New York, 1958, p. 332

[34] PEDERSEN, K. J. *Acta chem. scand.* 1948, **2**, 252, 385; 1952, **6**, 285

[35] STEINBERGER, R. and WESTHEIMER, F. H. *J. Amer. chem. Soc.* 1951, **73**, 429

[36] PRUE, J. E. *J. chem. Soc.* 1952, p. 2331

[37] BENDER, M. L. and TURNQUEST, B. W. *J. Amer. chem. Soc.* 1957, **79**, 1889

[38] BATES, R. G. *Electrometric pH Determinations*: Wiley, New York, 1954

[39] LONG, F. A. and PAUL, M. A. *Chem. Rev.* 1957, **57**, 935

[40] HAMMETT, L. P. and ZUCKER, L. *J. Amer. chem. Soc.* 1939, **61**, 2779, 2785, 2791

[41] BELL, R. P., DOWDING, A. L. and NOBLE, J. A. *J. chem. Soc.* 1955, p. 3106

[42] CHMIEL, C. T. and LONG, F. A. *J. Amer. chem. Soc.* 1956, **78**, 3326

[43] LONG, F. A. and PAUL, M. A. *Chem. Rev.* 1957, **57**, 938

[44] LONG, F. A., DUNKLE, F. B. and McDEVIT, W. F. *J. phys. Chem.* 1951, **55**, 829

[45] FRIEDEL, C. and CRAFTS, J. *C. R. Acad. Sci.*, Paris 1877, **84**, 1392, 1450

[46] PRICE, C. C. *Organic Reactions* Vol. III: Wiley, New York, 1946

[47] BADDELEY, G. *Quart. Rev. (Lond.)* 1954, **8**, 354

[48] PLESCH, P. H. *Cationic Polymerization and Related Complexes*: Academic Press, New York, 1953

[49] GOULD, E. S. *Mechanisms and Structure in Organic Chemistry*: Holt, New York, 1959, p. 447

[50] BROWN, H. C. and GRAYSON, M. *J. Amer. chem. Soc.* 1953, **75**, 6285

[51] BROWN, H. C., JUNGK, H. and SMOOT, C. R. *J. Amer. chem. Soc.* 1956, **78**, 2185

[52] BROWN, H. C. and JUNGK, H. *J. Amer. chem. Soc.* 1955, **77**, 5584

[53] SMOOT, R. C. and BROWN, H. C. *J. Amer. chem. Soc.* 1956, **78**, 6245

[54] WOHL, A. and WERTYPOROCH, E. *Ber. dtsch. chem. Ges.* 1931, **64B**, 1357

[55] FAIRBROTHER, F. *Trans. Faraday Soc.* 1941, **37**, 763

[56] FAIRBROTHER, F. *J. chem. Soc.* 1945, p. 503; 1937, p. 503; 1941, p. 293

[57] WHITMORE, F. C. *Industr. Engng Chem. (Industr.)* 1934, **26**, 94

HOMOGENEOUS CATALYSIS BY GROUP OR ELECTRON TRANSFER

3.1. GROUP AND ELECTRON TRANSFER IN SOLUTION

3.1.1. Introduction

MANY of the oxidation–reduction reactions which are important analytically, particularly the reactions of ions of metals and of oxy-anions, can be formulated as group transfer or as electron transfer reactions[1]. It may seem difficult to postulate that group transfer could occur in apparently simple reactions such as

$$2Fe^{2+} + I_2 \rightarrow 2Fe^{3+} + 2I^-$$

but it must be remembered that many ions are solvated and that part of a solvation molecule, such as a hydrogen atom or a hydroxyl group, may be transferred in some intermediate reactions[2].

Group and electron transfer reactions in solution are not easy to treat theoretically because the solvent is involved in the reaction, not only through changes in the solvation but also through reorganization of the solvent immediately around the reactants and the transition complex. Nevertheless, potential energy diagrams have proved very helpful in depicting the energy changes in these reactions and the factors that affect their rates[3]. Of course the same qualifications that were made in discussing *Figure 2.5* must be made. Halpern[4] has recently summarized the experimental and theoretical work on electron transfer reactions and has dealt with the energy changes involved in: (*i*) non-adiabatic electron transfer, when the reacting molecules have to be in states of equal energy and some rearrangement of the atomic configuration of the reactants must occur before the transfer; (*ii*) adiabatic electron transfer when the electronic interaction between the reactants is weak, a situation which apparently occurs for many transfers in aqueous solution, and (*iii*) adiabatic transfer when the electronic interaction is strong, for instance when two ions are linked by some complexing molecule and electron exchange occurs through overlapping orbitals. Halpern emphasizes that quantitative treatment is rarely possible, but that certain factors can be specified as affecting the rate of transfer and some qualitative discussion of them in particular cases is often helpful, especially in comparing rates or in predicting unknown from known rates. One important restriction on the transfers is, of course, that the electron spin cannot change readily in the transfer and any proposed change that requires an electron to change spin is likely to be slow. Such a change would probably proceed through an excited state of one reactant.

The other mechanism for oxidation–reduction reactions includes the transfer of an atom or group of atoms between the oxidant and the reductant. An obvious example is the transfer of an oxygen atom between oxy-anions. By labelling with ^{18}O, transfer has been shown[1] to occur between sulphite ions and hypochlorite, chlorite, chlorate or bromate ions. Taube[5] has demonstrated the transfer of chloride atoms from various oxidizing complexes such as $FeCl^{2+}.Cr^{2+}$ in the oxidation of chromous salts; the demonstration is possible because the chromic complex retains the chloride or other ions after transfer[6]. Hydrogen atom transfer between two aquo-ions can simulate electron transfer; Hudis and Dodson[7] have shown that the rate of electron transfer between isotopic ions of different oxidation states is often faster in water than in deuterium oxide, and have suggested mechanisms such as:

$$Fe^{2+}(H_2O)_6 + \overset{*}{Fe}^{3+}(OH)^-(H_2O)_5 \rightarrow \left[(H_2O)_5Fe^{2+}O-H\cdots\overset{-}{O}-\overset{*}{Fe}^{3+}(H_2O)_5\right]$$
$$\underset{H \qquad\qquad H}{}$$

$$Fe^{3+}(OH)^-(H_2O)_5 + \overset{*}{Fe}^{2+}(H_2O)_6$$

The ions $Fe^{3+}(H_2O)_6$, $Fe^{3+}(X)^-(H_2O)_5$ and $Fe^{3+}(X)_2^-(H_2O)_4$, where $X=$ Cl or F, exchange Fe with $Fe^{2+}(H_2O)_6$ at similar rates (but much more slowly than with $X=OH$). It has been suggested[7] that this indicates hydrogen atom transfer between the water of hydration of Fe^{2+} and Fe^{3+}, followed by rapid proton exchanges with the solvent. However, other possibilities have been discussed, such as the simultaneous exchange of a proton and a hydrogen atom[1], the participation of a solvent molecule in the transition complex[1,4] and the exchange of an electron through bridged complexes of the two ions[2,4].

It appears unlikely that electron transfer reactions occur by the transfer of an electron from the reducing agent to the oxidizing agent by way of transfer to a (solvent) water molecule not in the hydration sheath of an ion. Such a transfer may be possible with ammonia as a solvent[4].

In aqueous solution, it is still uncertain whether the transfer of two electrons can take place in one stage. After the detection of intermediates in some oxidations where two equivalents of reaction occurred—such as quinone, semiquinone, hydroquinone—it was supposed that all such changes took place in at least two steps with no more than one electron being transferred in any one step[8a,b]. The transition metals appear to react, as ions, in one-electron transfer reactions because they have so many stable oxidation states differing by one equivalent. Ions of non-transition metals often take part in two-equivalent reactions, such as $Sn^{2+}+Tl^{3+} \rightarrow Sn^{4+}+Tl^+$. Reactions like these could take place by successive single-electron transfers or by a variety of two-electron transfers. If the reaction involves a two-equivalent oxidant and a one-equivalent reductant, or vice versa, kinetic investigations may indicate a particular mechanism. For example, the reaction $2Fe^{2+}+Tl^{3+} \rightarrow 2Fe^{3+}+Tl^+$ may proceed in one step to give third-order kinetics, or in two steps such as

$$Fe^{2+}+Tl^{3+} \underset{k_2}{\overset{k_1}{\rightleftharpoons}} Fe^{3+}+Tl^{2+}$$
$$Tl^2+Fe^2 \underset{k_3}{\overset{k_2}{\longrightarrow}} Fe^{3+}+Tl^+$$

In the two-step mechanism, either the first step could be slow, when the rate would be proportional to the concentration of ferrous ion and of thallium ion and independent of ferric ion concentration, or the first reaction and its reverse may be in equilibrium, with the second step slow; in this case, the rate would be retarded by the ferric ion as it is formed or if it is added. It was found [9] that the kinetics fitted the second possibility, being in agreement with the law

$$\text{Rate} = \frac{k_1 k_3 [\text{Fe}^{2+}]^2 [\text{Tl}^{3+}]}{k_3 [\text{Fe}^{2+}] + k_2 [\text{Fe}^{3+}]}$$

Similar evidence that the oxidation $2\text{Co}^{2+} + \text{Pb}^{4+} \rightarrow 2\text{Co}^{3+} + \text{Pb}^{2+}$ proceeds by the stages

$$\text{Co}^{2+} + \text{Pb}^{4+} \rightleftharpoons \text{Co}^{4+} + \text{Pb}^{2+} \qquad \text{(fast equilibrium)}$$

$$\text{Co}^{2+} + \text{Co}^{4+} \rightarrow 2\text{Co}^{3+} \qquad \text{(slow reaction)}$$

is obtained by the retardation by Pb^{2+} ions, although other reaction steps occur [10]. When the oxidant and the reductant each show two-equivalent changes it appears that the rates are often proportional to the concentration of each ion, as with

$$\text{U}^{4+} + \text{Tl}^{3+} \rightarrow \text{U}^{6+} + \text{Tl}^{+}$$

This could be one two-electron step or two successive single electron transfers with the first rate-determining [11].

3.1.2. *Catalysis of electron-transfer reactions*

There is an obvious opportunity for catalysis where two electrons must be transferred, irrespective of the normal mechanism, by the introduction of another ion with two or more stable oxidation states. The $\text{Cu}^{+}.\text{Cu}^{2+}$ couple seems to be very effective in this way, and the $\text{Ag}^{+}.\text{Ag}^{2+}$ is also active. Copper ion catalyses various oxidation–reduction processes such as:

(*i*) The reaction $\text{V}^{3+} + \text{Fe}^{3+} \rightarrow \text{V}^{4+} + \text{Fe}^{2+}$. The rate is proportional to the concentration of V^{3+} ion and of cupric ion, indicating the steps

$$\text{V}^{3+} + \text{Cu}^{2+} \rightarrow \text{V}^{4+} + \text{Cu}^{+} \qquad \text{(slow reaction)}$$

$$\text{Cu}^{+} + \text{Fe}^{3+} \rightarrow \text{Fe}^{2+} + \text{Cu}^{2+} \qquad \text{(fast reaction)}$$

(*ii*) The oxidation of U^{4+} ions by molecular oxygen [12], apparently by

$$\text{U}^{4+} + \text{Cu}^{2+} \rightarrow \text{U}^{5+} + \text{Cu}^{+}$$

$$\text{Cu}^{+} + \text{O}_2 \rightarrow \text{Cu}^{2+} + \text{O}_2^{-} \xrightarrow{\text{H}^{+}} \text{HO}_2$$

The oxidation of the uranium probably continues by a chain reaction such as

$$\text{U}^{5+} + \text{O}_2 \xrightarrow{\text{H}^{+}} \text{U}^{6+} + \text{HO}_2$$

$$\text{U}^{4+} + \text{HO}_2 \xrightarrow{\text{H}^{+}} \text{U}^{5+} + \text{H}_2\text{O}_2$$

terminated by

$$\text{U}^{5+} + \text{HO}_2 \xrightarrow{\text{H}^{+}} \text{U}^{6+} + \text{H}_2\text{O}_2$$

Similar initiation of oxidation chains has been suggested for the auto-oxidation of sulphites, aldehydes, ferrous and V^{3+} ions. These auto-oxidations are discussed in section 11.2.

Silver ions can also act as catalysts for some electron transfer reactions, for example[13] the reaction

$$Tl^+ + 2Ce^{4+} \rightarrow Tl^{3+} + 2Ce^{3+}$$

The experimental rate law shows that several steps are involved, as in the mechanism:

$$Ce^{4+} + Ag^+ \rightleftharpoons Ce^{3+} + Ag^{2+} \qquad \text{(fast equilibrium)}$$

$$Ag^{2+} + Tl^+ \rightarrow Tl^{2+} + Ag^+ \qquad \text{(slow reaction)}$$

$$Tl^{2+} + Ce^{4+} \rightarrow Tl^{3+} + Ce^{3+} \qquad \text{(fast reaction)}$$

An interesting group of electron transfer reactions are involved in the catalysis by manganese ions of various oxidations. Taube[14,15] has studied the catalysis by manganic ion of the oxidation of oxalate ion by chlorine

$$Cl_2 + C_2O_4^{2-} \rightarrow 2CO_2 + 2Cl^-$$

and suggests that the following steps are indicated by the kinetics of the reaction

$$Mn^{3+} + C_2O_4^{2-} \rightarrow Mn(C_2O_4)^+$$

$$Mn(C_2O_4)^+ \rightarrow Mn^2 + CO_2 + CO_2^-$$

$$CO_2^- + Cl_2 \rightarrow CO_2 + Cl + Cl^-$$

$$Cl + Mn^{2+} \rightarrow Cl^- + Mn^{3+}$$

Either of the first two steps could be rate-determining. At very high concentrations of oxalate ion the rate passes through a maximum, so that another complex may be formed which is less reactive:

$$Mn(C_2O_4)^+ + C_2O_4^{2-} \rightarrow Mn(C_2O_4)_2^-$$

Duke[16] has suggested alternative oxalomanganic complexes.

The catalysis of the oxidation of oxalate ion by permanganate ion was one of the first reactions studied kinetically by Harcourt and Esson[17]; later work on oxidations by permanganate was reviewed by Ladbury and Cullis[18]. The reaction is catalysed by manganous ion, although the permanganate ion reacts very slowly with either manganous ion or oxalate ion. Malcolm and Noyes[19] suggested the steps:

$$Mn^{2+} + C_2O_4^{2-} \rightarrow MnC_2O_4$$

$$MnC_2O_4 + MnO_4^- \rightarrow MnO_4^{2-} + \text{(oxalomanganic complex } B^+\text{)}$$

$$B^+ \rightarrow Mn^{2+} + C_2O_4^- \rightarrow 2CO_2$$

The reaction of B^+ is the slow step.

Another very interesting group of catalysed reactions is centred around hydrogen peroxide[20,21]. This can be decomposed catalytically by a variety of metallic and halide ions, by metal surfaces and by enzymes. Many peroxidic substances undergo analogous catalysed reactions. The intermediates formed in these reactions have proved very effective in initiating polymerization reactions, and their use as 'redox' catalysts is discussed in Chapter 10.

In acid solution, hydrogen peroxide oxidizes iodide ion quantitatively to iodine, but in neutral or slightly alkaline solution iodine decomposes hydrogen peroxide:

$$2H^+ + 2I^- + H_2O_2 \rightarrow 2H_2O + I_2$$

$$I_2 + H_2O_2 \rightarrow 2I^- + 2H^+ + O_2$$

Although these reactions could be regarded as representing the catalysed decomposition, it actually proceeds through several simpler steps. At a time when it was thought that free radicals could not be formed in solution, Bray[22] and Abel[23] proposed that hypoiodous acid HOI or hypoiodite ions OI$^-$ were intermediates in reaction schemes like

$$I^- + H_2O_2 \rightarrow OI^- + H_2O$$

$$OI^- + H^+ \rightleftharpoons HOI$$

Alkaline solution:

$$OI^- + H_2O_2 \rightarrow I^- + H_2O + O_2$$

Acid solution:

$$HOI + I^- + H^+ \rightarrow I_2 + H_2O$$

There are several other possibilities. The initial oxygen atom transfer from H—O—OH is very unlikely. More likely is a combined electron transfer and a transfer of OH to the iodine

$$I^- + H_2O_2 \rightarrow HOI + OH^- \quad \text{or} \quad I + OH + OH^-$$

The formation of hypoiodous acid may be followed by the later steps of Bray's and Abel's schemes. The formation of iodine atoms and hydroxyl radicals may be followed by the reactions

$$OH + I^- \underset{OH^-}{\overset{H^+}{\rightleftharpoons}} I + OH^-$$

Acid solutions:

$$I + I \rightarrow I_2$$

Alkaline solutions:

$$OH + H_2O_2 \rightarrow \text{chain decomposition of } H_2O_2$$

On the whole, in this system the radical paths seem less likely than the paths involving hypoiodous acid and hypoiodite ions. With other catalysts, however, it is more certain that free radicals are formed by electron transfer. With ferrous ion, for instance, formally similar reactions to the pair at the top of the page can be written down. The oxidation by hydrogen peroxide of ferrous ion to ferric takes place quantitatively if the peroxide is added slowly to the ferrous solution, whereas if ferrous or ferric ions are added to hydrogen peroxide solution, the peroxide is catalytically decomposed:

$$2H^+ + 2Fe^{2+} + H_2O_2 \rightarrow 2H_2O + 2Fe^{3+}$$

$$2Fe^{3+} + H_2O_2 \rightarrow 2Fe^{2+} + 2H^+ + O_2$$

After the pioneer work of Haber and Weiss[8a], and further work by Baxendale et al.[24,25] there is general agreement that the following steps are involved:

$$Fe^{2+} + H_2O_2 \rightleftharpoons FeOH^{2+} + OH$$

$$Fe^{3+} + H_2O_2 \rightleftharpoons Fe^{2+} + HO_2 + H^+$$

$$OH + H_2O_2 \rightarrow H_2O + HO_2$$

$$HO_2 + H_2O_2 \rightarrow H_2O + OH + O_2$$

$$HO_2 + Fe^{3+} \rightarrow H^+ + Fe^{2+} + O_2$$

$$OH + Fe^{2+} \rightarrow FeOH^{2+}$$

At certain pH values the anions HO_2^- and O_2^- are important and take the places of HO_2 and H_2O_2 in some reactions[24].

3.1.3. Reductions by molecular hydrogen in solution[26,27]

Molecular hydrogen is not a strong reducing agent in solution unless a catalyst is present. The molecule can be split homolytically to two hydrogen atoms, which in aqueous solution probably requires about the same energy as in the gas phase (about 103 kcal), or heterolytically to a hydride ion H^- and a proton H^+ which are strongly hydrated, so that the energy required for this split is only about 33 kcal. The homolytic split is strongly catalysed by metal surfaces which are able to bind the hydrogen atoms, however, and where the binding is not too strong the surfaces are active catalysts for hydrogenation or reductions. Colloidal platinum or palladium, or finely divided nickel, have been used for many years as catalysts for hydrogenations. Much more recently, Calvin[28] showed that cuprous salts acted as homogeneous catalysts for the reduction of cupric ion or of benzoquinone in solution in pyridine. Similar activity has been found for a number of simple or complexed metal ions in solution in various solvents as well as for some anions. Thus in aqueous solutions silver, cupric and mercuric ions, permanganate and hydroxyl ions, and some complexes of the same metal ions, are catalysts for the reduction of dichromate, permanganate, iodate, ceric, cupric and mercuric ions as well as some exchange and conversion reactions. In organic solvents, organic salts of cuprous or silver are catalysts for similar reactions; dicobaltoctacarbonyl, $Co_2(CO)_8$, is a catalyst for reactions of hydroformylation and hydrogenation, as discussed in section 8.4. In ammonia, the anion NH_2^- is a catalyst for the orthohydrogen–parahydrogen conversion or the hydrogen–deuterium exchange.

Kinetic studies of these reactions have shown that the kinetics follow very similar patterns. The rate of the reduction, measured as the rate of consumption of hydrogen or of the substrate being used, is usually independent of the concentration of the substrate and is a function of the hydrogen pressure, the concentration of the catalyst, and sometimes of the pH of the solution. The rate seems to be determined by some reaction, not necessarily in a single stage, of the catalyst with the hydrogen. For this reason, it is often called[27] the 'activation' of hydrogen, although the catalyst is also involved in the active reducing agent in many cases.

The catalyses in aqueous solution may involve homolytic or heterolytic splitting of the hydrogen. This is clearly shown in the reduction of dichromate ion with silver as catalyst [29,30]. The rate of consumption of hydrogen is given by

$$-\frac{d[H_2]}{dt} = k_4[H_2][Ag^+]^2 + \frac{k_1 k_3 [H_2][Ag^+]^2}{k_3[Ag^+] + k_2[H^+]}$$

The first term, independent of pH, appears to be due to a homolytic splitting of hydrogen molecules to form two AgH^+ ions in a single termolecular step or in successive bimolecular steps; each AgH^+ ion reacts rapidly with the dichromate ion. The second term, dependent on pH, apparently involves several

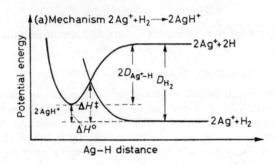

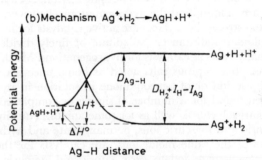

Figure 3.1. Potential energy curves for the homolytic (*a*) and heterolytic (*b*) splitting of H_2 by silver ions [30]

steps such as the heterolytic splitting of the hydrogen in a reversible reaction followed by a slow step (3) which is rate-determining:

$$Ag^+ + H_2 \underset{k_2}{\overset{k_1}{\rightleftharpoons}} AgH + H^+$$

$$AgH + Ag^+ \xrightarrow{k_3} 2Ag + H^+ \quad (\text{or } AgH^+ + Ag)$$

These reactions are followed by rapid reactions between dichromate ion and silver or AgH^+ ions. There is good evidence for the reversible reactions, because HD is formed when D_2O-enriched water is used [30]. The energetics of the homolytic and the heterolytic split have been examined by Halpern [27] with the help of the potential energy diagrams [30] shown in *Figure 3.1*. In the lower diagram, the ionization energy of the silver atom I_{Ag} is numerically equal to the electron affinity of the silver ion. The activation energies of the steps 1 and 4 have been measured; that of step 4 is low (14), while that of step 1 is high (23), but there are compensating changes in the pre-exponential factors; however, the k_1 path predominates at higher temperatures.

The reduction of dichromate ion is also catalysed by cupric ions, and the kinetics[31,32] show that the hydrogen is split heterolytically. In the absence of dichromate, the cupric ion is reduced to metallic copper, the kinetic expression for the rate of consumption of hydrogen being the same as when the substrate is present[33]. This suggests a common sequence of steps to the rate-determining step, followed by different rapid reactions:

$$Cu^{2+} + H_2 \underset{k_2}{\overset{k_1}{\rightleftharpoons}} CuH^+ + H^+$$

$$CuH^+ + Cu^{2+} \xrightarrow{k_3} 2Cu^+ + H^+ \quad (or \ CuH^{2+} + Cu^+)$$

followed by either $2Cu^+ \rightleftharpoons Cu^{2+} + Cu_{met}$

or $$6Cu^+ Cr_2O_7{}^{2-} + 14H^+ \rightarrow 2Cr^{3+} + 6Cu^{2+} + 7H_2O$$

There is also evidence that the first reaction should be written as

$$Cu(H_2O)_n^{2+} + H_2 \rightleftharpoons CuH(H_2O)_{n-1}^+ + H_3O^+$$

As the effective reducing agent is formed in step 3, and as cuprous ion is not an effective catalyst in aqueous solution (in contrast to organic solvents) it is questionable whether cuprous ion is the effective reducing agent in the fast later reactions; perhaps the CuH^{2+} ion shown in the alternative steps 3 is the true reducing agent, with silver hydride as the corresponding agent in the silver-catalysed reduction.

The addition of ions or molecules that can complex with the catalyst or any of the intermediates can produce marked changes in the rates of reaction. The relative strength of the complexing to different species will determine whether the rate is increased or inhibited. If the complexing substance is more basic than water, the first equilibrium may be displaced to the right, so increasing the rate by increasing $[CuH^+]$. But if the bond between the metal ion and the ligand is strong, k_1 will be decreased because a strong bond must be broken in step 1. These effects are shown in the cupric ion-catalysed reductions by the following observations[34]: (i) the increase in the catalytic activity in the series water, chloride, sulphate, acetate, propionate, butyrate, which is the order of increasing basicity of the anions, and (ii) the inhibition of the rate by the strongly complexing glycinate ion or ethlenediamine molecule.

water	chloride	sulphate	acetate	n-propionate n-butyrate	glycinate	ethylenediamine
1	2·5	6·5	120	150	0·5	0·1

With other ions as catalyst, the relative order of effectiveness is different because the relative stability of the complexes is different, but the same principles hold good.

The homogeneous activation of hydrogen has also been studied in non-aqueous solvents, particularly for copper and silver salts in inert or basic solvents. In the inert solvents like hydrocarbons or the long-chain acids, the

5—c.

unionized salts seem to react with hydrogen in a rate-determining step to cause heterolytic splitting. With copper, for example, cupric salts can be reduced by hydrogen with cuprous or cupric salts as catalysts:

$$-d[H_2]/dt = k_1[H_2][CuA_2] + k_2[H_2][CuA]$$

The cuprous salt is more effective, so that the reaction shows autocatalysis as the cupric salt is reduced; the reduction does not go beyond the cuprous stage (*Figure 3.2*). In the acid solvents, addition of the sodium salt of the acid seems to result in the formation of higher complexes that are inactive catalysts. In the basic solvents, it is possible that some homolytic splitting can occur.

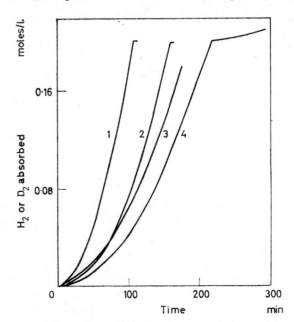

Figure 3.2. Autocatalysis in the reduction of cupric heptanoate (initially 0·4M) at 145° in various solvents[27] 1, diphenyl; 2, heptanoic acid; 3, octodecane; 4, heptanoic acid, using D_2 instead of H_2

The homogeneous activation of hydrogen is not of great importance as a reaction path in preparations or syntheses, but it is extremely important as an example of simple catalysis where the reaction path seems clearly established in a number of examples. It will be very interesting to see what results emerge from the comparison of the activities of different catalysts, for these results should give information about the factors such as bond strengths and electronic structure that control catalytic activity.

3.2. CATALYSIS BY ATOM TRANSFER IN NON-CHAIN GAS REACTIONS

There are some interesting examples of catalysis of non-chain reactions of the oxides of nitrogen and their halogen derivatives. They proceed by oxygen or chlorine atom transfer reactions between the catalyst and reactants. There seem to be very few other examples of the homogeneous catalysis of non-chain reactions such as molecular combinations, eliminations or isomerizations.

Ogg and Wilson[35] found evidence for the catalysis by nitrogen dioxide of the oxidation of nitrosyl chloride to nitryl chloride

$$2NOCl + O_2 \rightarrow 2NO_2Cl$$

In later work, Ray and Ogg[36] showed that the oxidation occurred by the following sequence of reaction steps:

$$NO_2 + NOCl \underset{2}{\overset{1}{\rightleftharpoons}} NO_2Cl + NO \quad K_{eq}$$

$$NO + O_2 + NO_2 \overset{3}{\longrightarrow} NO_3 + NO_2$$

$$NO_3 + NO \overset{4}{\longrightarrow} 2NO_2$$

$$NO + O_2 + NO \overset{5}{\longrightarrow} 2NO_2$$

The reactions 1 and 2 are fast and virtually balanced; step 3 and step 5 are slow, while step 4 is very fast. The rate of removal of oxygen is then

$$-\frac{d[O_2]}{dt} = \frac{k_3 K_{eq}[NO_2]^2[NOCl][O_2]}{[NO_2Cl]} + \frac{k_5 K_{eq}^2[NO_2]^2[NOCl]^2[O_2]}{[NO_2Cl]^2}$$

Ray and Ogg were able to evaluate the velocity constant k_3 and the equilibrium constant K_{eq}. The concentration of nitric oxide in this system is very low. The reaction scheme suggests that in these circumstances the oxidation of *nitric oxide* is catalysed by nitrogen dioxide. The normal path of oxidation of nitric oxide is thought[37] to be the single-stage process 5. When the concentration of nitric oxide is very low, however, and nitrogen dioxide is present, the reaction 3 may become faster than 5. An obvious question arises concerning the function of nitrogen dioxide in step 3. Does it act as a third body, or is there some chemical exchange? This may occur via:

$$ON + O_2 + NO_2 \rightarrow ON\text{····}O\text{····}O\text{····}NO_2 \rightarrow ONO + NO_3$$

which is comparable to reaction 5

$$ON + O_2 + NO \rightarrow ON\text{····}O\text{····}O\text{····}NO \rightarrow ONO + ONO$$

It is not easy to test whether other gases act as third bodies in step 3, because it is difficult to work with the low concentrations and small extent of reaction where 3 becomes comparable to 5. With ratios of $[NO]/[NO_2]$ above 10^{-2}, reaction 5, or some similar mechanism[38], is fast relative to step 3.

In the decomposition of nitrogen dioxide, the initial reaction can proceed by the reverse of step 5, or by the reverse of step 4 followed by the reverse of reaction 3. The second path is eliminated early in the reaction because reaction 4 becomes rapid compared with step 3 as nitric oxide is formed. There is thus an 'auto-inhibition' of the early fast rate; in addition, this early fast rate can be reduced by adding nitric oxide to the nitrogen dioxide[39a,b].

The decomposition of nitrosyl chloride is accelerated by the addition of inert gases[40]. This is because there are two parallel paths for the homogeneous decomposition, one the molecular path 6 and the other a two-stage mechanism 7, 8:

$$\overset{6}{NOCl + NOCl \rightarrow ON\cdots Cl\cdots Cl\cdots NO \rightarrow 2NO + Cl_2}$$

$$\overset{7}{NOCl + M \rightarrow NO + Cl + M}$$

$$\overset{8}{NOCl + Cl \rightarrow NO + Cl_2}$$

At temperatures above 300°C, the second path becomes relatively more important than the molecular reaction. At lower temperatures, the addition of nitrogen dioxide produces a fast catalysis of the decomposition[41], apparently because nitryl chloride is formed via the balanced reactions 1 and 2, and it decomposes[42] by two reactions comparable to, but faster than, 7 and 8:

$$NO_2 + NOCl \underset{2}{\overset{1}{\rightleftharpoons}} NO_2Cl + NO$$

$$NO_2Cl + M \overset{9}{\longrightarrow} NO_2 + Cl + M$$

$$NO_2Cl + Cl \overset{10}{\longrightarrow} NO_2 + Cl_2$$

When intermediates such as nitryl chloride, NO_2Cl, in the above scheme are postulated, the kinetic scheme is developed by the stationary-state treatment. It is important to check where possible that the concentration of the intermediate reaches a stationary level which is low compared with the concentration of the reactants, and that the level is reached in a time which is short in comparison with the half-life of the main reaction. Benson[43] has studied the problem for various combinations of the velocity constants of the reaction steps, for reaction schemes like the above and for chain reactions. The assumption of steady states can be checked in the nitryl chloride scheme, for the velocity constants k_1 and k_2 can be evaluated at temperatures around 200 to 400°C where the catalysed decomposition occurs. It appears[41] that for typical reaction mixtures the maximum concentration of nitryl chloride is about 10^{-3} of the reactant concentrations, and it is reached in a small fraction of a second compared with half-lives of many seconds.

It has been known for some time[44] that the combination of chlorine and nitric oxide is catalysed by nitrogen dioxide. The combination of nitric oxide and chlorine is also catalysed by bromine. It was proposed[44] that the bromine first forms nitrosyl bromide which then reacts with chlorine, and the rate equations fitted this assumption:

$$2NO + Br_2 \rightleftharpoons 2NOBr \quad K_{eq}$$

$$2NOBr + Cl_2 \overset{k'}{\longrightarrow} 2NOCl + Br_2$$

The rate of the catalysed portion of the reaction is

$$\frac{d[NOCl]}{dt} = K_{eq}k'[NO]^2[Br_2][Cl_2]$$

It would be interesting to discover whether reactions of bromine atoms or of the interhalogen compound, BrCl, are involved at suitable temperatures.

The decomposition of nitrogen pentoxide is a complex reaction[45] and nitrogen trioxide is formed as an intermediate

$$N_2O_5 \overset{1}{\underset{2}{\rightleftharpoons}} NO_2 + NO_3$$

It is then removed in the reactions

$$NO_3 + NO_2 \overset{3}{\longrightarrow} NO + O_2 + NO_2$$

$$NO_3 + NO \overset{4}{\longrightarrow} NO_2 + NO_2$$

Although reaction 3 is slow and determines the rate, addition of nitrogen dioxide does not accelerate the rate of decomposition because it increases by the same factor the rate of the reaction

$$NO_2 + NO_3 \rightarrow N_2O_5$$

The addition of nitric oxide does increase the rate of removal of nitrogen pentoxide by increasing the rate of step 4 at the expense of step 3, but the product is then nitrogen dioxide rather than nitrogen dioxide and oxygen; this acceleration is not a catalysis as defined in Chapter 1.

The decomposition of ozone is catalysed by the oxides of nitrogen[46]. With nitrogen pentoxide, the order of reaction is very unusual, the rate being proportional to $[N_2O_5]^{2/3}[O_3]^{2/3}$. Schumacher and Sprenger[46] showed that their results could be derived from the reaction scheme:

$$N_2O_5 \rightarrow 2NO_2 + \tfrac{1}{2}O_2$$

$$NO_2 + O_3 \rightarrow NO_3 + O_2$$

$$NO_3 + NO_2 \rightarrow N_2O_5$$

$$NO_3 + NO_3 \rightarrow 2NO_2 + O_2$$

The concentration of nitrogen pentoxide thus reaches a stationary state. In view of the later work on the decomposition of nitrogen pentoxide it is possible that reactions 1 and 3 should be included, as well as the reaction

$$NO_3 + O_3 \rightarrow NO_2 + 2O_2$$

The decomposition of ozone is also catalysed by nitric oxide and by nitrogen dioxide, probably through the same intermediates[47]. It is also catalysed by the halogens and by molecules (e.g. hydrogen peroxide or hydrocarbons) from which hydrogen atoms can readily be abstracted; the intermediates here can be written as X, formed by the reaction

$$\text{catalyst} + O_3 \rightarrow X \ldots$$

There is a possibility that X then reacts in a chain mechanism

$$X + O_3 \rightarrow XO + O_2$$

$$XO + O_3 \rightarrow X + 2O_2$$

so that the catalysed decomposition is a chain reaction.

There has been an immense amount of work on the thermal decomposition of nitrous oxide. The earlier work was summarized by Johnston[48] in 1951, and there have been several further attempts to interpret the earlier data and correlate it with fresh experimental work. The decomposition occurs at reasonable rates at temperatures around $700°C$, with pressures of gas around 1 atm. The main products are nitrogen and oxygen; nitric oxide is formed in the early stages of each decomposition, but the amount does not increase beyond a limiting value determined by the initial nitrous oxide pressure and the temperature. The decomposition appears to be unimolecular and the first-order velocity constant varies with the pressure as $k = \sum A_n p/(1+A_{n'} p)$, at least four values of the constants A_n and $A_{n'}$ being needed to describe k as the pressure is varied from low values to the highest investigated (about 40 atm). The activation energy is about 55 to 60 kcal. The decomposition is affected by inert gases, by the surface and by the presence of catalysts such as halogens or nitric oxide.

In recent work, Lindars and Hinshelwood[49] investigated in detail the variation of the velocity constant with pressure, Kaufman, Gerri and Bowman[50] examined the formation and fate of nitric oxide, and Kaufman, Gerri and Pascale[51] the effect of halogens on the decomposition. Reuben and Linnett[52] have examined this recent work and modified the reaction scheme of Kaufman, Gerri and Bowman to take account of the excitation of nitrous oxide to triplet states ($^3\Sigma$ and $^3\Pi$) and the production of 'hot' $3P$ oxygen atoms with excess energy.

It is generally agreed that the first reaction involves excitation of the nitrous oxide molecules and the subsequent formation of oxygen atoms. The alternative reaction to produce nitrogen atoms and nitric oxide has been ruled out by ^{15}N tracer experiments[53]. The oxygen atoms can be removed in the following reactions[51]:

$$O+N_2O \xrightarrow{2} N_2+O_2$$

$$O+N_2O \xrightarrow{3} 2NO$$

$$O+wall \xrightarrow{4} remove$$

$$O+NO \xrightarrow{5} NO_2^* \xrightarrow{M} NO_2+M$$
$$\longrightarrow NO_2+chemiluminescence$$

However, the nitrogen dioxide will decompose or react with nitrous oxide molecules or oxygen atoms:

$$2NO_2 \xrightarrow{6} 2NO+O_2$$

$$N_2O+NO_2 \xrightarrow{7} N_2+NO+O_2$$

$$O+NO_2 \xrightarrow{8} O_2+NO$$

It is therefore difficult to see how nitric oxide, once formed, can be removed from the system. The limiting pressure of nitric oxide must be due to some interference with reaction 3, either by nitric oxide itself or by another of the intermediates or products, without interference with step 2; this must be interpreted by assuming that the oxygen atoms are in different 'states' in steps 2 and 3. Reuben and Linnett[52] have developed schemes to include 'hot' oxygen atom reactions, and they explain the various features of the decomposition more successfully than has been done before, but their scheme is too complicated to be considered here.

The catalytic effect of nitric oxide on the decomposition is attributed to the reaction

$$NO + N_2O \xrightarrow{9} NO_2 + N_2$$

followed by reactions 6 or 7. The kinetics of the bimolecular reaction 9 have been studied by Kaufman and Kelso[54] at temperatures from 650 to 750°C. The reaction is first order with respect to each reactant and the activation energy is about 50 kcal. The catalysed reaction is thus less important at higher temperatures, as the uncatalysed reaction has a much higher activation energy. If the catalysed reaction were important in the higher temperature range, the decomposition would be autocatalytic.

The decomposition is also catalysed by halogens or by substances, such as alkyl halides, that decompose to give halogens. Early work showed that the rate is proportional to the nitrous oxide concentration, and suggested that the rate is also proportional to the halogen atom concentration assuming the atoms to be in equilibrium with the parent molecule. These kinetics have been confirmed in later investigations by Kaufman, Gerri, and Pascale[51]. They consider that the reaction scheme is:

$$Cl_2 + M \xrightarrow{10} 2Cl + M$$

$$Cl + N_2O \xrightarrow{11} N_2 + OCl$$

followed by reactions such as

$$2ClO \xrightarrow{12} Cl_2 + O_2$$

In earlier schemes, it was supposed that the catalysed decomposition was a chain reaction and that the ClO radicals continued the chain by

$$ClO + N_2O \xrightarrow{13} N_2 + O_2 + Cl$$

but Kaufman, Gerri and Pascale consider that its rate is too slow to compete with reaction 12. From their results, assuming reaction 10 and its reverse to be balanced, they find that the activation energy of reaction 11 is 33·5 kcal and that the corresponding energies with bromine or iodine are 37 and 38 kcal. The dissociation energy of reaction 10 is much higher than that of the corresponding reaction for bromine, which in turn is much higher than for iodine. Thus on a *molecular* basis, iodine is much the most effective catalyst. However, Benson and Buss[55] have criticized the two-stage scheme on the grounds that the rate of production of chlorine atoms by step 10 cannot be fast enough to keep up with step 11, and they return to a chain scheme in which ClO radicals yield chlorine atoms without reacting with nitrous oxide molecules. This could occur by the reactions

$$2ClO \rightarrow ClOO + Cl \rightarrow Cl_2 + O_2$$

Benson and Buss consider other possible reactions.

Although the formation of nitric oxide is inhibited by the addition of halogens, it is not negligible, and as soon as some is formed, chlorine atoms could be formed by the reactions

$$NO + Cl_2 \rightarrow NOCl + Cl$$

$$NOCl + M \rightarrow NO + Cl + M$$

It is, therefore, interesting to observe that the addition of nitric oxide and chlorine molecules, or of nitrosyl chloride, scarcely affects the rate of the chlorine-catalysed reaction[56]. This appears to support the contention[51] that the 'equilibrium' value of the chlorine atom concentration is reached rapidly in the chlorine-catalysed reactions. The problem of deciding between a two-stage or a chain reaction can only be settled if an inhibitor can be found and its action can be identified with the removal of ClO radicals before they can regenerate chlorine atoms. Any such inhibitor would probably react with chlorine, however, and the interpretation of the inhibition would be complicated. It may be noted that the activation energies of reaction 11 and the comparable bromine and iodine reactions are very high and this argues against any chain reaction, irrespective of the fate of the ClO radicals.

REFERENCES

[1] BASOLO, F. and PEARSON, R. G. *Mechanisms of Inorganic Reactions*: Wiley, New York, 1958, Chapters 7 and 8

[2] TAUBE, H. *Advanc. inorg. Chem. Radiochem.* 1959, **1**, 1

[3] DAINTON, F. S. *Spec. Publ. chem. Soc. (Lond.)* No. 1, 1954, p. 18

[4] HALPERN, J. *Quart. Rev. (Lond.)* 1961, **15**, 207

[5] TAUBE, H., MYERS, H. and RICH, R. L. *J. Amer. chem. Soc.* 1953, **75**, 4118

[6] TAUBE, H. *J. Amer. chem. Soc.* 1955, **77**, 4481

[7] HUDIS, J. and DODSON, R. W. *J. Amer. chem. Soc.* 1956, **78**, 911

[8a] HABER, F. and WEISS, J. *Proc. R. Soc. A* 1934, **147**, 332 (see p. 351)

[8b] MICHAELIS, L. *Chem. Rev.* 1935, **16**, 243

[9] ASHURST, K. G. and HIGGINSON, W. C. E. *J. chem. Soc.* 1953, p. 3044

[10] BENSON, D., PROLL, P. J., SUTCLIFFE, L. H. and WALKLEY, J. *Disc. Faraday Soc.* 1960, **29**, 60

[11] HARKNESS, A. C. and HALPERN, J. *J. Amer. chem. Soc.* 1959, **81**, 3526

[12] HALPERN, J. and SMITH, J. G. *Canad. J. Chem.* 1956, **34**, 1419

[13] HIGGINSON, W. C. E., ROSSEINSKY, D. R., STEAD, J. B. and SYKES, A. G. *Disc. Faraday Soc.* 1960, **29**, 49

[14] TAUBE, H. *J. Amer. chem. Soc.* 1947, **69**, 1418

[15] TAUBE, H. *J. Amer. chem. Soc.* 1948, **70**, 1216

[16] DUKE, F. R. *J. Amer. chem. Soc.* 1947, **69**, 2885

[17] HARCOURT, A. V. and ESSON, W. *Phil. Trans.* 1866, **156**, 193

[18] LADBURY, J. W. and CULLIS, C. F. *Chem. Rev.* 1958, **58**, 403

[19] MALCOLM, J. and NOYES, R. M. *J. Amer. chem. Soc.* 1952, **74**, 276g

[20] BAXENDALE, J. H. *Advanc. Catalys.* 1952, **4**, 31

[21] WEISS, J. *Advanc. Catalys.* 1952, **4**, 343

[22] BRAY, W. C. *Chem. Rev.* 1932, **10**, 161

[23] ABEL, E. *Z. phys. Chem. (Leipzig)* 1920, **96**, 1; 1928, **136**, 161; *Mh. Chem.* 1948, **79**, 178

[24] BARB, W. G., BAXENDALE, J. H., GEORGE, P. and HARGRAVE, K. R. *Trans. Faraday Soc.* 1951, **47**, 462, 591

REFERENCES

[25] BARB, W. G., BAXENDALE, J. H., GEORGE, P. and HARGRAVE, K. R. *Trans Faraday Soc.* 1955, **51**, 935

[26] HALPERN, J. *Quart. Rev. (Lond.)* 1956, **10**, 463

[27] HALPERN, J. *Advanc. Catalys.* 1959, **11**, 301

[28] CALVIN, M. *Trans. Faraday Soc.* 1938, **34**, 1181

[29] WEBSTER, A. H. and HALPERN, J. *J. phys. Chem.* 1956, **60**, 280

[30] WEBSTER, A. H. and HALPERN, J. *J. phys. Chem.* 1957, **61**, 1239, 1245

[31] HALPERN, J., MACGREGOR, E. R. and PETERS, E. *J. phys. Chem.* 1956, **60**, 1455

[32] PETERS, E. and HALPERN, J. *J. phys. Chem.* 1955, **59**, 793

[33] MACGREGOR, E. R. and HALPERN, J. *Trans. Amer. Inst. min. metall. petrol. Engrs* 1958, **212**, 244

[34] PETERS, E. and HALPERN, J. *Canad. J. Chem.* 1955, **33**, 356; 1956, **34**, 554

[35] OGG, R. A. and WILSON, M. K. *J. chem. Phys.* 1950, **18**, 900

[36] RAY, J. D. and OGG, R. A. *J. chem. Phys.* 1957, **26**, 984

[37] GERSHINOWITZ, H. and EYRING, H. *J. Amer. chem. Soc.* 1935, **57**, 985

[38] ASHMORE, P. G., BURNETT, M. G. and TYLER, B. J. *Trans. Faraday Soc.* 1962, **58**, 685

[39a] ASHMORE, P. G. and LEVITT, B. P. *Research, Lond.* 1954, **7**, 335

[39b] ASHMORE, P. G. and BURNETT, M. G. *Trans. Faraday Soc.* 1962, **58**, 253

[40] ASHMORE, P. G. and SPENCER, M. S. *Trans. Faraday Soc.* 1959, **55**, 1868

[41] ASHMORE, P. G. and BURNETT, M. G. *Trans. Faraday Soc.* 1961, **57**, 1315; 1962, **58**, 1801

[42] CORDES, H. F. and JOHNSTON, H. S. *J. Amer. chem. Soc.* 1954, **76**, 4264

[43] BENSON, S. W. *Foundations of Chemical Kinetics*: McGraw-Hill, New York, 1960

[44] VON KISS, A. *Rec. Trav. chim. Pays-Bas* 1923, **42**, 112; 1924, **43**, 68

[45] FROST, A. N. and PEARSON, R. G. *Kinetics and Mechanism*: Wiley, New York, 1953, Ch. 11H

[46] SCHUMACHER, H. J. and SPRENGER, G. Z. *phys. Chem. (Leipzig)* 1928, **A136**, 77; 1929, **B2**, 267

[47] BENSON, S. W. *Foundations of Chemical Kinetics*: McGraw-Hill, New York, 1960, p. 406

[48] JOHNSTON, H. S. *J. chem. Phys.* 1951, **19**, 663

[49] LINDARS, F. J. and HINSHELWOOD, C. N. *Proc. R. Soc. A* 1955, **23**, 162, 178

[50] KAUFMAN, F., GERRI, N. J. and BOWMAN, R. E. *J. chem. Phys.* 1956, **25**, 106

[51] KAUFMAN, F., GERRI, N. J. and PASCALE, D. A. *J. chem. Phys.* 1956, **24**, 32

[52] REUBEN, B. G. and LINNETT, J. W. *Trans. Faraday Soc.* 1959, **55**, 1543

[53] FRIEDMAN, L. and BIGELEISEN, J. *J. Amer. chem. Soc.* 1953, **75**, 2215

[54] KAUFMAN, F. and KELSO, J. R. *J. chem. Phys.* 1955, **23**, 602

[55] BENSON, S. W. and BUSS, J. H. *J. chem. Phys.* 1957, **27**, 1382

[56] ASHMORE, P. G. and HERTL, W.—unpublished

4

ENZYME-CATALYSED REACTIONS

4.1. INTRODUCTION

ENZYMES are catalysts for the reactions which occur in living matter. Many enzymes have now been isolated as pure crystalline substances. Some of these crystalline enzymes appear to be pure proteins; this is true of pepsin, one of the proteolytic enzymes which catalyse the hydrolysis of the peptide link (—CO—NH—) in proteins, and of urease which catalyses the hydrolysis of urea. Others contain a *prosthetic group*, essential for the catalytic activity, in addition to the protein; often the prosthetic group is a flavin, as in various enzymes which catalyse oxidation–reduction reactions, or a haem, as in catalase and peroxidases which catalyse certain reactions of hydrogen peroxide. Some other enzymes are only active if a *cofactor* is present in addition to the substrate. The cofactor, like the enzyme, takes part like the enzyme-catalysed reaction but is not destroyed; it may be a simple structure chemically, such as an inorganic ion, when it is called an *activator*, or it may be a complex organic molecule known as a *coenzyme*. The cofactors appear to function like prosthetic groups (or like parts of such groups) that are easily dissociated from the enzyme. Although the distinction between cofactors and prosthetic groups within an enzyme is obviously important biologically, it may be rather artificial as far as the catalytic mechanism is concerned.

The enzyme itself, or the enzyme in the presence of the cofactor, is thought to provide active sites or *active centres* at which the catalysed reaction occurs. It is probable that each molecule of activated enzyme contains only a few active centres (indeed often only one), and that each active centre is poly-functional in that certain parts of it may hold the substrate in a position where the other parts cause changes in the chemical bonding of the substrate and so *activate* it for the reaction being catalysed. The detailed configuration of the enzyme molecule—including the conformation of the protein in folds or coils as well as the chemical structure near the active centre—may be very impor-tant. Thus the activity of the enzyme can be destroyed by heat or by chemical reagents (such as acids, bases, or concentrated solutions of salts) which alter the conformation of the protein by *denaturation*. The activity can also be destroyed by *inhibitors*. These generally function by reaction with the active centres and have been used to determine the number of active centres in each enzyme molecule as well as to give some indication of their chemical structure.

The concept of an active centre with rather precise steric properties provides, at present, the most logical explanation of one of the important properties of enzymes as catalysts, that is their very high *specificity*. Enzymes are specific for certain types of reaction, such as the hydrolysis of certain links or the transfer of certain groups, and may even be specific for certain substrates among a

74

large number possessing those links. In most, if not all cases, enzymes catalyse the reactions of only one of a pair of optical enantiomorphs. Thus any detailed mechanisms of the reactions of enzymes must be able to account for chemical and stereochemical specificity. The problems involved are often similar to those encountered in the interpretation of the functioning of Ziegler-type catalysts (see section 10.4) in the preparation of stereoregular polymers.

These properties of enzymes have been summarized by Dixon and Webb[1] and in their definition 'an enzyme is a protein with catalytic properties due to its power of specific activation'.

The number of known enzymes is very large. In 1958, Dixon and Webb[2] were able to list more than 650, and it is certain that many more will be identified as different animal, plant, mould, bacterial and virus reactions are studied. In the absence of detailed knowledge about the structure of individual enzymes, and of the mechanisms of their action, it has been found convenient to arrange the enzymes in groups according to the type of reaction they catalyse. One very large group contains the *hydrolysing enzymes*, and it can be subdivided according to the particular link hydrolysed. Thus the peptidases catalyse the hydrolysis of the peptide link —CO—NH , the glycosidases catalyse the hydrolysis of the glycoside link in glycosides or polysaccharides, the esterases the ester link in carboxylic, phosphate or sulphate esters, and so on. Another large group contains the *transferring* enzymes which catalyse the transfer from a substrate to an acceptor molecule of a particular chemical group such as a hydrogen atom, a phosphate group, a glycosyl group or an acyl group. The reactions involving hydrogen-atom transfer are often concerned with the production of energy in living tissues, and the enzymes are called oxidases if the transfer is to or from molecular oxygen, but dehydrogenases if the transfer is to or from other molecules. Outside these two large groups are many smaller groups, for example those enzymes that catalyse non-oxidative decarboxylations, or additions to double bonds and the reverse decompositions, or changes of steric configuration.

There is no systemic nomenclature for enzymes. Some have a traditional name, such as pepsin, trypsin and rennin; others are named after a substrate in the reaction catalysed, for instance urease or fumarase; more recently, longer names which describe in more detail the reaction catalysed, such as maltose transglucosylase (catalysing the transfer of a glucose group from maltose to receptor molecules), have been adopted.

Although kinetic studies of some sort have been made on many of the enzymes now known, detailed and extensive investigations have been made on only a few. These include[3] the peptidases pepsin, trypsin, chymotrypsin and carboxypeptidase; the esterases cholinesterase and adenosinetriphosphatase; urease; fumarase; lactic dehydrogenase; and peroxidase and catalase.

These studies have shown that enzymes are extraordinarily effective catalysts compared with any others known in homogeneous non-chain reactions. The comparison has been made in many different ways by different investigators, and the two most useful measures (the *turnover number* and the *velocity constant*) are discussed in some detail later in this chapter. In any reasonable comparison, enzymes turn out to be many orders of magnitude more effective than, for example, hydrogen or hydroxyl ions as catalysts of hydrolyses, or metal ion catalysts in oxidation–reduction catalysis. For example, urease is about 10^{14} times as effective, molecule for ion, as hydrogen ions in the hydrolysis of urea, and catalase is about 10^6 times as effective as ferrous ion for the decomposition of hydrogen peroxide (see *Table 4.2*).

These very high 'yields' are reminiscent of photochemical chain reactions, and several investigators have suggested that enzyme reactions proceed by chain mechanisms. On this view, the high rates could be explained by the enzyme initiating chains, just as high rates of polymerization can be obtained with ionic or redox catalysts. Inhibitors could act by removing chain centres and so curtailing the chain length. Thus Haber and Willstätter[4] proposed that catalase initiated a chain decomposition in hydrogen peroxide

Initiation: $\quad H_2O_2 + catalase \rightarrow HO_2 + deoxycatalase$
Propagation: $\quad HO_2 + H_2O_2 \rightarrow H_2O + O_2 + OH$
$\qquad\qquad\qquad OH + H_2O_2 \rightarrow HO_2 + H_2O$

Rather similar schemes were given for the catalysis by dehydrogenases and oxidases, 'mutase', glyoxalase and peroxidases. Waters[5] also developed chain mechanisms for some oxidative enzymes. It is very difficult to account for the specificity of enzymes and also of coenzymes with chain mechanisms. The effectiveness of catalysts or initiators of chain reactions depends fundamentally upon the reaction having a high chain length, that is, a high value of the ratio rate of propagation/rate of termination. Once this is available, almost any substance that can decompose to give free radicals which can initiate chains at a moderate rate R_i will produce a fast rate of the chain reaction equal to $R_i \times$ (chain length). It is hard to reconcile this 'unspecific' behaviour of catalysts for free-radical chain reactions with the very specific behaviour of enzymes. In addition, no positive evidence for free radicals in enzyme reactions has been produced, indeed the evidence is that free radicals (formed for instance by irradiation) destroy the activity of enzymes. There is also evidence[6,7] against free radicals or free protons in some hydrogen transfer reactions, because the hydrogen transferred does not exchange with the solvent. It therefore seems very unlikely that enzymes act by initiating chains with either free radicals or free radical-ions as chain carriers. On the other hand, some of the difficulties mentioned above disappear if the enzyme is assumed to take part in a propagation step; this step could be highly specific. In fact, all catalysed reactions which proceed through intermediate complexes could be looked on as chain reactions. The catalyst disappears in one step—the reaction with the substrate—only to reappear in a later step just as the chain centre reappears in a propagation step. However, it is not very profitable to press this analogy further.

Some of the features of enzyme-catalysed reactions are similar to those found in heterogeneous reactions, for example the form of the rate laws and the action of inhibitors[8]. Bayliss suggested[9] a mechanism of enzyme catalysis based on the adsorption of the substrate at the surface of the enzyme, followed by reaction of the adsorption compound. There is now more detailed evidence[1,3,8] that specific chemical reaction occurs between substrate and enzyme, just as between substrate and heterogeneous catalyst surface, rather than mere physical adsorption. When more is known about the structure of the active sites in the enzyme molecule, there will be a real need to consider the 'surface geometry' of the enzyme molecule; in the meantime, it is often sufficient to consider the combination between the substrate S and the enzyme molecule E as a whole. Most enzyme mechanisms are modifications of the simple pattern of reaction of intermediate compounds or complexes which has been outlined in Chapter 1. The modifications have been proposed by many investigators, but the contributions by Michaelis and Menten[10] and by Briggs and Haldane[11] have proved particularly important and influential.

4.2. INTERMEDIATE COMPLEXES

The kinetics of enzyme reactions have been formulated in terms of these intermediate complexes for many years. The earliest systematic studies appear to be those of Henri[12] and of Brown[13] on the hydrolysis of sucrose in the presence of invertase from yeast. Brown found that the initial rates were proportional to the sucrose concentration at low concentrations but independent of it at higher concentrations. During a particular run the rates did not follow a simple law but decreased more rapidly than would be expected from the initial rate law with both the low and high concentrations. Brown showed that the initial rates could be explained if the enzyme and the sucrose form a complex which is hydrolysed to the products glucose and fructose; increasing the sucrose concentration eventually converts practically all the available enzyme into complex, so that the rate cannot further increase. The effects during a run were explained by postulating that the products inactivate the enzyme; it is now known that the fructose competes with the sucrose for the enzyme and produces an inactive complex.

These features are characteristic of the reactions of many enzymes. It has proved difficult to interpret the results obtained during the course of any single experiment, and investigators have concentrated upon the examination of initial rates. These initial rate studies have shown that the effects of substrate concentration, of enzyme concentration, of pH, of inhibitors (including inhibition by the products and, rather unexpectedly, by the substrate itself) and of temperature can all be explained in terms of intermediate complexes, each undergoing a limited number of reactions.

This theory requires that the intermediate complex is reactive and unstable, and hence it is very unlikely that any intermediate complex could be isolated and studied directly. On the other hand, the theory postulates that inhibitors also act by complexing with the enzyme to give comparatively stable compounds. The successful isolation and identification of some inhibitor–enzyme compounds provides important support for the theory. Such complexes are formed between trypsin[14] or chymotrypsin[15] and the inhibitor of formula $(iso\text{-}C_3H_7O)_2P{\overset{\nearrow O}{\underset{\diagdown F}{}}}$ (known widely as di-isopropylfluorophosphate, DFP, but more properly called di-isopropylphosphofluoridate, DPF) and in these and some other cases one molecule of enzyme combines with one molecule of inhibitor. There is additional evidence that the inhibitor combines with the enzyme only when the active centres are present, so these enzymes appear to contain one active centre per molecule. Similar conclusions have been reached from experiments with other less effective reversible inhibitors by studying[16] equilibria of the general type: $E + I = EI$. Other enzymes contain more than one active centre in each molecule; for example, studies [17] of the inhibition of urease by silver ions suggest three or four. Degradation studies of the enzyme–inhibitor compounds have given some information about the chemical nature of the active centres but detailed interpretation is complicated by the possibility of group transfer reactions during the degradations.

With some enzymes, relatively stable complexes are formed with the coenzymes. These can be studied by ultracentrifuging the solution and so separating the enzyme; in this way, it has been estimated [18,19] that one molecule of the enzyme glyceraldehyde-3-phosphate dehydrogenase combines with two molecules of Coenzyme I (diphosphopyridine nucleotide, DPN), and yeast alcohol dehydrogenase combines with four molecules of DPN; in each case combination occurs at the active centres.

Direct evidence for the existence of labile intermediates in the reactions of catalase and peroxidases with hydrogen peroxide have been obtained from spectrophotometric studies. Thus hydrogen peroxide and peroxidase give four complexes, two of which are catalytically inactive [20]. The kinetics of their interconversion, and of their reaction with hydrogen donors, have been studied extensively [21]. Laidler has indicated [22] sources of spectrophotometric evidence for other complexes.

Isotopic tracer studies and isotopic exchange reactions have also given some interesting information about the complexes formed between substrates and enzymes. Consider first the reaction catalysed by the enzyme sucrose trans-glucosylase (usually known as sucrose phosphorylase):

$$\alpha\text{-glucose-1-phosphate} + \text{fructose} \rightleftharpoons \alpha\text{-glucose-1-fructose} + \text{phosphate}$$

If this reaction proceeds in two steps in the presence of the enzyme, by successive transfer of the glucosyl group

$$\alpha\text{-G-1-P} + \text{E} \rightleftharpoons \alpha\text{-G-1-E} + \text{P}$$

$$\alpha\text{-G-1-E} + \text{F} \rightleftharpoons \alpha\text{-G-1-F} + \text{E}$$

and the phosphate and fructose groups are 'free', then it should be possible (i) to exchange labelled (^{32}P) phosphate with glucose-1-phosphate in the absence of fructose [23], and (ii) to exchange labelled (^{14}C) fructose with sucrose in the absence of phosphate [24]. Moreover, glucose-1-phosphate should exchange the phosphate group for arsenate to give glucose-1-arsenate, which is readily hydrolysed, in the presence of the enzyme. These reactions have been shown [23,24] to occur in the presence of the enzyme but not in its absence. The equations shown, with fructose and phosphate groups 'free', provide the simplest explanation of them. However, it is also possible that the phosphate and fructose are bound to the enzyme, but by weak bonds that allow some dissociation and hence some exchange. The reactions would then be written

$$\text{GF} + \text{E} \rightleftharpoons \text{GEF} \rightleftharpoons \text{F} + \text{GE}$$

$$\text{GP} + \text{E} \rightleftharpoons \text{GEP} \rightleftharpoons \text{P} + \text{GE}$$

Such a mechanism would require several sites at the active centre, and so may be more specific than the simpler mechanism. In a similar manner, the evidence [25] that the enzyme arylamine transacetylase catalyses the exchange in acetyl-arylamine of labelled arylamine but not of labelled acetate suggests that the acetyl group is attached to the enzyme, but the arylamine is free or very weakly bound; again, the results require the binding of at least part of the substrate to the enzyme.

Isotopic labelling of suitable atoms in the substrates has also been used to detect which bonds are broken in the reaction. Thus ^{18}O has been used to show that enzymes assist the cleavage of specific bonds in the phosphate esters; for example[26], when glucose-1-phosphate is hydrolysed with sucrose trans-glucoslyase (phosphorylase) the bond split is G—OPO_3 but with acid or alkaline phosphatase it is GO—PO_3. Similarly, 'sucrase' is specific for the O—fructosyl bond[27]. It is again very difficult to explain these specificities unless compounds are formed between groups in the substrate and the enzymes.

It must be emphasized, however, that there is ample evidence that *group* transfer between substrate and enzyme does not always occur. Thus the reaction catalysed by maltose phosphorylase

$$\beta\text{-G-1-P}+G \rightleftharpoons \alpha\text{-G-1-G}+P$$

appears formally to be similar to the reaction of α-G-1-P with fructose, except for the inversion. However, the reactions

$$\beta\text{-G-1-P}+P^* \rightleftharpoons \beta\text{-G-1-P}^*+P$$

$$\alpha\text{-G-1-G}+G^* \rightleftharpoons \alpha\text{-G-1-G}^*+G$$

are not catalysed by the enzyme[28]. To explain these results, and also the inversion, it is thought that the substrates complex with the enzyme without splitting, and that reaction then occurs between them as a direct transfer of the groups concerned.

Another example where group transfer to the enzyme apparently does not take place is provided by acetokinase, which catalyses the transfer of phosphate between acetate and adenosinetriphosphate (ATP) to give adenosinediphosphate (ADP) and acetylphosphate. However, this enzyme will not catalyse the incorporation of labelled ADP into ATP (unless acetate is also present), nor of labelled acetate into acetylphosphate (unless ADP is also added), nor of labelled phosphate into ATP[29]. Other examples have been listed[30].

In summary, although it has not been proved that intermediate complexes occur in all enzyme-catalysed reactions, there is enough evidence for their formation in some of the reactions to provide a sound basis for mechanisms based on intermediate complexes. With several enzymes, the evidence suggests that there are only a few active sites associated with each enzyme molecule, and that the bonds between substrate and enzyme are not always those involved in the reaction that is being catalysed.

4.3. KINETIC MECHANISMS FOR SINGLE SUBSTRATE REACTIONS (SCHEME I)

Most of the reactions catalysed by enzymes are bimolecular reactions, involving, for example, the transfer of a group between two substrates or the hydrolysis of a substrate. Historically, however, the treatment of the kinetics of enzyme reactions has been dominated by the early formulation of rate laws in terms of a single substrate. In the hydrolytic reactions, which have been studied extensively, the reactant water is in such great excess that its concentration changes only very slightly, with very little effect on the velocity of the reaction; only in concentrated solutions of very soluble substrates such as sucrose, or in mixed solvents, does the concentration of the water change sufficiently to affect the velocity[31]. Where the rate of hydrolysis is independent of the solvent concentration, the reaction scheme involving an intermediate complex between the substrate and the enzyme can be written:

Scheme I:

$$E + S \underset{k_2}{\overset{k_1}{\rightleftharpoons}} ES$$

$$ES \overset{k_3}{\longrightarrow} E + P$$

The first systematic treatment of Scheme I for the kinetics of single substrate reactions was given by Michaelis and Menten[10], but the steady-state treatment developed by Briggs and Haldane[11] is more versatile and more in line with the treatment of unstable reactive intermediates in other types of reaction. It assumes that the concentration of the intermediate complex rapidly reaches a stationary value. The rate expressions are also simplified by assuming—as is certainly true in all practical cases—that the concentration of the enzyme is much lower than that of the substrate. From the above reaction scheme

$$\frac{d[ES]}{dt} = k_1[E][S] - k_2[ES] - k_3[ES] = 0$$

$$[ES] = \frac{k_1[E][S]}{k_2 + k_3}$$

The rate of reaction is equal to $k_3[ES]$ and hence

$$V = \frac{d[P]}{dt} = \frac{k_1 k_3 [E][S]}{k_2 + k_3} \tag{4.1}$$

To derive the initial rate in terms of the initial concentrations $[E]_0$ and $[S]_0$, it is necessary to put $[E] = [E]_0 - [ES]$ and $[S] = [S]_0 - [ES]$ in the expression for the rate of change of $[ES]$ with time. However, $[ES]$ cannot be greater than $[E]_0$; whenever $[E]_0$ is much smaller than $[S]_0$ it is clear that $[S]_0 - [ES] \simeq [S]_0$. Then:

$$\frac{d[ES]}{dt} = k_1[S]_0([E]_0 - [ES]) - k_2[ES] - k_3[ES] = 0$$

$$[ES] = \frac{k_1[S]_0[E]_0}{k_2 + k_3 + k_1[S]_0} \tag{4.2'}$$

$$V_0 = \left(\frac{d[P]}{dt}\right)_0 = \frac{k_1 k_3 [S]_0 [E]_0}{k_2 + k_3 + k_1[S]_0} \tag{4.2}$$

As most investigations have been made using initial rates, the second equation is perhaps more important and certainly better known†. It predicts that initial

† The similarity of equation (4.2′) to the Langmuir equation relating amount of gas adsorbed ($\equiv [ES]$) on a surface to the pressure of the gas ($\equiv [S]_0$) may be noted; equation (4.2) is formally similar to the rate equations for heterogeneously-catalysed unimolecular reactions. The similarity is due to similar formulations of the problems, of course, and does not imply that enzyme and heterogeneous reactions proceed by similar molecular steps.

rate will be proportional to the initial concentration of the enzyme, if this is varied while the initial concentration of the substrate is held constant. If the concentration of the enzyme is constant, then the initial rate will be proportional to the initial concentration of the substrate provided that this concentration is low, but at higher concentrations the rate tends to a maximum value given by

$$V_{max} = k_3[E]_0 \qquad (4.3)$$

Thus k_3 can be determined from the values of V_{max} and $[E]_0$. An alternative expression for the initial rate is

$$V = \frac{V_{max}S}{S1 + \dfrac{K}{[S]_0}} \qquad (4.4)$$

where K is a ratio of velocity constants equal to $(k_2 + k_3)/k_1$ with the dimensions of concentration. K is numerically equal to the value of the initial substrate

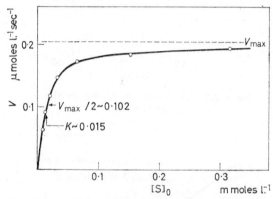

Figure 4.1. Hydrolysis of ATP catalysed by myosin
(From data given by Ouellet, Laidler and Morales[32])

concentration which gives an initial velocity equal to one-half of the maximum initial velocity V_{max}.

Some results which show the features mentioned above are plotted in *Figure 4.1*, from data given by Ouellet *et al.*[32], for the hydrolysis of ATP catalysed by myosin. Several methods of plotting the results have been devised which allow the determination of V_{max} without using very high values of $[S]_0$; they are similar to plots used to determine the constants of the Langmuir equation for the adsorption of gases on surfaces. Equation (4.4) can be transposed to give

$$\frac{1}{V} = \frac{1}{V_{max}} + \frac{K}{V_{max}[S]_0} \qquad (4.5)$$

Hence a plot of $1/V$ against $1/[S]_0$ should give a straight line of slope K/V_{max} and intercept of $1/V_{max}$ on the $1/V$ axis; from the slope and the intercept V_{max} and K can therefore be determined. An example is shown in *Figure 4.2*. Such plots are now known as Lineweaver–Burk[33] plots. In another similar method

$[S]_0 V$ is plotted against $[S]_0$; the slope is then $1/V_{max}$ and the intercept K/V_{max} Alternatively, by cross-multiplication the equation gives

$$V + \frac{K V}{[S]_0} = V_{max} \qquad (4.6)$$

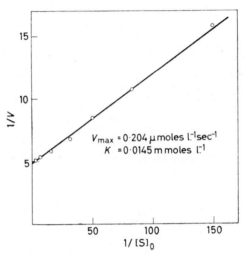

Figure 4.2. Lineweaver–Burk plot for the data of *Figure 4.1*

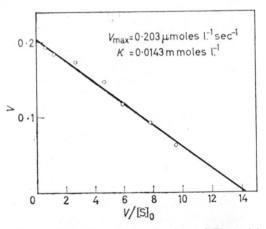

Figure 4.3. Eadie plot for the data of *Figure 4.1*

Hence a plot of V against $V/[S]_0$ should give a straight line of slope $(-K)$ and intercept on the V axis equal to V_{max}. An example is shown in *Figure 4.3*. Plots like these are known as Eadie plots[34]. They have the advantages of spreading the points evenly and of determining V_{max} and K separately.

It is not possible to determine k_1 and k_2 from these steady-state measurements on these simple single-substrate systems.

82

Rather more restrictive assumptions were made by Michaelis and Menten [10] in their derivation of an initial rate equation published some twelve years before the work of Briggs and Haldane [11]. They assumed that the rate of breakdown of the intermediate complex ES to give product ($k_3[ES]$) is very slow compared with its return to the initial reactants ($k_2[ES]$) so that the initial reversible reactions 1 and 2 control the concentration of ES. Their equation can be derived from equation (4.2) by neglecting k_3 in comparison with k_2, giving

$$V = \frac{k_1 k_3 [S]_0 [E]_0}{k_2 + k_1 [S]_0} = \frac{V_M}{1 + \dfrac{K_M}{[S]_0}} \tag{4.7}$$

The equations are seen to be of the same form as equations (4.2) and (4.4), but the constant K_M (the Michaelis constant) is the dissociation constant of the complex ES. The maximum rate is again equal to $k_3[E]_0$. The Lineweaver–Burk or Eadie plots should again be linear, and from them V_{max} and K_{max} could be determined. However, k_1 and k_2 could not be determined separately from these steady-state measurements.

Unfortunately, it is not possible to tell whether linear plots of steady-state rates (either Lineweaver–Burk or Eadie) give K or K_M. It would be interesting to derive K_M at different temperatures and so relate the stability of the complex, measured by K_M, and its reactivity, measured by k_3, to its chemical composition and eventually to its structure. Rather paradoxically it is possible to obtain this information for certain bimolecular reactions from steady-state kinetics—in fact to determine k_1 and k_2 as well as k_3—in spite of the fact that the kinetics are more complicated than those considered here; this arises because the other substrate allows the variation of another factor affecting the rate and hence the derivation of another equation connecting the constants in a different way. In some reactions of catalase and peroxidase, it has been possible to follow [20] the increase in concentration of the enzyme–substrate complex during the early stages of the reaction, using rapid mixing techniques and measuring the concentration of the complex spectrophotometrically. By these means, k_1 and k_2 can be determined.

Another useful method of separating the constants for the simple systems has been devised and applied to some hydrolyses. In this method the over-all kinetics of the brief pre-steady state are studied, using rapid mixing and analysis techniques. During this transient phase, it has been shown [35] that the amount of product P formed in time t is given by

$$P = k_1 k_3 [E]_0 [S]_0 t^2 / 2 \tag{4.8}$$

Thus the measurements allow the determination of the product $k_1 k_3$, and as k_3 can be determined from the maximum initial rate, k_1 can be determined. When P is plotted against t, the initial curve becomes linear as soon as the steady state is reached; the intercept obtained by extrapolating the linear portion to cut the time axis is related to k_1 and this gives another method of determining k_1. Measurements [36] made on the hydrolysis of synthetic amino acid esters in the presence of trypsin or chymotrypsin show that k_3 is certainly less than k_2 for each of these systems, and may be much less.

Laidler has listed [37] other methods by which it is possible to decide whether the Michaelis condition holds, i.e. $k_3 \ll k_2$. It appears that it holds for many of the systems studied, and that the reverse condition ($k_3 \gg k_2$) holds only for the decomposition of hydrogen peroxide with catalase, the oxidation of certain acceptors by hydrogen peroxide with peroxidase (these are strictly bimolecular reactions, proceeding by scheme II (page 89), but as explained later these kinetics are very similar to those of simple substrate reactions with k_3 replaced by $k_3[H_2O_2]$), and some hydrolyses with carboxypeptidase, among the systems studied up to 1958.

4.4.   INHIBITORS OF SINGLE-SUBSTRATE REACTIONS

Inhibitors of enzyme catalyses have often been classed as reversible or irreversible. This is based on the ease of removal, or otherwise, of the inhibitor from the enzyme by a physical method such as dialysis. Thus eserine is described as a reversible inhibitor, while the phosphorus compounds like DPF are irreversible inhibitors, of cholinesterase. As far as mechanisms of inhibition are concerned, however, the classification is rather misleading because it suggests that reversible and irreversible inhibitors act in different ways; in fact, they both act by combining with the enzyme to give inactive complexes, but with very different 'dissociation constants'. The irreversible inhibitors give complexes with very small dissociation constants, and so are removed from the complex by dialysis only very slowly, whereas the reversible inhibitors have high dissociation constants and there is plenty of uncombined inhibitor to dialyse at all stages of the removal.

However, a distinction which is more useful is that between competitive and non-competitive inhibitors (although many inhibitors show 'mixed' behaviour) for these operate in different ways and produce different rate laws. Competitive inhibitors combine with the enzyme at the same site as does the substrate and so block reaction 1 of the schemes. Non-competitive inhibitors combine with the enzyme at some other site to give a complex which can still combine with the substrate, but the resulting ternary complex is unreactive. It is obvious that where the reaction catalysed by the enzyme is really a bimolecular reaction proceeding by scheme III (page 89), then an inhibitor could be regarded as non-competitive with substrate 1 which combines with the enzyme at point 1′ on the active site when it is actually competitive with substrate 2 (or a coenzyme) combining at some other point 2′ on the active site. There are too few examples of complete investigations of the kinetics of inhibited bimolecular reactions to say whether this occurs. Although inhibitors have been used to identify intermediates in enzyme reactions, to determine the number of active sites and to obtain information about the chemical groups in those sites, these objects could be achieved without detailed study of the kinetics.

However, the results to be expected from competitive or non-competitive inhibition of a single substrate have been carefully worked out and several distinguishing tests have been described. With *competitive inhibition*, another reaction has to be added to the simple scheme I:

$$I + E \rightleftharpoons IE$$

It is assumed that the complex IE is unable to take part in the catalysis. The effect is a depletion of the active complex ES. If the dissociation constant of the complex is K_I (corresponding to the Michaelis constant, K_M, for the complex ES) and if $[IE] \ll [I]$, so that $[I] \simeq [I]_0$ it can be easily shown that the velocity is

$$V_I = \frac{V_{max}}{\dfrac{K}{[S]_0}\left(+\dfrac{[I]_0}{K_I}\right) + 1} \tag{4.9}$$

where V_{max} has the same value as before (i.e. $k_3[E]_0$) and K has the same meaning as before (i.e. $(k_2 + k_3)/k_1$). Thus the effect of the inhibitor is to introduce the factor $(1 + [I]_0/K_I)$ and as the value of k_3 is not altered while that of $[I]_0$ can be increased, the effect is to give the complex an apparently increasing dissociation constant. The equation can be transformed for the Lineweaver–Burk and the Eadie plots to give

$$\frac{1}{V_I} = \frac{1}{V_{max}} + \frac{K}{V_{max}[S]_0}\left(1 + \frac{[I]_0}{K_I}\right) \tag{4.10}$$

and

$$V_I = -\frac{KV_I}{[S]_0}\left(1 + \frac{[I]_0}{K_I}\right) + V_{max} \tag{4.11}$$

Hence the Lineweaver–Burk plots will all pass through the same point on the $1/V$ axis but their slope will increase as the concentration $[I]_0$ of inhibitor increases. From a plot of the slopes against the appropriate values of $[I]_0$, K_I can be determined. The Eadie plots similarly all pass through the same point, $V_I = V_{max}$, and their slopes $-K\{1 + ([I]_0/K_I)\}$ will also vary with $[I]_0$ so that from them K_I can be determined. Schematic plots of the lines are shown in *Figure 4.4*.

Dixon[38] has pointed out that if experiments are carried out with $[S]_0$ constant and $[I]_0$ varying, plots of $1/V_I$ against $[I]_0$ will be linear. Their slopes will be equal to $K/K_I V_{max}[S]_0$ and they will all intersect at a point $-[I]_0 = K_I$, $1/V = 1/V_{max}$, as shown schematically in *Figure 4.4*.

A simple scheme for *non-competitive inhibition* of single-substrate reactions can be set up by adding to scheme I the reaction

$$ES + I \rightleftharpoons ESI$$

However, it appears to be too simple to assume that ESI cannot be formed by the sequence $E + I \rightleftharpoons EI$, $EI + S \rightleftharpoons ESI$, and when these reactions are added, it is difficult to solve the stationary-state equations. The rate equations which are usually employed are derived[39] by making the additional assumptions that

(*i*) The Michaelis–Menten conditions apply, that is, the concentration of ES, EI and ESI are controlled by the equilibria (with *dissociation* constants as shown)

$$E + I \rightleftharpoons EI \qquad K_I$$

$$E + S \rightleftharpoons ES \qquad K_M$$

$$ES + I \rightleftharpoons ESI \qquad K'_I$$

$$EI + S \rightleftharpoons ESI \qquad K'_M$$

(*ii*) The combination of S with E does not affect the combination of I with E, so that $K_M = K'_M$ and $K_I = K'_I$. It can be shown that:

$$V_I = \frac{k_3[E]_0}{\left(1+\dfrac{[I]_0}{K_I}\right)\left(1+\dfrac{K_M}{[S]_0}\right)} \equiv \frac{V_{I,\,max}}{1+\dfrac{K_M}{[S]_0}} \qquad (4.12)$$

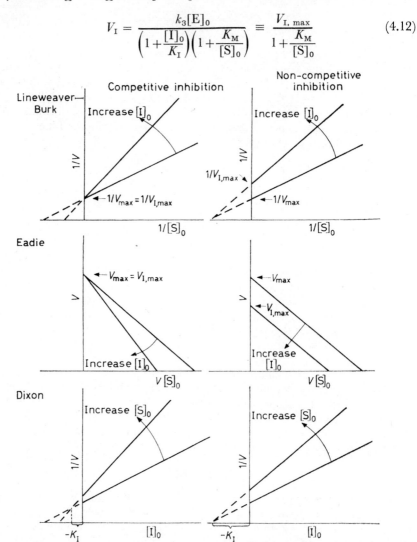

Figure 4.4. Schematic plots for competitive and non-competitive inhibition

Comparison with the equation for V in the absence of the inhibitor shows that the effect of the non-competitive inhibitor is to reduce the velocity of breakdown of the complex by the factor $1/(1+[I]_0/K_I)$ so that the maximum velocity $V_{I,max}$ (when $[S]_0$ is increased) is dependent on the concentration of inhibitor, $[I]_0$. K_I could be determined from the variation of the maximum velocities $V_{I,max}$ with $[I]_0$, these being determined as usual from Lineweaver–Burk or Eadie plots, or from Dixon plots, as illustrated in *Figure 4.4*.

A curious feature of some single-substrate reactions is that the rate increases to a maximum, but then diminishes, as the concentration of substrate is increased. This has been attributed to inhibition by the substrate itself. Competitive inhibition is conceivable; the substrate could combine with the correct point in the active site but with an incorrect, fixed orientation. However, substitution of $[I]_0$ by $[S]_0$ in equation (4.9) leads to an equation

$$V_I = V_{max}/\left(1+\frac{K}{K_I}+\frac{K}{[S]_0}\right)$$

and this would not show a decreasing rate at high substrate concentrations. On the other hand, the equation for non-competitive inhibitions would give

$$V_I = \frac{k_3[E]_0}{\left(1+\frac{[S]_0}{K_I}\right)\left(1+\frac{K_M}{[S]_0}\right)} = \frac{k_3[E]_0}{1+\frac{[S]_0}{K_I}+\frac{K_M}{[S]_0}+\frac{K_M}{K_I}} \qquad (4.13)$$

This expression now passes through a maximum as $[S]_0$ is increased. It predicts that the velocity will tend to zero at sufficiently high values of $[S]_0$. An example of this behaviour is shown in *Figure 4.9* (p. 99) for the hydrolysis of acetylcholine in the presence of acetylcholinesterase. In other examples (such as that

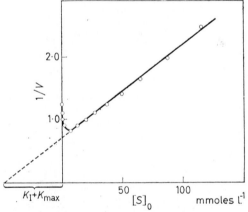

Figure 4.5. Dixon plot for the hydrolysis of acetyl-choline (see *Figure 4.9*)

of carbobenzoxyglycyl-L-tryptophan[40]) the rate passes through a maximum and tends to some limiting value, not zero; this may be because the complex ESS can decompose to give the products, but much more slowly than ES does. In other hydrolyses, such as that of sucrose in the presence of invertase, a maximum rate is reached at high substrate concentrations (~ 1 mole l.$^{-1}$) and thereafter the rate decreases because the concentration of *water* is no longer so large that it can be treated as constant.

Inhibition by substrate is revealed on a Lineweaver–Burk plot by the experimental value of V_I rising above the linear plot as $1/[S]_0$ tends to zero. Inhibition by substrate can also be revealed by plotting $1/V_I$ against $[S]_0$; as in the Dixon plots for inhibitors, a linear portion of *positive* slope can be attributed to the inhibitor—in this case the substrate. *Figure 4.5* shows the data of *Figure 4.9* plotted in this way. The linear portion intersects the axis $1/V_I = 0$ where

$$1 + \frac{[S]_0}{K_I} + \frac{K_M}{K_I} = 0 \quad \text{or} \quad -[S]_0 = K_I + K_M$$

4.5. BIMOLECULAR REACTIONS BETWEEN SUBSTRATES
(SCHEMES II and III)

True bimolecular reactions between two substrates, or between a substrate and a coenzyme, could take place by two different reaction schemes in the presence of an enzyme. In the first of these, scheme II, the enzyme intervenes to give two successive bimolecular steps:

$$E + S \underset{k_2}{\overset{k_1}{\rightleftharpoons}} ES$$

Scheme II:

$$ES + T \xrightarrow{k_3} E + P$$

The reactions of fructose with α-glucose-1-phosphate, and the corresponding exchange of phosphate with α-glucose-1-phosphate in the presence of sucrose transglucosylase are examples of this mechanism (see pages 78–79). All the simple 'single substrate' reactions can be regarded as particular cases of this scheme, provided that in developing the kinetics $k_3[T]$ is set equal to a constant corresponding to k_3 in equation (4.2). The development of this scheme II is very simple if the same assumptions as were made for scheme I can be made.

In the other scheme for bimolecular reactions, the bimolecular reaction occurs between the two substrates *after they have both* combined with the enzyme to form the intermediate complex. Many of the reactions of dehydrogenases are of this type, and the isotopic evidence mentioned earlier in this chapter suggests that the phosphorylation of maltose (G-1-G) and the transfer of phosphate between acetate and ATP may also be of this type. The complex may be formed in several ways, for example:

$$
\begin{array}{ccc}
E + S \rightleftharpoons ES & & E + T \rightleftharpoons ET \\
& \text{or} & \\
ES + T \rightleftharpoons EST & & ET + S \rightleftharpoons EST
\end{array}
$$

Scheme III:

$$EST \rightarrow E + P$$

The full steady-state treatment[41,42] of scheme III including all possible reactions is very complicated, but by making some further assumptions the equations can be simplified to forms that can be applied to experimental results[43-45].

It is interesting that there is little evidence for another possible reaction scheme for bimolecular reactions, in which one substrate molecule complexed with a particular enzyme molecule reacts with a molecule of the other substrate complexed with a different enzyme molecule:

$$E + \quad S \rightleftharpoons ES$$

$$E + \quad T \rightleftharpoons ET$$

$$ES + ET \rightarrow P + 2E$$

88

It can be easily shown that the velocity of reaction would then be proportional to $[E]_0^2$. There have been reports[46-48] of rates proportional to $[E]_0^x$ where x is greater than unity, but it seems likely that these results are sometimes due to impure enzymes, for example, to the presence of a dissociable 'activator' in the enzyme preparation. The great majority of investigations show the rate to be proportional to $[E]_0$. This interesting point suggests that mere *energetic activation*, followed by collision, is not sufficient, but that there are other requirements, for example, steric fit of certain parts of the two substrates which can only be achieved when they combine with the same molecule of enzyme. Even with scheme II, where only one substrate combines with the enzyme, it is probably necessary for the other substrate to be attracted to the complex by electrostatic forces, due to the charged groups or to hydrogen bonding, and this might be less effective if the second substrate were attached to another enzyme molecule.

Scheme II

In this scheme, one substrate forms a complex with the enzyme, and the other substrate reacts with the complex. By setting up the steady-state equation for [ES], as before, it is easily shown that the initial velocity is given by the equation

$$V_0 = \frac{k_1 k_3 [S]_0 [T]_0 [E]_0}{k_2 + k_3 [T]_0 + k_1 [S]_0} \qquad (4.14)$$

It will be seen that this equation is symmetrical in $[S]_0$ and $[T]_0$, and that a very similar equation would be obtained if it had been assumed that T complexes with the enzyme, followed by reaction of S with this complex. The equation shows that a maximum rate $k_1 [S]_0 [E]_0$ is reached if $[S]_0$ is held constant and $[T]_0$ is increased, and that a different maximum rate $k_3 [T]_0 [E]_0$ is reached if $[T]_0$ is held constant and $[S]_0$ is increased. Hence it is possible to determine k_1 and k_3 separately, and once these are known, k_2 can be determined. The 'constant' equivalent to K of equation (4.4) is now equal to $(k_2 + k_3 [T]_0)/k_1$ when $[S]_0$ is varied, and so depends upon the value chosen for $[T]_0$; a similar relationship holds when $[T]_0$ is varied. These 'constants' and the maximum rates can be determined from Lineweaver–Burk or Eadie plots as suggested for single-substrate reactions, and from them (and the determined values of k_1 and k_3) k_2 can be evaluated.

An interesting situation arises if there is competition between the substrates, as this can result in self-inhibition which can be revealed in plots such as those of *Figure 4.5*. Dixon, Massey and Webb[49] have shown that the oxidation of leucine with methylene blue as hydrogen acceptor, in the presence of an oxidase from snake venom, shows this effect. *Figure 4.6* shows the reciprocal of the rate plotted against the leucine concentration for various fixed concentrations of methylene blue. The slopes of the lines vary with the concentration of methylene blue, but the linear portions (which show the inhibition) pass through a common point.

Scheme III

When both substrates have to combine with the enzyme to give a complex EST, the reaction scheme is very like that developed for non-competitive inhibition. Moreover the rate equation can only be put into a simple form,

89

suitable for application to kinetic data, by making the same assumption that the Michaelis–Menten conditions apply[44,50]. The reaction scheme becomes the following:

$$E + T \rightleftharpoons ET \qquad K_T$$
$$E + S \rightleftharpoons ES \qquad K_S$$
$$ES + T \rightleftharpoons EST \qquad K'_T$$
$$ET + S \rightleftharpoons EST \qquad K'_S$$
$$EST \xrightarrow{k_3} P + E$$

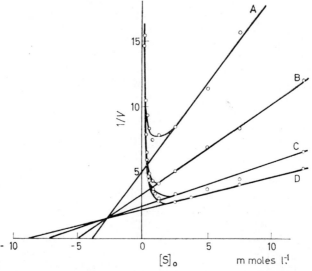

Figure 4.6. Inhibition by substrate (leucine) in the oxidation of leucine with methylene blue as hydrogen acceptor[1] Concentrations of methylene blue (in 10^{-5} moles/l.): A, 3·34; B, 6·7; C, 13·4; D, 26·7

and the rate equation is

$$V_0 = \frac{k_3[E]_0[T]_0[S]_0}{K_S K'_T + K'_T[S]_0 + \dfrac{K_S K'_T}{K_T}[T]_0 + [S]_0[T]_0} \tag{4.15}$$

When $K_T = K'_T$, that is the complex ES binds T as readily as does E, the equation becomes

$$V_0 = \frac{k_3[E]_0[T]_0[S]_0}{(K_S + [S]_0)(K_T + [T]_0)} \tag{4.16}$$

This comparatively simple equation has been shown to apply to some dehydrogenase systems[52,53]. It predicts that a maximum rate is reached as $[S]_0$ is increased, keeping $[T]_0$ constant, and a different maximum is reached if $[T]_0$ is increased, keeping $[S]_0$ constant. By suitable Lineweaver–Burk plots, the separate Michaelis-type constants K_S, K_T can be determined: this can also be done without assuming $K_T = K'_T$ [54].

One further point may be mentioned. In these schemes it has been assumed that the complexes ES or EST break down to product and enzyme in the step k_3. It is possible that there are intermediate steps, e.g.:

$$EST \underset{k_4}{\overset{k_3}{\rightleftharpoons}} EP \overset{k_5}{\longrightarrow} E+P$$

The effect of introducing such steps in the simple scheme I is to give a rate equation[51]

$$V_0 = \frac{\dfrac{k_3 k_5 [E]_0}{k_3+k_4+k_5}}{1+\dfrac{1}{[S]_0}\dfrac{k_2 k_4+k_2 k_5+k_3 k_5}{k_1(k_3+k_4+k_5)}} \qquad (4.17)$$

Thus the equation is similar to the simple equation with more complicated expressions for maximum velocity and the Michaelis constant. If $k_5 \gg k_4$ or k_3, the equation reduces to the simple equation. Dixon and Webb[51] have discussed other mechanisms where the rate is limited by the dissociation of the product. Similar mechanisms have been postulated for heterogeneous reactions, where the rate of desorption of products can limit the rate of reaction.

4.6.   THE INFLUENCE OF HYDROGEN ION CONCENTRATION

It has been known for a long time that the rates of enzyme-catalysed reactions are altered by changes in the hydrogen ion concentration of the solution. The

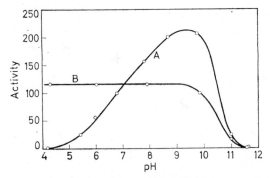

Figure 4.7.   Reversible and irreversible effects of pH
change on enzyme activity[1]
Curve A: activity was tested at the pH values given.
Curve B: enzyme was exposed for 5 minutes to the pH
values given and then the activity tested at pH 7·3

rate usually passes through a maximum value as the pH is increased, and provided that the pH is not changed too far from the 'optimum' value corresponding to the maximum rate, the changes of rate with pH are reversible and reproducible. However if the solutions are made very acid or alkaline the activity of the enzyme may be completely destroyed by denaturation of the protein of the enzyme; after this, the activity is not restored on returning to pH values near the optimum. This effect is clearly shown by the results[55] in *Figure 4.7*; the changes are reversible for pH values up to about 9, but

91

irreversible for more alkaline solutions. The 'optimum' pH usually has different values for different temperatures and for different substrate concentrations and cannot be regarded as a single characteristic value of the reaction.

The reversible part of the changes around the optimum pH is almost certainly due to changes in the amounts and activities of the various ionic forms of the enzyme, the substrate and the enzyme complex. Most of the results can be explained in terms of changes in the amount of enzyme and complex present. An explanation on these lines was first advanced by Michaelis and Davidsohn[56]. They proposed that three forms of the enzyme could exist, and only one of the forms is active in combining with the substrate to give the intermediate complex. The three forms are analogous to an unionized dibasic acid, for instance a dicarboxylic acid $A(COOH)_2$ and its singly- and doubly-ionized ions:

$$
\begin{array}{ccc}
\begin{array}{c} COOH \\ \diagup \\ A \\ \diagdown \\ COOH \end{array}
&
\begin{array}{c} -H^+ \\ \rightleftharpoons \\ +H^+ \end{array}
\quad
\begin{array}{c} COOH \\ \diagup \\ A \\ \diagdown \\ COO^- \end{array}
&
\begin{array}{c} -H^+ \\ \rightleftharpoons \\ +H^+ \end{array}
\quad
\begin{array}{c} COO^- \\ \diagup \\ A \\ \diagdown \\ COO^- \end{array}
\end{array}
$$

In the enzymes, the intermediate form is probably the neutral form of the amphoteric amino acid, thus:

$$
\underbrace{NH_3^+ \ COOH}_{\text{Acid form}} \ \overset{-H^+}{\underset{+H^+}{\rightleftharpoons}} \ \underbrace{NH_3^+ \ COO^-}_{\text{Neutral}} \ \overset{-H^+}{\underset{+H^+}{\rightleftharpoons}} \ \underbrace{NH_2 \ COO^-}_{\text{Alkaline form}}
$$

As other groups in the enzyme may be charged, it has been customary to ignore the charges when writing mechanisms of the reactions of the various forms of the enzyme and its complex with the substrate. However, the charges may be important when considering various mechanisms of the detailed molecular path of the enzyme reaction, and the arbitrariness of the custom must be kept in mind. Dixon and Webb[57] write the superscript n to denote the number of negative charges on the enzyme when the active group under consideration is in its neutral form.

The relative amounts of the three forms present at a given pH depend on the values of the dissociation constants of the 'acid' form EH_2 (K_a) and of the 'neutral' form EH (K_b). Strictly speaking, the dissociation constant of the particular *group* concerned in the active centre is important; there may be other groups present in the enzyme molecule which ionize at the same pH and contribute to the molecular dissociation constant but which do not affect the binding of the substrate. This problem has been carefully considered[57] and will be more important as more precise measurements of the effective dissociation constants are made by kinetic studies. The effect is exactly parallel to the effect of several groups in the molecule of an acid or base catalysing a reaction, an effect allowed for in the Brönsted treatment by the p and q factors.

If the two dissociation constants have widely separate values, it can be shown[57] that there is a wide range of values of pH between the pK values (i.e. the values $-\log K_a$ and $-\log K_b$) where almost all the enzyme will have its active group in the neutral form, as shown in *Figure 4.8(a)*. On the other hand, if the two constants are close, not only will there be a much shorter range of pH values over which the neutral form exists in any appreciable proportion, but the proportions may never approach 100 per cent (*Figure 4.8(b)*).

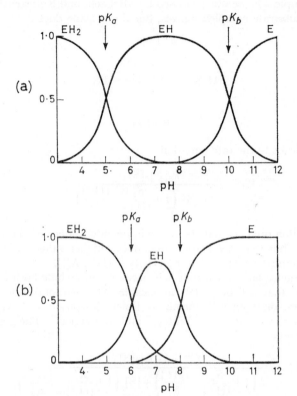

Figure 4.8. Relative proportions of enzyme present as EH$_2$, EH and E at various values of pH when K_a, K_b are (*a*) widely separated, (*b*) close together[1]

The steady-state treatment of the scheme proposed

$$EH_2 \rightleftharpoons EH \rightleftharpoons E$$
$$k_2 \| k_1[S]_0$$
$$ESH \xrightarrow[k_3]{} P+EH$$

leads to an equation for the pH-dependent rate of the reaction, V_H:

$$V_H = \frac{k_3[E]_0[S]_0}{K\left(1+\dfrac{K_a}{[H^+]}+\dfrac{[H^+]}{K_b}\right)+[S]_0} \tag{4.18}$$

This equation predicts that for any chosen value of $[S]_0$ that is not too large, the rate will pass through a maximum value as the $[H^+]$ is altered. The maximum will always occur when $[H^+] = \sqrt{(K_a K_b)}$. However, at very large

93

values of $[S]_0$ the rate will be independent of $[H^+]$. By comparison with equation (4.9), equation (4.18) could be interpreted as showing competitive inhibition of the reaction by hydrogen ions or hydroxyl ions.

Another simple scheme was proposed by Michaelis and Rothstein[58]. In this the enzyme–substrate complex ionizes, but the enzyme does not:

$$
\begin{array}{c}
\text{EH} \\
k_2 \Big\Updownarrow k_1[S]_0 \\
\text{EH}_2\text{S} \rightleftharpoons \text{EHS} \rightleftharpoons \text{ES} \\
\Big\downarrow k_3 \\
\text{P} + \text{EH}
\end{array}
$$

This scheme leads to the rate equation

$$
V'_{\text{H}} = \frac{k_3[\text{E}]_0[\text{S}]_0}{K + [\text{S}]_0\left(1 + \dfrac{K'_a}{[\text{H}^+]} + \dfrac{[\text{H}^+]}{K'_b}\right)}
\tag{4.19}
$$

and this equation predicts that the rate will be independent of pH at very *low* values of $[S]_0$, but that it will show maxima at higher values of $[S]_0$ with a limiting maximum of $k_3[\text{E}]_0/\{1 + (K'_a/[\text{H}^+]) + ([\text{H}^+]/K'_b)\}$.

Later experience has shown that it is necessary to include both ionizations in any scheme that will be widely applicable. The two ionizations were incorporated into one general scheme by Euler, Josephson and Myrbäck[59]. Later derivations were given by Waley[60] and by Laidler[61]. The general rate equation becomes

$$
V_{\text{H}} = \frac{k_3[\text{E}]_0[\text{S}]_0}{K\left(1 + \dfrac{K_a}{[\text{H}^+]} + \dfrac{[\text{H}^+]}{K_b}\right) + [\text{S}]_0\left(1 + \dfrac{K'_a}{[\text{H}^+]} + \dfrac{[\text{H}^+]}{K'_b}\right)}
\tag{4.20}
$$

This equation is able to explain most of the experimental results found so far, and clearly reduces to the simpler equations by putting either $K'_a = 1/K'_b = 0$ or $K_a = 1/K_b = 0$. Thus it will explain equally well any results that the simpler equations explained satisfactorily. In addition, it can explain some results that were very puzzling in either of the simpler schemes. Thus both the simple equations predict that the plot of rate against pH should change shape when $[S]_0$ is changed at moderate concentrations. However, for the hydrolysis of sucrose with 'sucrase' it was found that there was a change on the acid side with the optimum but not on the alkaline side. The full equation can account for this type of behaviour, for if the dissociation constants K_a and K'_a are equal, then on the alkaline side of the optimum where the terms $[\text{H}^+]/K_b$ and $[\text{H}^+]/K'_b$ can be neglected, the equation becomes

$$
V_{\text{H,alk}} = \frac{k_3[\text{E}]_0[\text{S}]_0}{\left(1 + \dfrac{K_a}{[\text{H}]^+}\right)(K + [\text{S}]_0)}
\tag{4.21}
$$

This will vary in the same way with pH whatever the value of $[S]_0$. This equation suggests that the hydroxyl ion is a non-competitive inhibitor of the reaction. On the other hand, on the acid side the equation becomes

$$V_{H,acid} = \frac{k_3[E]_0[S]_0}{K\left(1+\dfrac{[H^+]}{K_b}\right)+[S]_0\left(1+\dfrac{[H^+]}{K'_b}\right)}$$

(4.22)

and here the shape will depend upon the value of $[S]_0$.

Using the full equation, the analysis of results at low concentrations of the substrate concentrations allows the determination of K_a and K_b, while an analysis at high substrate concentrations allows the determination of K'_a and K'_b. A knowledge of these dissociation constants is a useful guide to the nature of the groups in the complex and the free enzyme, indicating which have been affected by the complexing and so giving some information about the groups which are active in complexing the substrate. Laidler[62] has assembled a table showing the effect on K values of complexing at the sites which ionize and relating those effects to changes in the rate and the Michaelis constant as the pH changes. Where the information is incomplete, it can sometimes be treated by an analysis suggested by Dixon[38] to estimate K_a or K_b. Information about the groups concerned in complexing has been obtained for the interconversion of fumarate and malate ions with fumarase[63], the hydrolysis of sucrose with sucrose[64] the hydrolysis of acetylcholine with cholinesterase and with acetyl-cholinesterase[65] and the oxidation of 2-amino-4-hydroxypteridine in the presence of xanthine oxidase[38].

4.7.   THE INFLUENCE OF TEMPERATURE ON ENZYME-CATALYSED REACTIONS

The rates of enzyme-catalysed reactions are markedly affected by changes of temperature. As the temperature is raised from room temperature, the rate of reaction of a given initial mixture is increased, as is common with chemical reactions. At quite moderate temperatures, however, the rate ceases to increase and at higher temperature it falls. The temperature at which the rate is a maximum varies with the composition of the mixture and the pH of the solution. The rate in fall at higher temperatures is very rapid, and it is ascribed to inactivation of the enzyme by denaturation. At a given temperature, the rate of denaturation is a minimum at a certain pH, and it is increased sharply by extremes of pH. This denaturation causes certain changes in other properties besides changes in chemical reactivity; there may be a decrease in solubility and in the ease of crystallization of the enzyme. On a molecular scale, the shape of the enzyme molecule may be changed considerably by breaking of hydrogen bonds and similar bonds, and chemical dissociation of the molecule may occur. The activation energies of the denaturation processes are very high and so are the pre-exponential factors, and so the processes can pass from a negligible rate to an extremely rapid one over a range of temperature of 20 to 30°C. Under extreme conditions, either by heating for a long time at a moderate temperature (e.g. 40 to 50°C) or for a short time at a higher temperature (e.g. 60°C), the denaturation becomes irreversible. Under 'mild' conditions in solution the process may be reversible. It is interesting that the formation of the complex with the substrate often appears to stabilize the enzyme against denaturation.

At lower temperatures, where the rate of inactivation is negligible, the rate of the enzyme-catalysed reaction increases with rise of temperature because of changes in the values of the velocity constants and the equilibrium constants that occur in the rate equation. If equation (4.20) is taken as typical of many single-substrate reactions—and of molecular reactions of scheme II if k_3 is replaced by $k_3[T]$—it appears that changes may occur in the constants K, K_a, K_b, K'_a and K'_b which are all of the form of equilibrium constants, and also in the velocity constant k_3. In principle, it is possible to determine[3,66] from kinetic data the way in which each of these constants varies with temperature, and in the ideal situation to split K into k_1, k_2 and k_3 and so determine how k_1 and k_2 as well as k_3 vary with the temperature. Each of the equilibrium constants K could then be related to the free energy change $\Delta G°$ of the reaction concerned by the isotherm $-\Delta G° = RT \ln K$ and to the heat of reaction $\Delta H°$ by the isochore $d \ln K/dT = \Delta H°/RT^2$. Once $\Delta G°$ and $\Delta H°$ are known it is easy to calculate $\Delta S°$ for the reaction. Parallel information could be obtained from the variation of the velocity constants with temperature about the activation process of each reaction (e.g. $ES \rightleftharpoons ES^* \rightarrow P+E$). The velocity constants k can be expressed as

$$k = \frac{kT}{h}e^{\Delta S^*/R}\cdot e^{-\Delta H^*/RT} \qquad (4.23)$$

where ΔH^* and ΔS^* are the heats and entropies of activation. The Arrhenius activation energy is E where $d \ln k/dT = E/RT^2$ and hence E can be determined from a plot of $\ln k$ against $1/T$. Then $\Delta H^* = E - RT$, and ΔS^* can be determined from the relationship for k.

At present comparatively little progress has been made in the systematic determination of values of ΔH and ΔS for the various equilibrium and velocity constants mentioned above for any number of enzyme reactions, although there is partial information for several reactions.

Fairly extensive investigations have been made of the reversible fumarate–malate ion interchange in the presence of the enzyme fumarase[67-69]. A thermodynamic 'balance sheet' for this reaction has been given by Dixon and Webb[70]. The same authors also discuss various possible causes of the discontinuities found in the $\ln$ (constant) (or $\ln$ (initial rate)) versus $1/T$ plots; in these and in other discussions of these discontinuities there may be a tendency to overlook the effect on the Arrhenius plot of errors in the measurement of the individual values of initial rates, especially when the temperature range studied is comparatively short.

Table 4.1. Activation energies of enzyme-catalysed reactions

Catalyst	Substrate†	T	pH	Over-all reaction			Decomposition of complex		
				k' l.moles^{-1}sec^{-1}	E kcal	ΔS^* e.u.	k_3 sec^{-1}	E kcal	S^* e.u.
Pepsin	Z	31·6	4·0	0·79	20·2	2·6	0·0014	17·2	−21·8
Chymotrypsin	X	25·0	7·8	6·66	9·6	−23·2	0·026	16·8	−11·8
Carboxypeptidase	Y	25·0	7·5	$1·7 \times 10^4$	9·9	− 8·5	89	9·9	−19·8
Myosin	ATP	25·0	7·0	$8·2 \times 10^6$	21·1	44·0	104	13·0	− 8·0
Urease	Urea	20·8	7·1	$5·0 \times 10^6$	6·8	− 6·8	2×10^4	9·7	− 7·2

† X = methyl hydrocinnamate, Y = carbobenzoxyglycl-L-tryptophan, Z = carbobenzoxy-L-glutamyl-L-tyrosine

Otherwise the information is fragmentary. Laidler has assembled useful tables showing how the constant k_3, and its E and ΔS^* values, change for different enzymes, and also similar values for the composite velocity constant k' for very low substrate concentrations. Some representative values of the parameters given by Laidler[3,66] are shown in *Table 4.1*. Examination of equation (4.20) shows that the initial rate at low concentrations of substrate is equal to

$$V = k'[\text{E}]_0[\text{S}]_0 \quad \text{where} \quad k' = k_3/K\left(1 + \frac{K_a}{[\text{H}^+]} + \frac{[\text{H}^+]}{K_b}\right)$$

The constant k' is clearly a complex function of temperature and it is not wise to attempt too detailed an interpretation of the apparent values of E and ΔS for it. As far as k_3 is concerned, it is interesting that the activation energies are fairly large, and that the entropies of activation are always negative and so lead to comparatively low A factors. The negative ΔS^* values are rather surprising, if the breakdown of the complex is thought of as unimolecular, for the formation of the activated complex in a unimolecular reaction usually involves a stretching of the bonds about to be broken, with a consequent increase in the entropy. However, the activation may involve some association with other parts of the enzyme, or the protein conformation may change to a 'tighter' one, or the interaction with the solvent may increase. Some of the values for ΔS^* for the over-all reaction are also negative, but some are positive and several are positive and large. In so far as this can be reckoned as a large

positive ΔS^* associated with the factor $1/K\left(1 + \frac{K_a}{[\text{H}^+]} + \frac{[\text{H}^+]}{K_b}\right)$ this could be

interpreted as a large positive ΔS for the association $\text{E} + \text{S} \rightleftharpoons \text{ES}$. This might arise if charges on E and S were neutralized when the complex is formed, or if there were a considerable loss of orientation of solvent molecules as the complex is formed, more than balancing the loss of entropy due to the association itself.

4.8. THE EFFECTIVENESS OF ENZYMES

The effectiveness of enzymes as catalysts has been expressed in many ways. One which is much used is the *turnover number*, *TN*. This is defined[1] as the number of cycles undergone by one prosthetic group of the enzyme per minute during the course of the catalysis, or the number of molecules of substrate reacting per minute per active centre of the enzyme. However, several other definitions of TN have been used; any measurement of TN should indicate the substrate concentration, and whether this was high enough to give the maximum rate. Another measure[8,3] is the initial velocity constant k' of the reaction at low substrate concentrations where $V = k'[\text{S}]_0[\text{E}]_0$ for single substrate or $k'[\text{S}]_0[\text{E}]_0[\text{T}]_0$ for bimolecular reactions. This has the advantage of being an accessible measure for many enzyme-catalysed reactions and also for the same reactions with other catalysts which may not, for example, give a limiting maximum rate. There may, however, be great advantages in correcting k' for the number of active centres per molecule of enzyme, just as in acid–base catalysis the catalytic constant is divided by the number of available protons in the catalyst acid. In a similar way, when the enzyme catalase is compared with colloidal platinum for the decomposition of hydrogen peroxide, each *particle* may be as active as one enzyme molecule[8]. However, each particle of radius 500 Å exposes roughly 3×10^5 metal atoms, each of which may be an active centre, so that, site for site, the enzyme is much more efficient. As shown in *Table 1.2*, the enzyme reaction has the lower activation energy by about 10 kcal; this can easily account for the difference in efficiencies. In *Table 4.2* some enzymes are compared with other ions as catalysts.

Table 4.2. The effectiveness of enzymes

Substrate reaction	Catalyst	k 25°C	A	E kcal
Hydrolysis of urea	H_3O^+	$2 \cdot 3 \times 10^{-8}$	$1 \cdot 8 \times 10^{10}$	24·6
	Urease	$5 \cdot 6 \times 10^6$	$5 \cdot 6 \times 10^{11}$	6·8
Hydrolysis of ATP	H_3O^+	$7 \cdot 3 \times 10^{-7}$	$2 \cdot 35 \times 10^9$	21·2
	Myosin	$8 \cdot 2 \times 10^6$	$1 \cdot 64 \times 10^{22}$	21·1
Hydrolysis of ethyl benzoate	OH^-	$5 \cdot 5 \times 10^{-4}$	$5 \cdot 3 \times 10^9$	17·7
Hydrolysis of methyl hydro- cinnamate	Chymotrypsin	6·7	$8 \cdot 4 \times 10^7$	9·6
Decomposition of H_2O_2	Fe^{2+}	61	$1 \cdot 8 \times 10^9$	10·1
	Catalase	$3 \cdot 8 \times 10^7$	$6 \cdot 4 \times 10^8$	1·7

(After Laidler[3])

As illustrated in *Table 4.2* it is usual to find that the very great efficiency of enzymes is associated with very low activation energies. However, there are some examples where the rate with an enzyme catalyst is very much greater than with some ion catalyst, yet the activation energies are the same or nearly so. In the hydrolysis of ATP there is an extraordinary increase in the pre-exponential factor in passing from hydrogen ion to myosin. When more is known about the entropy changes in forming the activated complex in reactions like this it may be possible to see the chemical reason for the change.

It seems very likely that most of the active centres on enzyme molecules have more than one chemical group capable of bonding with parts of the substrate. The low activation energies may result from concerted attack by several groups, rather like the 'push–pull' mechanisms suggested for acid- and base-catalysed hydrolyses. There it was found that the occurrence of an acid and a base site in suitable positions on a single molecule could be far more effective than the same sites each on a separate molecule. In oxidation and reduction reactions, it is likely that radicals rather than ions are transferred from substrate to enzyme and vice versa. Again, the simultaneous transfer to and from adjacent sites, rather than a sequence of breaking and making of bonds, may be more favourable energetically. A reasonably apt parallel from heterogeneous catalysis may be the Rideal mechanisms in hydrogenation reactions, where one hydrogen atom is removed from the surface as another one is put on an adjacent site from the gas phase.

4.9. THE ACTIVE CENTRES

Several methods for obtaining information about the active centres of enzymes have been mentioned in the preceding sections. Some indication will now be given of the application of these methods to a particular example, the enzyme acetylcholinesterase[71]. This enzyme catalyses the hydrolyses of several esters and especially the reaction

$$(CH_3)_3\overset{+}{N}CH_2CH_2OCO\cdot CH_3 + H_2O \rightleftharpoons (CH_3)_3\overset{+}{N}CH_2CH_2OH + CH_3COOH$$

Many preparations of cholinesterases have been described, but the preparations[72,73] from the electric eels *Electrophorus electricus* and *Torpedo marmorata* appear to yield an enzyme with properties which allow it to be called 'true' acetylcholinesterase. These properties are its very high activity for the hydrolysis of acetylcholine itself and the appearance of self-inhibition at higher concen-

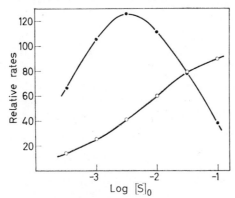

Figure 4.9. Relative rates of hydrolysis of acetylcholine in the presence of true acetyl-cholinesterase ($\bullet$) and pseudo-acetylcholin-esterase (o)
(From data given by Augustinsson[72])

trations of acetylcholine. 'Pseudo-cholinesterases' are less active and do not show self-inhibition, as illustrated in *Figure 4.9*. The cholinesterases do not contain a prosthetic group; the molecular weight of true acetylcholinesterase is between 2,000,000 and 3,000,000 and inhibitor studies[74] have shown that there may be 100 active centres on each molecule.

Information about the active centres has been obtained from study of the type of substrate molecule hydrolysed—especially the nature of the bonds present and, from isotope studies, the fate of various fragments of the molecules—from the variation of activity with pH and from the effect of inhibitors.

The enzyme will catalyse the hydrolysis of organic esters, although at a slower rate than that of acetylcholine, and of thiol esters and acid anhydrides. On the other hand, it will not react with thiono-esters with the group $-C\overset{\displaystyle OH}{\underset{\displaystyle S}{\big<}}$ present[75]. In parallel with these reactions, it will react with molecules like DPF with the group P=O but not with molecules with the group P=S. Moreover, experiments with DPF containing labelled phosphorus have shown[76] that the group $(C_2H_5O)_2\overset{+}{P} : O$ is attached to the enzyme, while the fluoride ion goes into solution; this seems to be an electrophilic attack on the enzyme. If the acetylcholine–enzyme complex is formed in the same way, it is argued, the carbon end of the C=O group is probably attached to the enzyme. The absence of reaction with C$=$S is because carbon is not then positive enough; there is some support for this idea from the effect of other substituents on the carbon concerned.

It has been established that it is the acyl C—O that is broken. Thus with water labelled with $H_2{}^{18}O$ the ^{18}O appears in the acid, not the choline[77]; and with thiol esters, the product is thiocholine[78]:

$$(CH_3)_3\overset{+}{N}CH_2CH_2\text{—}O\text{—}\overset{||}{\underset{O}{C}}\text{—}CH_3 \qquad (CH_3)_3\overset{+}{N}CH_2CH_2\text{—}S\text{—}\overset{||}{\underset{O}{C}}\text{—}CH_3$$

$$H\text{—}{}^{18}OH \qquad\qquad\qquad H\text{—}OH$$

It seems likely that the acetyl group is attached to the enzyme in the complex, via the carbonyl carbon, and is hydrolysed later. A mechanism in keeping with these ideas and capable of explaining the observed kinetics is as follows[79]:

acetylcholinesterase (E) + acetylcholine (S) $\rightleftharpoons$ complex (ES)

complex (ES) $\rightleftharpoons$ complex' (ES') + choline (ROH)

H_2O + complex (ES') $\rightarrow$ acetylcholinesterase (E) + acetic acid

With true acetylcholinesterase the inhibition found at higher concentrations of substrate can be explained by a reaction of ES with S to give an inactive complex.

The evidence suggests that there are three sites concerned in the reactions; the first binds the acetyl group, the second may give a hydrogen atom to the ethereal —O— of the ester, and the third may be concerned with holding the molecule of ester in position. The reaction scheme and these sites can be depicted as follows:

$$CH_3\text{—}\overset{O}{\overset{||}{C}}\text{—}O\text{—}CH_2\cdot CH_2\cdot\overset{+}{N}(CH_3)_3 \rightleftharpoons CH_3\text{—}\overset{\bar{O}}{\overset{|}{C}}\text{—}O\text{—}CH_2\cdot CH_2\cdot\overset{+}{N}(CH_3)_3$$

$$\text{—①—②————③———} \qquad \text{—①—②————③———}$$

$$\rightleftharpoons CH_3\text{—}\overset{\bar{O}}{\overset{|}{C}} \quad HOCH_2\cdot CH_2\cdot\overset{+}{N}(CH_3) \xrightarrow{H_2O} CH_3\text{—}\overset{O}{\overset{||}{C}}OH \quad HOCH_2\cdot CH_2\cdot\overset{+}{N}(CH_3)_3$$

$$\text{—①—②————③———} \qquad \text{—①——②————③———}$$

Information about the site at which the carbon is attached comes from studies of the effect of changes of pH on the activity of the enzyme[80]. As shown in *Figures 4.10* and *4.11* the activity with various esters of acetic acid is low in acid solution, rising to a maximum at about pH 8, and thereafter either remaining roughly constant (with thiol- and phenol-esters) or decreasing sharply (with acetylcholine and esters of aliphatic alcohols). The acid branch of the curve is substantially independent of the substrate. This branch is probably concerned with the formation in more acid solutions of the 'acid' form of the group responsible for binding the common part of the esters hydrolysed, i.e. the carbonyl carbon. This carbon would be less likely to bind to an 'acid' site. The other, and variable, branch may be concerned with bonding of the alcohol part of the ester. The inhibitors like DPF and pyrophosphates ($(RO)_2PO\cdot O\cdot PO\cdot(OR)_2$) probably attack the first site. Some clue to the nature of this site is provided by the pK corresponding to the 'neutralization' represented by the left-hand branch of the curve in *Figure 4.10*. By comparison

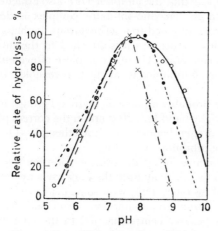

Figure 4.10. pH–activity curves of human cholinesterase[80]
o, 10^{-2}M acetylcholine; ●, 10^{-2}M n-propyl chloroacetate; X, $3\cdot6\times10^{-2}$M n-propyl fluoroacetate

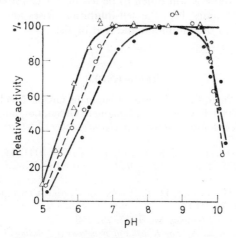

Figure 4.11. pH–activity curves for the system eel esterase—phenyl acetates[75]
Δ, 4×10^{-4}M *p*-nitrophenyl acetate; ●, 10^{-3}M phenyl acetate; o, 10^{-3}M *p*-methoxyphenyl acetate

with *Figure 4.8*, the pK evidently lies between 6 and 7. Now imidazole has a pK of 6·9, and its derivatives like histidine and its peptides have pK values between 5·9 and 7·1. Also, imidazole does combine with acetyl groups and it does catalyse the hydrolysis of some esters, including some thiol-esters but not the corresponding thiono-esters[75]. For these and other reasons, it is believed that the acetyl group attaches itself to the group $\overset{\displaystyle -N}{\underset{\displaystyle -NH}{>}}CH$ in the active centre. It would appear that the inhibitor DPF also attaches itself to the same site; however, when the enzyme–inhibitor complex is degraded, the phosphorus always appears attached to a serine group. Perhaps it is only attached to this in the complex, or perhaps it is attached to the imidazole site and is transferred to the serine later. There is one piece of evidence in favour of the latter proposal—the inhibition is at first reversible, but later becomes irreversible[81].

The second site is probably a phenolic hydroxyl group; it can hardly be the serine itself, as the right-hand branch is not in the correct pH range for serine. This site may be hydrogen-bonded on to the ethereal —O— of the ester, or on to the F^- ion of the inhibitors like DPF.

There is some evidence[82] that the presence of a positive centre in the substrate, sited about 6 to 7 Å away from the ester carbonyl, greatly increases the rate of hydrolysis of an ester. This, with some evidence[82,83] on the inhibition by ions such as substituted ammonium ions, drugs such as curare, and substituted esters with a positive centre, has led to the view that there are also anionic sites concerned in bonding the acetylcholine to the enzyme by its positive charge. There may be two such sites per active centre.

The evidence outlined here shows that a good deal of information has been accumulated about the site of the catalysis and the function of the active centres. However, there is still much to be learnt, for example, just when the water molecule intervenes, how the self-inhibition arises and what is the role of the serine group in the inhibition and hydrolysis.

REFERENCES

[1] DIXON, M. and WEBB, E. C. *Enzymes*: Longmans Green, London, 1958

[2] DIXON, M. and WEBB, E. C. *Enzymes*: Longmans Green, London, 1958, Chapter V

[3] LAIDLER, K. J. *The Chemical Kinetics of Enzyme Action*: Oxford University Press, London, 1958

[4] HABER, F. and WILLSTÄTTER, R. *Ber. dtsch. chem. Ges.* 1931, **64**, 2844

[5] WATERS, L. A. *The Chemistry of Free Radicals* 2nd edn: Oxford University Press, London, 1948

[6] WESTHEIMER, F. H., FISHER, H. F., CONN, E. E. and VENNESLAND, B. *J. Amer. chem. Soc.* 1951, **73**, 2403

[7] VENNESLAND, B. *Disc. Faraday Soc.* 1955, **20**, 240

[8] MOELWYN-HUGHES, E. A. *The Kinetics of Reactions in Solution*: Oxford University Press, London, 1947, pp. 380 *et seq.*

[9] BAYLISS, W. M. *The Nature of Enzyme Action* 4th edn: Longmans Green, London, 1919

[10] MICHAELIS, L. and MENTEN, M. L. *Biochem. Z.* 1913, **49**, 333

[11] BRIGGS, G. E. and HALDANE, J. B. S. *Biochem. J.* 1925, **19**, 338

[12] HENRI, V. *C.R. Acad. Sci., Paris* 1901, **133**, 891; 1902, **135**, 916

[13] BROWN, A. J. *J. chem. Soc.* 1902, p. 373

[14] JANSEN, E. F. and BALLS, A. K. *J. biol. Chem.* 1952, **194**, 721

REFERENCES

[15] JANSEN, E. F., BAUS, A. K. et al., J. biol. Chem. 1949, **179**, 189, 201; 1950, **185**, 209

[16] LOEWUS, M. W. and BRIGGS, D. R. J. biol. Chem. 1952, **199**, 857

[17] AMBROSE, J. F., KISTIAKOWSKY, G. B. and KRIDL, A. G. J. Amer. chem. Soc. 1951, **73**, 1232

[18] VELICK, S. F., HAYES, J. E. and HARTING, J. J. biol. Chem. 1953, **203**, 527

[19] HAYES, J. E. and VELICK, S. F. J. biol. Chem. 1954, **207**, 225

[20] CHANCE, B. Arch. Biochem. Biophys. 1949, **22**, 224; 1952, **41**, 416

[21] CHANCE, B. A Symposium on the Mechanism of Enzyme Action (Ed. W. D. McElroy and B. Glass): Johns Hopkins Press, Baltimore, 1954, p. 399 (also p. 389)

[22] LAIDLER, K. J. The Chemical Kinetics of Enzyme Action: Oxford University Press, London, 1958, p. 58

[23] DOUDOROFF, M., BARKER, H. A. and HASSID, W. Z. J. biol. Chem. 1947, **168,** 725

[24] WOLOCHOW, H., PUTMAN, E. W., DOUDOROFF, M., BARKER, H. A. and HASSID, W. Z. J. biol. Chem. 1949, **180**, 1237

[25] BESSMAN, S. P. and LIPMANN, F. Arch. Biochem. Biophys. 1953, **46**, 252

[26] COHN, M. J. biol. Chem. 1949, **180**, 771

[27] KOSHLAND, D. E. and STEIN, S. S. J. biol. Chem. 1954, **208**, 139

[28] FITTIG, C. and DOUDOROFF, M. J. biol. Chem. 1952, **199**, 153

[29] ROSE, I. A., GRUNBERG-MANAGO, M., KOREY, S. R. and OCHOA, S. J. biol. Chem. 1954, **211**, 737

[30] LAIDLER, K. J. The Chemical Kinetics of Enzyme Action: Oxford University Press, London, 1958, pp. 180–1

[31] NELSON, J. M. and SCHUBERT, M. P. J. Amer. chem. Soc. 1928, **50**, 2188

[32] OUELLET, L., LAIDLER, K. J. and MORALES, M. F. Arch. Biochem. Biophys. 1952, **39**, 37

[33] LINEWEAVER, H. and BURK, D. J. Amer. chem. Soc. 1934, **56**, 658

[34] EADIE, G. S. J. biol. Chem. 1942, **146**, 85

[35] ROUGHTON, F. J. W. Disc. Faraday Soc. 1954, **17**, 116
LAIDLER, K. J. Canad. J. Chem. 1955, **33**, 1614

[36] GUTFREUND, H. Disc. Faraday Soc. 1954, **17**, 220; 1955, **20**, 167; Trans. Faraday Soc. 1955, **51**, 441

[37] LAIDLER, K. J. The Chemical Kinetics of Enzyme Action: Oxford University Press, London, 1958, pp. 187 et seq.

[38] DIXON, M. Biochem. J. 1953, **55**, 161, 170

[39] DIXON, M. and WEBB, E. C. Enzymes: Longmans Green, London, 1958, p. 176

[40] LUMRY, R., SMITH, E. I. and GLANTZ, R. R. J. Amer. chem. Soc. 1951, **73**, 4330

[41] BOTTS, J. and MORALES, M. F. Trans. Faraday Soc. 1953, **49**, 696

[42] LAIDLER, K. J. Trans. Faraday Soc. 1956, **52**, 1374

[43] HALDANE, J. B. S. Enzymes: Longmans Green, London, 1930, pp. 83–4

[44] LAIDLER, K. J. and SOCQUET, I. M. J. phys. Chem. 1950, **54**, 519, 530

[45] MORALES, M. F. J. Amer. chem. Soc. 1955, **77**, 4169

[46] DIXON, M. and WEBB, E. C. Enzymes: Longmans Green, London, 1958, p. 71

[47] IRVING, G. W., FRUTON, J. S. and BERGMANN, M. J. biol. Chem. 1941, **138**, 231

[48] ROY, A. B. Biochem. J. 1953, **55**, 653

[49] DIXON, M., MASSEY, V. and WEBB, E. C. Enzymes: Longmans Green, London, 1958, p. 87

[50] DIXON, M. and WEBB, E. C. Enzymes: Longmans Green, London, 1958, p. 99

[51] DIXON, M. and WEBB, E. C. Enzymes: Longmans Green, London, 1958, p. 110

[52] SOCQUET, I. M. and LAIDLER, K. J. Arch. Biochem. 1950, **25**, 171

[53] SCHWERT, G. W. and HAKALA, M. T. Arch. Biochem. Biophys. 1952, **38**, 55

[54] FLORINI, J. R. and VESTLING, C. S. Biochim. biophys. Acta 1957, **25**, 575
ALBERTY, R. A. J. Amer. chem. Soc. 1953, **75**, 1928

[55] HARE, M. L. C. Biochem. J. 1928, **22**, 968

[56] MICHAELIS, L. and DAVIDSOHN, H. *Biochem. Z.* 1911, **35**, 386

[57] DIXON, M. and WEBB, E. C. *Enzymes*: Longmans Green, London, 1958, p. 134

[58] MICHAELIS, L. and ROTHSTEIN, M. *Biochem. Z.* 1920, **110**, 217

[59] EULER, H. VON, JOSEPHSON, K. and MYRBÄCK, K. *Hoppe-Seyl. Z.* 1924, **134**, 39

[60] WALEY, S. G. *Biochim. biophys. Acta* 1953, **10**, 27

[61] LAIDLER, K. J. *Trans. Faraday Soc.* 1955, **51**, 528

[62] LAIDLER, K. J. *The Chemical Kinetics of Enzyme Action*: Oxford University Press, London, 1958, p. 141

[63] MASSEY, V. and ALBERTY, R. A. *Biochim. biophys. Acta* 1954, **13**, 347, 354
ALBERTY, R. A. *J. cell. comp. Physiol.* 1956, **47**, supplement 1, 245

[64] MYRBÄCK, K. and BJÖRKLUND, U. *Ark. Kemi* 1952, **4**, 567

[65] WILSON, I. B. and BERGMANN, F. *J. biol. Chem.* 1950, **186**, 683

[66] LAIDLER, K. J. *Disc. Faraday Soc.* 1955, **20**, 83

[67] ALBERTY, R. A. *Advanc. Enzymol.* 1955, **17**, 1

[68] BOCK, R. M. and ALBERTY, R. A. *J. Amer. chem. Soc.* 1953, **75**, 1921

[69] MASSEY, V. *Biochem. J.* 1953, **53**, 72

[70] DIXON, M. and WEBB, E. C. *Enzymes*: Longmans Green, London, 1958, p. 169

[71] BERGMANN, F. *Advanc. Catalys.* 1958, **10**, 130

[72] AUGUSTINSSON, K. B. *Arch. Biochem.* 1949, **23**, 111

[73] ROTHENBERG, M. A. and NACHMANSOHN, D. *J. biol. Chem.* 1947, **168**, 223

[74] BOURSNELL, J. C. and WEBB, E. C. *Nature, Lond.* 1949, **164**, 875

[75] BERGMANN, F., RIMAN, S. and SEGAL, R. *Biochem. J.* 1958, **68**, 493

[76] MICHEL, H. O. and KROP, S. *Fed. Proc.* 1949, **8**, 320

[77] STEIN, S. S. and KOSHLAND, D. E. *Arch. Biochem. Biophys.* 1953, **45**, 467

[78] KOELLE, G. B. and FRIEDENWALD, J. S. *Proc. Soc. exp. Biol., N.Y.* 1949, **70**, 617

[79] WILSON, I. B. and CABIB, E. *J. Amer. chem. Soc.* 1956, **78**, 202

[80] BERGMANN, F., SEGAL, R., SHIMONI, A. and WURZEL, M. *Biochem. J.* 1956, **63**, 684

[81] NACHMANSOHN, D., ROTHENBERG, M. A. and FELD, E. A. *J. biol. Chem.* 1948, **174**, 247

[82] WILSON, I. B. and BERGMANN, F. *J. biol. Chem.* 1950, **185**, 479

[83] WILSON, I. B. *J. biol. Chem.* 1952, **197**, 215

PART III

HETEROGENEOUS CATALYSIS

HETEROGENEOUSLY CATALYSED REACTIONS

5.1. INTRODUCTION

As EXPLAINED in Chapter 1, 'heterogeneous catalysis' could include reactions proceeding at a variety of interfaces, but the most interesting surfaces are those between solids and gases and between solids and liquids. The catalysis by solid surfaces of reactions between gases has proved particularly important and will be given most prominence here, although some catalysed reactions in condensed phases will also be discussed. Some idea of the range of reactions catalysed by solids can be obtained from *Table 5.1*, which has been compiled from the extensive and well-referenced tables assembled by Innes[1].

Table 5.1. Heterogeneous catalysts for some important reactions

Type of reaction	*Examples*	*Catalysts*
Cracking reactions	Alkylation, isomerization, polymerization	Silica + alumina + titania + zirconia Fluorides, chlorides, fluorborates on carrier Activated montmorillosite and other clays
Hydrogenation–dehydrogenation	of olefins and aromatics $\diagdown C = C \diagup \rightleftharpoons \diagdown CH \cdot CH \diagup$ of $\diagdown C = O \rightleftharpoons \diagdown CH(OH)$	Transition and Group I metals Transition metal oxides and sulphides Copper
	of $\diagdown C = O$ or $\diagdown CH(OH) \rightarrow \diagdown CH_2 + H_2O$	Nickel, chromia
	Hydroforming (aromatization)	Chromia, molybdena
Ammonia synthesis	$N_2 + 3H_2 \rightleftharpoons 2NH_3$	Iron, molybdenum, osmium, uranium, etc. Promoted iron (K_2O, Al_2O_3)
Methanol synthesis and allied Fischer–Tropsch reactions	$CO + 2H_2 \rightleftharpoons CH_3OH$	Copper, zinc oxide Zinc oxide with chromia
	Higher alcohol formation Methane formation Higher hydrocarbon formation Aromatic formation	As above, with alkali Nickel Cobalt, iron Al_2O_3

Table 5.1—continued

Type of reaction	Examples	Catalysts
Oxo-reaction	$CO + H_2 + RCH{=}CH_2$ $\rightarrow RCH_2 \cdot CH_2 \cdot CHO$	Cobalt + thoria
Hydrosulphurization	$RSH + H_2 \rightarrow RH + H_2S$	Cobalt-molybdia Iron and tungsten sulphides
Hydration–dehydration	$\diagdown C{=}C\diagup \rightleftharpoons \diagdown CH + C(OH)\diagup$ $-C{\equiv}C- \rightleftharpoons -CH_2{-}CHO$	Alumina, silica + alumina Phosphoric and other acids on carriers
Dehydration + dehydrogenation	$2C_2H_5OH \rightarrow CH_2{=}CH{-}CH$ $= CH_2 + 2H_2O + H_2$	Silica + magnesia Copper, Cu + Ni + Cr_2O_3
Oxidation	Ammonia $\rightarrow$ oxides of nitrogen $SO_2 \rightarrow SO_3$, $C_{10}H_8 \rightarrow$ phthallic anhydride $CO \rightarrow CO_2$ $CO + H_2O \rightleftharpoons CO_2 + H_2$ $C_2H_4 \rightarrow$ ethylene oxide	Platinum (Pt, PtO) Vanadium pentoxide (V_2O_5, V_2O_4) Manganese dioxide (MnO_2, Mn_2O_3) Iron (Fe, Fe_3O_4) Silver (Ag, Ag_2O)
Halogenation–dehalogenation	$4HCl + O_2 \rightleftharpoons 2Cl_2 + 2H_2O$ $RH + O_2 + HCl \rightleftharpoons RCl + H_2O$ $RH + Cl_2 \rightarrow RCl + HCl$ $CO + Cl_2 \rightleftharpoons COCl_2$ Fluorination of hydrocarbons	Chlorides of copper, zinc or mercury on carriers Chlorides of copper, zinc or mercury on carriers Chlorides of copper or silver on carriers, charcoal Charcoal Fluorides of silver or copper on carriers
Exchange reactions	D_2 with H_2 or RH or NH_3 R'D with RH ^{18}O with ^{16}O in oxides, N_2O, H_2O $^{30}N_2$ with $^{28}N_2$ NH_3 with ND_3	Transition metals, ammonia catalysts, cracking catalysts As above Many oxides Ammonia catalysts Ammonia catalysts

Some of the reactions mentioned in this Table were among those listed by Berzelius as examples of catalysed reactions. He included the dehydrogenation of alcohol vapour at metal surfaces to give acetaldehyde, and its dehydration at clay surfaces to give ethylene, as well as the catalytic action of the surfaces of metals or oxides upon several oxidations.

During the nineteenth century, attempts to explain the action of heterogeneous catalysts were based on one or other of two general theories. The *intermediate compound theory* proposed that a reaction took place between the bulk solid and the reactant to give an intermediate compound. This intermediate compound decomposed, or reacted with any other necessary reactant, to give the products of the main reaction and to regenerate the catalyst. Thus in the reaction of hydrogen and oxygen in the presence of copper, cuprous oxide was found to appear. A possible route for the catalysed reaction could be:

$$2Cu \xrightarrow{\frac{1}{2}O_2} Cu_2O \xrightarrow{H_2} \frac{1}{2}H_2O + 2Cu$$

In other cases, for example the oxidation of ammonia over platinum, changes in the catalyst surface could be seen without precise identification of the intermediate. However, in many cases there was no direct evidence for intermediates, and it was often difficult to suggest plausible ones. So long as the intermediates were considered as bulk compounds, the intermediate compound theory was of limited applicability.

The other theory had its origin in ideas put forward in 1834 by Faraday[2] in the course of his experiments on electrolysis. He noticed that there was a loss of hydrogen and oxygen from his water voltameter while using electrodes of platinum, related this effect to Döbereiner's experiments on the oxidation of hydrogen over platinum[3] and suggested that 'the phenomena . . . are dependent upon the natural conditions of gaseous elasticity combined with the exertion of that attractive force possessed by many bodies, especially those which are solid, in an eminent degree, and probably belonging to all; by which they are drawn into association more or less close, without at the same time undergoing chemical combination, through often assuming the condition of adhesion; and which occasionally leads, under very favourable circumstances, as in the present instance, to the combination of bodies simultaneously subjected to this attraction'.

This picture of adhesion and combination, termed *contact action* by Mitscherlich[4], appears startlingly like our present theories of reaction in a chemisorbed layer. For many years it was thought that the contact action merely brought the reactants together, and after the formulation of the law of mass action it was considered that the increased concentration in the condensed layer was responsible for the increased rate of reaction in the presence of the catalyst. The chief evidence that this simple idea is inadequate is that some substances can decompose to give quite different products in the presence of different catalysts. Thus it is well known that ethyl alcohol vapour will decompose to give ethylene and water when passed over alumina at 300°C, whereas it forms acetaldehyde and hydrogen when passed over heated copper or silver. As the rate of reaction is proportional to the concentration of ethyl alcohol vapour in each case, the preference for one route or another cannot be due to differential compression in the adsorbed layers. Sabatier[5] has listed hundreds of these alternative catalyses, and it is now accepted[6] that only specific interaction with the catalyst surface can account for them.

The nature of this specific interaction became clear after Langmuir's work on adsorption† and its applications[7] to chemical reactions. Previously, many studies had been made of adsorption, and many attempts had been made to formulate equations which would relate the amount of gas adsorbed (x) to its pressure (p). The Freundlich isotherm, $x = ap^{1/n}$, where a and n are constants

---

† In this book, 'adsorption' is used in a general sense for chemisorption or physical adsorption when it is not necessary (or sometimes not possible) to distinguish which is occurring.

($n > 1$) for a given gas and solid and temperature, was found to be very useful over moderate ranges of pressure, but it was an empirical equation and suffered from the disadvantage of indicating that x increases indefinitely as p increases. Experiments showed, however, that the adsorption often reached a constant maximum value as the pressure increased, for example, as shown by Langmuir, in the adsorption of oxygen or hydrogen on metal wires. Langmuir attributed this kind of adsorption with 'saturation' to short-range attractions between surface and adsorbent, giving bonds which are essentially chemical in nature and limited in number by the number of 'sites' available for bonding in the surface; this type of adsorption has become universally known as *chemisorption*, to distinguish it from *physical* (or *van der Waals*) *adsorption*.

In physical adsorption[8], the molecules are held to the surface by weak forces, comparable to the forces holding a liquid together. This type of adsorption does not lead to any activation of the reactant, although there have been suggestions that a physically adsorbed molecule can react with a chemisorbed molecule or radical; and the physically adsorbed state, however briefly the molecule stays in it, is the precursor of the chemisorbed state. The heats of physical adsorption are very similar in magnitude to the heat of condensation of the gas being adsorbed, although somewhat larger for the gases of low boiling point. There are, however, changes in the value of the heat of adsorption with the extent of coverage of the surface, a phenomenon which does not occur with heats of condensation but does with heats of solution; it is essential to consider differential heats of adsorption, just as with solutions. The rates of physical adsorption and desorption are rapid, provided the surface is accessible, and the processes are readily reversible. The lifetime of the physically adsorbed molecule is very short (see page 167).

During chemisorption[9], considerable changes occur in the distribution of the electrons in the molecule of the adsorbate. The molecule can be held to the surface by covalent or by ionic bonds, or even dissociated into atoms or radicals bound to the surface by similar bonds[10,11]. The heat evolved is usually large, especially in the initial stages of the adsorption, but it may fall considerably as the surface becomes covered with the adsorbate (*Figures 6.9* and *6.12*). The rate of chemisorption and the rate of desorption from a chemisorbed layer vary enormously from system to system. Some chemisorptions occur extremely rapidly at all temperatures, even where the molecule is split into atoms, as with oxygen, nitrogen or hydrogen on tungsten. Other chemisorptions are slow and appear to have an activation energy like that of a chemical reaction, so that their rates increase rapidly as the temperature is raised. The high heats of chemisorption, comparable with those of chemical reactions, mean that rates of desorption from chemisorbed layers are often very slow, and especially at low temperatures the chemisorptions of many gases are irreversible in a chemical sense.

In principle, therefore, the study of heterogeneously catalysed reactions is intimately bound up with studies of chemisorption. The rate of the reaction may be controlled by the rate of chemisorption of the reactants, or by a later reaction between chemisorbed molecules, radicals or ions, or by the rate of desorption of a product. It has proved particularly difficult to identify the surface intermediates with any certainty, so that there are many simple reactions where different investigators are not at present agreed upon the rate-determining step and the mechanism.

The first step in any study of a heterogeneously catalysed reaction is the measurement of the rate over different catalysts. In order to obtain rate measurements that give any indication of the true mechanism, it is necessary to know a good deal about the physical and chemical nature of the catalyst surface, and especially about its area and accessibility and its physical and chemical homogeneity. Accordingly, the next sections deal briefly with these topics. As the one common feature of all these reactions is that one or more reactants are chemisorbed, it is appropriate in the next chapter to discuss our present ideas upon the nature of chemisorption, the type and strength of the bonds that hold the chemisorbed species to the surface, and the rates of adsorption and desorption. In later chapters, the mechanisms of particular reactions are discussed.

5.2. RATES OF SURFACE REACTIONS OF GASES

In almost all investigations of heterogeneous catalysis, the rate of reaction has been determined as the rate of disappearance of a reactant from the gas phase or the rate of release of a product to the gas phase. In only one type of heterogeneous reaction can the variation of the properties of the catalyst be used to follow the rate of the reaction; this is when the only chemical reaction is the chemisorption or desorption of atoms or molecules and there is no further reaction between the chemisorbed fragments. In this case, changes in surface properties such as the accommodation coefficient[7,12], the contact potential[13], the emissivity of electrons[14] or the surface conductivity[15] can be used. Such studies are important to our knowledge of catalysis because chemisorption is a vital step in all heterogeneously catalysed reactions and changes in surface properties can be used to decide what chemisorptions are occurring *during* the catalysed reactions, and hence what are possible mechanisms. For example, Dowden[10] has related the dehydrogenation–hydrogenation properties of certain mixed oxides to their semiconducting properties. These methods are discussed in the following chapter.

The experimental methods used to investigate the rates of the majority of catalysed reactions are therefore similar to those used for homogeneous reactions[16]. The reactants can be flowed past the catalyst, suitably supported or 'fluidized' to allow intimate contact between gas and catalyst. These flow systems allow the collection at leisure of ample quantities of products for analysis; the fluidized bed is particularly suited to give steady-state conditions, but there may be changes of rate along a fixed catalyst bed due to changes in the amounts of reactants adsorbed as the proportions of reactants and products change. Alternatively, the reactants can be enclosed in a reaction vessel and the rate followed as the concentrations of reactants fall, and this static method has often been used in laboratory studies. In either case, the reacting mixtures can be analysed by chemical or physical means, the former being particularly suited to flow systems and the latter to static systems but requiring, of course, substantiation and calibration by chemical analyses. The mass spectrometer provides the most versatile and reliable method[17] of analysis; it can give a continuous record[18], without disturbing the reaction mixture, of a wide range of products, including isotopically substituted molecules. Infra-red absorption

111

spectra have also proved useful[19, 20]. In deuterium–hydrogen exchange reactions, it is often possible to isolate from the reaction products a binary mixture of hydrogen and deuterium which can be analysed by thermal conductivity measurements with a Pirani gauge; the same method has been used to follow the orthohydrogen–parahydrogen reaction[21]. In many decompositions or reactions which proceed with a change, known from chemical analyses, in the number of molecules, the pressure change has been used[22] to follow the reaction—perhaps used rather too freely, for without detailed analysis of the products, many finer but revealing points about the reaction are missed. A good example of this is provided by the comparatively recent discovery of the self-hydrogenation of ethylene upon chemisorption on nickel surfaces (section 8.2).

In the preliminary investigations of a catalysed reaction, perhaps concerned with the effectiveness of various catalyst preparations, it is often sufficient to report the rates of reaction as percentage conversions for various standard conditions of reactant flow rates, composition and temperature. This practice, although convenient, conceals the effects on the reaction rates of the specific surface of the catalyst and the concentrations of the reactants and the products. In more fundamental studies, the rate, expressed as the rate of change of concentration of a reactant or product in the gas phase, is related to the concentrations by kinetic laws similar to those used for reactions in homogeneous phases. A brief reference to *Tables 7.1* to *7.5* (pp. 177–79) will show the complicated form of some typical rate laws. They are clearly similar to the equations derived in Chapter 1 for the rates of complex reactions involving several stages, with the complication that the concentration of the *product* can occasionally affect the rate. These complicated equations would not have been deduced without the help of some suggested mechanism of reaction, and in fact, most of these presented in *Tables 7.1* to *7.5* were based on mechanisms which regarded a *reaction step within the surface* as the rate-determining step; these are the Langmuir–Hinshelwood (LH) mechanisms[22,23]. As explained in more detail later, there are other basic mechanisms. There is a variation of the LH mechanisms due to Rideal[24] and Eley[25] which involves interaction between a chemisorbed species and a molecule held briefly in a physically adsorbed layer; this is entitled the van der Waals–chemisorbed interaction (VCI) theory. There is another quite different type of mechanism, developed by Temkin and Pyzhev[26], in which the desorption of product or the chemisorption of reactant determines the rate. The LH mechanisms have been used extensively, and in later sections they will be treated in a general manner and compared with the transition state theory of heterogeneous reactions. The other two mechanisms mentioned above have not yet been applied so extensively nor have they been formulated in such a general way. They are well established for several reactions, however, and it seems better to discuss the reasons for adopting them for individual reactions such as some hydrogenations, exchanges and syntheses, rather than to attempt any generalized treatment of the kinetics which result from these mechanisms.

It cannot be emphasized too strongly that rate determinations alone do not distinguish between various possible mechanisms for heterogeneous reactions. This was pointed out as long ago as 1928 by Schwab and Pietsch[27], who showed that identical forms of the rate equation were obtained by assuming that the rate was controlled either by activated adsorption or by a surface reaction. Even the absolute rates do not allow discrimination, as shown by Schwab and Drikos[28]. Nor is the transition state theory any help, as shown in section 7.2. To some extent, therefore, the success of the LH mechanisms has been over-emphasized, for it is unlikely that they give the unique explanation for the rates of many reactions. The recognition that other mechanisms are more likely for some reactions makes it advisable to consider testing them for many more reactions.

5.3. HETEROGENEOUS CATALYSTS

Table 5.1 shows that the principal heterogeneous catalysts for industrial and laboratory processes are metals, oxides, sulphides or combinations of these substances. Molecular crystals are rarely useful as catalysts. The metals in chief demand are the transition metals and Group IB metals. As will be seen

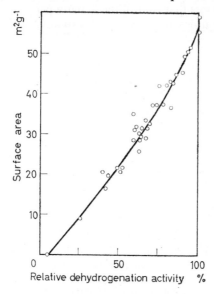

Figure 5.1. Relative rates of dehydrogenation of butane on chromia–alumina catalysts of different area/g[29]

later, they do not function in the same way in all the reactions listed. The oxidation catalysts, for example, often have an oxide easily prepared from and reduced to the metal, or a pair of oxides that are readily interconvertible, as shown in brackets after each catalyst. The hydrogenation catalysts undoubtedly chemisorb hydrogen with dissociation, and the more effective metals have vacant d-orbitals which may bond the hydrogen atoms. In the Fischer–Tropsch syntheses, the ability to chemisorb carbon monoxide (without dissociation) seems to be important, whereas similar catalysts used for the synthesis of ammonia function by splitting nitrogen into atoms. The oxides fall into two distinct categories. The insulator oxides are useful in cracking, isomerization and dehydration reactions, and their activity may be connected

8—c.   113

with their surface acidity and the ability to form carbonium ions from hydro-carbons. The semiconductor oxides are useful for hydrogenation reactions, exchange reactions, oxidations and some decompositions. They seem to adsorb the reactants as ions, and interesting correlations have been found between the catalytic activity and the conductivity of the surface of these semiconduct-ing oxides.

The ideal catalyst for the industrial preparation of a chemical would be very active, very robust and very stable and reproducible. Unfortunately, very active surfaces do not always have a long life, and the expense of renewing or reactivating a spent catalyst has often led to the use of a less active but more durable catalyst.

The activity of a given weight of catalyst can be increased by increasing the activity per unit area and by increasing the area of catalyst per gramme. Because of the difficulties of determining the surface composition, far less is known about the factors that control the activity per unit area than is known about the effects of various methods of preparation upon the area per gramme.

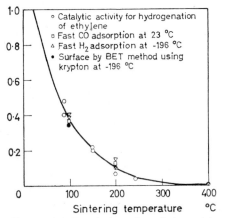

Figure 5.2. Correlation of catalytic activity with adsorption and surface area [30] (The ordinate represents fraction of respec-tive values obtained for films sintered at 23°C)

It is certain that the specific activity is very sensitive to the method of prepara-tion, and the only way to ensure reproducibility is to use a proven 'recipe'. It is generally assumed that a standard method of preparation from a specified source will produce a catalyst with an activity proportional to its area. The proportionality will be exact only if the surface is strictly uniform, or has a uniform pattern of activity over the whole surface, and is uniformly accessible to the reactants. An example of this behaviour is shown in *Figure 5.1* for a chromia–alumina catalyst used for the dehydrogenation of butane [29]. Another interesting example for a very different catalyst is shown in *Figure 5.2*; this is for an evaporated film of nickel prepared as described in a later section and used for the hydrogenation of ethylene [30].

In order to obtain a large area for a given weight, the catalyst is usually prepared in the form of a fine powder or as a thin film spread out over a support or carrier of a relatively inert powder or porous solid, or as a porous mass. The obvious method of powdering by grinding larger particles is sometimes used, for example with the mixed metal–metal oxide catalysts used in the Fischer–Tropsch syntheses (section 8.4). A direct precipitation is sometimes possible for sulphides or oxides. In many preparations, an intermediate is precipitated and then converted to the catalysts, for example oxides from nitrates or hydroxides, or the metal by reduction of oxides. The importance of thorough reduction is seen in the behaviour of iron catalysts for the ammonia synthesis (see section 8.3), but it is acknowledged that it is extremely difficult to reduce some metals such as iron and tungsten; moreover, oxide below the surface can considerably alter the adsorption characteristics, as for hydrogen on tungsten (section 6.2). In the precipitation, and in the calcining or drying, the surface area per gramme of catalyst can be profoundly altered by the presence of promoters; indeed one of the main functions of promoters may be to increase the specific area of the catalyst, but there is often an effect on the activity per unit area as well. Metals and alloys have been used as foils or wires.

Supported metal or oxide catalysts are prepared by precipitating a salt in the presence of the carrier, or soaking the carrier in a solution of a salt, and calcining the salt on the carrier with further reduction if needed. Promoters can be incorporated in catalysts by similar methods. It has been suspected for long that few carriers are completely inert. This was difficult to test until the area of the metal could be measured accurately, for different thicknesses of the same weight of film might present very different surface areas to the reactants. Recent work on the hydrogen–deuterium exchange has revealed that a film of copper is much more effective when spread on a base of magnesia than on a base of alumina, and Taylor[31] and Kwan[32] have quoted other examples.

It is well known that porous masses of silica or alumina can be prepared by drying the gels of these oxides, and these have often been used as supports for metal films. Metals that are not attacked by caustic alkali can be prepared in a very porous form by alloying with aluminium and 'leaching-out' the aluminium with caustic alkali. The enormous increase in area is illustrated by a preparation[33] of Raney nickel from an alloy of specific area $0.4 \text{ m}^2\text{g}^{-1}$. By extrapolation of the time–area curve, the area immediately after preparation was about $142 \text{ m}^2\text{g}^{-1}$, estimated by the physical adsorption of a gas and the 'point B' method which is described in the next section. The adsorption curves shown in *Figure 5.3* with the point B marked on each curve show that the area decreases on aging, probably owing to the slow growth of the larger crystals at the expense of the smaller.

It is necessary to know a good deal about the surface of a catalyst before the mechanism of the catalysed reaction can be known. In order to avoid the difficulties and doubts about the precise nature of the surface of industrial catalysts, which are very complex, strenuous efforts have been made to prepare clean and uniform surfaces for special studies of chemisorption and rates. Some of these experiments are described in the next chapter. However, these studies have brought their own problems, and the view has been expressed that extrapolations from 'clean' to 'industrial' surfaces are not without danger.

5.4. PHYSICAL CHARACTERIZATION OF HETEROGENEOUS CATALYSTS

Studies of chemisorption and of the rates and mechanisms of heterogeneous reactions have been greatly helped by the development of methods of measuring the surface areas of catalysts and the size and porosity of the particles[34]. In addition, methods have been found for investigating the atomic geometry

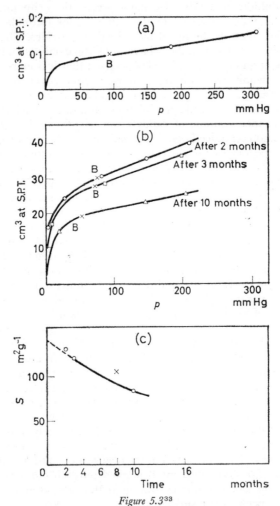

Figure 5.3[33]

(*a*) Multilayer adsorption on original aluminium–nickel alloy used to prepare Raney nickel
(*b*) Multilayer adsorption on Raney nickel
(*c*) Surface area (*S*) of Raney nickel
× = particle size measurements

of the surface and the distribution of promoter molecules between bulk and surface catalyst. It seems appropriate to summarize here some of these methods for characterizing the catalyst; some applications of these methods are mentioned in later sections.

5.4.1. *Particle size of catalysts*

The obvious method of determining the size and shape of larger particles is with the optical microscope; the lower limit of the radius which can be investigated in this way is about 2,000 Å. For smaller particles (which can contribute substantially to the area and to the catalytic activity of the powder) the older methods involve suspension in a liquid and studies of the sedimentation rate or equilibrium under gravity or in a centrifuge. These methods are tedious but give good results for the distribution among various radii. Another procedure of limited utility is to use the surface area measurements by gas adsorption and an assumed shape to calculate an average radius. Much more direct and useful information can now be obtained by studying the low-angle scattering of x-rays, by using an electron microscope and by examining the broadening of the diffraction patterns of x-rays at wide angles of scattering.

The electron microscope uses high-speed electrons of short equivalent wavelength to extend the range of measurement down to 10 to 50 Å. The powder is spread as a thin film on a support of collodion and silhouettes of the particles are obtained by suitable focusing of the beams with the magnetic and electric fields which serve as lenses. By calibration of the instrument with a standard grating replica as object the size of particles can be determined to within a few ångströms. The number of particles covered with one beam is not large, but distribution functions can be determined and have been used to follow the growth of particles during aging, sintering and reaction[35]. With different focusing of the emergent beams from the film, the electron-diffraction patterns can give information about the atomic spacings in the layers near the surface, although reflection electron diffraction has been used more often for this purpose[36].

The scattering of x-rays[37] at low angles (1 to 2°) from a powder leads to a diffraction pattern and the intensities, I, are related theoretically to the radius of the particles as well as to the angle of scattering, θ. The radii of the particles can be calculated from the slopes of plots of $\log I_\theta$ against a suitable function of the scattering angle and the wave-length of the x-rays. The particles are assumed to be spherical, but distribution functions among radii between 50 and 1,000 Å can be determined. The method has been used to follow the history of particle size during aging and other treatments of catalysts.

Rather different information is provided by studying the width of the lines in the patterns of x-ray diffraction at wider angles[38]. When the dimensions of the crystallites (of which there may be many in each particle) are below about 100 Å, the angular width of the line at half the maximum intensity is inversely proportional to the number of reflections N from the planes distance d apart, so that the lines get broader as the crystallite size gets smaller. It has been found that considerable differences in crystallite size occur with changes in the details of the method of preparation (see section 8.5) and with annealing or sintering of the catalyst.

5.4.2. *The surface area of catalysts*

The surface area of a sample of a catalyst is obviously a major factor in determining its activity, and a good deal of confusion about the activity of various preparations has arisen from the assessment of activity per unit weight rather than per unit surface; only recently has it become clear that the specific area of a catalyst is quite variable with details of the source and the subsequent history of the catalyst sample. Fortunately, a relatively simple and accurate method of measuring the surface area of a catalyst, by the physical adsorption of a gas near its boiling point, has become available, and the measurement of the surface area is now a standard part of any investigation of catalytic activity[39]. Other methods have proved useful in particular studies and in the testing of the gas adsorption method, however, and will be mentioned briefly. The methods available can conveniently be divided into two groups. Those in the first group leave the surface unaltered and ready for further studies; those in the second group so affect the surface of the solid that it has to be regenerated, or else the further studies made on a parallel sample.

Group I. Methods leaving the surface unaltered

(*i*) *From measurements of the geometrical area*—The geometrical area of extensive, non-porous solids such as plates, foils, wires or spheres can readily be calculated by measurement of linear dimensions. As indicated in the previous section, the optical and the electron microscope allow the determination of shape and cover practically the whole useful range of radii between them. Metal powder and colloidal particles are often spherical, but some oxides are fibrous or plate-like in shape.

The geometrical area is converted into a true or adsorption area by multiplying by a 'roughness factor' which is taken as unity for a liquid surface and close to unity for non-porous powders[40] (see section 5.5 for the determination of porosity). For bulk metals, however, it is difficult to know what factor to use. Factors between one and two have often been used; but Rideal, Bowden and their co-workers[41] have demonstrated that factors of three and higher were common for aged drawn or electropolished metals and could be as high as 13 for new polished nickel. In principle, detailed information can be obtained about surface roughness from multiple-beam interferometry[42] or from electron microscope studies using the shadow technique. In the interferometry method the surface is placed near an optically flat surface of quartz to form a thin wedge, and this wedge forms interference fringes (obtained in reflection or transmission) which are displaced by irregularities on the surface. If the surface and the 'flat' have a thin uniform layer of silver evaporated on to them before use, the displacement of the pattern of fringes formed by multiple reflections is clearer. The surface topography can be plotted by 'contouring' at about 30 Å intervals. In the shadow method, projections or hollows are revealed after their slopes or steps have been covered by gold atoms from a molecular beam directed at an oblique angle at the surface. Such studies as these have been used to follow detailed changes in the growth of crystals and the formation of films of metals, and the evaluation of surface roughness factors is probably not worth while. On the other hand, a detailed knowledge of the surface topography of the faces of single crystals will probably be essential in relating the activity of the faces to the presence of surface dislocations, edges, kinks and so on.

(*ii*) *By flow of an inert gas past a powder*—These permeability methods are very accurate for powders consisting of discrete particles of radius greater than 10μ, but not for finer particles. The surface area of the powder, S, is evaluated from the permeability K by empirical equations such as that used by Carman[43]

$$S = 14\sqrt{\frac{\varepsilon^2}{K\nu(1-\varepsilon)^2}}$$

where ν is the kinematic viscosity of the fluid used, and ε is the 'porosity' of the bed, calculated as the ratio of total pore space to the volume of the bed (see page 121). K is determined from the flow experiments, for it relates the rate of flow per unit area of cross-section of the bed (V/A) to the pressure gradient down the bed (P/L): $V/A = K(P/L)$. The equations used have some theoretical basis, but a thorough treatment is made difficult by surface migration of the fluid as well as bulk flow. Interest in these methods has increased with the advent of gas-phase chromatography. The problems of flow in a bed of powdered catalyst are obviously of great importance in industrial processes.

(*iii*) *By the physical adsorption of gases*[39,44]—This method is widely used, for the apparatus is simple, the experimental work is straightforward and the calculations are not too tedious. The results are accurate absolutely to about ± 25 per cent, but relative areas can be determined to a much higher degree of accuracy and often to ± 5 per cent. The experimental basis of the method is the measurement of the amount of gas adsorbed on the surface at various pressures of the gas at a temperature near its boiling point. From these results the amount of gas required to complete a monolayer of physically adsorbed gas on the surface is determined, and this is converted to an area assuming that the molecules are packed on the surface in the same way as in the liquefied gas at that temperature†. With certain gases, like nitrogen, the results fit isotherms like those of *Figure 5.3*, in which the amount of gas adsorbed is reported as v (the volume of that amount of gas at S.T.P.) for various pressures p. The point where the linear portion of the graph begins (point B) was chosen by Brunauer and Emmett[44] as a measure of v_m, the volume of gas which would fill the monolayer. A more refined way of determining v_m is to apply the BET equation[45]

$$\frac{v}{v_m} = \frac{cx}{(1-x)(1+(c-1)x)}$$

The quantity x is the relative pressure, p/p_0, and c is a constant; writing the equation as

$$\frac{x}{v(1-x)} = \frac{1}{cv_m} + \frac{x(c-1)}{cv_m}$$

it can be seen that a plot of $x/v(1-x)$ against x should be a straight line and that v_m and c can then be determined from the slope and intercept.

† Usually hexagonal close packing is assumed, so that the cross-sectional area of the molecule can be calculated from the expression

$$a = 1.091\left(\frac{M}{N_0\rho}\right)^{2/3}$$

where M is the molecular weight and ρ the density of the liquid adsorbate, and N_0 is Avogadro's number. For the gases most widely recommended as adsorbates, the following areas have been used:

Gas	NH$_3$	A	CO	N$_2$	n-C$_4$H$_{10}$
Temperature used (°C)	-36	-183	-183	-183	0
Area (Å^2)	12·9	14·1	16·8	17·0	32·1

Group II. Methods which require regeneration of the catalyst

(*i*) *By adsorption from solution*—The adsorbate can be any solute that is adsorbed to give a monolayer on the surface, provided that its concentration in solution can be easily determined. Acids, phenols or coloured dyes are often used. An interesting variation for a salt or metal powder is to adsorb from solution a radioactive ion of the salt or metal on to the surface of the powder; at equilibrium, the relationship

$$\frac{\text{active isotope on surface}}{\text{normal isotope on surface}} = \frac{\text{active ion in solution}}{\text{normal ion in solution}}$$

allows the evaluation of the number of normal atoms or ions on the surface and hence the surface area. The method was first used by Paneth for a lead sulphate powder, using thorium B as the isotope; a recent application is mentioned by Schwab and Marhenkel[33].

(*ii*) *By chemisorption from the gas phase*—The method is basically the same as in (*i*) above and determines the number of sites available for chemisorption[9,12]. This is determined from the amount of gas required to complete a monolayer on the surface, and some assumption about the state of adsorption as molecules or atoms or radicals. Hydrogen or carbon monoxide have usually been used, with an appropriate equation to evaluate v_m and hence N_m. The calculation of the area involves further assumptions about the area per site— this is usually taken as the crystallographic area per 'lepton' but it is not always known which crystallographic planes are exposed, still less in what proportions. Nevertheless, as the correlation of the area determined by some other method, such as the BET method, with the number of sites available for chemisorption involves these same assumptions in the reverse manner, it has often proved useful to determine 'sites available' directly from chemisorption rather than from other area measurements.

(*iii*) *From heats of wetting*—The heat of wetting q_w is related to the surface area S and the surface tension γ of the liquid

$$S = -q_w/e\left(\gamma - T\frac{\partial \gamma}{\partial T}\right)$$

Most of the experimental methods suggested[8] involve the evaluation of the constant e by calibration. An ingenious method, avoiding the evaluation of the constant e, was devised by Harkins and Jura[46]. They adsorbed water vapour on to a powder, to give multilayer adsorption, and then dipped the adsorbent with the adsorbate into liquid water; this destroyed S cm^2 of water surface,

Table 5.2

Solid powder	Relative area by heat of immersion	Relative area by BET N_2	Relative area by BET C_7H_{16}
TiO$_2$ (standard)	1·00	1·00	1·00
TiO$_2$ II	0·63	0·62	0·63
SiO$_2$	0·23	0·23	0·26
BaSO$_4$	0·17	0·17	0·17

evolving $118S$ ergs of energy (i.e. the value of $\left(\gamma - T\dfrac{\partial \gamma}{\partial T}\right)S$) which was measured, and so S was obtained. The method would clearly not work for a porous adsorbent, but for various powders it gave good agreement with the BET method, as shown in *Table 5.2*.

4.3.5. *Structure of porous catalysts*

Porous catalysts include activated charcoals, activated clays, silica gel, Raney nickel and pelletted powders. It is useful to know something about the volume of the pore spaces, the inner surface area of the pores, the average radii of the pores and the distribution of the volume and the surface area among pores of different radii. By combining gas adsorption measurements with what are virtually measurements of the density of the solid, information can be obtained about pores of radii of all sizes above a few ångströms. Gas adsorption measurements are particularly useful for investigating pores with small radii, less than about 100 Å, while larger pores can be investigated by forcing a liquid under pressure into the pores.

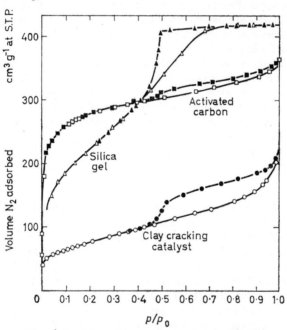

Figure 5.4. Adsorption curves on porous catalysts[49]

The volume V_P of the pores can be determined from experiments which measure separately the total external volume V_T and the actual volume V_A of solid, for $V_P = V_T - V_A$. V_T is measured by immersion in a liquid such as mercury which does not penetrate the pores at low pressures. V_A is determined by immersion in helium gas which penetrates all the pores but is not adsorbed on the surface at room temperature. The 'displacement' of the helium is measured by putting the sample of catalyst into a vessel of known internal volume V_V and evacuating thoroughly; helium stored at pressure P in a container of volume V_C is shared with the evacuated vessel containing the sample, and assuming the temperature is uniform the conservation of mass leads to the equation

$$V_C P = p(V_C + V_V - V_A)$$

where p is the final (measured) pressure. With attention to the relative sizes of V_V, V_C and V_A and to temperature control, the method is very accurate and good estimates of V_A can be made, and hence of the pore volume V_P. The ratio V_P/V_T is called the porosity (ε) of the sample.

The inner surface of the porous catalyst can usually be equated to the total area determined by the adsorption of nitrogen gas. This is especially true if the adsorption isotherm is of the form shown in *Figure 5.4* for silica gel. The flat portion of the isotherm at high pressures indicates that a negligible amount of adsorbate is taken up as soon as the pores are filled; the rising portion of the curve for adsorption or desorption at rather lower pressures (with p/p_0 between 0·4 and 0·8) is attributed to capillary condensation of the adsorbate as a liquid. The portion at still lower pressures, due to monolayer adsorption, can be used to determine the surface area, as explained in the last section.

If the capillaries are assumed to be cylindrical in shape, the average radius of the capillaries can be determined from the surface area and the volume of the pores, for $\bar{r} = 2V_P/S_P$.

Better estimates of the radii of the smaller pores can be obtained from the portions of the curves attributed to capillary condensation. In the earlier treatment of Zsigmondy[47], developed by Patrick and others[8], adsorption is visualized as starting in fine capillaries where the liquid would have a lower vapour pressure, and successively filling wider pores as the pressure is increased. This allows the pressure p to be related to the pore radius r by the Kelvin equation

$$\ln \frac{p_0}{p} = \frac{2\gamma V}{rRT}$$

where γ and V are, respectively, the surface tension and the molar volume of the liquid adsorbate at the temperature T and R is the gas constant. However, this view of adsorption takes no account of the formation of a monolayer or of multilayers and can only be applied to the high-pressure regions. Where the adsorption and desorption branches show a loop, it is plainly better to apply the Kelvin equation to the desorption branch, when the liquid is present in the capillaries, rather than to the adsorption branch where the multilayers on the inner surface of the pores have not bridged the pore. In the simplest treatment, the change in volume adsorbed between two pressures gives the volume of the pores with radii between the two corresponding radii calculated from the Kelvin equation. In more complicated and accurate treatments, due to Shull[48], Barrett, Joyner and Halenda[49] and to Wheeler[50], corrections are made for the slow stripping of multilayers from wider capillaries after the 'emptying' of the condensate and also for the effect of the thickness of the monolayer or average multilayer on the condensation radius of each capillary. A good brief account of these methods, without examples however, has been given by Jacobs and Tompkins[34]. A more detailed discussion has been given by Ries[51].

The type of distribution curves found experimentally is illustrated in *Figure 5.5* which were determined[49] from the isotherms shown in *Figure 5.4*. By assuming that the capillaries are cylindrical and that the distribution of the *length* of the capillaries with r is of some standard form such as a Maxwellian

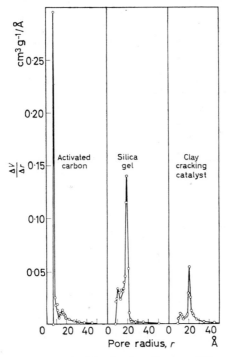

Figure 5.5. Distribution of pore radii[49]

or Gaussian curve, the volume of gas desorbed between the saturation pressure and chosen pressures can be calculated and compared with the experimental volumes; this is done for various values of the parameters of the standard form of the distribution function, and the best match with experiment is taken to give the best distribution function. If this is $L(r)$ then the surface area and the volume of the pores of radii between r_1 and r_2 can be determined separately as functions of the radii, for

$$S_{r_1, r_2} = \int_{r_1}^{r_2} 2\pi r L(r)\, dr$$

$$V_{r_1, r_2} = \int_{r_1}^{r_2} \pi r^2 L(r)\, dr$$

The radii of larger pores are determined by forcing into them mercury under pressure. If the radius of a pore mouth is r, then liquid of surface tension γ will enter when the pressure is given by

$$Pr = -2\gamma \cos \text{(angle of wetting)}$$

123

The volume of liquid entering between pressures P_1 and P_2 thus gives the volume of the pores with radii between the corresponding values r_1 and r_2.

Very large pores, of radii $> 10^3$ Å, can sometimes be measured with an optical microscope if the structure of the catalyst allows the cutting or preparation of good sections.

REFERENCES

[1] INNES, W. B. Catalysis (Ed. P. H. Emmett) Vol. II: Reinhold, New York, 1955, Chapter 1

[2] FARADAY, M. Phil. Trans. 1834, **114**, 55

[3] DÖBEREINER, J. Schweigger's J. 1822, **34**, 91; 1823, **38**, 321

[4] MITSCHERLICH, E. Liebigs Ann. 1842, **44**, 186

[5] SABATIER, P. La Catalyse en Chemie Organique: Béranger, Paris, 1920

[6] LAIDLER, K. J. Catalysis (Ed. P. H. Emmett) Vol. I: Reinhold, New York, 1954, Chapter 3

[7] LANGMUIR, I. Phys. Rev. 1915, **6**, 79; J. Amer. chem. Soc. 1915, **37**, 1139

[8] BRUNAUER, S. The Physical Adsorption of Gases and Vapours: Oxford University Press, London; Princeton University Press, Princeton, 1943

[9] TRAPNELL, B. M. W. Chemisorption: Butterworth, London, 1955

[10] DOWDEN, D. A. J. chem. Soc. 1950, p. 242

[11] EISCHENS, R. P. and PLISKIN, W. A. Advanc. Catalys. 1958, **10**, 1

[12] ROBERTS, J. K. Some Problems in Adsorption: Cambridge University Press, London, 1939

[13] CULVER, R. V. and TOMPKINS, F. C. Advanc. Catalys. 1959, **11**, 68

[14] BECKER, J. A. Advanc. Catalys. 1955, **7**, 135
GOMER, R. Advanc. Catalys. 1955, **7**, 93

[15] SUHRMANN, R. Advanc. Catalys. 1955, **7**, 303

[16] LAIDLER, K. J. Catalysis (Ed. P. H. Emmett) Vol. I: Reinhold, New York, 1954, Chapter 4

[17] ROBERTSON, A. J. B. Mass Spectrometry: Methuen, London, 1954

[18] KEMBALL, C. Proc. R. Soc. A 1951, **207**, 539; Proc. chem. Soc. 1960, 264

[19] TWIGG, G. H. Disc. Faraday Soc. 1950, **8**, 152

[20] BOND, G. C., SHERIDAN, J. and WHIFFEN, D. H. Trans. Faraday Soc. 1952, **48**, 715

[21] FARKAS, A. Orthohydrogen, Parahydrogen and Heavy Hydrogen: Cambridge University Press, London, 1935

[22] HINSHELWOOD, C. N. The Kinetics of Chemical Change: Clarendon Press, Oxford, 1940, Chapter 8

[23] SCHWAB, G. M. Catalysis (Trans. H. S. Taylor and R. Spence): Macmillan, London, 1937

[24] RIDEAL, E. K. J. Soc. chem. Ind., Lond. 1943, **62**, 335

[25] ELEY, D. D. Advanc. Catalys. 1948, **1**, 157; Quart. Rev. 1949, **3**, 209

[26] TEMKIN, M. and PYZHEV, V. Acta phys.-chim. U.R.S.S. 1940, **12**, 327

[27] SCHWAB, G. M. and PIETSCH, E. Z. phys. Chem. (Leipzig) 1928, **B1**, 385

[28] SCHWAB, G. M. and DRIKOS, G. Z. phys. Chem. (Leipzig) 1942, **B52**, 234

[29] OWEN, J. R. J. Amer. chem. Soc. 1947, **69**, 2559

[30] BEECK, O. Advanc. Catalys. 1950, **2**, 151

[31] TAYLOR, H. S. Advanc. Catalys. 1957, **9**, 1

[32] KWAN, T. Advanc. Catalys. 1954, **6**, 67

[33] SCHWAB, G. M. and MARHENKEL, H. Solid–Gas Interface, Proceedings of the Second International Congress of Surface Activity (Ed. J. H. Schulman) Vol. II: Butterworth, London; Academic Press, New York, 1957, p. 64

[34] JACOBS, P. W. M. and TOMPKINS, F. C. Chemistry of the Solid State (Ed. W. E. Garner): Butterworth, London, 1955, Chapter 4

REFERENCES

[35] Ashley, K. D. and Innes, W. B. *Industr. Engng Chem.* (*Industr.*) 1952, **44**, 2857
Adams, C. R. and Voge, H. H. *J. phys. Chem.* 1957, **61**, 722

[36] Bassett, G. A., Menter, J. W. and Pashley, D. W. International Conference on the Structure and Properties of Thin Films: Wiley, New York, 1959, p. 11

[37] Guinier, A. *J. Chim. phys.* 1943, **40**, 133

[38] Clarke, G. I. and Rhodes, H. D. *Industr. Engng Chem.* (*Anal.*) 1940, **12**, 66

[39] Emmett, P. H. *Catalysis* (Ed. P. H. Emmett) Vol. I: Reinhold, New York, 1954, Chapter 2

[40] Barrett, H. M., Birnie, A. W. and Cohen, M. *J. Amer. chem. Soc.* 1940, **62**, 2839
Kenrick, F. B. *J. Amer. chem. Soc.* 1940, **62**, 2838

[41] Rideal, E. K. and Bowden, F. P. *Proc. R. Soc. A* 1928, **120**, 59, 80

[42] Tolansky, S. *Proc. roy. Soc. A* 1945, **184**, 41, 51

[43] Carman, P. C. *J. Soc. chem. Ind., Lond.* 1938, **57**, 225; 1939, **58**, 1

[44] Brunauer, S. and Emmett, P. H. *J. Amer. chem. Soc.* 1937, **59**, 1553

[45] Brunauer, S., Emmett, P. H. and Teller, E. *J. Amer. chem. Soc.* 1938, **60**, 309

[46] Harkins, W. D. and Jura, G. *J. Amer. chem. Soc.* 1944, **66**, 919, 1362, 1366

[47] Zsigmondy, R. *Z. anorg. Chem.* 1911, **71**, 356

[48] Shull, C. G. *J. Amer. chem. Soc.* 1948, **70**, 1405

[49] Barrett, E. P., Joyner, L. G. and Halenda, P. P. *J. Amer. chem. Soc.* 1951, **73**, 373

[50] Wheeler, A. *Advanc. Catalys.* 1951, **3**, 250

[51] Ries, H. E., Jr. *Advanc. Catalys.* 1952, **4**, 87

HETEROGENEOUS CATALYSIS AND CHEMISORPTION

6.1. INTRODUCTION

In the last chapter, it has been explained that the *chemisorption* of a reactant on the catalyst surface is an essential part of a heterogeneously catalysed reaction, and that it consists of a chemical reaction between a free molecule and the surface. Almost all chemisorptions are exothermic, and there is ample evidence from simple and unequivocal calorimetric experiments that the strengths of the bonds with the surface are in the same range as the strengths of the bonds in molecules. Examination of *Table 6.4* shows that the heats of adsorption of diatomic molecules such as H_2 or O_2 on various transition metals are very high. It is highly unlikely that these large amounts of energy could be released if the molecules were adsorbed as such; it is far more likely that the molecules are split into atoms as they react with the surfaces to form covalent M—H links, or even become ionized to form M^-H^+ or M^+H^- links. Without prejudicing a decision between these possibilities, it is helpful to consider[1] the potential energy changes as the molecule approaches the surface, is attracted by the van der Waals forces, and dissociates; for simplicity, it will first be assumed that covalent M—H bonds are formed.

In *Figure 6.1* the curves ABC and AB′C′ represent the potential energy changes upon physical adsorption of a molecule X_2 on metals M and M′. Because the forces are the non-specific van der Waals forces, the curves will be practically identical and the heats of physical adsorption, q_p and q'_p, will be nearly the same. As explained, it will first be assumed that the molecule X_2 is chemisorbed on the metals as atoms; the heat of dissociation is D_{X_2} and the curve DFG represents the energy changes upon adsorption of the atoms on the metal M; DF′G′ is the equivalent curve for M′. The points F and F′ represent the stable equilibrium conditions of chemisorption of the atoms, and their depth below D is equal to the heat of chemisorption of two atoms of X. F and F′ will lie to the left of B because the internuclear distances of the chemisorbed bonds M—X and M′—X will be less than the equilibrium distance of physical adsorption, the chemisorption bonds being much stronger.

Considering *Figure 6.1 (a)* first, there is a path for the chemisorption of the molecule X_2 depicted by the heavy line; this chemisorption could occur without need for activation, as all points of the path to F lie below A. The heat of chemisorption of the molecule X_2 would be equal to q_c and the heat of chemisorption of each atom is $\frac{1}{2}(q_c + D_{X_2})$. In *Figure 6.1 (b)*, on the other hand, the curves have been drawn to intersect at a higher point, and the chemisorption of the molecule now needs activation energy E. In practice, the magnitude of the activation energy will depend upon the shape of the potential energy curves, and in particular upon the length of the chemisorbed bond and the heat of chemisorption. The relationship between these and other properties of the atoms and metals are not known well enough to predict the value of E. There is no doubt about the existence of an activation energy of chemisorption for a variety of chemisorptions, and many examples have been found since Taylor[2] first drew attention to 'activated adsorption'. Some of them are dis-

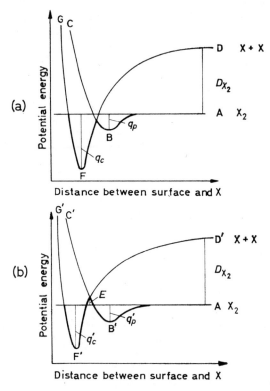

Figure 6.1. Potential energy curves for chemisorption with dissociation

cussed in section 6.6.2, where it is pointed out that a high value of q often seems to be connected with a low value of E.

If a molecule were chemisorbed without dissociation, as appears to be true for carbon monoxide on some metals, similar potential energy curves could be drawn with DFG representing the molecule in some excited state capable of bonding to the surface. Moreover, similar curves could be drawn to represent ionization of the atoms or molecules; if, for example, a hydrogen atom lost an electron which was passed into the metal, the energy required would be equal $eI-e\phi$ where I is the ionization potential of hydrogen and ϕ is the work function of the metal. The ion and its image charge in the metal are attracted and provide 'image energy' equal to $e^2/4R$ where $2R$ is the distance between ion and image. The energy of adsorption is therefore: $-\tfrac{1}{2}D_{H_2}-eI+e\phi+e^2/4R$. Gundry and Tompkins[3] show that with reasonable values for R and ϕ the process

127

would be *endothermic* to the extent of 200 kcal g-atom^{-1}. An alternative calculation with the hydride ion H^- suggests that the gain of an electron from the metal would require 115 kcal g-atom^{-1}. On the other hand, calculations of Eley[4] on the energy released if covalent bonds M—H were formed are in reasonable agreement with the experimental heats of chemisorption for tungsten (73·4 compared with 74·1 experimentally), nickel (60·2 compared with 67·1 experimentally) and other transition metals. It therefore seems likely that hydrogen is chemisorbed on transition metals as atoms with localized covalent M—H bonds; however, the precise site of the adsorption may vary with the coverage, and this point will be discussed again later.

Similar calculations show that sodium, potassium and caesium are probably chemisorbed on tungsten as cations, but the majority of molecules appear to be held on metals by covalent bonds.

Hydrogen is also chemisorbed on oxides. With semiconductor oxides, such as zinc oxide or cuprous oxide, the conductivities of the surface layers change during chemisorption and the changes show that electrons are transferred from the hydrogen to the oxide[5]. In addition, the chemisorption is not reversible, for on heating the system loses water rather than hydrogen[6]. These results can depicted for zinc oxide as follows:

$$\tfrac{1}{2}H_2 + O^{2-} \rightarrow OH^- + e$$

$$2OH^- \rightarrow H_2O + O^{2-}$$

In general, this pattern of covalent bonding to metals, and the formation of ions on oxides, is found for many gases. In detail, the picture is complicated by the presence of impurities on real surfaces—for example, unreduced oxides on metals—and by the presence of defects in the crystal surfaces, by the finite size of the crystallites and the occurrence of edges, joints and steps, and by the possibility of multiple bonding of chemisorbed molecules or atoms to several surface atoms. Now the surfaces of effective catalysts are far from simple, and it proved very difficult to examine theories of chemisorption on them. One very profitable way round this difficulty has been to prepare surfaces of metals that can be freed from impurities and in addition are fairly uniform. The fundamental studies of chemisorption have been made on these surfaces. Some of these studies are described in the next section, and this is followed by a discussion of chemisorption on oxides. The important experimental work on the heats of adsorption is summarized briefly before dealing with the theoretical basis of the isotherms that describe chemisorption.

6.2. CHEMISORPTION OF GASES ON METALS

Many studies of chemisorption on the surface of catalysts have been made with the aim of testing proposed reaction schemes. These investigations are essential, and their frequency has increased rather than decreased. However, they are not very suitable for testing theories of chemisorption, for the surfaces are usually too complex and too ill-defined for this purpose; in fact, chemisorption studies are often used to help to define the surface structure of these catalysts. Special methods have been used to clean metal surfaces for fundamental studies of chemisorption, and other methods have been developed for forming fresh surfaces *in situ*.

The methods used for cleaning the surfaces of metals depend upon the use of very high vacua to remove gases from the surface and to prevent recontamination. With pressures below 10^{-5} mm Hg, strong heating of the surface will remove most dissolved and chemisorbed gases from oxides. With metals, a preliminary reduction in hydrogen at moderate temperatures, followed by heating *in vacuo* to remove chemisorbed hydrogen, is more effective than attempts to desorb oxygen directly[7]. Besides reduction with molecular hydrogen, oxygen can be rapidly removed by atomic hydrogen produced in an electrodeless discharge[8], but solution of the hydrogen below the surface then proves troublesome. Another interesting technique is bombardment of the surface with positive ions of inert gases[9], but again dissolved gases may cause trouble and it seems that atoms of the bombarding gas replace the desorbed layer[10]. Many workers have shown that it is difficult to keep metal surfaces free from oxygen and nitrogen. In a stimulating discussion of vacuum techniques, Becker[11] has summarized the evidence that completely clean tungsten surfaces can only exist for a very short time unless the vacuum is better than 10^{-8} mm Hg. At 10^{-6} mm, tungsten adsorbs a layer of nitrogen atoms in about 1 second, at 10^{-8} mm, in about 100 seconds; the rate for oxygen atoms is probably similar or faster.

The first of the special techniques for studying clean surfaces were developed by Langmuir and his associates during their investigations of adsorption equilibria and the rates of adsorption and desorption[12]. They utilized the great advances in vacuum techniques which were made at the beginning of the twentieth century, and by thorough heating of glass and metal parts *in vacuo* were able to prepare cleaner and more definite catalyst surfaces than had been used before. Their principal studies were on the adsorption of hydrogen, oxygen, water vapour and caesium vapour on to refractory metals such as tungsten, and they used changes in the contact potential of the surfaces as well as changes in the pressure and volume of the adsorbate gas to follow the extent of adsorption. They established that dissociation of molecules could occur at hot tungsten surfaces, that caesium could be adsorbed as atoms or as ions, that the energies evolved in these adsorptions were similar in magnitude to the energies of exothermic chemical reactions, that the adsorption reached saturation and that the adsorbed fragments could migrate on the surface.

Rather similar techniques were used by Roberts[13] and by Rideal[14] and their co-workers in Cambridge between 1935 and 1939. They measured the extent of adsorption by changes in contact potentials or in the accommodation coefficients of various gases (see section 6.6.1), and showed that the number of hydrogen atoms adsorbed on tungsten wires was very nearly equal to the number of metal atoms exposed on the surface. This gave reality to the idea of a chemisorbed monolayer. Besides measuring the heat of adsorption of different gases on different metals, they showed that the heat of adsorption fell off with increasing coverage, whatever the adsorbate–adsorbent system. This change was thought to be due either to the surface having a variety of sites which form bonds of different strengths, or to interactions between the adsorbed fragments on a uniform set of sites; on the whole, Roberts and Rideal favoured the second possibility.

Roberts showed that very clean surfaces of metals with high melting points could be obtained by heating electrically a wire of the metal *in vacuo* to evaporate the surface layers and all but the most tenacious impurities. With tungsten, for instance, the oxide WO_3 will evaporate at temperatures above 1,200°C and the surface layer of oxygen atoms above 2,000°, while at a temperature a few hundred degrees higher the oxygen dissolved in the interior will be rapidly removed. Even silica can be removed. The 'flashing' results in a polycrystalline surface with many crystal planes exposed, although the (100), (110) and (111) planes may predominate. Many studies of chemisorption have been made on surfaces of tungsten, tantalum and similar metals prepared by this method, and it was used to clean the tungsten points used in recent field emission studies.

There are two other methods for obtaining very clean metal surfaces which have the advantage of allowing some control of the geometry and the orientation of the crystal plane exposed. In the first[15-17], single crystals of the metal are grown and treated to expose predominantly one crystal plane; this results in a surface which is precisely defined on an atomic scale but is small in area, i.e. a few square centimetres. In the second[18,19], the metal is evaporated by heating a clean wire of the metal to form a film on a cooled surface; the orientation of the crystals in the film can be controlled by the conditions of evaporation and more exactly by suitable choice of the backing material for the film, and with many metals the films can have substantial specific areas, for instance, about 100 cm^2 mg^{-1} of film is quite common.

6.2.1. Preparation of single crystal faces

The methods available for preparing the single crystal faces are very varied. With non-metals, large crystals have been grown and single faces obtained from them by cleavage; such faces have been used for studies of chemisorption, but are of little interest for catalysis. With metals, the cleavage method often produces buckling and dislocations. It is better[15] to grow a single crystal in the form of a rod by solidification of the melt in a vacuum, and to machine the crystal into a slice exposing one face or into a sphere exposing all faces. Selected faces can be polished mechanically and electrolytically, and after washing they are usually further cleaned by annealing in hydrogen. Electron diffraction and electron microscope studies have shown[17] that these faces are essentially flat on an atomic scale, and show an undistorted structure characteristic of a given crystal plane.

Rhodin[17,22] has developed a very sensitive gravimetric method for measuring the amounts of gas adsorbed on these single crystal faces. If an area of 1 cm^2 is covered by a monolayer of nitrogen molecules, the increase in weight is about 5×10^{-8} g. This is below the sensitivity of the older spiral spring microbalances, such as that of McBain and Bakr[23], but within that of beam microbalances which can measure the adsorption on single metal crystals or on metal wires. Rhodin[17] has given a critical survey of the various types of spring and torsion or knife-edge or cantilever beam microbalances. A typical assembly used by Rhodin for measuring adsorption on single crystals of copper of area 1 cm^2 is shown in *Figure 6.2*; he prefers to measure the deflection of the beam rather than to use a null method. A good idea of the results obtained is given by *Figure 6.3*, showing the physical adsorption of nitrogen.

Some surprising results have emerged from studies of adsorption and of catalysed reactions on these single crystal faces. The extent of adsorption, both

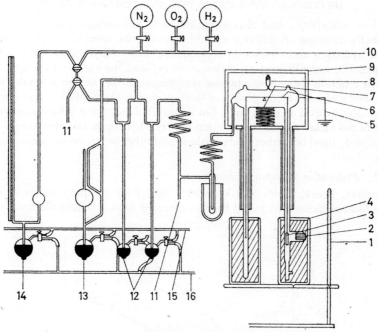

Figure 6.2. Vacuum microbalance assembly for measuring low-temperature adsorption[22a]

1. elevator platform
2. evaporator (not used)
3. single crystal plate
4. dewar
5. electrical earth
6. microbalance beam
7. shock mounting
8. ionization gauge
9. air thermostat
10. purified gases
11. high-vacuum manifold
12. mercury cut-offs
13. McLeod gauge
14. gas burette
15. air line
16. vacuum line

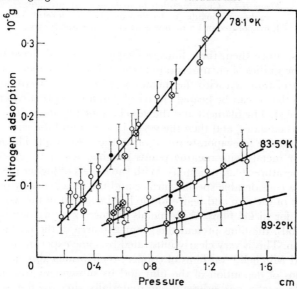

Figure 6.3. Physical adsorption of nitrogen on a single face of a copper crystal[22b]

physical adsorption and chemisorption, and the heats of adsorption are markedly different on different faces[22]; the reaction rates of the reaction between hydrogen and oxygen on copper, and those of hydrogen and ethylene on nickel[15], are different on different faces; and during the hydrogen and oxygen reaction there is substantial rearrangement of the metal crystal with roughening of some faces, growth of facets of preferred orientation and growth of powdered metal on some faces. On the other hand, there is little rearrangement of the nickel during the reaction between hydrogen and ethylene. There is obviously need of further study of these and other reactions on single crystal faces.

6.2.2. *Preparation of evaporated films*

In 1941, Beeck, Smith and Wheeler[18] described the preparation of very clean films of metal which had been evaporated from a heated filament on to

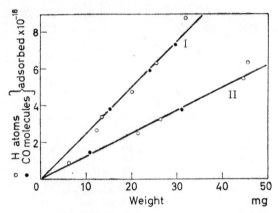

Figure 6.4. Chemisorption of hydrogen (atoms) and carbon monoxide (molecules) on films of nickel[18]
I, evaporated in 1 mm nitrogen; II, evaporated *in vacuo*

glass surfaces. Since then, these films of evaporated metals have been extensively used for studies of chemisorption and catalysis. A filament of the metal, or a filament of tungsten with the metal coated on it by electrodeposition, is suspended so that it can be heated electrically in a vessel that can be strongly heated or cooled. The filament and the vessel are first heated with pumping to remove adsorbed gases, and then the vessel is cooled and the wire heated to a higher temperature to evaporate metal on to the vessel wall. The method has been used for metals with melting points ranging from low (e.g. potassium) to high temperatures (e.g. tungsten). With the metals of higher melting points the film has a considerable specific surface and the area is nearly proportional to the weight of the film and hence to the loss in weight of the wire, as shown in *Figure 6.4* for nickel films. With metals of lower melting points, and with Group I metals, the films present the geometric area of the backing material for adsorption. This is very clearly illustrated by some experiments carried out by Allen and Mitchell[24] on films of copper; their results also emphasize that the conditions of deposition of the film and its subsequent treatment before adsorption or catalysis experiments can materially alter the film surface. The apparatus which they used to prepare the films and to study the adsorption of oxygen upon them is illustrated in *Figure 6.5.*

The copper films were prepared in the spherical bulb B (diameter 8 cm) by evaporation from a thoroughly outgassed bead mounted on a tungsten filament, after the bulb had been baked and evacuated and sealed off at C. Oxygen was stored in the tubes G after these had similarly been cleaned, and admitted to the manifold M by breaking the 'pigtail' seals. The pressure was measured on the Pirani gauge P, the seal S was broken after the film had been prepared and the pressure measured at suitable time intervals. The volumes of various parts of the system were measured after each experiment by weighing them first empty and then full of water. The number of molecules of gas adsorbed were then calculated by application of the simple gas laws. This system eliminates dead-space corrections and the method of operation ensures that the initial surfaces are uncontaminated by evaporating some copper from the film just before sealing off at a pressure of 10^{-7} mm Hg. The films were prepared with the bulb under three different conditions: (*i*) at room temperature, and cooled after deposition to $-183°C$, (*ii*) at $-183°C$, then warmed to room temperatures for 2 hours and cooled to $-183°C$ again, and (*iii*) prepared and maintained at $-183°C$. The colour of these films was copper-red if they were prepared or annealed *in vacuo* at room temperature; but the colour was bronze if the film was prepared and maintained at $-183°C$, and if oxygen was adsorbed at $-183°C$, this colour was kept and no oxygen desorbed upon subsequent warming to room temperature.

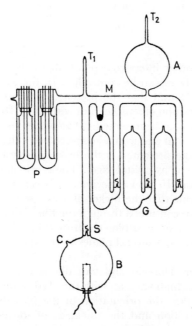

Figure 6.5. Apparatus for the preparation of evaporated films[24]

Table 6.1 shows some of Allen and Mitchell's results for these films, reporting the molecules of oxygen adsorbed at various temperatures per square centimetre of the geometric area of the film. As an oxygen molecule adsorbed as such would occupy an area of about 16Å^2 or $1\cdot6 \times 10^{-15}$ cm^2 (and roughly the same site area if adsorbed as atoms), it appears that the films prepared at room temperature present, as said, the geometric area (allowing for a small roughness factor for the area on an atomic scale), that the films prepared at $-183°$C with oxygen adsorbed at $-183°$C have a larger specific area and maintain this area when warmed even to $74°$C, while the films warmed before adsorption lose most of their area. This is in keeping with other experiments which show the ready sintering of copper films. Allen and Mitchell consider that the extra oxygen taken up on films of types (*i*) and (*ii*) at $20°$C and at $74°$C oxidizes the bulk metal.

Table 6.1. Chemisorption of oxygen on copper films[24]

Method of preparation	*Film weight* 10^5 gcm^{-2}	*Number of Molecules*/10^{-15} cm^2 of geometric area with adsorption at:			
		$-183°$C	$-78°$C	$20°$C	$74°$C
i	6·2	1·1	1·0	2·6	—
	6·5	1·3	1·3	3·1	10·3
	6·4	1·5	1·4	3·0	9·4
ii	6·9	1·8	1·9	5·0	6·6
	7·0	2·4	2·0	6·0	7·5
iii	4·7	8·1	10·6	12·9	12·6
	6·6	10·7	12·1	12·0	11·7
	6·9	10·0	10·0	10·0	9·9
	10·8	15·0	15·0	14·9	12·6
	15·5	22·2	26·0	26·0	26·0

Oriented films—Another interesting point about the films is that the orientation of the crystal faces can be controlled. In the early work by Beeck and co-workers[18], it was found that the presence of 1 mm of an inert gas like argon led to the deposition of a nickel film with the (110) planes parallel to the glass backing, whereas iron presented (111) planes to the glass. Nickel has a face-centred cubic crystal and iron a body-centred cubic crystal structure, and in each case the plane presented is the least densely occupied of the planes which commonly occur as crystal faces. These orientations were determined by electron diffraction. In later experiments, Beeck and Ritchie[19] showed by adsorption experiments that the nickel film exposed (110) planes to the gas, so that the orientation continued through the film. When films were laid down in as high a vacuum as possible, electron diffraction and gas adsorption measurements showed that several planes were exposed to the glass and to the gas.

However, Sachtler, Dorgelo and van der Knaap[20] found it possible to deposit nickel films in high vacuum with the (110) planes parallel to the backing, and suggested that the orientation of the film depends mainly on the temperature of deposition and the thickness of the deposit. Their electron microscope studies of the films cast some doubt on the continuity of the orientation through the film.

Beeck, Smith and Wheeler studied[18] the adsorption of carbon monoxide, hydrogen, oxygen, nitrogen and ethylene on films of iron, nickel, tantalum, tungsten, rhodium and protactinium. Some of their results are shown in *Figure 6.6*. Broadly speaking, their results, and those of other workers such as Trapnell, Kemball and Eley who used evaporated films, were in agreement with those of Langmuir and Roberts, but the significant discovery was made that chemisorption takes place to different extents on different crystal planes, and there are parallel differences in catalytic activity. Later work on single crystals has confirmed this specificity of crystal planes on the rate[16,17].

Beeck's results showed[21] that the heats of chemisorption of hydrogen on oriented and unoriented films are the same. This suggests that the same bonds

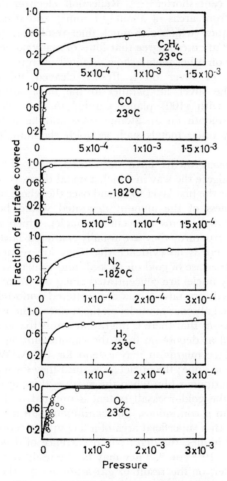

Figure 6.6. Chemisorption of gases on nickel films[18]

are formed between the hydrogen and the metal atoms in different crystal planes. Heats of physical adsorption of gases vary with the orientation, however[17].

135

Some other useful methods of controlling the orientation of films have been investigated, of which the most interesting is that of oriented overgrowth or 'epitaxy'[25]. If a vapour is condensed on to a crystalline substrate, the crystal structure of the film is oriented in relation to the face of the substrate. The structure of the metal film is identical with that of the bulk metal, except perhaps for a very short distance from the interface, but the crystal is oriented so that there is as little misfit as possible at the interface. There is little evidence to support older ideas[26] that the substrate enforces its own crystal spacing on the deposit, with a change in the crystal planes normal to the surface (basal plane pseudomorphism). Thus a monolayer of lead on the (111) face of silver has a spacing only 2 per cent smaller than that of bulk lead, whereas the silver spacing is 19 per cent shorter[27,28]. Reflection electron diffraction (which gives an average from areas of about 0·1 mm^2) and transmission electron microscopy techniques (which give much finer resolution, particularly when Moiré patterns[29,30] are used) agree that films of many noble metals deposited on ionic crystals or on other metals show oriented overgrowths. Of particular interest are those of silver on a freshly cleaved mica surface, when (111) planes of the silver lie parallel to the mica surface, or silver on a rocksalt surface with (100) planes parallel to the surface. These silver surfaces are very smooth on an atomic scale and have been used as the substrate for many other metals such as gold, rhodium, platinum, copper and nickel.

Already these overgrowths have been used, with the electron microscope[29,30], to investigate the way in which a metal deposits on to a crystalline surface. It is rare for the first layer to extend over the whole surface, even when the average thickness of the amount deposited would be several tens of ångströms. The growth seems to occur on nuclei, which rapidly assume a three-dimensional structure; they are usually scattered fairly uniformly over the surface, and there is no evidence that they are related to any surface features except in the case of gold on rocksalt and similar ionic crystals. With these systems, many nuclei are concentrated along the linear edges of steps on the surface of the salt crystals; others are scattered uniformly over the steps, but there is a marked absence of nuclei on the surfaces where the steps are very close together. It seems that there is migration across the surfaces towards the edge nuclei, as well as deposition from the vapour, during the thickening of the film. This surface migration may extend for 100 Å. With all films, the history is roughly the same; the nuclei grow until they form a network, which later becomes a continuous film when the average thickness is around 100 to 200 Å but again, the gold–rocksalt system is unusual and is 700 to 800 Å thick before the film is continuous. The continuous film is virtually one large oriented crystal, with a superficial area of a few square centimetres. By use of Moiré pattern techniques, the density of occurrence of dislocations has been estimated as 10^{10} to 10^{11} cm^{-2}. They may be the result of the meeting of the growths from nuclei, or the result of gas adsorbed on the substrate before deposition of the film. There is some evidence[31] that a monolayer of oxygen on titanium inhibits the deposition of copper. Further studies of the conditions of deposition—the vacuum, the rate of evaporation of the metal, the effects of surface singularities and adsorbed molecules—will be most welcome.

6.2.3. Infra-red spectra of chemisorbed species

It has recently been found that the techniques of infra-red spectroscopy can be adapted to allow the determination of the spectra of adsorbed molecules[32,33]. Both physically adsorbed and chemisorbed molecules can be studied, and the (absorption) spectra have been obtained by transmission[32] and also by reflection from films evaporated on to the mirrors of a multiple reflection cell[34].

For transmission, spectra are well defined if the radiation passes through a layer of close-packed molecules about 10^5 Å thick. Such thicknesses of chemisorbed molecules can be obtained by using layers of adsorbent in the form of very small particles. The particles should be smaller than the wave-length of the radiation used in order to minimize scattering, and it has been found best to spread metals as still finer particles (about 500 Å diameter) on silica or alumina particles of 1 to 2×10^3 Å diameter. These supports are transparent for radiation of wave-lengths between 2 and 8×10^5 Å.

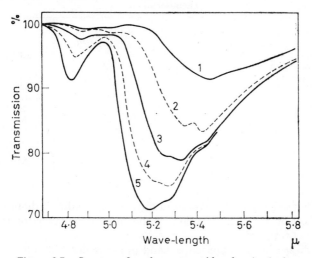

Figure 6.7. Spectra of carbon monoxide chemisorbed on palladium as influenced by surface coverage, with curves numbered according to increasing surface coverage[35]

The spectra observed are compared with those of the free adsorbate molecule and with those of compounds with structures similar to the possible structures of the chemisorbed species. When the molecules are physically adsorbed, there are comparatively small changes in the frequencies of the bands of the free molecule. There may also be small changes in the frequencies of bands due to groups in the surface, for example, hydroxyl groups on glass or silica surfaces. If the molecule is chemisorbed, entirely new bands may appear and the frequencies of original bands may be changed appreciably. The effect of the vibrations of the surface atoms is to broaden the original bands, and the supporting material may also modify the spectra.

These points are illustrated by the figures in *Table 6.2* which show the frequencies of strong bands in the isolated carbon monoxide molecule, in various metal carbonyls and in the chemisorbed layers on metals.

When the chemisorption of carbon monoxide on palladium is studied at increasing coverage, both the 2,070 band and the 1,820 band increase in intensity, but the 2,070 increases relatively more, as shown in *Figure 6.7*. These changes[35] are reversible, and it appears that there may be a change in the type of the bonding as the surface becomes covered. It is believed that the intensity of the 1,820 band at low coverage shows that practically all the chemisorbed carbon monoxide is then in the bridged form.

On rhodium surfaces, supported on alumina, it was shown[36] that an unsintered surface gave a simpler spectrum than a sintered surface; however, there appeared to be water adsorbed on the unsintered surface. In passing, it might be noted that the metal surfaces used in the infra-red studies are not as 'clean' as is really needed for certain interpretation; it may be that evaporated films on particles will improve this. Also, it is clear from the work

Table 6.2. Frequencies (cm^{-1}) of bands in carbon monoxide, its compounds and its chemisorptions

Stretching frequency of the CO molecule in $Ni(CO)_4$, $Fe(CO)_5$, etc.	2,120, 2,175 2,000–2,083	
in $Fe_2(CO)_9$, $CO_2(CO)_8$		1,818–1,852
CO chemisorbed on evaporated platinum[35]	2,050	—
on platinum–silica[3]	2,070	1,820 (weak)
on platinum–alumina	2,045	1,820 (strong)
on palladium–silica[35]	2,070	1,820 (1,925)
Probable structure	Linear	Bridged
		M
		\\
	$M{=}C{=}O$	C$=$O
		/
		M

on carbon monoxide and likewise from nitric oxide studies[37] that the support has some effect on the chemisorption, as shown by the changes of frequencies with change of support.

When hydrogen is chemisorbed, a band in the region 2,000 to 3,500 cm^{-1} might be expected if the bond is a covalent H—M bond. Such bands evaded detection for a long time, but have been seen at 2,058 to 2,110 for chemisorption on platinum supported on alumina[38]. There was evidence for two different types of chemisorption, however, and Eischens and Pliskin[38] suggested that the hydrogen atom might bridge two platinum atoms, as well as forming a bond to one atom. It has also been found that several bands appear when hydrogen is admitted to rhodium films, but the interpretation is difficult and uncertain.

Some comparatively early work[39] on the chemisorption of hydrogen added to a film of platinum on which carbon monoxide had been presorbed appeared to show that the species $M{=}C{<}^{H}_{OH}$, which has been proposed in the Fischer–Tropsch syntheses, did not occur with platinum. However, there was a shift of the 2,040 band and an increase in intensity of the 1,840 band. It might be interesting to examine this again, and also to examine cobalt surfaces, with improved techniques.

When hydrocarbons are adsorbed on metals, it is possible to identify C—H bonding when present in: (*i*) —CH$_3$, —CH$_2$ or —CH groups, with the carbon fully saturated by single bonds to other groups; (*ii*) —CH$_2$ or —CH groups with the carbon doubly bonded to some other atom, or (*iii*) —CH groups with the carbon triply bonded. The identification is from the position of the peaks and some estimate of the ratio of the various types can be made from the relative intensities. These studies have confirmed[32,34,40], for instance, that ethylene can be adsorbed through the π-bonds, leaving saturated —CH$_2$ groups, or by dissociation, leaving —CH groups; but it has been shown that some of the carbons of the —CH group are singly bonded to three other atoms, in addition to some as HC≡CH. There is thus a strong possibility that there are multiple bonds to the surface in the sense that a carbon atom can be bonded to more than one surface atom. In addition, there is evidence that the presence of hydrogen on or beneath the surface has a marked effect on the bonding of the molecule. These points are discussed later; but three very important possibilities emerge that must have bearing on all consideration of the chemisorption of large or unsaturated molecules: (*i*) there is a variety of bonds to the surface, including bonding to several atoms in the surface; (*ii*) that very extensive reformation of the adsorbed molecules can occur, even at moderate temperatures, and (*iii*) that the presence of other gases, such as hydrogen used in the reduction of the surface, can have a profound effect on the adsorption. The last point should be emphasized, for it indicates that chemisorption studies on each of a pair of reactants in some bimolecular reaction do not necessarily give reliable information about chemisorption from mixtures. This is particularly important in studying catalysed reactions over surfaces, and indicates the immense value of searching for direct methods of investigating the surface species actually present during the catalysed reaction.

6.3. CHEMISORPTION ON OXIDES

Attention has been drawn in Chapter 5 to the types of oxides that are useful as catalysts. The insulator oxides form a group useful in cracking, isomerization and dehydration reactions. The semiconductor oxides are useful for hydrogenations, exchange reactions, oxidations and some decompositions.

6.3.1 The insulator oxides

The insulator oxides are used as porous particles or as gels, and it appears essential to have mixtures of oxides for catalytic activity[41]. Thus magnesia, alumina and silica are each inactive, but mixtures of magnesia and silica, or alumina and silica, are active and so are natural clays. The active catalysts probably contain networks of covalently bonded atoms, such as

$$-\text{O}-\overset{\displaystyle\diagdown\!\!\!\diagup}{\underset{\displaystyle\diagup\!\!\!\diagdown}{\text{Al}}}-\text{O}-\overset{\displaystyle|}{\underset{\displaystyle|}{\text{Si}}}-\text{O}-$$

It has also been found that the activity of these catalysts is lost if they are dehydrated completely, and that the activity is restored by suitable treatment with water or acids. The activity seems to be directly related to the acidity of the surface, and it is supposed that the surface reacts with hydrocarbons to produce carbonium ions; the subsequent reactions of these ions produce the cracking and other reactions[42,43]. There have not been many chemisorption studies on these catalyst surfaces. The chemisorption of water[44], the use of ammonia or quinoline vapour to titrate the acid sites on the surface[42], and some studies of the chemisorption of alcohols in dehydration reactions are examined in section 8.7.1 in relation to particular reactions.

6.3.2. *Semiconductor oxides*

Molecules are often adsorbed (with or without dissociation) as ions on the surfaces of semiconductor oxides[45]. These oxides all have ionic crystals and can be classed as *n*- or *p*-type semiconductors[46–48]. Conduction in the *n*-type oxides is due to free electrons associated with anion vacancies in the crystal lattice, or free electrons balancing interstitial cations. In the *p*-type oxides, conduction occurs by changes of charge on a sequence of lattice cations, equivalent to the motion of 'positive holes' through the lattice. The charge changes may originate from a cation vacancy, for instance, if a *cuprous* ion is missing from a lattice point in the Cu_2O crystal, an adjacent lattice point must carry a *cupric* ion; alternatively and more rarely, an interstitial anion may be balanced by a higher charge on some cation in the lattice. Examples of these non-stoichiometric oxides are given in *Table 6.3*.

In addition, impurity cations can occupy lattice points; if their charge is less than that of the normal lattice cation, electrical neutrality can be restored by increases in charge of normal cations at nearby lattice points, while cations of higher charge can be balanced by electrons.

The type of semiconductor and its charge carrier can be identified by certain physical tests[47,48]. If a gas is chemisorbed and tends to increase the type of charge carrier, the conductivity will increase, and vice versa. Consequently, chemisorption can be *cumulative* and increase the number of carriers, or *depletive* when the number of carriers is decreased. Adsorption of a gas as anions would mean a withdrawal of electrons from the oxide, and on an *n*-type oxide this would be depletive chemisorption and the conductivity would decrease; on a *p*-type, it would be cumulative chemisorption and the conductivity would increase. Conversely, if the chemisorption releases electrons to the oxide, it is cumulative on an *n*-type but depletive on a *p*-type oxide. Hence, if the type of oxide is known, the changes in conductivity during chemisorption give information about the chemisorbed species and the bonding to the surface.

In this way, it has been shown[49–51] that oxygen is chemisorbed as O^{2-} ions, taking electrons from the oxide; and nitrous oxide probably gives oxygen and nitrogen via O^- ions as a surface species[52]. On the other hand, hydrogen and carbon monoxide release electrons on chemisorption, probably by the reactions[5,53,54]

$$H_2 + 2O^{2-} \rightarrow 2OH^- + 2e$$

$$CO + 2O^{2-} \rightarrow CO_3^{2-} + 2e$$

A very interesting feature of the last chemisorption is that space is left for another O^{2-} ion; it has been found that extra oxygen can be chemisorbed[55] on chromic oxide and $ZnO.Cr_2O_3$, and on cupric oxide the extra oxygen molecules are nearly half as many as the carbon monoxide molecules pre-adsorbed[53]. Carbon dioxide is also adsorbed as CO_3^{2-} ions, and as expected there is no extra oxygen adsorption possible afterwards. Many oxygenated hydrocarbons (alcohols, ketones) and water vapour chemisorb in the same way as do hydrogen and carbon monoxide.

These 'ionic' chemisorptions occur more rapidly at higher temperatures, and are then irreversible[45]. With hydrogen chemisorption, the product desorbed at high temperatures is water, and with carbon monoxide chemisorption the product is carbon dioxide. With each of these gases, there is also a low-temperature reversible[55] chemisorption, on many oxides, including zinc oxide; they are weaker than the high-temperature chemisorptions[45]. The low-temperature chemisorptions may be using the metal ions as adsorption sites; but hydrogen is not adsorbed on evaporated films of zinc metal, and it is hard to see how hydrogen could be covalently bonded to zinc ions. Morrison[56] offers another explanation. A special feature of hydrogen chemisorption on zinc oxide is the 'activating' effect of pretreatment with hydrogen at high temperatures (around 450°C); this may prepare more defects in the form of interstitial zinc ions by removing oxygen, and so speed the process of chemisorption at lower temperatures. The speed of chemisorption is considered again in section 6.6.

Table 6.3. Non-stoichiometric semiconductor oxides

	n-*Type* (excess cation)	p-*Type* (excess anion)
Examples with interstitial ions	ZnO, CdO	UO_2
Examples with lattice vacancies	TiO, ThO_2, CeO_2	Cu_2O, NiO, FeO
Effect of adding M_2^+O	Conductivity decreased	Conductivity increased
Effect of adding $M_2^{3+}O_3$	Conductivity increased	Conductivity decreased
Effect of O_2, N_2O	Depletive chemisorption	Cumulative chemisorption
Effect of H_2, CO	Cumulative chemisorption	Depletive chemisorption
Conduction	Electron	Positive hole

The movement of electrons to or from the adsorbent will produce a charged double layer on the surface and this will hinder the chemisorption of any more of the gas molecules on the surface. Application of simple barrier-layer theory[47, 56-58] suggests that the number of molecules that can be chemisorbed with depletion of carriers is small; unless the interstitial ions or vacancies are mobile, the carriers in the surface layers are soon used up. Calculations show that the coverage should be about 1 per cent at equilibrium. Experimental results agree with this; in fact, the chemisorption is so small that conventional volumetric or gravimetric methods are not sensitive enough and conductivity measurements must be used to determine the chemisorption.

With cumulative chemisorption, however, the surface layers can accommodate comparatively large numbers of carriers and chemisorption can continue to high coverages and be studied by conventional methods. In some cases, for example oxygen on cuprous oxide[53], the chemisorbed species may travel into the lattice forming cation vacancies, so that the oxygen chemisorbed apparently occupies more than a monolayer and not all of it may be available for chemical reaction with some other gas.

The deliberate addition of small quantities of oxides with cations of different valency from the parent cation can be used to increase the conductivity of the semiconductors[59,60]. Consider the addition of lithium oxide or indium oxide to a typical p-type oxide. The additives alter the balance of the Ni^{3+} and Ni^{2+} ions by reactions which can be written

$$Li_2O + 2Ni^{2+} + \tfrac{1}{2}O_2 \rightarrow 2Li^+ + 2Ni^{3+} + 2O^{2-}$$
$$In_2O_3 + 2Ni^{3+} \rightarrow 2In^{3+} + 2Ni^{2+} + \tfrac{1}{2}O_2 + 2O^{2-}$$

In the first reaction, the increase in Ni^{3+} is equivalent to an increase in the number of positive holes, with an increase in the conductivity and an increase in the capacity to accept surface electrons. With indium oxide, the conductivity is decreased. There are parallel changes in the capacity to chemisorb gases *depletively*; with cation-forming gases such as carbon monoxide, the chemisorption will be increased by the incorporation of lithium, whereas with anion-forming gases, chemisorption will be increased by incorporating indium. These controlled changes of chemisorption potential have been used to obtain information about the rate-determining step in reactions catalysed by oxides[52].

Although many of the details of these experiments and theories are unsettled, the main picture seems clear: chemisorption on these oxides occurs as ions; the amount of chemisorption can be dependent on the type and concentration of lattice vacancies; small proportions of 'impurities' can markedly affect the adsorption of gases.

6.4.   HEATS OF ADSORPTION

In all physical adsorptions and in most chemisorptions, heat is evolved, and the amount can be measured by suitable adaptation of the direct calorimetric or indirect thermodynamic methods used for measuring the heats of chemical reactions. An evolution of heat upon spontaneous adsorption would be expected for the following reasons. There must be a decrease in the free energy of the

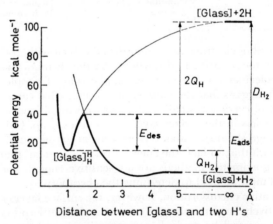

Figure 6.8.   Endothermic chemisorption of hydrogen atoms on glass and their associative desorption[61]

system adsorbent–adsorbate for the spontaneous process at constant temperature and pressure, and as the adsorbate is more localized it loses some of its translational entropy and some of its rotational entropy. Thus ΔG and ΔS are both negative and so $\Delta H(= \Delta G + T\Delta S)$ must also be negative, i.e. heat is evolved. However, de Boer[61] has pointed out that in some chemisorptions where dissociation occurs ΔS may be positive, and at high temperatures $(+T\Delta S)$ may outweigh ΔG and cause a positive ΔH. This endothermic adsorption is rare, and not many examples are established; but it must be remembered that exothermicity is not an invariable occurrence for adsorption. The potential energy changes for the endothermic adsorption of hydrogen on glass are shown in *Figure 6.8*.

Direct calorimetric methods, and indirect thermodynamic methods, can be used to measure heats of adsorption, the latter being particularly suited to measuring the heat of adsorption at different coverages; often the two methods agree as well as could be expected in view of the possible experimental errors, but there have been unexplained differences for some adsorbents. With chemisorption, this may often be due to the adsorption of some other gas before one set of experiments, or to the use of different methods of preparation in the two experiments or to an error in the calculation of the fraction of surface covered

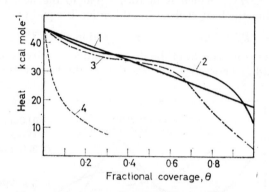

Figure 6.9. Heats of chemisorption of hydrogen on tungsten[62]

in one experiment; similar reasons have been advanced to explain the differences between the results of different investigators using the same method. A particularly notorious example of this is shown in *Figure 6.9*. There is tolerable agreement for curve 1 (calorimetric on a wire)[13] and curve 2 (calorimetric on an evaporated film)[63]; there are important differences near $\theta = 1$ with curve 3 (thermodynamic on an evaporated film)[61,64]; and a quite different picture for curve 4 (thermodynamic on a powder prepared by reduction of the oxide)[7]. Trapnell[45] considers that curve 4 represents results on a partially oxidized surface, and the differences between curves 1, 2 and 3 are due to the difficulties of measuring θ accurately as it approaches 1.

In calorimetric measurements, both isothermal and adiabatic calorimeters have been used. With either, the chief difficulties are to ensure a rapid access of the adsorbent and a rapid flow of the heat evolved to the calorimeter in spite of the poor thermal conductivity of many catalysts. Brief accounts of some of the calorimeters used have been given by Brunauer[65] and by Trapnell[45]. An interesting comparison of the two types of calorimeter can be obtained readily by looking at the description of the adiabatic calorimeter designed by Beeck, Cole and Wheeler[63] to determine the heats of adsorption of gases on evaporated films of metals, and the low-temperature isothermal calorimeter of Morrison and Los[66]. The Beeck-type calorimeter has been improved by Brennan, Hayward and Trapnell[67], who paid particular attention to: (*i*) achieving uniform temperatures throughout the calorimeter, and (*ii*) the accurate determination of the heat capacity of the calorimeter.

The principle of the indirect method is to measure the equilibrium constant of the adsorption process at different temperatures, and to apply the isochore to the results

$$\frac{d \ln K}{d T} = \frac{\Delta H}{RT^2}$$

The equilibrium constant is taken as the pressure of the gas for a fixed coverage of the surface, and so refers to the process

$$\text{adsorbed gas} \rightleftharpoons \text{gas} + \text{surface}$$

The value of ΔH is thus the change in the heat content during desorption which is equal to $-(\Delta H)_{ads}$ which is in turn equal to the heat evolved q_{ads} in adsorption. Thus the heat evolved in adsorption is equal to

$$RT^2(d \ln p/dT)_\theta \quad \text{or} \quad +R(d \ln p/d(1/T))_\theta$$

The experiments thus consist of the determination at a series of temperatures of the relationship between θ, the fraction of the surface covered, and the

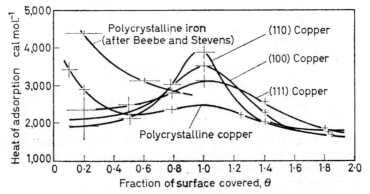

Figure 6.10. Heats of adsorption of nitrogen on copper crystals[22b]

pressure; pairs of values of p, T at a suitable value of θ are then plotted as $\ln p$ versus $1/T$ and the value of q_{ads} determined from the slope. The procedure can be repeated for a number of values of θ. The heats obtained are known as *isosteric heats of adsorption*, and it can be shown that the calorimetric values of the heat should lie between $q_{isosteric}$ and $q_{isosteric} - RT$; the difference is usually smaller than the errors involved in either experimental method.

It should be mentioned here that in recent years, attention has returned to the more detailed determination of heats of physical adsorption on more clearly defined surfaces. Thus Rhodin[22] has measured isosteric heats of adsorption of nitrogen on various faces of single copper crystals and on polycrystalline copper, with the interesting results shown in *Figure 6.10*. The single faces show a *low* heat at low coverages, and a maximum as the second layer begins to form; this is perhaps due to the lateral interactions. On oxidized surfaces, however, the curves are of quite different shape and in a slightly higher range (*Figure 6.11*). This emphasizes very clearly the need for accurately defining the surface studied, even for physical adsorption. Field emission studies suggest strongly preferential adsorption of rare gases on certain parts

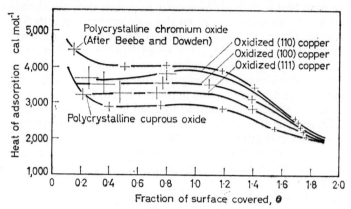

Figure 6.11. Heats of adsorption of nitrogen on oxidized copper crystals[22b]

of the tungsten crystal, and this may well be a general phenomenon connected with different heats of adsorption on different areas of the crystal. The heat of adsorption of argon on the (100) faces is 2,100 kcal mole^{-1}, but on the (111) faces it is 2,600 kcal mole^{-1}.

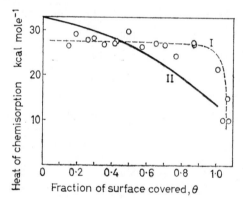

Figure 6.12. Heats of chemisorption of hydrogen on evaporated iron film at $-183°C$ (I) and at $23°C$ (II) [21]

Heats of chemisorption cover a greater range of values and show more variation with the experimental conditions of preparation. The most concordant results for chemisorption on metals have been obtained with evaporated films and wires, which are as clean and as uniform as can be obtained without extraordinary precautions. Even these films show heats which decrease as the coverage increases, and this lends strong support to the view that the fall is due to the process of adsorption as well as to any inherent heterogeneity of the surface. On the other hand, the differences between the heats of chemisorption of a gas on a film and on powdered metals are probably due to differences in the surfaces—both in composition and in the details of the non-uniformities. Thus the heat of adsorption of hydrogen on powdered nickel has been reported as low as 15 kcal at low coverages, whereas the value on a film is 31 kcal. Molecular hydrogen does not chemisorb on a copper film at room temperature; on the powder, heats of 9 to 20 kcal have been reported. The great difference between powdered tungsten and the metal wire or film is shown in *Figure 6.6*. The effect of pretreatment of the oxide with oxygen (oxidized) or hydrogen (reduced) on the adsorption of gases is shown in *Table 6.4*[45]. The heats of chemisorption change rather rapidly with temperature (*Figure 6.12*); this may be due in many cases to the adsorption occurring on different sites at different temperatures, but in some cases there is believed to be a different type of bonding to the surface at low temperatures, for example with nitrogen on iron (10 kcal at $-183°C$, 40 kcal at room temperature). On chromia, the heat of adsorption of oxygen changes from 25 kcal at $-183°$ to 50 kcal at $-78°$ to 98 kcal at room temperature. The change seems to be less on evaporated films.

In the *Tables 6.4* and *6.6*, some initial heats of chemisorption of various gases on evaporated metal films and on pretreated oxides are given. The values have been determined at room temperature.

Table 6.4. Heats of chemisorption on metals at low coverages[45]

Gas	Adsorbent								
	Cr	Fe	Ni	Ta	W	Pt	Rh	Cu	Au
H_2	45	32	31	45	45	30	28	—	—
O_2	—	75	130	—	155	—	—	—	—
N_2	—	40	—	140	95	—	—	—	—
CO	—	32	35	—	—	—	—	9	9
C_2H_4	102	68	58	138	102	—	50	18	21
C_2H_2	—	—	67	—	—	—	—	19	21
NH_3	—	45	37	—	66	—	—	—	—

Table 6.5. Heats of chemisorption on oxides at low coverages[45]

Gas	Adsorbent state	Adsorbent					
		ZnO	Cr_2O_3	Mn_2O_3	$ZnO.Cr_2O_3$	$Mn_2O_3.Cr_2O_3$	Cu_2O
H_2	Red.	†	36	44	13	†	27
	Ox.	†	72	30	48	†	42
O_2	Red.	—	98	22	43	52	55
	Ox.	—	37	24	†	22	—
CO	Red.	20	29	67	15	33	28
	Ox.	18	28	62	44	47	27
CO_2	Red.	—	31	17	18	14	—
	Ox.	13	18	23	15	20	—

† No adsorption occurs at room temperature.

There have been many attempts to relate heats of chemisorption to the type of bonding in the adsorbent, the adsorbate molecule and the possible bonding in the chemisorbed species. There have also been many attempts to relate heats of chemisorption on metals to chemical or electronic properties.

The heats of chemisorption of the gases hydrogen, nitrogen, ammonia, carbon monoxide, ethylene, acetylene all change in the same order with different metals

$$Ta > W, \quad Cr > Fe > Ni > Rh > Cu, \quad Au$$

thus indicating that a common property of the metal is dominant[45]. Eley's calculations[4] of the heat of chemisorption of gases on various transition metals, assuming that covalent M—X bonds are formed, give the right order of magnitude for many gases; the calculations lay the main emphasis on the heat of sublimation of the metal, and less emphasis on the contribution from the partial ionic nature of the M—X bond which is calculated from the dipole moment of the chemisorbed bond. Unfortunately, the sequence of sublimation heats is quite different:

$$W > Ta > Rh > Ni > Fe > Cr > Au > Cu$$

It may be that the heat of sublimation is not related in a straightforward way to the strength of the M—X bond, as assumed, but depends on changes of bonding in the metal that differ with, for example, the electronic structure of the metal atoms. Also, the dipole moments may need revision[68]. Stevenson[69] has used a different method to estimate the ionic contribution, and obtains better agreement for the heats.

Attempts have also been made to relate the heats to the electronic structure of the metals as measured by the percentage d-character of the metallic bonds[70]. The 'correlation' is really most unconvincing. Inspection of *Figures 56* and *57* of Trapnell[45] (taken from the work of Beeck[70]) show that for hydrogen and for ethylene the heats change markedly where the percentage d-character scarcely changes at all, and vice versa. The idea that empty d-orbitals in the metal are needed for bonding is attractive, but it is doubtful whether the true picture of surface bonding has yet been presented. There is evidence from the infra-red spectra, as explained in section 6.2, that multiple bonding to the surface atoms occurs at low coverage, whereas bonding to one surface atom predominates at higher coverages. The initial 'sites' may be between the surface metal atoms rather than on them. The bonding may involve complex changes in the hybridization of the metallic orbitals, affecting several atoms as each adsorbate atom is chemisorbed, rather than a simple bonding with a vacant orbital[3].

Other interesting approaches to the problem have been the assumption of purely ionic bonds, which gives quite the wrong heats for chemisorption on metals, and the assumption[67,71] of charge-transfer no-bonding complexes, which appears to be successful for hydrogen on various metals but has been criticized[3].

The heat of chemisorption of oxygen on many metals is very high (*Table 6.4*). Moreover, very different values have been reported by different workers; some examples have been summarized by Brennan, Hayward and Trapnell[67]. They point out that the maximum heats of chemisorption on titanium, tantalum, aluminium, niobium, tungsten, chromium, molybdenum, manganese, iron, nickel and cobalt are close to the heats of formation of the bulk oxides of the

147

metals and vary linearly with the atomic radius of the metal. The heats of chemisorption on rhodium, palladium and platinum are nearly double the heats of formation of the stable oxides and show a separate linear relationship with the atomic radii. Bortner and Parravano[72] examined the heats of chemisorption of oxygen on silver and on palladium and their alloys, and found the heat of chemisorption on silver to be much greater than the heat of formation of the bulk oxide. With alloys, the results suggested that silver is concentrated in the surface layers of the alloys.

6.4.1. The fall in heat of chemisorption with increasing coverage

This phenomenon, almost always observed except at low temperatures, is profoundly important for catalysis and has proved very puzzling. The importance for catalysed reactions can be indicated briefly at this point, as it is mentioned in more detail in several later sections. The high heats of initial chemisorptions mean that the chemisorptions are chemically irreversible at all but extremely high temperatures, as the desorption process must have a very high activation energy. There is a parallel effect on the activation energy of any surface reaction of the species, which therefore are very unreactive. At higher coverages, the heat is lower and the activation energies of desorption or of surface reactions are lower. There is ample evidence of these correlations, and it is clear that a catalytically active surface must hold its chemisorbed species lightly rather than tightly.

The following appear to be the main explanations offered for the fall in heat with increasing coverage:

(*i*) *Inherent heterogeneity of the surface*—It has always been obvious that edges of crystallites and similar discontinuities might present more active sites for chemisorption, on any adsorbent[73]. The connection between defects and chemisorption on oxides suggests a different type of heterogeneity–crystal defects. The metal and anion sites in an oxide or sulphide present another obvious heterogeneity, as do promoter oxides in the surfaces of metals. Different faces of crystals also chemisorb with different heats[20].

(*ii*) *Mutual repulsions between adsorbed species on a uniform surface*—This might be repulsion between the dipoles of the chemisorbed bond and this possibility was explored by Roberts[13,74]. There is now general agreement[75] that the effect is not large enough except perhaps with alkali metals on transition metals where the dipoles are large. A more recent suggestion[76] is that the metal structure may cause bonding orbitals to spread into other atoms and allow electrons to interact with closed shells, so extending the repulsive forces.

(*iii*) *Changes in the work function of the metal due to the chemisorbed gas*, so that adsorption affects the empty sites through the electronic structure of the metal†—Different investigators have applied this idea in different ways, arriving at different formulations of the relationship between the change in the work function and the change in the heat of chemisorption. Rather strangely, they all find data on the work function to support their theories with calculations showing reasonable agreement with the experimental fall in the heat of chemisorption.

---

† Boudart[77] calls this *induced heterogeneity*; de Boer[78] calls it *surface potential effect*; other workers have criticized these ideas and treatments.

(*iv*) *Changes in the type of bonding between adsorbate and surface, and between surface atoms, as the coverage changes*[3,79]—There is much experimental support for changes in the bonding of atoms such as hydrogen and nitrogen, and molecules such as carbon monoxide and ethylene, as the coverage changes, as indicated in previous sections. The specific effects of crystal face may also be due to the possibility or otherwise of multiple bonding of an atom to several surface atoms. This is an interesting variation of the 'geometric' requirements, previously emphasized for adsorption of aromatic and olefinic molecules by chemisorption of two or more carbon atoms to surface atoms.

The problem of deciding whether, for example, all the iron atoms in a sample of an ammonia catalyst are capable of bonding with equal strength to the first hydrogen atom which approaches the surface is a very difficult one. In the past, it has been claimed[73] that the small amount of poison needed to deactivate some catalysts is evidence that only a fraction of surface sites are active; however, other quantitative studies[80] of poisoning of metal surfaces indicate homogeneity of the surface. De Boer[78] and Wheeler[81] have pointed out that the great effect of some poisons might be caused by the poison blocking off a large proportion of the surface by occupying the mouth of pores in the catalyst. It was hoped at one time that the use of isotopes would provide a crucial test of inherent heterogeneity[82]. If one isotope is adsorbed first and occupies the more active sites, and then the other is adsorbed on to less active sites, and the relative activity of various sites does not change *after* adsorption, then upon desorption we might expect the second isotope to come off before the first; but if all sites were originally homogeneous, or some equalization took place after adsorption, there would be isotopic mixing. The experimental evidence has been contradictory. Thus Keier and Roginskii[83] found that nickel and zinc oxide appeared heterogeneous to hydrogen–deuterium mixtures, whereas Schuit[84] found that a nickel catalyst on silica was homogeneous to the same isotopes. Emmett and Kummer[85] found that half the surface of an iron-ammonia catalyst was homogeneous to carbon monoxide. In any case, it would seem that the method investigates the mobility of the adsorbate, or the possibility of changes of bond strength after adsorption by a mechanism similar to that operating in induced heterogeneity, rather than inherent initial heterogeneity. Another cause of initial heterogeneity might be the edges, corners and cracks of crystallites; it is generally agreed that these sites might contribute significantly to heterogeneity in physical adsorption where the energy changes are small; but there is controversy over the idea that they could account for the much larger changes found in chemisorptions[75]. There is certainly heterogeneity for chemisorption and for rates of reaction on different crystal planes in the surface of pure metals[18,15] but the study of the effect of orientation of various crystal faces has not yet progressed very far.

6.5. DERIVATION OF ADSORPTION ISOTHERMS

The evidence presented in the last three sections has shown that there is no single pattern of chemisorption. Some gases are adsorbed as ions, others covalently bonded to one or more atoms in the solid surface, others dissociated and bound as ions or as radicals. Some gases cover the whole surface, others are adsorbed to a very limited extent. The adsorption sites may be crystal defects, or the whole surface may be capable of chemisorbing particular gases. The energetics of the processes depend on the extent of the chemisorption. Many catalyst surfaces are obviously heterogeneous, with mixed oxides or promoters in the surface, and even metal crystals show specificity of crystal faces and heterogeneity due to edges, steps, dislocations and defects.

It is plain that it is very difficult to devise a comprehensive theory of chemisorption which will take account of all these variations, and it will be a long time before quantitative information will be available for the testing of such a theory. Limited but important success has been achieved by developing the Langmuir theory of adsorption on an array of uniform sites[86], and applying it to various hypothetical yet reasonable distributions of energies of adsorption. These distributions allow simplifications of the mathematical task of dealing with a heterogeneous surface, and they result in certain isotherms which fit adsorption on real surfaces rather better than do the simple Langmuir isotherms.

There is another very different approach. The study of depletive chemisorption on semiconductor oxides (page 140) led to the application of boundary-layer theory to the kinetics and extent of chemisorption[56,57]. Isotherms were derived that described the chemisorption accurately, and the rate of chemisorption could be expressed as equations which fitted the slow chemisorptions described in section 6.6.2. The theory was also extended to cumulative chemisorption, with claims to success. Now cumulative chemisorption appears very like chemisorption on metals, and as the adsorbate provides its own 'defects' in cumulative chemisorption, it is reasonable to examine this as a basis for chemisorption on metals. Instead of an array of sites identical with the metal lattice, Volkenstein[87] suggested that the defects in the crystal acted as the initial points for chemisorption, and that besides a 'biographical' array of defects in the surface, new centres could be formed thermally and upon adsorption of a gas at a defect. Slow chemisorptions are regarded as due to a slow formation of sites thermally, the formation of sites being activated and rate-controlling, rather than the interaction of the site with the gas. He showed that the common isotherms could be derived by suitable choice of the kinetics of the reactions producing the defects. This treatment has not yet been widely developed or tested. Similar treatments have been used by Taylor and Thon[88] to explain slow, activated chemisorptions. The suggestions that the fall in heat of adsorption with increasing coverage [(iii) of page 148] is due to changes in the work function[77,78], so that the gas adsorbed already affects the sites available for the remainder of the adsorptions, are in line with Volkenstein's treatment. There is undoubtedly some evidence that chemisorption on films starts on or near defects; on the other hand, the almost complete and very rapid chemisorption at low temperatures of so many gases on metals of great cleanliness makes it difficult to believe that the surface atoms are not the sites for adsorption.

Attempts have often been made to identify the adsorption sites from the amounts of gases adsorbed on a unit area of the surface. Measurements of this kind were made by Roberts[13] on the adsorption of hydrogen by tungsten (see section 6.2) and from the amount of hydrogen required to saturate the surface of a wire of known geometrical area it was estimated that one hydrogen atom was chemisorbed for each tungsten atom in the surface. More exact measurements of the area of the adsorbents were made by Frankenburg[7], using tungsten powder, and by Beeck[18,19] and his associates using evaporated films of tungsten, nickel and other metals. Striking agreement between the number of atoms of hydrogen chemisorbed and the number of metal atoms exposed was found, as shown in *Table 6.6*.

Table 6.6. Chemisorption of hydrogen on nickel and tungsten

Adsorbent	Plane	10^{14} *metal atoms* cm^{-2}		10^{14} H *atoms adsorbed* cm^{-2}
Nickel	100	16·3	Unoriented film	16·2
	110	11·5	Oriented film	11·4
Tungsten	100	14·2	Metal powder A	11·0
	110	10·1	Metal powder B	10·8
			Metal wire	11·4

Kwan[89] has utilized some experiments of Maxted *et al.*[80] on the poisoning of platinum or nickel catalysts to show that all the atoms in the surface of the metal are available for chemisorption. He has also shown that the surface of an oxide can be fully occupied by chemisorbed species.

The results of these experiments on metal surfaces are usually interpreted[45] as showing that there is localized bonding between the chemisorbed atoms and the metal atoms, the pattern of Langmuir sites thus being the surface atoms. On this basis, the chemisorption studies with other gases have shown that some, like carbon monoxide, are adsorbed as molecules on single sites (although infra-red studies have also produced evidence of bonding of carbon monoxide to more than one site), while others, such as ethylene or acetylene, occupy several sites. It has always proved difficult to interpret the adsorption of nitrogen and oxygen on nearly saturated surfaces. On some films, Beeck and Ritchie[19,70] reported that nitrogen occupies far less of the area of the surface than does hydrogen. On clean tungsten, Roberts[13], and later Becker[11], reported that nitrogen may occupy several sites, but that it can, like oxygen[18], form a second layer held by weaker bonds. It is essential to bear in mind that it is not easy to determine with certainty the total number of sites in the surface. Some recent evidence (see page 139) suggests that the pattern of sites may be *between* the surface atoms at low coverage, but changing to the surface atoms at higher coverage[3].

In developing the Langmuir treatment of adsorption to derive isotherms, it is therefore better to do so in terms of a pattern of 'sites' assumed to be uniform or to vary in a known way, for example, in the heat of adsorption. In particular cases, even if some isotherm is found to apply, the surface sites must still be identified. The derivation of various isotherms for uniform and for non-uniform surfaces is dealt with in Appendix II. There are, of course, other methods of developing isotherms, and the barrier-layer treatment so successful for chemisorption on semiconductors has been mentioned in section 6.3. Although these alternative treatments have not been used so much in work on catalysed reactions, it is quite possible that extension of the Volkenstein theory of chemisorption processes may lead to an increased use of them.

The isotherms derived in Appendix I are summarized here for reference.

The isotherms for *uniform* surfaces are:

A. Localized adsorption

1. One molecule on one site: $\qquad\qquad\qquad\qquad \theta = Bp/(1+Bp)$

2. One molecule on two sites as atoms or molecules: $\qquad\qquad\qquad\qquad \theta = B'p^{1/2}/(1+B'p^{1/2})$

3. Two gases A and B, one per site, competing for site:

$$\theta_A = \frac{B_A p_A}{1+B_A p_A + B_B p_B}$$

$$\theta_B = \frac{B_B p_B}{1+B_B p_B + B_A p_A}$$

B. Non-localized adsorption $\qquad\qquad\qquad \theta = B''p \text{ for } p < 1/B''$
$\qquad\qquad\qquad\qquad\qquad\qquad\qquad\quad \theta = 1 \text{ for } p > 1/B''$

(B, B', B'', B_A and B_B are of the form $B = B_0 e^{q/RT}$ where q is the constant heat of adsorption of the species concerned.)

The isotherms for *non-uniform* surfaces all assume certain dependences of the heat of adsorption on the coverage. They each assume that one molecule is adsorbed on one site, except for C2 which assumes the molecule dissociates and occupies two sites. None of these equations are valid as θ approaches zero or unity:

Name of isotherm	Expression for θ	Variation of q with θ
C1 Freundlich	Cp^{RT/q_m}	$q = q_m \ln D/\theta$ C, D are related temperature-dependent constants
C2 Freundlich	$C'p^{RT/2q_m}$	As above
C3 Halsey	$C''p^{RT/q_m(1-r\theta)}$	As above
C4 Sips	$(p/C''+)p^{1/n}$	As above
C5 Temkin	$(RT/\alpha) \ln Bp$	$q = q_0 - \alpha\theta \quad B = B_0 e^{q_0/RT}$

6.6. RATES OF ADSORPTION

The rate of adsorption of a substance on a surface can be controlled by the approach to the surface or by the actual 'reaction' with the surface, whether this involves chemisorption or 'sticking' for a brief time in a physically adsorbed layer.

The approach to the surface can be by molecular diffusion through a more or less stagnant gas or by bulk flow of the gas. The bulk flow may be the slow step in some industrial reactions over very active catalysts, but the problems are engineering ones rather than chemical. Molecular diffusion may well control the rate in many chemisorptions and physical adsorptions, for it turns out that the 'sticking coefficient' on impact is very near to unity at the temperatures of interest. There are two cases of particular interest, the molecular approach to a plane surface open to the gas, and the molecular approach through a long pore in a porous catalyst to the inner surface; with catalysts such as Raney nickel or metals deposited on silica or charcoal, this inner area may be many times the outer area of the particles.

The rate of impact on a plane surface is given by the kinetic theory of gases as $n\bar{c}/4$ molecules cm^{-2} sec^{-1}, where n is the number of molecules per cubic centimetre of the gas and $\bar{c}$ is their mean velocity. Substituting well-known expressions for n and $\bar{c}$, the rate of impact in terms of the temperature T, the pressure p (in dynes per square centimetre) and the mass m of the molecules is

$$\text{Rate of impact} = \frac{p}{(2\pi mkT)^{1/2}} \text{ molecules cm}^{-2} \text{ sec}^{-1} \quad (6.1)$$

Following Langmuir's treatment of adsorption[86], this rate is multiplied by a 'sticking coefficient' α and by the fraction of bare surface $(1-\theta)$, while the rate of desorption is put equal to $\beta\theta$. The coefficients α and β include terms $e^{-E/RT}$ to allow for the possibility of activation energies of adsorption and desorption (see section 6.1).

The net rate of adsorption is then given by

$$\frac{dN}{dt} = \frac{\alpha p(1-\theta)}{(2\pi mkT)^{1/2}} - \beta\theta \quad (6.2)$$

Now θ equals N/N_{max} where N_{max} is the maximum number of molecules which can be adsorbed on the surface in a monolayer. At constant pressure and temperature, the approach to equilibrium can be expressed by the equation

$$\frac{dN}{dt} = k_1(N_{max} - N) - k_2 N \quad (6.3)$$

where $k_1 = \alpha p/N_{max}(2\pi mkT)^{1/2}$ and $k_2 = \beta/N_{max}$. This equation integrates, with $N = 0$ at $t = 0$, to give

$$N = N_{max}\frac{k_1}{k}(1 - e^{-kt}) \quad (6.4)$$

where $k = k_1 + k_2$. At equilibrium, $N = N_{eq}$ and $N_{eq} = N_{max}k_1/k$ so that

$$N = N_{eq}(1 - e^{-kt}) \quad \text{or} \quad \ln\frac{N_{eq}}{N_{eq} - N} = kt \quad (6.5)$$

Thus the rate of approach to adsorption equilibrium is a first-order process with a half-life equal to $\ln 2/k$.

It is interesting to make an estimate of this half-life (τ) for a physical adsorption. Markham and Benton[90] found that oxygen at a pressure of 50 mm Hg covered about $\frac{1}{20}$ of the surface of a silica gel at 0°C. Hence $N_{eq}/N_{max} = 1/20$, and $k = 20k_1$. It can be assumed that a monolayer of oxygen would require about 10^{15} molecules cm^{-2}, and so

$$k_1 = \frac{\alpha \times 5\cdot0 \times 13\cdot6 \times 981}{10^{15}(2\pi \times \frac{32}{6\cdot3 \times 10^{23}} \times 1\cdot4 \times 10^{-16} \times 273)^{1/2}}$$

$$= 2\alpha \times 10^7 \text{ sec}^{-1}$$

$$\therefore \tau = \frac{0\cdot69}{40\alpha \times 10^7} = 1\cdot7 \times 10^{-9}/\alpha \text{ sec}$$

153

Thus the equilibrium is established in a very short time unless α is extremely low; as will be seen, at $0°C$ α is close to unity, so that $\tau \sim 10^{-9}$ sec.

Some early attempts to test Langmuir's treatment of adsorption in a mono-layer were based on measurements of the rate of certain adsorptions and the use of equations (6.5). The amount of gas adsorbed at time t is N molecules which occupy V cm^3 as gas at S.T.P.; hence a plot of $\ln V_{eq}/(V_{eq}-V)$ against t should be a straight line of slope k.

The adsorption of some gases on active charcoal was found to be slow enough to measure the uptake at various times, and a plot of $\ln V_{eq}/(V_{eq}-V)$ was indeed linear (*Figure 6.13*); but the value of k was so small that τ was several minutes.

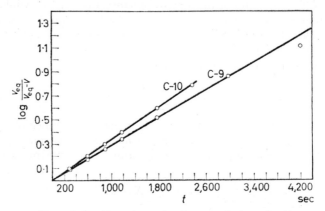

Figure 6.13. Test of equation for rate of adsorption [64]

This apparent conflict was resolved by Damköhler[91], who showed that the experimental work on these slow adsorptions on charcoal and silica could be explained quantitatively if it is assumed that the rate of diffusion through the pores of these porous adsorbents is the rate-determining process. He derived an equation of the form

$$\frac{N}{N_{eq}} = 1 - \frac{8}{\pi^2} \sum_{m=0}^{\infty} \frac{e^{-\delta(2m+1)^2}}{(2m+1)^2} \tag{6.6}$$

In this equation, $\delta = \{(2\pi)^2/L\}Dt$ where D is a diffusion coefficient which took note of surface diffusion as well as gas diffusion, and is a function of the radius of the capillary pores, while L is the length of the pores. If the earliest stages of the adsorption are ignored, the first term of the series gives a reasonable approximation to the summation.

The equation thus becomes

$$\frac{N}{N_{eq}} = 1 - \frac{8}{\pi} e^{-\frac{4\pi^2 Dt}{L}} \tag{6.7}$$

The formal resemblance between this equation and equation (6.5) makes it clear why straight lines were found for the plots of $\ln V_{eq}/(V_{eq}-V)$ versus time. *Figure 6.14* shows that equation (6.6) fits the results very well, as does a similar equation due to Wicke[92]. The most striking feature of *Figure 6.14*, however, is that the rate of desorption is equal to the rate of adsorption at all stages of the adsorption; this is only true for the Langmuir mechanism at equilibrium whereas in this example the adsorption and the desorption pass through the same 'bottleneck', i.e. the capillary pores.

In recent years, a good deal of work has been done on diffusion in the pores of adsorbents and catalysts by Barrer[93] and by Wheeler[94] and their associates. From this work, a fairly clear picture has emerged of the conditions under which the rate of adsorption on to porous catalysts, or in beds of very active granular catalysts, can be so limited by the rate diffusion as to become the slowest step in a catalysed reaction.

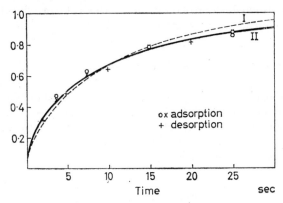

Figure 6.14. Rate of adsorption of carbon dioxide on charcoal[65], calculated on the basis of: I, Damköhler's equation (6.6) and II, the equation due to Wicke[92]

There has also been a number of very ingenious experiments designed to measure the rate of adsorption on plane surfaces and so to evaluate the sticking coefficient α. The theoretical evaluation of this quantity was made by Lennard-Jones and Devonshire[95] as 'condensation coefficients'. Calculations of the probability of transfer of a quantum of energy from the gas molecule to one of the solid molecules was assumed to be equivalent to calculating the coefficient; the probability of transfer was found to depend upon the Debye characteristic temperature θ of the solid and the temperature, and for many solids at room temperature α lies between 0·2 and 0·4. Another method of calculating α is provided by a statistical mechanical calculation of the velocity of chemisorption and comparison with the kinetic theory calculation. The treatment[96] can be outlined as follows. The potential energy changes during a chemisorption are shown by the heavy line of *Figure 6.1(b)*, taking this as the general case and *Figure 6.1(a)* as a particular case with $E=0$. At the peak of the path, which represents the energy and configuration of the 'transition complex', there is assumed to be a stationary population of activated molecules which can pass to the chemisorbed state or return to the reactants. If there are N_s sites per unit area, and a fraction θ of them are occupied, the concentration c_s of vacant sites waiting for the incoming gas molecules is $c_s = N_s(1-\theta)$. The concentration of activated molecules, $c^{\ddagger}$, is thus derived from an equilibrium

gas molecule + vacant site $\rightleftharpoons$ activated molecules

and if the concentration of gas molecules is c_g and the equilibrium constant is

155

K_c, then $c^{\ddagger}/c_s c_g = K_c$. Now this equilibrium constant can be connected with the 'partition functions' of the species concerned ($f^{\ddagger}$, f_g and f_s) as explained in more detail in Appendix I; it can be shown that

$$\frac{c^{\ddagger}}{c_s c_g} = \frac{f^{\ddagger}}{(f_g/V) f_s}\, e^{-E_{\text{ads}}/RT} \tag{6.8}$$

It is assumed that the frequency ν with which the activated molecules pass over the peak is the frequency of the weak vibration that the molecule and the site make along the bond joining them. Now $f^{\ddagger}$ contains a factor for the vibrational partition function of the complex which also involves this frequency, and as the frequency is weak the factor is $kT/h\nu$. Hence the rate of chemisorption is

$$\nu c^{\ddagger} = c_s c_g \nu f^{\ddagger} e^{-E_{\text{ads}}/RT}/(f_g/V) f_s = \frac{kT}{h} c_s c_g f^{\ddagger}_{\text{res}} e^{-E_{\text{ads}}/RT}/(f_g/V) f_s \tag{6.9}$$

The residual partition function $f^{\ddagger}_{\text{res}}$ is the total partition function for the complex after the vibrational function has been factorized out. For a tightly bound immobile complex, formed in the chemisorption of an atom, $f_{\text{res}} \sim 1$, $f_s \sim 1$, and $f_g = (2\pi m k T)^{3/2} V/h^3$; $c_g kT$ is equal to p and $c_s = N_s(1-\theta)$, so the velocity of chemisorption equals

$$\frac{p(1-\theta)}{(2\pi m k T)^{1/2}} \frac{h^2 N_s}{2\pi m k T}\, e^{-E_{\text{ads}}/RT}$$

Comparing this with the kinetic expression (equation 6.2) it is seen that

$$\alpha = \frac{h^2 N_s}{2\pi m k T}\, e^{-E_{\text{ads}}/RT} \tag{6.10}$$

When $E_{\text{ads}} = 0$, α is of the order 10^{-1} for hydrogen atoms. A similar treatment shows that $\alpha \sim 1$ for physical adsorption, but may be as low as 10^{-5} for a polyatomic molecule which gives an immobile transition complex. It is therefore of considerable interest to see how the experiments check these values.

6.6.1. Experimental measurements of the rates of adsorption on plane surfaces

The best way to lengthen the half-life of the adsorption process is to work with very low pressures of gas, and all investigators have adopted this plan.

Volmer and Estermann[97] did this by evaporating mercury from a surface at $-10°C$ to one at $-65°C$, and watching the condensate grow as extraordinarily thin plates—as do crystals—which incidentally demonstrated an interesting mobility of the mercury atoms over the surface, for they must have collected on the flat face of the crystal and moved to the edge, or else 'shunted' a row of atoms along the crystal face. Volmer and Estermann found that the rate of accumulation of the condensate continued to be high and almost equal to the rate of impact, irrespective of the fact that the surface was filling up. Thus α is close to unity and remains so; it is doubtful whether the $(1-\theta)$ factor in the basic rate equation (6.2) is justified on this evidence.

Roberts[98] investigated the adsorption of many substances on wires of tungsten by changes in the accommodation coefficient of a monatomic inert gas such as neon on the surface as adsorption of some other gas proceeded. The accommodation coefficient of the neon, a_c, is related to the heat loss from the wire to the gas molecules. It measures the efficiency of the energy transfer to the gas molecule. For a gas molecule whose kinetic energy corresponds to a temperature T_1 striking a surface at T_2 and leaving it with an energy corresponding to temperature T'_2, a_c is defined as

$$a_c = \frac{(T'_2 - T_1)}{(T_2 - T_1)} \tag{6.11}$$

The theoretical value for a_c for a monatomic gas on a clean surface is 0·05. If the wire is cleaned by repeated heating *in vacuo*, the experimental value approaches the theoretical value; when gases are adsorbed, it rises very considerably. The heat loss from the wire, measured by the electrical energy needed to maintain its temperature, is equal to $1·74 \times 10^{-4} a_c p (T_2 - T_1)/MT$ calories per square centimetre per second with p in dynes per square centi-

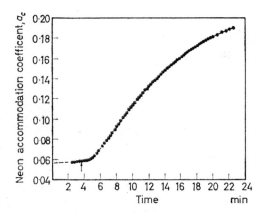

Figure 6.15. Rate of adsorption of oxygen on tungsten[99]. The arrow indicates the moment at which oxygen was admitted

metre. Hence a_c can be calculated. It is assumed that the accommodation coefficient changes linearly with the fraction of the surface covered, so that

$$\theta = \frac{a_{c,t} - a_{c,0}}{a_{c,\infty} - a_{c,0}} \tag{6.12}$$

Roberts and Morrison[99] measured the rate of adsorption of oxygen on tungsten by allowing oxygen to flow through a fine capillary past the wire to a trap containing charcoal cooled in liquid air; in the capillary the flow was restricted by the walls and in the adsorption vessel by diffusion through the neon. A typical curve, obtained with an oxygen pressure of $2·3 \times 10^{-8}$ mm, is shown in *Figure 6.15*, while *Figure 6.16* shows the effect of the oxygen pressure on the *final* value of the accommodation coefficient. Roberts and Morrison suggested that the limiting value at very low pressure ($a_c = 0·226$) corresponds to a stable film, while the extra gas adsorbed at higher pressures is in a more mobile superposed layer; however, the stable film seemed to consist of two parts, one evaporating at 1,100°K but the other part not until 1,700°K. They considered that the second layer, and the more easily evaporated part of the first layer, consisted of oxygen molecules, and that even the most firmly held layer might be molecules, but should be taken as the basis for calculating θ. However, it is certain that the sticking coefficient for the earlier stages lies between 0·2 and 0·4, depending upon the interpretation of θ. It is also certain that the rate in the middle stages of the adsorption is faster than predicted by the Langmuir postulate that the incoming molecules stick only on the bare surface, if the values of $a_{c,\infty}$ given by Roberts and Morrison are used. If the molecules chemisorb one to each site, then as expressed by equation (6·2) the rate of adsorption should fall off as the surface fills up, even if the desorption

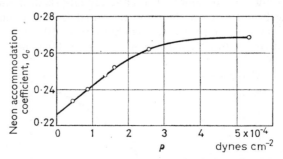

Figure 6.16. Relationship between the *final* steady value of accommodation coefficient of neon and the partial pressure of oxygen in adsorption of oxygen on tungsten[99]

is ignored. The rate should be proportional to $(1-\theta)$. If the chemisorption is dissociative and the incoming molecule has to find two adjacent vacant sites, the rate should be proportional to $(1-\theta)^2$. The relative rate, measured from curves like those of *Figure 6.5*, is much faster than either of these proportionalities suggest, as shown in *Table 6.7*. However, it must be remembered that

Table 6.7. Relative rates of adsorption of oxygen on tungsten at various coverages

Coverage, θ	0·0	0·2	0·4	0·6	0·8
Relative rate, measured	1·00	0·86	0·70	0·56	0·40
Assuming rate $\propto (1-\theta)$	1·00	0·80	0·60	0·40	0·20
Assuming rate $\propto (1-\theta)^2$	1·00	0·64	0·36	0·16	0·04

there is some doubt about the precise calculation of θ, especially the value taken for $a_{c,\infty}$. The coverages for which the figures are given were calculated on the assumption that there is a real difference between the binding of the gas desorbed at 1,100 and that desorbed at 1,700°K. If, however, all this gas was counted as the monolayer, the values of θ would be lower and the predicted rates more in keeping with the measured. Also, the heat evolved in the adsorption of hydrogen changes with coverage, and Roberts' values again appear (in the light of later experiments, see *Figure 6.9*) to correspond to lower values of θ than he calculated.

An ingenious use of a flow system for determining the amount of adsorption, and the rate of adsorption, on a wire which can easily be heated or cooled has been described by Becker and Hartmann[100,101]. Their apparatus, shown in *Figure 6.17*, consisted of a large bulb (about 2·3 l.) containing a tungsten ribbon FF of surface area 2·3 cm² and connected to an ionization gauge PG1. A gas such as nitrogen could be admitted by a controlled gas leak and be pumped away at a steady rate through a pinhole (area 0·01 cm²) in a plate PSC which can also be removed for rapid pumping. Another ionization gauge PG2 measures the pressure in the manifolds and traps leading to the mercury diffusion and backing pumps. The ribbon is cleaned and 'aged' by heating *in vacuo* to 2,400°K for several hours, with shorter periods at 2,600°K, and then cooled to room temperature and reheated several times. The gas is leaked in at a rate giving, with the steady pumping, a steady pressure p_0 of about 10^{-7} mm with the ribbon hot. When the ribbon is cooled to room temperature,

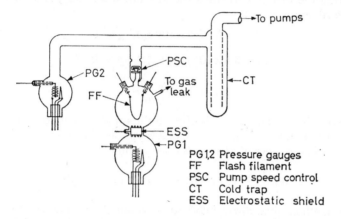

Figure 6.17.   Becker and Hartmann's apparatus for measuring rates of adsorption[100]

the pressure drops abruptly, not because of cooling, for the ribbon heats a negligible volume, but due to adsorption. However, the pressure settles at some lower steady value p_1, showing a constant rate of adsorption by the ribbon, and then rises slowly to its original value as the ribbon becomes

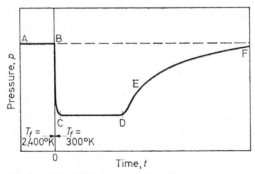

Figure 6.18.   Pressure–time relationships during adsorption of nitrogen on tungsten[101]

159

saturated (*Figure 6.18*). These processes can be analysed as follows. The number of gas molecules impacting 1 cm² of surface in 1 second is $p/(2\pi mkT)^{1/2}$ and for nitrogen at 300°K and 1 mm pressure, this is $3 \cdot 8 \times 10^{20}$. Thus the rate at which molecules hit the pinhole of area a and are removed from the system is $3 \cdot 8 \times 10^{20} pa$ and the rate at which others are adsorbed is $3 \cdot 8 \times 10^{20} pa_R s$, where a_R is the area of the ribbon and s is the sticking coefficient. If the rate of entry through the leak is L molecules per second, then the rate of increase of the molecules in the bulb is

$$L - 3 \times 8 \times 10^{20} p(a + a_R s) - g \tag{6.13}$$

where g is a correction for molecules adsorbed on the glass, etc.; as the system had become saturated before the ribbon was cooled, this correction was small. Considering the two periods when the pressure was steady, and setting $s = 0$ when the ribbon was hot:

$$L - 3 \cdot 8 \times 10^{20} p_0 a - g = 0$$

and

$$L - 3 \cdot 8 \times 10^{20} p_1 (a + a_R s) - g = 0$$

$$\therefore s = \frac{a(p_0 - p_1)}{a_R p_1} \tag{6.14}$$

Now the number of molecules adsorbed in the rapid pressure drop from p_0 to p_1 is $3 \cdot 2 \times 10^{19} V(p_0 - p_1)$, and the rate of adsorption after this is $3 \cdot 8 \times 10^{20} p \, a_R s$. Hence the total number of atoms adsorbed at time t is

$$N_{\text{ads, } t} = 2 \times 3 \cdot 2 \times 10^{19} V(p_0 - p_1) + 2 \times 3 \cdot 8 \times 10^{20} \int_{t=0}^{t=t} a(p_0 - p_1) \, dt \tag{6.15}$$

Thus the method gives direct information about the rate and the extent of adsorption. Becker and his associates have extended it to other high-melting metals such as molybdenum and tantalum, using nitrogen, oxygen and hydrogen.

A useful check on the calculations can be made by stopping the adsorption at a chosen time by heating the ribbon suddenly. The gas adsorbed up to time t, $(N_{\text{ads},t})$ is released to the volume V giving a pressure rise Δp, and

$$N_{\text{ads},t} = 6 \cdot 4 \times 10^{19} V \, \Delta p \tag{6.16}$$

From these results, the number of, for instance, nitrogen atoms adsorbed on 1 cm² of ribbon can be calculated; unfortunately there is not agreement about the interpretation of the value of N_{ads} at 'saturation' of a monolayer. Becker[100,101] produces evidence from the rates of evaporation and the heats of adsorption that there are two layers of nitrogen atoms, and by taking the first layer as 'filled' when there is one nitrogen atom adsorbed for every four tungsten atoms in a (100) plane, arrives at curves of s versus θ shown in *Figure 6.19*. On the other hand, Trapnell[102] assumes that there is one nitrogen atom for every two tungsten atoms and changes Becker and Hartmann's curves as shown in *Figure 6.20*; moreover, he calculates that the fall in s at high coverages is principally due to the decreased area available, i.e. to the term $(1 - \theta)^2$, although in the early and middle ranges of coverage the rate of adsorption does not fall off as rapidly as proportionality to $(1 - \theta)^2$ suggests.

While the interpretation of the later stages of the adsorption may be uncertain, there is no doubt at all from Becker's results that: (*i*) several gases adsorb very rapidly at room temperatures on clean tungsten, molybdenum and tantalum metals, (*ii*) the sticking coefficient for low coverages is between 1 and 0·1 for quite a range of temperatures, and *decreases* as the temperature

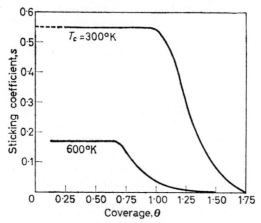

Figure 6.19. Becker's interpretation of coverage and sticking coefficient of nitrogen adsorbed on tungsten [101]

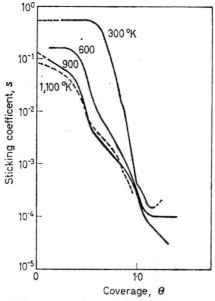

Figure 6.20. Nitrogen adsorption on a tungsten ribbon [102]

increases (this means that it is rather pointless to speak of an activation energy for the early stages of the adsorption), and (*iii*) the sticking coefficient is constant for a considerable extent of adsorption at a fixed temperature, especially at low temperatures (*Figure 6.8*).

There is also evidence[103] that the sticking coefficient of metal atoms on the same bulk metal, of caesium atoms on tungsten[104] and of silver atoms on molybdenum[104] at temperatures up to 800°K, are all close to unity. So also is the probability for xenon or nitrogen on tungsten at quite low temperatures: 0·3 for xenon at 82°K and 0·5 for nitrogen at 115°K. There is also a large amount of semiquantitative data for chemisorption on evaporated films of metals which points clearly to rapid rates of adsorption for most gases, even at low temperatures.

In *Table 6.8* the adsorptions listed in columns 2 and 3 are fast at room temperature, while those in column 4 are fast initially but are often followed by a slow uptake of the gas. This often happens with oxygen[105], and with metals that are easily oxidized, such as iron, copper and aluminium, the bulk oxide is probably formed. With oxygen on nickel, the presence of NiO in the lattice has been shown by electron diffraction studies[21]. It is not easy to explain the slow uptake of oxygen on stable metals such as platinum, however, nor the slow uptakes of hydrogen on nickel or iron, nor those of carbon monoxide on iron, tungsten or platinum. In most cases the slow effect seems connected with the bulk metal rather than the surface, although slow chemisorption from some sites to less active sites on the surface has been suggested for some slow residual uptakes[106–108]. It occurs on oxides also[109].

Table 6.8. Rapid chemisorptions[45]

Gas	On oxides	On metal films	On metal films, but often followed by slow chemisorptions
H_2	—	W, Ta, Fe, Ni, Ti, Zr, Pd, Rh, Pt, Ba	Ni, W, Fe
CO	$ZnO.Cr_2O_3$, MnO,Cr_2O_3	As for H_2, plus Cu, Au, Al	Fe, W, Pt, Pa, Ni
C_2H_4	$ZnO.Cr_2O_3$, ZnO, Cu_2O	As for H_2, plus Cu, Au	—
C_2H_2	—	As for H_2, plus Cu, Au, K	—
N_2	—	W, Ta, Mo, Ti, Zr, Ba	W
O_2†	$ZnO.Cr_2O_3$, MnO	On most metals	On most metals

† The adsorption of oxygen on some oxides goes beyond a monolayer: the first portion of the chemisorption is fast, the later stages, beyond the monolayer, slow, obeying the Elovich equation.

6.6.2. Slow activated chemisorptions

There is a quite different type of chemisorption, however, which is slow from the moment the gas and surface are brought into contact. Many years ago, Taylor[2] noticed that the adsorption of hydrogen on manganous[110] oxide and on other[111] oxides is very slow compared with the rate that the molecules hit the surface. In one example, the rate of impact of the molecules was 10^{31} cm^{-2} h^{-1} whereas the rate of chemisorption was 10^{15} cm^{-2} h^{-1}. Taylor showed that the rate of adsorption increased very rapidly with temperature, and that the main cause of the large discrepancy between expected and observed rates could be accounted for by a need for the molecules to be activated. The activation energy for chemisorption of hydrogen on manganous oxide was about 12,400 for initial adsorptions and about 20,800 for adsorption on a nearly full surface, at temperatures above 180°C. For zinc oxide, two ranges of chemisorption were observed; between 0 and 110°C the activation energy was 3 to 6 kcal, whereas above 180°C it was 8 to 15 kcal mole^{-1}. These high activation energies make it very unlikely that the slow process is a diffusion, which was one of the alternative proposals put forward to account for the slow chemisorptions. Another proposal, made by Allmand and Chaplin[108, 103], was that the surfaces were occupied by chemisorbed oxygen, and that the slow process was displacement of the oxygen or reaction of the hydrogen with it. The slow chemisorption of hydrogen on nickel, iron or tungsten powders is almost certainly due to inadequate reduction of the surface, for the chemisorption on evaporated films of these metals is very rapid. The observation that hydrogen and carbon monoxide often desorb from oxides as water and carbon dioxide respectively may be due to reaction of the gases with oxide ions in the lattice, but similar desorption products from charcoal must arise from reaction of the gases with pre-adsorbed oxygen.

Table 6.9. Slow, activated chemisorptions[45]

Gas	On oxides	On metals		Metal film, negligible at 0°C	Other surfaces
		Powders	Films		
H$_2$	UO$_2$, ThO$_2$, MnO, ZnO, Cr$_2$O$_3$, NiO	Cu, Ni, W	? Ca	As for CO, plus Cu, Au, Al	Glass, CaF$_2$, Al$_2$O$_3$ gel
CO	NiO, MnO$_2$, ZnO.MnO, Cr$_2$O$_3$.MgO	Pt	—	Zn, Cd, In, Sn, Pb, Ag, K	—
C$_2$H$_4$	Cr$_2$O$_3$	Many	Al	As for CO	—
C$_2$H$_2$	—	Many	Al, K	As for CO, except K	—
CH$_4$, C$_2$H$_6$	ZnO, Cr$_2$O$_3$	Many	W, Mo, Ta, C, Fe, Co, Ni, Rh, Pd, Ti	—	—
N$_2$	—	Fe, W	Fe, ? Ca	As for H$_2$, plus Ni, Pd, Rh, Pt	—
O$_2$	NiO, CoO, CoO.Cr$_2$O$_3$	Ag, Au	Ag	Au	—
NH$_3$	—	—	W, Ni, Fe	—	—

The fact that slow chemisorptions have been reported on some evaporated films (Table 6.9, column 4) with some gases, but not with others, does suggest that activated chemisorption is a real phenomenon on clean metals, although not as common as on oxides nor as on metal powders with surfaces not entirely free from oxygen. Generally, it is unreactive gases like nitrogen, or gases with the central atom in the molecule somewhat shielded from the surface, that seem to chemisorb slowly. Table 6.9 also lists a number of metals which give films which do not chemisorb certain gases at 0°C, and this may mean a very high activation energy, perhaps because the adsorptions are endothermic (see page 143).

163

The velocity of these slow chemisorptions often obeys a most interesting rate law now known (in the integrated form) as the Elovich equation. If v is the volume of gas chemisorbed at time t, then

$$\frac{dv}{dt} = ae^{-bv} \tag{6.17}$$

where a and b are constants for each system at a particular temperature; b normally decreases as the temperature rises, while a increases. The equation can be integrated to give

$$v = \frac{1}{b} \ln \frac{t+t_0}{t_0} \quad \text{(where } t_0 = 1/ab) \tag{6.18}$$

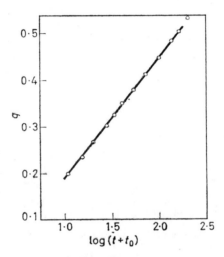

Figure 6.21. Test of the Elovich equation (6.18) ($q \equiv v$, in cm³, at S.T.P. of H_2 on 1 g of $2MnO.Cr_2O_3$; at 1 atm and 100°C)

The rate equation was first reported by Roginskii and Zeldovitch[113] for the chemisorption of carbon monoxide on manganese dioxide and applied by Elovich and Zhabrova[114] to other slow chemisorptions. An extensive survey of the reactions to which the equation applies was made by Taylor and Thon[88]. *Figure 6.21* shows the fit of the equation to some of their results.

It can be seen from equation (6.17) that the constant a is equal to the rate of adsorption at $t=0$ if the chemisorption is slow from the beginning. The equation applies quite well to the slow processes which sometimes follow fast initial chemisorptions, but the value of a is then much smaller than the volume v_1 adsorbed in the first unit of time. There is some indication in these cases that a and b are insensitive to the actual pressure of the gas, and so the slow process might not involve reaction between the gas and the surface. It might be some slow formation of sites for adsorption which has been initiated by the initial adsorption, or it might be a slow migration of adsorbed molecules in the surface.

Taylor and Thon[88] interpret the slow chemisorptions and the form of equation as due to the formation of a number of sites when the gas and the solid first came into contact, followed by a decay of the sites. If initially n_0 sites are formed, then at time t the number n of sites must be given by

$$n = n_0 e^{-bv} \tag{6.19}$$

in order that equation (6.17) may hold. Hence by differentiating and using equations (6.17) and (6.19)

$$\frac{dn}{dt} = -b\frac{dv}{dt}n_0 e^{-bv} = -bn\frac{dv}{dt} = -\frac{ab}{n_0}n^2 \tag{6.20}$$

This equation represents a bimolecular decay in the number of sites. Other formulations by Taylor[115] and by Landsberg[116], which depend on the generation of sites as proposed by Volkenstein, have been summarized by Low[117].

The more conventional views[118, 119] are based upon the postulate of non-uniform sites, either due to an inherent heterogeneity or to an induced one. It will be noticed that equation (6.17) could be interpreted as representing a slow reaction in which the activation energy increases as the reaction proceeds. On the model of chemisorption proposed by Lennard-Jones[1] this increase in activation energy could be linked with the almost universal decrease in the heat of chemisorption with higher coverages. This is shown in *Figure 6.22* which is based on a figure of Zwietering *et al.*[120] The lower potential energy curve b_1 for

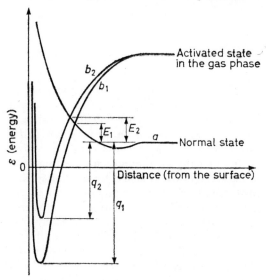

Figure 6.22. Heats and activation energies of adsorption at different coverages[120]

chemisorption of the atoms (or suitably activated molecules) corresponds to the chemisorption at low coverages, with heat of adsorption q_1 and activation energy E_1; the higher curve b_2 corresponds to chemisorption at higher coverages with a smaller value c_2 of the heat of adsorption, and this could clearly lead to a larger activation energy E_2. Unfortunately, there does not seem any certain way of showing that the potential energy curves do lie as drawn, with the smaller heat of adsorption on top; it obviously would if the length of the metal–adatom bond were the same, but it might be anticipated that the stronger bond (q_1) is the shorter, so bringing the curves together and perhaps even leading to a transposition near the intersection with the van der Waals curve.

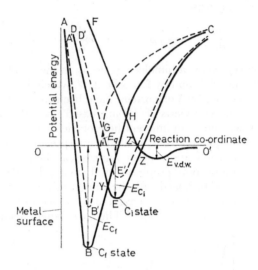

Figure 6.23. Activated migration on surface[107]

Yet another possibility, especially relevant to the slow adsorptions which sometimes follow rapid initial adsorptions, is that the adsorbed molecules or atoms migrate slowly from sites of higher potential to sites of lower potential on a heterogeneous surface. This can be envisaged from *Figure 6.23*, which differs from *Figure 6.22* by showing two sites C_i and C_f. At low coverages there would be no activation energy for the molecule starting from O' to reach C_i or C_f, but at the later stages (represented by the dotted lines) an activation energy might appear and cause the migration from C_i to C_f to be slow. From their experiments on the later slow adsorption of carbon monoxide and hydrogen on iron films, Porter and Tomkins[106] adopted this mechanism; but later experiments by Grundy and Tomkins[107] led to a rather different view. They studied the amounts of gas taken up after each stage of 'thermal cycling' of the film and adsorbate between 90 and 273 °K, with and without evacuation, and concluded that instead of migrating on a heterogeneous surface, the adsorbed species might change its bonding to the surface metal atoms; following Dowden's suggestions[121], the first state might involve d-orbitals of the metal only, and the final state some hybridized bonds with different metal–metal bonds and fresh surface sites for adsorption from the gas phase. These are extremely interesting ideas, and it is to be hoped that some experimental check upon the existence of surface migration, or its absence, will be devised.

6.7. RATES OF DESORPTION

Just as for adsorption, the rate of desorption can be estimated from theoretical formulae or measured experimentally.

The kinetic treatment of adsorption allows the calculation of rates of desorption from the rate of adsorption and the equilibrium conditions. Reference to section 6.6 shows that the rate of desorption at coverage θ is equal to $\beta\theta$, and at the equilibrium value of θ_{eq}

$$\beta\theta_{eq} = \frac{\alpha p(1-\theta_{eq})}{(2\pi m k T)^{1/2}} \tag{6.21}$$

For the example which was examined on page 153, $\theta_{eq}=1/20$ when $p=50$ mm, $T=273°$K and therefore

$$\beta = 38\times 10^{22}\alpha \text{ molecules cm}^{-2} \text{ sec}^{-1}$$

This is the rate of evaporation of molecules from each square centimetre of filled surface of silica; for each square centimetre of *total* surface under the same conditions, the rate of evaporation is $2\times 10^{22}\alpha$ molecules cm^{-2} sec^{-1} (i.e. $\beta\theta_{eq}$).

The average lifetime of the molecules on the silica surface can be defined as the ratio

$$\frac{\text{number of molecules on each cm}^2 \text{ of total surface}}{\text{rate at which molecules leave each cm}^2 \text{ of total surface}}$$

$$= \frac{N_{max}\theta_{eq}}{\beta\theta_{eq}} = \frac{10^{15}}{38\times 10^{22}\alpha} = 2.5\times 10^{-9}/\alpha$$

The value of α is likely to be near unity for temperatures near 273°K so that the rate of evaporation or desorption is about 2×10^{22} molecules sec^{-1} for each square centimetre of total surface, and the average lifetime of an adsorbed molecule is about 2.5×10^{-9} sec for this example of oxygen on silica gel.

The rate of desorption will increase very rapidly with the temperature. β contains a factor $e^{-E_{des}/RT}$, and reference to *Figure 6.22* will show that $E_{des}(=E_{ads}+q_{ads})$ is likely to be a few kilocalories for physical adsorption and several tens of kilocalories for chemisorption. Thus the rate of physical desorption reaches a given level at a far lower temperature than does a chemisorption; the ratio of temperatures for the same rates of desorption from each square centimetre of *covered* surface is given fairly accurately by the expression

$$\frac{T_{physical}}{T_{chemisorption}} = \frac{\text{Heat of physical adsorption}}{\text{Heat of chemisorption}}$$

The practical effect of this relationship is that physically adsorbed layers start to unstrip at quite low temperatures, but chemisorbed layers must be heated to a high temperature for desorption. The change of the heat of adsorption with coverage at a given temperature has a profound effect upon the rate of desorption at different coverages. For example, the heat of adsorption of hydrogen on tungsten falls from about 40 kcal at low coverage to about 10 kcal at high coverage; this means that at room temperature the molecules adsorbed in the last stages of filling the surface evaporate $10^{21.7}$ times as fast as those which first entered the adsorbed layer—this means that the half-lives are 1 sec to 10^{14} years!

If the adsorption process is activated, it is likely that the activation energy of adsorption increases as the surface fills, while the heat of adsorption falls. Often these effects seem to compensate each other, although there is not a great deal of evidence on which to suggest general trends. The slow chemisorption of nitrogen on iron catalysts[122] has an activation energy of 10 kcal and a heat of adsorption of 44 kcal at low coverages, and an activation energy of 21·5 and a heat of adsorption of 32 kcal at high coverages; here the activation energy of desorption is nearly constant at 53·5 to 54 kcal. Hydrogen on an iron film[105] gives $26+0=26$ kcal at 50 per cent coverage and $18+3=21$ kcal at 85 per cent coverage.

On the other hand, if the activation energy of adsorption is zero, the activation energy of desorption will equal the heat of adsorption. It will thus vary very much with the coverage for many adsorbent–adsorbate systems; the coverage will vary in turn with the temperature, and if the heat of adsorption does not change much with the temperature at each coverage, a very unexpected effect can occur; if the rate of desorption is measured after equilibration at constant ambient pressure, and the gases are then removed to give the highest possible vacuum, *the rate of desorption can be less at higher temperatures!* This is best seen by taking an example. Trapnell quotes[123] the figures shown in *Tables 6.10* and *6.11* for the coverage of an evaporated film of tungsten by hydrogen, and also the heats of adsorption at various coverages. Assuming

Table 6.10. Percentage of the surface atoms of a tungsten film covered by hydrogen[122,123]

Pressure mm	Temperature (°C)				
	0	−36	−78	−126	−183
10^{-6}	76	80	86	92	97
10^{-4}	81	85	90	95	100
10^{-2}	86	90	94	99	103

Table 6.11. Heat of adsorption on tungsten films[123]

Isothermal heat (kcal mole^{-1})	15·2	12·4	9·3	6·1	3·0
Coverage θ (%)	80	85	90	95	100

that the rate of desorption is proportional to $\theta^2 e^{-q_\theta/RT}$, interpolation of the figures given leads to the following relative rates after equilibration at a pressure of 10^{-6} mm Hg:

0°C	−36°C	−78°C
1	0·36	5·21

Thus if the rates at 0 and −36°C were used to calculate an apparent activation energy for the rate of desorption, it would appear to be about 4 kcal, but if the rates at 0 and −78°C were used, it would appear to be −2 kcal.

This point has been mentioned by Trapnell[123] in discussing the low activation energy for the orthohydrogen–parahydrogen conversion over metals; the rate-determining step appears to be the desorption of hydrogen atoms, yet the activation energy is lower than the heat of adsorption of either hydrogen atoms or molecules. Trapnell gives qualitatively the explanation outlined above. Of course, in reality the heat of adsorption may change with temperature in such a way that the real effect is not as extreme as that calculated above (see *Figure 6.12*, for example). Especially at higher temperatures all isobars show that the rate of change of coverage with temperature is less, and when the level of coverage is lower the rate of change of heat with coverage is usually less; thus the activated energy of desorption is closer to the heat of adsorption at higher temperatures. It seems to be necessary to exercise great caution in interpreting experimental rates at different *low* temperatures, however, where the coverage is high.

The point is one of obvious importance for all reactions with rates depending upon the rate of desorption. It emphasizes that the effective part of the reaction may be occurring in a small section of the total surface, and a section which is different at different temperatures—either another part of a heterogeneous surface or another part of an adsorbed film with induced heterogeneity. It also helps in understanding why so many surface-catalysed hydrogenations can proceed rapidly at temperatures as low as $-195°C$.

As will be seen in the next few paragraphs, the experimental activation energies for desorption are often lower than the heats of desorption. The explanation may lie in the suggestion above; but there are not yet enough data on heats of adsorption at different coverages and at different temperatures to test the suggestion properly.

There have been several measurements of the rate of desorption from tungsten wires or filaments, and these rates have been compared with the calculated rates based on the theory of absolute reaction rates. When the adsorbed species and the desorbed gas have the same molecularity, the theoretical expression is quite simple[124]:

$$-\frac{dc_{ads}}{dt} = c_{ads}\frac{kTf^{\ddagger}}{hf_{ads}}e^{-E_{des}/RT} \qquad (6.22)$$

where c_{ads} is the concentration of the adsorbed species, $f^{\ddagger}$ and f_{ads} are the partition functions of the transition complex and the adsorbed species, E_{des} is the activation energy of desorption, and k and h are Boltzmann's and Planck's constants, respectively. If the rate-determining step of a desorption is not the formation of the complex but the desorption of the complex *as a diatomic molecule*, the rate expression[125] is

$$-\frac{dc_{ads}}{dt} = \frac{c^2_{ads}c_{s_2}}{c^2_{s_1}}\frac{kT}{h}\frac{f^{\ddagger}f^2_{s_1}}{f^2_{ads}f_{s_2}}e^{-E_{ads}/RT} \qquad (6.23)$$

where c_{s_2} and f_{s_2} are the surface concentration and partition functions of the sites holding the complex. The rate-determining step is step 2 of the sequence

$$2XS \underset{-1}{\overset{1}{\rightleftharpoons}} X_2S_2 \overset{2}{\longrightarrow} X_2 + 2S$$

A first-order law has been found, as might be expected, for the desorption of alkali metal atoms or ions; as shown in *Table 6.12*, due to Ehrlich[103], there is

Table 6.12. Rates of desorption of alkali metals or ions[103]

Alkali metal	E_{des}	$10^{13}A_{des}$	$10^{13}kT/h$
Na	62·9	0·5	2·7–3·0
K$^+$	58·8	3·3	1·1–1·5
Rb	60·0	0·4	2·9–3·1
Rb$^+$	43·8	0·03	1·2–1·4
Cs	64·4	0·17	0·9–2·1
Cs$^+$	47·1	0·09	0·9–1·2

fair agreement, if the partition functions are assumed to be equal, between the value of kT/h and the experimental pre-exponential factor A_{des} given by

$$-\frac{\mathrm{d}c_{ads}}{\mathrm{d}t} = c_{ads}A_{des}\mathrm{e}^{-E_{des}/RT} \tag{6.24}$$

Laidler[125] has also shown that there is fair agreement between the experimental rate for desorption of carbon monoxide from platinum and of oxygen from tungsten, both of which are first order in c_{ads}, and the absolute rate, although the observed rates are 20 times faster for carbon monoxide and 300 for oxygen: rather better agreement for oxygen was found by Ehrlich[103] who used the activation energy determined by Johnson and Vick[126] rather than the older value of Langmuir and Villars[127], for he finds $A_{des} \sim 1·25 \times 10^{13}$ compared with $kT/h \sim (4·9–5·4) \times 10^{13}$ sec^{-1}. It is rather surprising to find a first-order law for oxygen, as this is almost certainly adsorbed as atoms, and if it desorbs as molecules, a second-order law would be expected. The desorption might be as atoms, or the slow step might be migration across the sparsely occupied surface to find a partner. Becker[101] has made accurate measurements of the rate of desorption of nitrogen from a tunsgten surface, and a second-order rate law is found, with an activation energy of 71 kcal[128].

REFERENCES

[1] LENNARD-JONES, J. E. *Trans. Faraday Soc.* 1932, **28**, 333
[2] TAYLOR H. S. *J. Amer. chem. Soc.* 1931, **53**, 578
[3] GUNDRY, P. M. and TOMPKINS, F. C. *Quart. Rev. (Lond.)* 1960, **14**, 257
[4] ELEY, D. D. *Disc. Faraday Soc.* 1950, **8**, 34
[5] BEVAN, D. J. M., SHELTON, J. P. and ANDERSON, J. S. *J. chem. Soc.* 1948, p. 1729
[6] GARNER, W. E. and KINGMAN, F. E. T. *Trans. Faraday Soc.* 1931, **27**, 322
[7] FRANKENBURG, W. G. *J. Amer. chem. Soc.* 1944, **66**, 1827, 1838
[8] COUPER, A. and ELEY, D. D., *Disc. Faraday Soc.* 1950, **8**, 172
[9] EGGLETON, A. E. J. and TOMPKINS, F. C. *Trans. Faraday Soc.* 1952, **48**, 738
[10] LECK, J. H. *Chemisorption* (Ed. W. E. Garner): Butterworth, London, 1957, p. 162
[11] BECKER, J. A. *Advanc. Catalys.* 1955, **7**, 135
[12] LANGMUIR, I. *et al.*—for summary see: ADAM, N. K. *Physics and Chemistry of Surfaces*: Oxford University Press, London, 1941, p. 255
[13] ROBERTS, J. K. *Some Problems in Adsorption*: Cambridge University Press, London, 1939

REFERENCES

[14] RIDEAL, E. K. *Sabatier Lecture: J. Soc. chem. Ind.* 1943, **62**, 335

[15] CUNNINGHAM, R. E. and GWATHMEY, A. T. *Advanc. Catalys.* 1957, **9**, 25

[16] CUNNINGHAM, R. E. and GWATHMEY, A. T. *Advanc. Catalys.* 1958, **10**, 57

[17] RHODIN, T. N., Jr. *Advanc. Catalys.* 1953, **5**, 39

[18] BEECK, O., SMITH, A. E. and WHEELER, A. *Proc. R. Soc. A* 1941, **177**, 62

[19] BEECK, O. and RITCHIE, A. W. *Disc. Faraday Soc.* 1950, **8**, 159

[20] SACHTLER, W. M. H., DORGELO, G. and KNAAP, W. VAN DER *J. Chim. phys.* 1954, **51**, 491

[21] BEECK, O. *Advanc. Catalys.* 1950, **2**, 151

[22] RHODIN, T. N., Jr. *J. Amer. chem. Soc.* 1950, **72** (*a*) 4343; (*b*) 5691

[23] McBAIN, J. W. and BAKR, A. M. *J. Amer. chem. Soc.* 1926, **48**, 690

[24] ALLEN, J. A. and MITCHELL, J. W. *Disc. Faraday Soc.* 1950, **8**, 309

[25] PASHLEY, D. W. *Advanc. Phys.* 1956, **5**, 173

[26] FINCH, G. I. and QUARRELL, A. G. *Proc. R. Soc. A* 1933, **141**, 398

[27] NEWMAN, R. C. *Phil. Mag. Ser. 8* 1957, **2**, 750

[28] GRUNBAUM, E. *Proc. phys. Soc. Lond.* 1958, **72**, 459

[29] BASSETT, G. A., MENTER, J. W. and PASHLEY, D. W. International Conference on the Structure and Properties of Thin Films: Wiley, New York, 1959, p. 11

[30] BASSETT, G. A., MENTER, J. W. and PASHLEY, D. W. *Disc. Faraday Soc.* 1959, **28**, 7

[31] SCHLEIR, R. E. and FARNSWORTH, H. E. *J. Phys. Chem. Solids* 1958, **6**, 271

[32] EISCHENS, R. P. and PLISKIN, W. A. *Advanc. Catalys.* 1958, **10**, 1

[33] CRAWFORD, V. *Quart. Rev. (Lond.)* 1960, **14**, 378

[34] PICKERING, H. L. and ECKSTROM, H. C. *J. phys. Chem.* 1959, **63**, 512

[35] EISCHENS, R. P., FRANCIS, S. A. and PLISKIN, W. A. *J. phys. Chem.* 1956, **60**, 194

[36] YANG, A. C. and GARLAND, C. W. *J. phys. Chem.* 1957, **61**, 1504

[37] CRAWFORD, V. *Quart. Rev. (Lond.)* 1960, **14**, 388 *et. seq.*

[38] EISCHENS, R. P. and PLISKIN, W. A. Symposium on Instrument Technique in the Study of Catalysis Mechanism, Boston, 1959

[39] EISCHENS, R. P., PLISKIN, W. A. and FRANCIS, S. A. *J. chem. Phys.* 1954, **22**, 1786

[40] PLISKIN, W. A. and EISCHENS, R. P. *J. chem. Phys.* 1956, **24**, 482

[41] RYLAND, L. B., TAMELE, M. W. and WILSON, J. N. *Catalysis* (Ed. P. H. Emmett) Vol. VII: Reinhold, New York, 1960, Chapter 1

[42] TAMELE, M. W. *Disc. Faraday Soc.* 1950, **8**, 270

[43] MILLIKEN, T. H., MILLS, G. A. and OBLAD, A. G. *Disc. Faraday Soc.* 1950, **8**, 279

[44] KIPLING, J. J. and PEAKALL, D. B. *Chemisorption* (Ed. W. E. Garner): Butterworth, London, 1957, p. 59

[45] TRAPNELL, B. M. W. *Chemisorption*: Butterworth, London, 1955

[46] STONE, F. S. and GRAY, T. J. *Chemistry of the Solid State* (Ed. W. E. Garner): Butterworth, London, 1955, Chapters 2, 15 and 5

[47] HAUFFE, K. *Advanc. Catalys.* 1955, **7**, 213

[48] FENSHAM, P. J. *Quart. Rev. (Lond.)* 1957, **11**, 227

[49] GARNER, W. E., GRAY, T. J. and STONE, F. S. *Disc. Faraday Soc.* 1950, **8**, 246

[50] BAUMBACH, H. H. and WAGNER, C. Z. *phys. Chem. (Leipzig)* 1933, **B22**, 199

[51] BEVAN, D. J. M. and ANDERSON, J. S. *Disc. Faraday Soc.* 1950, **8**, 238

[52] WAGNER, C. *J. chem. Phys.* 1950, **18**, 69

[53] GARNER, W. E., STONE, F. S. and TILEY, P. F. *Proc. R. Soc. A* 1952, **211**, 472

[54] GARNER, W. E., STONE, F. S. and TILEY, P. F. *Disc. Faraday Soc.* 1950, **8**, 254

[55] GARNER, W. E. *J. chem. Soc.* 1947, p. 1239

[56] MORRISON, S. R. *Advanc. Catalys.* 1955, **7**, 259

[57] HAUFE, K. and ENGELL, H. J. *Z. Elektrochem.* 1952, **56**, 366
AINGRAIN, P. and DUGAS, C. *Z. Electrochem.* 1952, **56**, 363

[58] WEISZ, P. B. *J. chem. Phys.* 1952, **20**, 1483; 1953, **21**, 1531

[59] VERWEY, E. J. W., HAAYMAN, P. W. and ROMEYN, F. C. *Chem. Weekbl.* 1948, **44**, 705

[60] HAUFFE, K. and VIERK, A. L. *Z. phys. Chem.* (*Leipzig*) 1950, **196**, 160

[61] DE BOER, J. H. *Advanc. Catalys.* 1957, **9**, 472

[62] ELEY, D. D. *Catalysis* (Ed. P. H. Emmett) Vol. III: Reinhold, New York, 1955, p. 56

[63] TRAPNELL, B. M. W. *Proc. R. Soc. A* 1951, **206**, 39

[64] BRUNAUER, S. *The Physical Adsorption of Gases and Vapours*: Oxford University Press, London; Princeton University Press, Princeton, 1943

[65] BEECK, O., COLE, W. A. and WHEELER, A. *Disc. Faraday Soc.* 1950, **8**, 314

[66] MORRISON, J. A. and LOS, J. M. *Disc. Faraday Soc.* 1950, **8**, 321

[67] BRENNAN, D., HAYWARD, D. O. and TRAPNELL, B. M. W. *Proc. R. Soc. A* 1960, **256**, 81

[68] CULVER, R. V. and TOMPKINS, F. C. *Advanc. Catalys.* 1959, **11**, 68

[69] STEVENSON, D. P. *J. chem. Phys.* 1955, **23**, 203

[70] BEECK, O. *Disc. Faraday Soc.* 1950, **8**, 118

[71] MIGNOLET, J. C. P. *J. chem. Phys.* 1953, **21**, 1298
BRODD, R. J. *J. phys. Chem.* 1958, **62**, 54

[72] BORTNER, M. H. and PARRAVANO, G. *Advanc. Catalys.* 1957, **9**, 424

[73] TAYLOR, H. S. *J. phys. Chem.* 1926, **30**, 145

[74] ROBERTS, J. K. *Proc. R. Soc. A* 1935, **152**, 445

[75] KWAN, T. *Advanc. Catalys.* 1954, **6**, 67

[76] GRIMLEY, T. B. *Chemisorption* (Ed. W. E. Garner): Butterworth, London, 1957, p. 17

[77] BOUDART, M. *J. Amer. chem. Soc.* 1952, **74**, 1531, 3556

[78] DE BOER, J. H. *Advanc. Catalys.* 1956, **8**, 17

[79] DOWDEN, D. A. *Chemisorption* (Ed. W. E. Garner): Butterworth, London, 1957, p. 3

[80] MAXTED, E. B., MOON, K. L. and OVERGAGE, E. *Disc. Faraday Soc.* 1950, **8**, 135

[81] WHEELER, A. *Advanc. Catalys.* 1951, **3**, 250

[82] TAYLOR, H. S. *Disc. Faraday Soc.* 1950, **8**, 9

[83] KEIER, M. P. and ROGINSKII, S. Z. *Izvest. Akad. Nauk S.S.S.R., Otdel Khim. Nauk* 1950, p. 27

[84] SCHUIT, G. C. A. *Proceedings of the International Symposium on Reactivity Solids*, 1952: Elander, Gothenburg, 1954, p. 571

[85] EMMETT, P. H. and KUMMER, J. T. *J. Amer. chem. Soc.* 1951, **73**, 2886; *J. Chim. phys.* 1950, **47**, 67

[86] LANGMUIR, I. *J. Amer. chem. Soc.* 1918, **40**, 1361; *Trans. Faraday Soc.* 1932, **17**, 607

[87] VOLKENSTEIN, F. F. *Zh. fiz. Chim.* 1948, **22**, 311; 1949, **23**, 317, 917; *Advanc. Catalys.* 1960, **12**, 189

[88] TAYLOR, H. A. and THON, N. *J. Amer. chem. Soc.* 1952, **74**, 4169

[89] KWAN, T. *Advanc. Catalys.* 1954, **6**, 67 (cf. p. 102)

[90] MARKHAM, E. C. and BENTON, A. F. *J. Amer. chem. Soc.* 1931, **53**, 497

[91] DAMKÖHLER, G. *Z. phys. Chem.* (*Leipzig*) 1935, **A174**, 222

[92] See BRUNAUER, S. *The Physical Adsorption of Gases and Vapours*: Clarendon Press, Oxford, 1943, p. 465

[93] BARRER, R. M. *Structure and Properties of Porous Materials* (Ed. D. H. Everett and F. S. Stone): Butterworth, London, 1958, p. 6

[94] WHEELER, A. *Catalysis* (Ed. P. H. Emmett) Vol. II: Reinhold, New York, 1955, Chapter 2

[95] LENNARD-JONES, J. E. and DEVONSHIRE, A. F. *Proc. R. Soc. A* 1936, **156**, 6

[96] LAIDLER, K. J. *Catalysis* (Ed. P. H. Emmett) Vol. I: Reinhold, New York, 1954, Chapter 5

REFERENCES

[97] VOLMER, M. and ESTERMANN, I. *Z. Phys.* 1921, **7**, 1, 13

[98] ROBERTS, J. K. *Some Problems in Adsorption*: Cambridge University Press, London, 1939, p. 109

[99] ROBERTS, J. K. and MORRISON, J. L. *Proc. R. Soc. A* 1939, **173**, 1, 13

[100] BECKER, J. A. and HARTMAN, C. D. *J. phys. Chem.* 1953, **57**, 153

[101] BECKER, J. A. *Advanc. Catalys.* 1955, **7**, 159

[102] TRAPNELL, B. M. W. *Chemisorption*: Butterworth, London, 1955, p. 58

[103] EHRLICH, G. *Molecular Processes at Gas–Solid Interfaces*: Conference on the Properties and Structure of Thin Films: Wiley, New York, 1959

[104] TAYLOR, H. S. and LANGMUIR, I. *Phys. Rev.* 1933, **44**, 423

[105] TRAPNELL, B. M. W. *Proc. roy. Soc. A* 1953, **218**, 566

[106] PORTER, A. S. and TOMPKINS, F. C. *Proc. R. Soc. A* 1953, **217**, 529

[107] GUNDRY, P. M. and TOMPKINS, F. C. *Chemisorption* (Ed. W. E. Garner): Butterworth, London, 1957, p. 152

[108] BEEBE, R. A. and DOWDEN, D. A. *J. Amer. chem. Soc.* 1938, **60**, 2912

[109] RUDHAM, R. and STONE, F. S. *Chemisorption* (Ed. W. E. Garner): Butterworth, London, 1957, p. 205

[110] TAYLOR, H. S. and WILLIAMSON, A. T. *J. Amer. chem. Soc.* 1931, **53**, 2169

[111] TAYLOR, H. S. and STROTHER, C. O. *J. Amer. chem. Soc.* 1934, **56**, 586

[112] ALLMAND, A. J. and CHAPLIN, R. *Trans. Faraday Soc.* 1932, **28**, 223

[113] ROGINSKI, S. and ZELDOVITCH, Z. *Acta phys.-chim. U.R.S.S.* 1934, **1**, 595

[114] ELOVICH, S. Y. and ZHABROVA, G. M. *Zh. fiz. Khim.* 1939, **13**, 1761, 1775

[115] TAYLOR, H. A. *Ann. N.Y. Acad. Sci.* 1954, **58**, 798

[116] LANDSBERG, P. T. *J. chem. Phys.* 1955, **23**, 1079

[117] LOW, M. J. D. *Chem. Rev.* 1960, **60**, 267

[118] TRAPNELL, B. M. W. *Chemisorption*: Butterworth, London, 1955, p. 103

[119] HALSEY, G. D. *J. phys. Chem.* 1951, **55**, 21

[120] BOKHOVEN, C., VAN HEERDEN, C., WESTRIK, R. and ZWIETERING, P. *Catalysis* (Ed. P. H. Emmett) Vol. III: Reinhold, New York, 1955, Chapter 7

[121] DOWDEN, D. A. *J. chem. Soc.* 1950, p. 242

[122] BRUNAUER, S., LOVE, K. S. and KEENAN, R. G. *J. Amer. chem. Soc.* 1942, **64**, 751

[123] TRAPNELL, B. M. W. *Catalysis* (Ed. P. H. Emmett) Vol. III: Reinhold, New York, 1955, Chapter 1

[124] TRAPNELL, B. M. W. *Proc. R. Soc. A* 1951, **206**, 39

[125] LAIDLER, K. J. *Catalysis* (Ed. P. H. Emmett) Vol. I: Reinhold, New York, 1954, Chapter 5, p. 195

[126] JOHNSON, M. C. and VICK, F. A. *Proc. R. Soc. A* 1935, **151**, 308

[127] LANGMUIR, I. and VILLARS, D. S. *J. Amer. chem. Soc.* 1931, **53**, 486

[128] EHRLICH, G. *J. phys. Chem.* 1956, **60**, 1388

MECHANISMS OF HETEROGENEOUSLY CATALYSED
REACTIONS   I

7.1. INTRODUCTION

THE EXPERIMENTAL material presented in the last chapter has shown that the velocities of chemisorption and of desorption vary enormously. This wide variation makes it necessary to consider that any one of the three steps chemisorption of reactant, surface reaction or desorption of product, may control the rate of a heterogeneous reaction. In the past, there has been a marked emphasis on the mechanisms in which the surface reactions are assumed to control the rate. Partly because of the early success of these mechanisms, and partly because of the absence until recently of information about rates of chemisorption and desorption, there has been some neglect of the other possibilities.

Langmuir's[1] conception of the chemisorption of molecules or atoms in monolayers led to the derivation of simple isotherms connecting the fraction of the surface occupied with the pressure of the gas being adsorbed. By assuming that the rate of a heterogeneous reaction is controlled by the reaction of the adsorbed molecules, and that all adsorption and desorption processes are in equilibrium, it is possible to take the rate as proportional to the fraction of surface covered. Hence the rates can be connected with the gas pressures. In this way, expressions were derived for the rates of decompositions and simple bimolecular reactions on the surface of metals, glass, porcelain and silica. These expressions were very successful in accounting for quite complex rates. *Tables 7.1* to *7.5* summarize some of the varied expressions found for the surface rate laws. Inhibition of the rate by products and even by reactants, fractional orders of reaction, and orders that change with the range of pressure have been found. These mechanisms have become known as Langmuir–Hinshelwood (LH) mechanisms[2-4].

Most of the reactions to which the LH mechanisms were applied, whether unimolecular or bimolecular, took place at high temperatures where it is reasonable to expect the rate of desorption of reactants or products to be fast in spite of the high activation energy of such processes. In the decade 1930–40, however, several reactions were studied which proceed readily at low temperatures, and of these the reversible conversion of orthohydrogen to parahydrogen and the exchange reaction between hydrogen and deuterium are particularly interesting. Their rates on transition metals such as tungsten are very similar at $-80°C$ and the order of reaction is the same although the reactions have different activation energies. Bonhoeffer and Farkas[5] suggested a mechanism which seemed very reasonable, involving the adsorption of hydrogen as atoms with subsequent conversion or exchange upon desorption of the atoms. Doubt was cast on this mechanism, however, by Roberts's measurements[6] of the extent and rate of adsorption and the rate of desorption of hydrogen on clean tungsten wires. He showed that hydrogen did indeed adsorb very rapidly as atoms, even at low temperatures, with a heat of adsorption which fell from about 40 kcal mole^{-1} at low coverages to about 18 kcal as the surface became nearly saturated; but desorption occurred extremely slowly at temperatures below about 400°C. It seemed most improbable that the desorption required by the Bonhoeffer–Farkas mechanism could be fast enough to account for the rates of conversion and exchange at -80°C. These considerations led Rideal[7] to propose that the reactions occurred between adsorbed atoms (held by strong bonds) and molecules which were held to the surface by comparatively weak van der Waals forces, forming a physically adsorbed or van der Waals layer. Exchange of a chemisorbed atom with one of those of the physically adsorbed molecule (it was thought that these were held over gaps in the chemisorbed layer) would be almost thermoneutral and so might have a low energy of activation which would allow it to proceed at a low temperature. Thus the exchange reaction was depicted as follows:

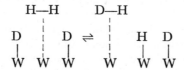

This type of mechanism became known as van der Waals–chemisorbed interaction (VCI) and was extensively applied by Rideal and his school[7,8] to other exchange and hydrogenation reactions, for example those between deuterium and unsaturated hydrocarbons. The VCI mechanism gave as satisfactory an account of the kinetics of the bimolecular reactions studied as did the LH mechanism, and until recently appeared more reasonable energetically. However, as will be shown more fully in a later chapter, there is now some evidence that a different interpretation can be put on Roberts's experiments on hydrogen adsorption at high coverages, and that some desorption can occur readily at low temperatures. If this is confirmed, doubts about the Bonhoeffer-Farkas mechanisms may disappear.

The VCI mechanism was really a refinement of some older ideas that certain bimolecular catalyses occurred by reaction between a molecule and a chemisorbed species upon a suitable collision of the gas molecule with the chemisorbed layer. Thus Bodenstein[9] suggested that the catalysed oxidation of ammonia took place when a gas-phase ammonia molecule reacted with oxygen adsorbed on the platinum surface. Benton and Thacker[10] suggested a similar mechanism for the reaction between nitrous oxide and hydrogen on a silver surface, a gaseous hydrogen molecule reacting with adsorbed oxygen atoms. Temkin and Mikhailova[11] proposed that gaseous carbon dioxide molecules removed adsorbed hydrogen atoms (though not in the rate-determining step) in the reaction: $H_2 + CO_2 \rightarrow H_2O + CO$ over platinum. More recently, Eucken[12] has explained his experimental observations on the hydrogenation of hexene vapour over nickel by assuming that a cyclohexene molecule reacts on impact with a layer of chemisorbed hydrogen atoms. Schuler and Laidler[13] have discussed the recombination of atoms such as hydrogen at glass surfaces in terms of a reaction between gaseous and chemisorbed atoms. Bond[14] has discussed the hydrogenation of acetylene in terms of the collision of gaseous hydrogen with a nearly saturated layer of chemisorbed acetylene on nickel, iron and other metals. As the collision with the surface includes the stage of a brief adsorption into a van der Waals layer, it will be convenient to describe all such reaction schemes as VCI mechanisms.

In many heterogeneously catalysed reactions, however, it appears that the rate-determining step is not a reaction in the adsorbed layer in the sense that the reacting fragments and the product are all adsorbed, nor is it a reaction between a gaseous molecule and a chemisorbed fragment. In one very simple reaction, the orthohydrogen–parahydrogen conversion over metals, the Bonhoeffer–Farkas mechanism is not really a LH mechanism: it is unlikely that the product *molecule* is adsorbed, and the rate-determining step is either the adsorption of the hydrogen molecule or its desorption.

As long ago as 1931, it was suggested[15] that in the decomposition of ammonia the slow step might be the desorption of nitrogen atoms. In the following decade, very thorough work on the synthesis and decomposition of ammonia under the conditions used in industrial processes, in particular work under the direction of Temkin, Brunauer and Emmett, Frankenburg and H. S. Taylor, showed that the rate of adsorption of nitrogen controlled the rate of synthesis and the rate of desorption the decomposition. Excellent reviews[16,17] of these researches have appeared recently, which emphasize the variety of techniques used to supplement determinations of the kinetics of the reactions. Isotopically labelled compounds were used[18] to show that the surface reactions of adsorbed species were rapid. Measurements of the surface areas of the catalysts[19] allowed stricter comparisons of the rates over different catalysts. Careful comparisons[20-22] were made, too, between rates of adsorption and rates of reaction. The chemisorption of each species was studied and various isotherms were tested against the results. The bulk catalysts, and their surfaces, were examined by x-rays in attempts to correlate[16] crystal structure and catalytic activity, and x-ray and surface area measurements were used to show that some promoters are concentrated in the surfaces of promoted iron catalysts. Certain features of these studies mark them as the beginning of really systematic investigations of heterogeneous catalyses. In particular, the study of the chemisorption of individual substances, the use of isotopes and the examination of the bulk and surface structure of the catalyst, represented a marked advance on the earlier reliance on kinetic data alone.

7.2. SOME REACTIONS PROCEEDING BY LANGMUIR–HINSHELWOOD MECHANISMS[2-4]

These mechanisms assume that the surface reactions control the rate, the adsorption and desorption processes being in equilibrium. The concentrations of the adsorbed species are thus related to the gas pressures by a suitable form of the Langmuir isotherm, and this allows the rate of reaction to be expressed in terms of the gas pressure. The treatment has been frequently discussed, and it will suffice to explain the most general form of the rate equation for a unimolecular decomposition; more complicated reactions can readily be examined by applying the same principles.

If the reaction is $X \to Z$ and it is assumed that X is adsorbed as one molecule on one site, and therefore localized, and that Z also competes for the same sites the fraction of surface covered by X (see p. 152) is

$$\theta_X = B_X p_X / 1 + B_X p_X + B_Z p_Z$$

The rate of reaction is then put equal to $k_1 \theta_X$, so that the rate

$$\frac{dp_Z}{dt} = -\frac{dp_X}{dt} = \frac{k_1 B_X p_X}{1 + B_X p_X + B_Z p_Z} \tag{7.1}$$

Table 7.1. Langmuir–Hinshelwood mechanisms for unimolecular decomposition: $X \to Z$

Adsorption of Z	Adsorption of X	Rate expression	Order	Apparent activation energy	Examples Gas	Examples Adsorbent
Weak	Weak	$k_1 B_X p_X$	First	$E - q_X$	AsH_3 or PH_3 N_2O HI	Glass, silica or porcelain Au Pt
	Moderate	$\dfrac{k_1' B_X p_X}{1 + B_X p_X}$	Variable with p_X	Variable with p_X	Formic acid SbH_3	Glass or metals Sb
	Strong	k_1''	Zero	E''	NH_3 HI	W, Mo, Nb Au
Strong	Weak	$\dfrac{k_1''' B_X p_X}{B_Z p_Z}$ $\left.\begin{array}{c}\\ \\ \end{array}\right\}$	First for X	$E''' - q_X + q_Z$	NH_3	Pt(H_2 retards)
		$\dfrac{k_1''' B_X p_X}{1 + B_Z p_Z}$	Inverse for Z	Variable	N_2O	Pt(O_2 retards)

Table 7.2. Kinetic laws in the decomposition of nitrous oxide[4]

Rate law	Catalyst	Temperature range °C	Activation energy kcal mole^{-1}	Reference
$v = k[N_2O]$	Au MgO, CaO, SrO$_2$, Al$_2$O$_3$	830–990 800–1,200	29·0 37·1, 34·8, 32·0, 29·3	25 a
$v = \dfrac{k[N_2O]}{1 + b[O_2]}$	Pt Ag CuO CdO, In$_2$O$_3$	600–1,200 450 495–590	32·5 — 27·0 36·6, 28·5	b c d a
$v = \dfrac{k[N_2O]}{(1 + b'[N_2O])(1 + b[O_2])}$	Pt	850–875	31·8	e

a. Schwab, G. M., Staeger, R. and von Baumbach, H. H. *Z. phys. Chem.* (*Leipzig*) 1933, **B21**, 65
b. Hinshelwood, C. N. and Prichard, C. R. *J. chem. Soc.* 1925, p. 327
c. Steacie, E. W. R. and Folkins, H. O. *Canad. J. Res.* 1937, **15B**, 237
d. Schwab, G. M. and Staeger, R. *Z. phys. Chem.* (*Leipzig*) 1934, **B25**, 418
e. Miyazaki, S. *J. chem. Soc. Japan* 1951, **72**, 723

Various cases can then arise, depending on the relative values of the terms in the denominator of the expression (7.1). For example, if the reactant is fairly strongly adsorbed (B_X large) and the product weakly adsorbed (B_Z small) the rate will be proportional to $B_X p_X/1 + B_X p_X$ and may well be first order at low pressures and zero order at high pressures with a fractional order in between.

Table 7.3. Kinetic laws in the decomposition of phosphine over tungsten (at 610 to 720°C) and molybdenum (at 570 to 645°C) [4]

Rate law	Catalyst	Pressure range mm Hg	Activation energy kcal	Reference
$v = k[PH_3]$	W	10^{-3}–10^{-2}	26·5	31
	Mo	Very low	15·1	32
$v = \dfrac{k[PH_3]}{1+b[PH_3]}$	W	0·2	32·0	31
	Mo	0·06	20·8	32
$v = k[PH_3]^\circ$	W	~1	31–34	31
	Mo	0·20	22·3	32

Table 7.4. Langmuir–Hinshelwood mechanisms for bimolecular reaction: $X+Y \rightarrow$ products

Adsorption of X	Adsorption of Y	Adsorbent	Reference
Weak	Weak		
NO	O_2	Glass (−190°C)	a
H_2	C_2H_4	Cu(150–200°C)	b
Weak	Strong		
O_2	CO	Quartz	c
		Pt	d
O_2	H_2	Pt	d
H_2	C_2H_4	Cu(0–20°C)	e
H_2	CO_2	Pt	f
D_2	NH_3	Promoted iron	g

a. Temkin, M. and Pyzhev, V. *Acta phys.-chim. U.R.S.S.* 1935, **2**, 473
b. Pease, R. N. *J. Amer. chem. Soc.* 1923, **45**, 2235
c. Bodenstein, M. and Ohlmer, F. *Z. phys. Chem.* 1905, **53**, 166
d. Langmuir, I. *Trans. Faraday Soc.* 1921, **17**, 621
e. Pease, R. N. *J. Amer. chem. Soc.* 1923, **45**, 1196
f. Prichard, C. and Hinshelwood, C. N. *J. chem. Soc.* 1925, 865
g. Weber, J. and Laidler, K. J. *J. chem. Phys.* 1951, **19**, 1089

An example is quoted in *Table 7.3.* If the product is extremely strongly adsorbed, however, the predicted rate will be proportional to $B_X p_X/B_Z p_Z$. Many examples of these rate laws have been given in the literature, especially by Hinshelwood[2], Schwab[3] and Laidler[4]. *Table 7.1* shows some of the possible relationships, with examples, and *Tables 7.2* and *7.3* show the variety of laws found for individual decompositions.

Similar principles can be applied to bimolecular reactions, and some examples are given in *Table 7.4* for reactions of the type: $X + Y \rightarrow$ products, where there are no complications. *Table 7.5* shows some rather more complicated laws observed in the reactions between hydrogen and nitrous oxide.

Table 7.5. Kinetic laws in the reaction between hydrogen and nitrous oxide[4]

Rate law	Catalyst	Temperature range °C	Activation energy kcal mole^{-1}	Reference
$v = \dfrac{k[N_2O]}{[H_2]}$	Pt (high pressure)	500–580	25·0	a
$v = \dfrac{k[N_2O]}{1 + b[N_2O]}$	Pt (low pressure)	300–1,100	—	b
$v = \dfrac{k[H_2][N_2O]}{(1 + b[N_2O])(1 + b'[H_2])}$	Au	704–880	—	c
$v = k[N_2O]$	Pt	260–471	22–23	d

a. Hinshelwood, C. N. *Proc. R. Soc. A* 1924, **106**, 292
b. Cassel, H. and Glückauf, E. *Z. phys. Chem. (Leipzig)* 1932, **B19**, 47
c. Hutchinson, W. K. and Hinshelwood, C. N. *J. chem. Soc.* 1926, p. 1556
d. Dixon, J. K. and Vance, J. E. *J. Amer. chem. Soc.* 1935, **57**, 818

Unfortunately most of these and other examples lack quantitative corroboration of the mechanism offered. In the case of unimolecular decompositions, it is very difficult to examine the chemisorption of the reactant by itself (let alone with product present) without the decomposition occurring. Hence the only evidence about the correct choice of isotherm comes from the comparison of the mathematical form of the experimental rate equation and predicted rate equation. The variety of possible mechanisms is then great, as will be shown by the following example. The appropriate forms of the isotherms are taken from page 152.

Phosphine decomposes on glass with a first-order rate law. The mechanism could be any one of the following:

(*i*) The gas is adsorbed *weakly* (B small) as molecules on a localized site and the rate is controlled by the first step: $(PH_3)_a \rightarrow$ fragments.

$$\text{Rate} = k_1[PH_3]_a = k_1 \frac{Bp_{PH_3}}{1 + Bp_{PH_3}} \sim k_1 Bp_{PH_3} \tag{7.2}$$

(*ii*) The gas is weakly adsorbed as atoms (H) and radicals (PH_2) on localized sites. The rate depends on a bimolecular reaction of two of these atoms or radicals, such as $H_a + H_a \rightarrow H_{2,g}$ or $H_a + PH_{2,a} \rightarrow H_{2,g} + PH_a$, and is equal to $k_1[H_a][H_a]$ or $k_1[H_a][PH_{2,a}] = k_1(B'p_{PH_3}^{1/2})^2 = k_1 B'^2 p_{PH_3}$.

(*iii*) The gas is adsorbed in a non-localized layer, with the same rate-determining step as in (*i*).

$$\text{Rate} = k_1[PH_{3,a}] = k_1 B'' p_{PH_3}$$

(*iv*) The rate is determined not by surface reactions but by the rate of (activated) chemisorption. This rate would be proportional to the pressure p_{PH_3}, irrespective of the way in which the phosphine is adsorbed.

The mechanism usually adopted in this and other similar decompositions is that shown under (i). This has the merit of simplicity, but it would be very valuable to have some definite evidence that the phosphine is adsorbed as a molecule and not directly as fragments. What is required, of course, is some quantitative check on the possible mechanisms, similar to that used to distinguish between diffusion-controlled and surface reaction-controlled rates of chemisorption (section 6.6). It was hoped that the theory of absolute reaction rates applied to surface reactions would allow some discrimination. Unfortunately, additional assumptions about the nature of the surface transition complex have to be introduced and cannot be checked independently; the flexibility of the method allows several possible models to 'explain' results.

The neatest development[4] of the absolute rate equations regards the vacant adsorption sites of concentration c_s as reactants, and the gas-phase molecules react with these to form the complex of concentration $c^{\ddagger}$. There is no distinction between the chemisorption or some later step linked by equilibria to the chemisorption as the rate-controlling step. For a first-order step involving one molecule on one site, with symbolism similar to that used on page 155:

$$\frac{c^{\ddagger}}{c_g c_s} = K_{eq} = \frac{f^{\ddagger}}{(f_g/V)f_s}e^{-\Delta E_0^o/RT} \tag{7.3}$$

The value of ΔE_0^o cannot be determined and the experimental activation energy E_a is usually substituted; some comments on this follow in the next section. The complex is considered to have a weak vibration along the decomposition axis (the bond being broken) of frequency ν, and the rate of reaction is set equal to $\nu c^{\ddagger}$. If the partition function corresponding to the weak vibration is factorized out of the total partition function of the complex, leaving f_{res}, then

$$f^{\ddagger} = (1-e^{-h\nu/kT})^{-1}f_{res} \simeq \frac{kT}{h\nu}f_{res}$$

Hence the rate is equal to

$$\nu c^{\ddagger} = \frac{kT}{h}c_g c_s\frac{f_{res}}{(f_g/V)f_s}e^{-E_a/RT} \tag{7.4}$$

If the complex is adsorbed on a localized site, and is rigid apart from the decomposition vibration, f_{res} is unity; and f_s is also unity. Hence for a polyatomic molecule with strong bonds (so that $f_{g,vib}$ is unity) the rate becomes

$$\text{rate} = c_g c_s \frac{kT}{h}\frac{h^3 e^{-E_a/RT}}{(2\pi mkT)^{3/2}f_{g,rot}} \tag{7.5}$$

For many surfaces, and certainly those of metals at low coverages, $c_s \simeq N_s$ and N_s is about 10^{15} sites cm^{-2}. If c_g is in molecules per cubic centimetre, the rate is in molecules per square centimetre per second.

In comparing this calculated rate with the experimentally measured rate, it is necessary to know the surface area A of the catalyst and the volume V of the reaction vessel. The rate of production of molecules *for the whole vessel* is

$$V(\text{rate in molecules cm}^{-3}\text{ sec}^{-1}) = A \times (\text{rate in molecules cm}^{-2}\text{ sec}^{-1})$$

therefore:

measured rate (molecules cm^{-3} sec^{-1})

$$= \frac{A}{V} \times \text{calculated rate (molecules cm}^{-2}\text{ sec}^{-1})$$

There are few data in the literature to test the theory, for it was rare for the area of the catalysts to be known. Indeed, this is why there are no collections of velocity constants for heterogeneous reactions; the velocity constants of *Tables 7.1* to *7.5* are not fundamental, for they conceal the arbitrary vessel parameter V and catalyst parameter A. Only recently has more attention been paid to the calculation of 'true' velocity constants, independent at least of the reaction vessel geometry. In a few older experimental arrangements the values of V and A were given, and these provide the following comparisons.

Temkin[23] calculated the rate of decomposition of phosphine on a glass surface from an equation similar to equation (7.5), and found good agreement with the experimentally measured rate. Glasstone, Laidler and Eyring[24] reported fair agreement of calculated rates for: (*i*) the decomposition of nitrous oxide on gold, compared with the experimental data of Prichard and Hinshelwood[25], and (*ii*) the decomposition of hydrogen iodide on platinum, compared with the measured rates of Hinshelwood and Burk[26]. The comparison as presented by Laidler[4] is shown in *Table 7.6*.

Table 7.6. Observed and calculated values of surface reactions[4]

| Decomposition of | Surface | Temperature °K | Gas-phase rate constant sec^{-1} | | Reference (obs. value) |
			calc.	obs.	
PH_3	Glass	684	$2 \cdot 2 \times 10^{-8}$	$4 \cdot 7 \times 10^{-7}$	23
HI	Platinum	836	$1 \cdot 2 \times 10^{-3}$	$1 \cdot 0 \times 10^{-3}$	26
N_2O	Gold	1,211	$3 \cdot 4 \times 10^{-6}$	$1 \cdot 2 \times 10^{-4}$	25

Unfortunately, Robertson[27] calculates very different absolute rates for the last two reactions, although agreeing with the calculations for phosphine. He considers (in the present author's opinion correctly) that the calculated rate for nitrous oxide suggests a first-order velocity constant for the gas phase $(-dp/dt=kp)$ of $4 \cdot 3 \times 10^{-10}$ sec^{-1}. If the complex is assumed to be *mobile*, however, the discrepancy is removed, according to Robertson. While this is not unlikely at the high temperatures used, and while the phosphine results were obtained at lower temperatures where the assumption of mobility would not be so plausible, it is most desirable to have some independent check on the assumption; at present this is lacking. The fundamental weakness of all approaches to the mechanisms of surface reactions is our present ignorance of the structure of the chemisorbed species.

The theory of the absolute rates of surface reactions cannot distinguish between the mechanisms with dissociative adsorption or with molecular adsorption. Upon first thought, chemisorption with localized dissociation might be written

$$AB+2S \rightleftharpoons \left(\begin{array}{cc} A\cdots B \\ \vdots \quad \vdots \\ S \quad S \end{array} \right)_n \rightarrow \begin{array}{cc} A & B \\ | & | \\ S & S \end{array} \qquad (7.6)$$

If the same treatment is followed as for molecular adsorption, the rate expression would include a factor c_s^2 in place of c_s, and this would appear to make such a large numerical difference between the two treatments that discrimination should be possible. It is not the *totality* of sites which are available for adsorbing A and B, however, but the number of *adjacent pairs*. The reaction should be written [28] as

$$AB + S_2 \rightleftharpoons \begin{pmatrix} A\cdots B \\ \vdots \quad \vdots \\ S \quad S \end{pmatrix}_n \rightarrow \begin{matrix} A & B \\ | & + | \\ S & S \end{matrix} \qquad (7.7)$$

The resulting expression contains c_s multiplied by a numerical factor which varies with the atomic geometry of the surface but is not substantially different from unity; neither theory nor experiment are good enough to test such a small difference.

It was remarked earlier that the theory of absolute reaction rates of surface reactions does not distinguish between chemisorption or some later step, in equilibrium with the chemisorption step, as rate determining. This can be illustrated by the calculation of the rate of the exchange reaction between methane and deuterium. In careful experimental studies of the rate of formation of the various deuteromethanes over an evaporated film of nickel, Kemball[29] concluded that nearly all the methyl radicals formed from the dissociative chemisorption of methane reacted with deuterium atoms to form CH_3D. Laidler[4] derived an expression for the chemisorption of methane as CH_3 and H on a surface practically covered with deuterium atoms:

$$\text{Rate} = c_{CH_4,g} / c_{D_2,g}^{1/2} c_s \frac{kTf^{1/2}_{D_2} e^{-q_0 - q'_0 / RT}}{hf_{CH_4}} \qquad (7.8)$$

and showed that the rate of adsorption was nearly equal to the rate of formation of CH_3D (*Table 7.7*). q_0 and q'_0 are (strictly) the heats of adsorption of a

Table 7.7. Rate of chemisorption of methane and its reaction with deuterium[4]

Temperature °K	p_{D_2}	p_{CH_4}	$Rate \times 10^{-13}$ molecules mg^{-1} sec^{-1}	
	mm	mm	calc.	obs.
499·4	2·49	12·4	13·0	19·0
503·2	4·82	3·26	2·3	3·0
499·4	4·85	9·69	6·9	6·9
498·6	14·4	3·20	1·3	1·5
498·6	14·5	6·46	2·6	4·6

methane molecule and a deuterium atom at absolute zero: the values used were measured values at T with $\frac{1}{2}RT$ subtracted. This is excellent agreement, but an inspection of a later table of Laidler[4] (Table 9, page 228) shows that the calculated rate is extremely sensitive (as would be expected) to the value taken for q_0. In any but the most careful investigations where q_0 or q'_0 are determined for the conditions of the experiment, it cannot be expected that the theory can give results of the accuracy shown in *Table 7.7*. Also, in the example given, the calculations are really dealing only with the rates of chemisorption and desorption of methanes (H or D); in other calculations of rates of chemisorption the theory seems fairly successful, more so than in calculating rates of reactions where the rate-determining step occurs on the surface.

7.3. VELOCITY CONSTANTS OF SURFACE REACTIONS

The velocity constants that are calculatxd from experiments that measure the rate of change of gas-phase concentrations can be converted into surface velocity constants. The surface velocity constant can be defined for a unimolecular reaction in the surface by the equation

$$\text{Rate} = k_s c_a \text{ molecules cm}^{-2} \text{ sec}^{-1} \tag{7.9}$$

The experimental gas-phase velocity constant, k_e, is defined by

$$\text{Rate} = k_e c_g \text{ molecules cm}^{-3} \text{ sec}^{-1} \tag{7.10}$$

It follows that $k_s c_a A = k_g c_g V$ where A is the area of catalyst and V the volume of the gas phase. There is no difficulty over measuring c_g for it equals p/kT. There is difficulty over c_a, for it cannot be measured directly and it must be inferred from the model of the chemisorption or mechanism chosen for the reaction. If it is thought that the reaction proceeds through the chemisorption of molecules on a fixed pattern of sites to give localized chemisorption, like mechanisms (7.2) or (7.5) of the last section, then

$$c_a = N_s \theta = N_s Bp/(1+Bp) \tag{7.11}$$

Hence, combining equations (7.9) to (7.11), we obtain an expression for k_s:

$$k_s = k_e \frac{V(1+Bp)}{AN_s BkT} \tag{7.12}$$

In equations (7.10) and (7.12), k_e is determined from the measurements of the rate of reaction; V, p and T are measured as usual; k is known; A can be measured by the BET method as described on page 119; N_s can be calculated assuming that certain crystal planes are exposed in the surface, although some doubt will usually remain about the range of values of N_s. It is possible, though not reliable, to estimate B from measurements of the extent of chemisorption at lower temperatures where the reaction is slow enough to allow its investigation, but a better method is to determine both k_s and B from the values of k_e. Writing the equations in the form:

$$\frac{k_s AN_s kT}{V} \times \frac{1}{k_e} = \frac{1}{B}+p \tag{7.13}$$

it can be seen that, by plotting $1/k_e$ against p, the slope and the intercept allow the determination of both k_s and B. Eley and his collaborators have developed equations of this type during their studies of the orthohydrogen–parahydrogen conversion on metal foils, wires and evaporated films. *Figure 7.1*, taken from a paper presented by Eley and Rossington [30] at the Chemical Society Symposium on Chemisorption in 1956, illustrates the use of equation (7.13). Good linear plots are found. However, the values of k_s so obtained do not fit an Arrhenius plot very well. Eley and Rossington justify their choice of the activation energy from this plot, but it appears that some assumption made in their analysis—

such as the particular form used for the adsorption isotherm—may be incorrect (see also section 6.5).

It must be admitted that there is extremely little information in the literature about the velocity constants of the actual rate-determining step of any heterogeneous reaction, and correspondingly little about the activation energy of such steps.

The activation energy E_e that is usually reported is a composite one. In the Langmuir–Hinshelwood treatments, E_e is regarded as a function of the activation energy E_s of the surface step and the heats of adsorption of the reactants

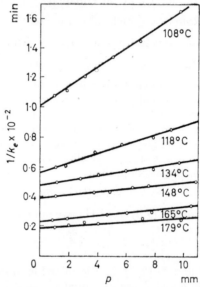

Figure 7.1. Reaction velocity isotherms for the orthohydrogen–parahydrogen conversion over an evaporated copper film[30]

and sometimes of the products as well (see *Table 7.1*). With unretarded reactions and very low pressures of the reactants, when $Bp \ll 1$, the relationship is: $E_e = E_s - q$. When the pressure is high and the surface well covered, the activation energy may change to E_s' and the experimental value E_e' may equal E_s'. There is a corresponding change of order from one towards zero. These changes with pressure have been observed[31] for the decomposition of phosphine on tungsten, where the activation energy changed from 26·5 kcal at pressure 10^{-3} mm Hg to 31·5 kcal at 1 to 5 mm pressure. A similar change was found[32] in the kinetics and activation energy of the decomposition over molybdenum, where E_e changed from 15·1 to 22·3 kcal. Although the relation between E_e, E_s and q, and the possible changes with θ, have been emphasized from the earliest days of the Langmuir–Hinshelwood treatments, no simple pattern of behaviour has emerged, and it seems that the three quantities vary in an unpredictable way with coverage θ.

When the rate-determining step is not a surface reaction but the rate of adsorption or desorption, it is again quite possible that the experimental activation energy is not the true activation energy of adsorption or desorption. As explained in section 6.7, the variation of the heat of adsorption with coverage and changes in the extent of coverage with temperature, can in some circumstances lead to a very low apparent activation energy of desorption.

It is rather surprising that the activation energies of a reaction on several different catalysts can be the same, although the pre-exponential factors differ greatly. As the activation energy is the quantity first derived, with the other factor following from the Arrhenius expression, one cannot help wondering whether changes in the true activation energy of the rate-determining step have not been obscured by changes in the heat of adsorption. There can be little doubt that the change in the extent of adsorption with temperature means that different parts of the surface are in action at different temperatures, and this means that the relevant heats of adsorption are different. It seems likely that a site with a high heat of adsorption will lead to a strongly bound adsorbed state which will require a large activation energy. Thus a high 'q' means a high 'E_s' and when the experimental activation energy E_e equals $E_s - q$, there may be little change in E_e. This could occur for several catalysts. However, it is very unlikely that a close balance should always occur, so it is not very surprising that several different patterns of behaviour have been found, as mentioned in Chapter 1.

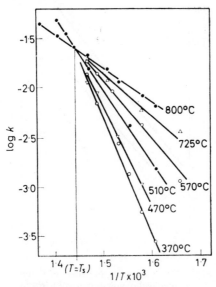

Figure 7.2. Arrhenius plots for decomposition of formic acid vapour over magnesite (MgCO$_3$–MgO)[34b]

For instance, it is quite common to find that there is a relationship between the values of E_e and the pre-exponential factors A, for a series of catalysts of a given reaction, of the form

$$\log A = \alpha E_e + \beta \qquad (7.14)$$

This has been called the 'theta rule' by Schwab[33] and the 'compensation effect' by Cremer[34]. It was first noticed by Constable[35] when studying the dehydrogenation of ethanol over copper catalysts. Catalysts prepared at different temperatures showed different values for E_e, but high values of E_e were accompanied by high values of A and vice versa. A detailed investigation of the decomposition of formic acid over magnesite decomposed at various temperatures shows similar results (*Figure 7.2*)[34]. As all the Arrhenius plots pass through one point, or extremely close to it, at temperature T_s, it follows that

$$A_1 e^{-E_1/RT_s} = A_2 e^{-E_2/RT_s} = \ldots$$

$$\ln A_1 - E_1/RT_s = \ln A_2 - E_2/RT_s = \ldots \qquad (7.15)$$

and the relation (7.14) must hold.

Another marked compensating change in A with E was found[34] for the decomposition of nitrous oxide by Mikovsky and Waters with platinum–alumina as the catalyst, and by Cremer and Marschall[36] with cupric oxide, prepared at different temperatures, as the catalyst.

Eley and Rossington[30] showed that a similar effect can occur with the orthohydrogen–parahydrogen conversion reaction over foils, wires and evaporated films (*Figure 7.3*).

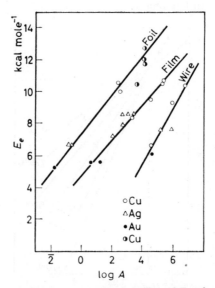

Figure 7.3. Compensating effect of E and A in the orthohydrogen–parahydrogen conversion over metal foils[30]

An explanation of this relationship between A and E_e for catalysts prepared at different temperatures may lie in the effect of temperature on the distribution of sites in the surface. It seems reasonable that there may be many more sites of high energy (like sites C_i of *Figure 6.23*) formed at the higher temperatures of preparation. These are the sites most active in catalysis, for they have low heats of adsorption and so low activation energies for the surface reactions. Thus the high-temperature preparations might be expected to have low activation energies, as found in *Figure 6.23*. The low-temperature preparations would have too few of these sites to contribute much to the rate of reaction, which will therefore occur on sites of higher activation energy; however, the slower rate on these sites is compensated by their greater numbers. Moreover, some type of Boltzmann ditribution of sites with temperature would lead to the correct form of equation (7.14). However, the whole of this argument depends upon E_s changing more than q, so that E_e changes in the same sense as E_s. Cremer[34] quotes some results for the orthohydrogen–parahydrogen conversion on nickel foils prepared at different temperatures where A changes but E_e is almost constant (*Figure 7.4*); perhaps the changes in E_s and q balance here. There is still evidence for the distribution of sites, however, for the absolute level of k and hence of A is in agreement with the idea of a few sites of high activity in the high-temperature preparations and many sites of lower activity in the low-temperature preparations.

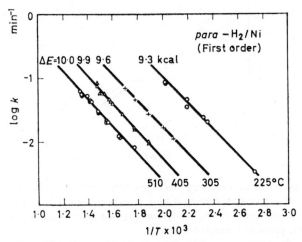

Figure 7.4. Change of A factor with nearly constant E_e in the orthohydrogen–parahydrogen conversion over annealed nickel foils[34]

Another suggestion which deserves serious consideration is that there are errors in the determination of E_e arising from the experimental conditions usually used to measure k at the different temperatures. Any error in E_e, for a given value of k, will obviously produce a corresponding error in A which is of the form

$$\delta \ln A \propto \delta E_e$$

and which leads therefore to the relationship (7.14). Ignoring any plain experimental errors in obtaining k and E_e, as there are too many examples of the effect to make this a tenable explanation, there remain some more subtle effects of the experimental conditions usually used. Generally no effort has been made to measure the velocities at different temperatures *at the same coverage*. If different coverages are used, then the number of sites in action at different temperatures is different. A plot of log (rate) against $1/T$ (*Figure 7.5*) which would lie at A if the number of sites were constant, might lie at B if there

187

were fewer sites at lower temperatures or at C if there were more. Thus if two catalysts B and C do not change the distribution of sites in the same way as the temperature changes, and $T_{B,C}$ is the temperature at which the Arrhenius plots cross, it follows that

$$E_B - RT_{B,C} \ln A_B = E_C - RT_{B,C} \ln A_C$$

For a series of catalysts, if the temperatures at which the pairs of Arrhenius plots cross are not very different, it could easily appear that $\delta E \propto \delta \ln A$. Thus the compensation effect may be caused wholly or in part by the form of the Arrhenius expression rather than a particular distribution of sites of different energies. Linking the pre-exponential factor to the entropy of activation is only another way of examining a spread over sites; until this entropy can be evaluated by independent means [37] it cannot add much to our know-

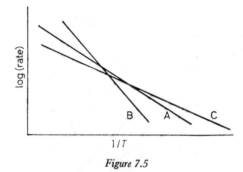

Figure 7.5

ledge. The essential step is some discovery that will allow the measurement of the number of active sites during a kinetic experiment. Until this is done, and the simpler suggestions tested, it seems premature to invoke effects like the tunnel effect, possible though these are.

7.4. INHIBITION OF SURFACE REACTIONS

In discussions of heterogeneously catalysed reactions, mention is often made of poisons which reduce markedly the effectiveness of the catalysts. These poisons may be present in the raw material of the catalyst, or introduced with the reactants. They function by blocking the reaction between the reactant and the surface and must themselves be strongly chemisorbed by the surface. It has usually been assumed that they are chemisorbed on the sites that would otherwise be active in the catalysis, and so behave like the competitive inhibitors of enzymes discussed in Chapter 4. The extension of the Langmuir–Hinshelwood treatment to include inhibitors leads to equations very like those listed in *Tables 7.2* and *7.5*, where inhibition by the product or self-inhibition by the reactant are included as some examples. A careful analysis of the inhibition of the decomposition or ammonia by the product hydrogen is described on page 218; this analysis uses an integrated form of the rate equation. There have not been many other detailed quantitative treatments of inhibition of surface reactions, however, and very few attempts to use the various plots discussed in Chapter 4.

Maxted and his colleagues[38,39] have carried out the most systematic quantitative treatment of poisoning. This work suggests that a different form of equation is applicable, at any rate to the inhibition of the hydrogenation of various liquid substrates. For example, *Figure 7.6* shows results for the inhibition of the hydrogenation of cyclohexene on platinum by methyl sulphide[39]. The lines follow the equation

$$V_P = V_0(1 - \alpha P) \qquad (6.16)$$

where V_P is the rate inhibited by an amount P (moles) of poison, and α is called the sensitivity constant or poisoning coefficient. The surface is fully poisoned when $P = 1/\alpha$, and Kwan[40] has shown that this amount of methyl

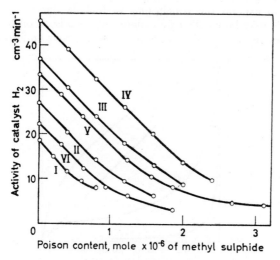

Figure 7.6. Inhibition of hydrogenation of cyclohexene over platinum by methyl sulphide[39]

sulphide would lead to about $2 \cdot 2 \times 10^{14}$ molecules of methyl sulphide and $1 \cdot 6 \times 10^{15}$ molecules of hydrogen sulphide per square centimetre of the platinum surface. This second figure is close to the number of platinum atoms per square centimetre (compare page 151) and so it appears that nearly all the sites available are active in this reaction. The 'tail-off' observed in practice may be due to the difficulty of filling all the sites with the comparatively bulky inhibitor molecules. Maxted and Evans[41] have shown that the size of the poison is important, less being required of a poison with larger molecules. Thus measuring the effectiveness by α, they showed that two surfaces of very different areas showed the same *relative* values of α for the hydrogenation of crotonic acid:

Poison	H_2S	CS_2	Thiophene	Cysteine
Platinum black	1	1·9	4·4	5·0
Nickel on kieselguhr	1	2·4	4·5	5·0

Furthermore, they showed that with a given 'adsorption point' in the poison such as a sulphur atom, the value of α increased steadily with the length of

189

the alkyl radical chain attached to the sulphur atom. Lastly they examined the effect of a given poison on the hydrogenation of several different substrates and found the same relative reduction of the rates for the hydrogenation of benzene, nitrobenzene, crotonic acid, oleic acid and benzoic acid over platinum by either carbon disulphide or mercuric chloride. Similar poisoning curves are found for a wide range of hydrogenations in the liquid phase and for the decomposition of hydrogen peroxide and the gas-phase oxidation of sulphur dioxide. With these curves, it is found that the activation energy does not change with the extent of the poisoning, so that the catalyst surfaces are homogeneous (cf. Schwab and Photiadis[42]). However, the bulk of the evidence quoted is for liquid-phase reactions, and it may well be argued that it is dangerous to expand the conclusions to include the gas phase without further tests. It may be recalled that many solutes adsorb on to metals from solution to obey the Langmuir equation, suggesting that uniformity of sites is

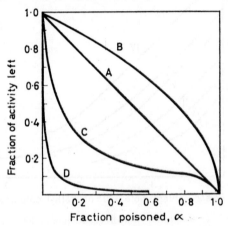

Figure 7.7. Poisoning curves for porous catalysts[44]
A, Non-porous catalyst; B, Homogeneous poisoning of porous catalyst; C, D, Selective poisoning at pore mouths of porous catalysts

connected in some way with the solvent; perhaps displacing the solvent from the site produces some levelling effect in the energetics of adsorption in solution.

Herington and Rideal[43] also examined the likely shape of the poisoning curve for adsorption on sites where both the substrate and the poison occupied several sites, and concluded that uniform curves, or curves with linear portion followed by sharper curvature, could be found even if the surface were homogeneous.

Wheeler[44] has carried this type of analysis a stage further and considered the poisoning of porous catalysts. He considers first the effect of a poison which is adsorbed uniformly over the external and the internal (i.e. pore) surface of the catalyst, for example with a less effective poison that can collide many times with the surface before being adsorbed and so can penetrate into the catalyst pores. This 'non-selective' poisoning reduces the active surface uniformly, as in curve A of *Figure 7.7*, if the reaction being catalysed is slow; but if the reaction is fast, in the absence of the poison, the activity of the poisoned catalyst may fall less slowly along curve B. If the poison is rapidly adsorbed by the catalyst, however, the mouths of the pores will be selectively poisoned and the rate of approach to the internal surface will be controlled by the diffusion at the pore mouth; this can give poisoning curves C and D especially with small-diameter pores in the catalyst. Wheeler also discusses the changes of activation energy with temperature caused by the change from surface to diffusion control.

The curves C and D are similar to the curves shown in Maxted's work[39,45]. In both cases, the curves are obtained for surfaces that are essentially homogeneous. It has often been assumed that curves such as these are typical of 'selective' poisoning of a few active sites. It is clear that curves of this type can be attributed to causes other than surface heterogeneity.

There are several descriptions of selective poisoning that can hardly be attributed to any cause other than heterogeneity, however. The poisoning of ammonia catalysts with oxygen from oxygen or water vapour in the reactant gases is one example. Almquist and Black[46] found that enough oxygen to cover 10 to 15 per cent of the catalyst surface reduced the rate by about 70 per cent. *Figure 8.8* (page 212) shows the poisoning effect of a gas containing 0·32 per cent of water vapour, and the reversibility of the poisoning when the gas is replaced at 60 minutes with dry gas[47]. Oxygen similarly inhibits the orthohydrogen–parahydrogen conversion over tungsten[48].

The poisoning of a platinum catalyst by hydrogen for the decomposition of ammonia, without inhibiting the decomposition of hydrogen iodide, has often been quoted[49] as an example of selective poisoning and interpreted as indicating that the two reactions proceed on different sites. In the ammonia decomposition, the nitrogen atoms must be attached to the surface, and it is easy to see that the strong adsorption of hydrogen may prevent this chemisorption. In the decomposition of hydrogen iodide, however, it is possible that the chemisorbed hydrogen atoms can react with molecules of hydrogen iodide on impact from the gas phase, or with molecules in the van der Waals layer; free hydrogen atoms readily attack hydrogen iodide but do not attack ammonia so readily, and it is likely that the surface atoms have the same relative rates of attack.

Again, the hydrogenation of ethylene over copper is inhibited by the decomposition of nitrous oxide, although the decomposition proceeds freely[50]. It is possible that the nitrous oxide reacts with the surface to give oxygen atoms or ions, and that the hydrogenation is inhibited by this oxygen. However, the decomposition is inhibited by oxygen also (see *Table 7.2*) although it is known to proceed on the surface of oxides. In the presence of the hydrogen a new reaction between hydrogen and nitrous oxide would appear to be possible (see *Table 7.5*). Hence this observation may be explained by new reactions rather than separate sites for the two reactions originally considered.

In summary, it would appear that the occurrence of selective poisoning can be interpreted by the presence of different active sites for different reactions but that other interpretations are possible. The extreme effectiveness of some poisons may be due to the adsorption of the poison at the pore mouths of porous catalysts. Some quite effective poisons appear to indicate a uniform surface of the catalyst when the problem is treated quantitatively.

Maxted[45] has pointed out that the catalysts most susceptible to poisons are the metals. The oxides and sulphides used as catalysts are more robust, but it will be seen in section 8.6.3 that the Hopcalite used in the oxidation of carbon monoxide is poisoned by water vapour, and several dehydration catalysts are similarly poisoned. Of course, the cracking catalysts are poisoned by alkalis and by basic gases. The metal catalysts are poisoned by: (*i*) molecules containing elements of Groups VB and VIB, provided that the key atoms in these molecules are not fully saturated or can be converted to unsaturated forms under the conditions of the reaction; (*ii*) compounds or ions of certain metals, and (*iii*) molecules or ions with multiple bonds such as carbon monoxide or cyanides. Further details of these groups are given below.

(*i*) The elements nitrogen, phosphorus, arsenic, antimony of Group VB are notorious as poisons. Maxted has shown that the poisoning is due to bonding to the surface of the key atom. This is possible, for instance, with hydrogen sulphide, phosphine or sulphites where there are free electron pairs on the atom, but not in sulphates nor in phosphates. An interesting point is that dry ammonia can act as a poison in hydrogenation reactions, but the presence of water reduces the effect considerably. The elements of Group VIB are less active and more selective as poisons, but the same principle holds. Maxted has developed methods for converting many of the poisons from toxic to non-toxic forms[45].

(*ii*) From systematic examination of the toxic effects of metals, Maxted[45] has come to the conclusion that a metal is only toxic if all the *d*-orbitals are empty or full, whether the metal is in an ion or in a covalent compound. He interprets this as the need for *d*-electrons to form bonds with the surface. An alternative way of looking at the classification, however, is that metals with unoccupied *d*-orbitals cannot bond to the surface; those with partially occupied *d*-orbitals can bond to the surface but also chemisorb other molecules and so do not act as poisons; but those that have fully occupied orbitals can bond to the surface but cannot add on any other reactant molecules, and so act as poisons.

(*iii*) The multiple-bond poisons include carbon monoxide and derivatives of cyanogen, and olefins and aromatic compounds. They operate by competitive adsorption, as described earlier in this section. They can be detoxicated by reduction or by oxidation[45].

7.5 ON ACTIVE SITES

A good deal has been said in this and in the last chapter about the sites in the surface that chemisorb the reactants and so activate them. Taylor[51] first suggested that catalyst surfaces might contain some sites specially active for chemisorption and catalysis, but pointed out that: 'The amount of surface which is catalytically active is determined by the reaction catalysed. There will be all extremes between the cases in which all the atoms in the surface are active and that in which relatively few are so active.' The wisdom of this statement is in refreshing contrast to the assumption made by many other writers that all heterogeneous catalysis is due to 'edges, corners and discontinuities in the surface'.

Consider first the evidence on chemisorption discussed in sections 6.2 and 6.3. The proportion of sites active in chemisorption ranges from all the atoms in the surface of metals (although several surface atoms may be required to bind one chemisorbed species) and all the lattice points in 'cumulative' adsorption on oxides to the comparatively few crystal defects used for 'depletive' adsorption on oxides. The almost universal fall of the heat of adsorption as the surface is covered is a clear indication that not all sites are equally active in binding the adsorbed species. The usual shape of the heat–coverage curves suggests that rather than a few very active and many inactive sites there is a fairly steady drop of activity on clean surfaces which may be due to inherent heterogeneity or to the effect of the initial adsorption on the later adsorption. Unfortunately the use of isotopic labelling does not give clear evidence whether the strong binding on the sites initially occupied remains stronger than that on the sites occupied later. There is evidence that several chemisorptions of gas can occur on oxides, differing in the heat of adsorption and possibly in the site of adsorption, at different temperatures. Thus Taylor's remark still summarizes our present knowledge about chemisorption reactions.

Again, with catalysed reactions there are some in which all the surface sites are used and some in which a small fraction are active. In the oxidation of ammonia to nitric oxide, over platinum, the reaction is so rapid that practically every molecule hitting the surface reacts (see section 8.6). The same is true of the decomposition of ozone on a silver oxide surface[52] and of the decomposition of ammonia or germane on surfaces of germanium[53]. On the other hand, there can be little doubt that the need to remove the last traces of oxide from the surfaces of iron catalysts for the exchange of nitrogen or the synthesis of ammonia means that only a small proportion of the sites is active, and this is supported by the effect of promoters such as potassium monoxide, which may remove 'acid sites' effective for the cracking of hydrocarbons but not for the synthesis of ammonia (see section 8.3). There is clear evidence (see section 8.7) that such 'acid sites' are active in the cracking reactions over natural clays and silica–alumina catalysts, whether they are present as Brönsted acids or as Lewis acids, and they do not by any means cover the surfaces of the catalysts. The use of ^{18}O in the surface of oxides has shown that in some oxidations only a small fraction of the sites is active at any one time[54].

Kwan[40] has argued strongly against the idea that the edges and corners of crystals are especially active in catalysed reactions, although agreeing with Taylor[55] that there is evidence that these isolated spots can affect the heat of physical adsorption. There is plenty of evidence, however, that the different planes of metal or ionic crystals can give different rates of reaction, whether exposed in single crystals or in evaporated films. There is also some evidence that a minimum area—or a minimum number of sites—is needed for catalytic activity.

The action of inhibitors or poisons has provided two kinds of evidence that reactions occur on a few active sites (see section 8.5). Firstly, very small quantities of poison are needed, and in some examples the activation energy of the partially inhibited reaction is higher than that of the uninhibited reaction, suggesting that the more active sites are eliminated first. Secondly, poisoning the surface for one reaction may not poison it for another apparently similar reaction. However true these inferences are for some reactions, it is certain that there are examples of poisoning where the whole surface seems to be

13—c.   193

active and where the poisoning seems to leave the same activation energy—in other words, the surface appears to be uniformly active.

One conclusion can be drawn from the evidence. It is that the sites most active in chemisorption may bind the chemisorbed fragments so strongly that they are not active for a surface reaction. This is especially clearly seen in the arguments about simple reactions of hydrogen, such as the orthohydrogen-parahydrogen conversion or the exchange between hydrogen and deuterium (see section 8.1). In these reactions, the reacting atoms are those in the 'tail' of the adsorption, and the reaction goes through a small fraction of the sites on which chemisorption has occurred. Although less obvious, similar energetic factors must control the site of other surface reactions. The measurement of these factors—as the activation energy of the surface reaction—and the determination of the number of sites actually active, remain the objectives rather than the achievement of any theory of catalysis.

REFERENCES

1 LANGMUIR, I. *Phys. Rev.* 1915, **6**, 79; 1916, **8**, 149; *J. Amer. chem. Soc.* 1915, **37**, 1139; 1916, **38**, 2221; 1918, **40**, 1361; *Trans. Faraday Soc.* 1921, **17**, 607

2 HINSHELWOOD, C. N. *The Kinetics of Chemical Change*: Clarendon Press, Oxford, 1940

3 SCHWAB, G. M. *Catalysis* (Trans. H. S. Taylor and R. Spence): Macmillan, London, 1937

4 LAIDLER, K. J. *Catalysis* (Ed. P. H. Emmett) Vol. I: Reinhold, New York, 1954, Chapters 3, 4 and 5

5 BONHOEFFER, K. F. and FARKAS, A. *Z. phys. Chem.* (*Leipzig*) 1931, **B12**, 231
BONHOEFFER, K. F., FARKAS, A. and RUMMEL, K. W. *Z. phys. Chem.* (*Leipzig*) 1933, **B21**, 225

6 ROBERTS, J. K. *Some Problems in Adsorption*: Cambridge University Press, London, 1939; *Proc. R. Soc. A* 1935, **152**, 445

7 RIDEAL, E. K. *Sabatier Lecture: J. Soc. chem. Ind.* 1943, **62**, 335

8 ELEY, D. D. *Quart. Rev.* (*Lond.*) 1949, **3**, 209
TWIGG, G. H. *Disc. Faraday Soc.* 1950, **8**, 152

9 BODENSTEIN, M. *Trans. electrochem. Soc.* 1937, **71**, 353

10 BENTON, A. F. and THACKER, C. M. *J. Amer. chem. Soc.* 1934, **56**, 1300

11 TEMKIN, M. and MIKHAILOVA, E. *Acta phys.-chim. U.R.S.S.* 1935, **2**, 9

12 EUCKEN, A. *Disc. Faraday Soc.* 1950, **8**, 128

13 SCHULER, K. E. and LAIDLER, K. J. *J. chem. Phys.* 1949, **17**, 1212

14 BOND, G. C. *Catalysis* (Ed. P. H. Emmett) Vol. III: Reinhold, New York, 1955, p. 133

15 WINTER, E. *Z. phys. Chem.* (*Leipzig*) 1931, **B13**, 401

16 NIELSEN, A. *Advanc. Catalys.* 1953, **5**, 1

17 FRANKENBURG, W. G. *Catalysis* (Ed. P. H. Emmett) Vol. III: Reinhold, New York, 1955, p. 17

18 TAYLOR, H. S. and JUNGERS, J. C. *J. Amer. chem. Soc.* 1935, **57**, 660

19 EMMETT, P. H. and BRUNAUER, S. *J. Amer. chem. Soc.* 1937, **59**, 310, 1553

20 EMMETT, P. H. and BRUNAUER, S. *J. Amer. chem. Soc.* 1934, **56**, 35

21 BRUNAUER, S., LOVE, K. S. and KEENAN, R. G. *J. Amer. chem. Soc.* 1942, **64**, 751

22 LOVE, K. S. and EMMETT, P. H. *J. Amer. chem. Soc.* 1941, **63**, 3297

23 TEMKIN, M. *Acta phys.-chim. U.R.S.S.* 1938, **8**, 141; *Zh. fiz. Khim.* 1938, **11**, 169

24 GLASSTONE, S., LAIDLER, K. J. and EYRING, H. *Theory of Rate Processes*: McGraw-Hill, New York, 1941

REFERENCES

[25] PRICHARD, C. R. and HINSHELWOOD, C. N. *Proc. R. Soc. A* 1925, **108**, 211

[26] HINSHELWOOD, C. N. and BURK, R. E. *J. chem. Soc.* 1925, p. 2896

[27] ROBERTSON, A. J. B. *J. Colloid Sci.* 1956, **11**, 308

[28] TRAPNELL, B. M. W. *Chemisorption*: Butterworth, London, 1955, p. 90

[29] KEMBALL, C. *Proc. R. Soc. A* 1951, **207**, 539

[30] ELEY, D. D. and ROSSINGTON, D. R. *Chemisorption* (Ed. W. E. Garner): Butterworth, London, 1957, p. 137

[31] BARRER, R. M., *Trans. Faraday Soc.* 1936, **32**, 490

[32] MELVILLE, H. W. and ROXBURGH, H. L. *J. chem. Soc.* 1933, p. 586

[33] SCHWAB, G. M. *Advanc. Catalys.* 1950, **2**, 251

[34] (a) CREMER, E. *Advanc. Catalys.* 1955, **7**, 75; (b) CREMER, E. and KULLICH, E. *Radex Rdsch.* 1950, **4**, 176

[35] CONSTABLE, F. H. *Proc. R. Soc. A* 1925, **108**, 355

[36] CREMER, E. and MARSCHALL, E. *Mh. Chem.* 1951, **82**, 840

[37] KEMBALL, C. *Advanc. Catalys.* 1950, **2**, 233

[38] MAXTED, E. B. *Ann. Rep. Progr. Chem.* 1935, **32**, 109

[39] MAXTED, E. B., MOON, K. L. and OVERGAGE, E. *Disc. Faraday Soc.* 1950, **8**, 135

[40] KWAN, T. *Advanc. Catalys.* 1954, **6**, 67, see p. 103

[41] MAXTED, E. B. and EVANS, H. C. *J. chem. Soc.* 1937, p. 603

[42] SCHWAB, G. M. and PHOTIADIS, D. *Ber. dtsch. chem. Ges.* 1944, **77**, 296

[43] HERINGTON, E. F. G. and RIDEAL, E. K. *Trans. Faraday Soc.* 1944, **40**, 505

[44] WHEELER, A. *Advanc. Catalys.* 1951, **3**, 249

[45] MAXTED, E. B. *Advanc. Catalys.* 1951, **3**, 129

[46] ALMQUIST, J. A. and BLACK, C. A. *J. Amer. chem. Soc.* 1926, **48**, 2814

[47] EMMETT, P. H. and BRUNAUER, S. *J. Amer. chem. Soc.* 1930, **52**, 2682

[48] ELEY, D. D. and RIDEAL, E. K. *Proc. R. Soc. A* 1941, **178**, 429

[49] HINSHELWOOD, C. N. *The Kinetics of Chemical Change*: Clarendon Press, Oxford, 1940, p. 227

[50] RUSSELL, W. W. and GHERING, L. G. *J. Amer. chem. Soc.* 1935, **57**, 2544

[51] TAYLOR, H. S. *Proc. R. Soc. A* 1925, **108**, 105 (see p. 109)

[52] HINSHELWOOD, C. N. *The Kinetics of Chemical Change*: Clarendon Press, Oxford, 1940, p. 3

[53] TAMARU, K., BOUDART, M. and TAYLOR, H. S. *J. phys. Chem.* 1955, **59**, 801
TAMARU, K. and BOUDART, M. *Advanc. Catalys.* 1957, **9**, 699

[54] WINTER, E. R. S. *Chemisorption* (Ed. W. E. GARNER): Butterworth, London, 1957, p. 189

[55] TAYLOR, H. S. *Advanc. Catalys.* 1957, **9**, 1

8

MECHANISMS OF HETEROGENEOUSLY CATALYSED REACTIONS II

8.1. THE ORTHOHYDROGEN–PARAHYDROGEN CONVERSION AND THE HYDROGEN–DEUTERIUM EXCHANGE

THE INTERCONVERSION of ortho- and parahydrogen can be catalysed by two distinct types of substance. One type provides an inhomogeneous magnetic field in which the probability of conversion is increased; the other type splits the molecule into hydrogen atoms which recombine to give the ortho–para proportions appropriate to the temperature. The hydrogen–deuterium exchange occurs on the second type but not on the first type of catalyst.

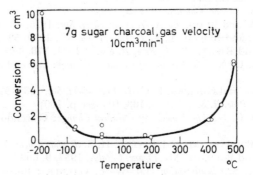

Figure 8.1. Rate of the orthohydrogen–parahydrogen conversion at different temperatures[1]

The magnetic conversion is catalysed by paramagnetic gases like nitric oxide and nitrogen, by ions of rare-earth elements and transition metals in solution, and by adsorption on some surfaces at very low temperatures. A curve of rate against temperature is shown in *Figure 8.1* for charcoal surfaces, which have been often investigated[1]. The low-temperature rate is the magnetic one; the high may be atomic. The balance of evidence is that the rate is very slow on outgassed charcoals, and that it is increased by adsorbed oxygen molecules (paramagnetic) but not by adsorbed oxygen atoms (diamagnetic), in keeping with the relative rates over other paramagnetic or diamagnetic solids. Charcoal itself is diamagnetic in bulk and there is not much evidence for surface paramagnetism.

The chemical or atomic mechanism, similar to the thermal mechanism, occurs on the surface of metals and oxides at both high and low temperatures, for both conversion and exchange. Generally these have comparable speeds, kinetics and activation energies on the same surface, although discrepancies have been noted[2]. The reactions occur only slowly on the surfaces of metals that have been exposed to oxygen or carbon monoxide or ethylene. The orders of the low-temperature reaction are low, often about 0·5, and the activation energy is then often low, e.g. about 2 kcal on the transition metals; the order is nearer 1 on foils or wires of the Group IB metals, and the activation energies are larger and more varied[2]. The activation energy over zinc oxide appears to be very variable with the temperature of investigation.

The history of the suggestions about these 'atomic' mechanisms of the two reactions is very interesting. In 1931, Bonhoeffer and Farkas[3] suggested an obvious mechanism for the conversion, which could also operate for the exchange:

$$p\text{-}H_2 + 2S \rightleftharpoons 2H\text{---}S \rightleftharpoons 2S + o\text{-}H_2$$

Two experimental discoveries seemed to make this mechanism untenable: (i) Although this conversion occurred on a tungsten filament at $-110°C$, Frankenburger and Hodler[4] found very little adsorption of hydrogen on tungsten powders below about 150°C. (ii) Roberts[5] measured the heats of adsorption of hydrogen on very clean tungsten filaments and found very high heats of adsorption at all coverages (*Figure 6.9*, curve 1, page 143) although adsorption did occur rapidly at quite low temperatures. Thus, it seemed that Frankenburger and Hodler's results could be attributed to surface contamination of their powder (a conclusion confirmed by later work of Frankenburg[6] on rigorously reduced powders) but that a fresh and apparently insuperable difficulty had arisen—the high rates of adsorption meant very slow rates of desorption, far too slow to account for the observed rates of conversion.

This difficulty led Rideal[7] to propose a most ingenious mechanism involving the interaction between chemisorbed hydrogen atoms and van der Waals adsorbed hydrogen *molecules*. These molecules were thought to be held over the gaps in the chemisorbed layer left by the chemisorption of hydrogen on to two adjacent sites, so that the exchange can be illustrated as

van der Waals layer			D_2					HD		
chemisorbed layer	H	H		H	H	H		D	H	H
						$\rightleftharpoons$				
metal	S	S	S	S	S	S	S	S	S	S

This VCI theory would require only a small activation energy, as the process is almost thermoneutral. Other forms of it were applied to the hydrogenation of ethylene and substituted olefins.

Later experiments[8] on the adsorption of hydrogen on tungsten films with a much larger area than the filaments used by Roberts suggest that there is a slow adsorption after the rapid chemisorption; the technique of measuring the adsorption by the change in the accommodation coefficient of neon gas on the filament would not have detected this slow adsorption. Rideal and Trapnell consider[8] that it does represent chemisorption as atoms in the monolayer, and not a secondary layer of adsorbed molecules. As the slow chemisorption has a low heat of adsorption (*Figure 6.9*, curve 3), it is possible for the conversion and exchange reactions to take place on this 'tail-end' of the film where the desorption will be much faster than at lower coverages. It appears that the estimates of the coverage on the filaments used by Roberts were too high at the higher coverages; for other reasons, this has been suggested elsewhere (see section 6.6).

The kinetics of the reactions do not discriminate between the two mechanisms, although it has always been difficult to account for the low order of the low-temperature reactions without assuming an unlikely extent of adsorption in the van der Waals layer. Calculations of the rate of the conversion on tungsten have been made by Trapnell[1], assuming that the rate-determining step is the desorption of hydrogen, and are close to the measured values. Somewhat similar calculations based on the transition state expressions for the rate of chemisorption have been made by Laidler[9] for the conversion over tungsten and he concludes that the conversion proceeds almost wholly by the Bonhoeffer–Farkas mechanism. This mechanism is also preferred by Couper and Eley[10] for the interpretation of their work on the conversion over alloys of gold and palladium, and by Eley and Rossington[2] for the conversion over copper and Group IB metals at temperatures above 300°C, and likewise for the conversion over oxide surfaces.

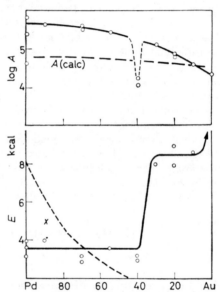

Figure 8.2. Activation energies and A factors for the orthohydrogen–parahydrogen conversion over palladium–gold alloys[10]

Thus the Bonhoeffer–Farkas mechanism is almost certainly the mechanism of conversion at high temperatures and is not excluded at low temperatures for metals where the heat of chemisorption falls markedly with increasing coverage. For example, Kummer and Emmett[11] found that a singly-promoted iron catalyst (for the ammonia synthesis) catalysed the conversion at -195°C, and that hydrogen is adsorbed reversibly by this catalyst at -195°C. On the other hand, a doubly promoted catalyst did not catalyse the conversion nor was the hydrogen reversibly adsorbed on it at -195°C.

The activation energy of the conversion seems to show great variation when metals are used as catalysts. Cremer and Kerber[12] found values for different nickel foils that were all near 10 kcal (*Figure 7.4*). Values of 11 to 13 kcal have been reported for copper foil[13], and 17·5 kcal for gold foil[10]; rather surprisingly, the activation energy for the hydrogen–deuterium exchange is higher over copper (23·1) than over silver (16·5) or gold (13·9)[14]. Later work by Eley and Rossington[2] suggested even lower values for the activation energy of the conversion reaction over metal foils, wires and films of the Group IB metals. They found nearly constant values for the various forms of gold (5 to 6 kcal) and of silver (7 to 9 kcal), with rather more variation for copper (7 to 11). On the other hand, Couper and Eley[10] investigated the conversion over alloys of palladium and gold and found a low activation energy (3 to 4 kcal) over palladium-rich alloys, with an abrupt increase at about 60 per cent of gold to 8 to 9 kcal, and a still greater increase for pure gold (*Figure 8.2*). It is interesting to note that the high values were obtained in experiments where the surface was probably sparsely covered, and the low values with more completely covered surfaces. Thus Eley and Couper worked at 500 to 800°C for pure gold, whereas Eley and Rossington's results were obtained at 0 to 200°C. Moreover, the activation energy over gold has been reported as increasing steadily as the temperature is raised[15]. As explained in section 6.8, if the desorption is the rate-determining step, then at low coverages where the heat of adsorption changes less with coverage, the activation energy may appear high, whereas at high coverages, with the heat changing more rapidly, the activation energy may appear artificially low. Thus the results seem to tie up with the idea of desorption as the rate-determining step.

The abrupt change in the activation energy with change of composition of the gold and platinum alloys occurs when the paramagnetic susceptibility drops from high values in palladium-rich alloys to zero. Couper and Eley[10] concluded that the palladium was effective because the hydrogen could bond to the vacant d-orbitals of the surface atoms of the transition metal, and when these are filled at 60 per cent of gold the activation energy rises sharply. This suggestion seemed very reasonable and has been widely quoted as an example of the 'electronic effect' in catalysis. However, if this is the explanation, it is rather hard to see how the conversion can proceed on various forms of gold in the lower temperature range 0 to 200°C with the low activation energy found by Eley and Rossington.

It really seems as though the limitations of the experimental techniques available at present prevent the examination of a very wide range of rates at any one temperature. To overcome this, experiments on different metals, or by different investigators on the same metal, have been carried out over widely different temperature ranges. Even the experiments over the palladium–gold alloys used the ranges 150 to 350, 370 to 1,000, and 500 to 800°C and very different parts of the surfaces must have been involved. It seems highly dubious to try to relate activation energies obtained over different ranges of temperature with different metals to any properties of the metals, whether chemical, electronic or geometric. Far too many comparisons have been made in the past between isolated values of activation energies determined under very different conditions. The results obtained by Eley and his collaborators serve as a warning against doing this.

It is of great interest that the rates of these simple reactions depend upon the rate of desorption of atoms to give molecules in the gas phase. There is no 'surface reaction' in the sense used in the older Langmuir–Hinshelwood treatments, as the hydrogen is not chemisorbed as a molecule. The reactions have, in fact, been used as a diagnostic for the occurrence of hydrogen atoms on surfaces. Another interesting point brought out by the discussion on page 169 is that the experimental activation energy of reactions controlled by the rate of desorption is not necessarily as high as the heat of desorption, if this changes with coverage, and values of experimental activation energies should be used with caution in selecting possible mechanisms.

8.2. HYDROGENATION–DEHYDROGENATION REACTIONS

The addition of hydrogen to double or triple carbon–carbon bonds is catalysed by many substances. The industrial application of this catalytic process started with the work of Sabatier in France studying vapour-phase hydrogenations at moderate pressures, and with Ipatieff in Russia working on the hydrogenation of liquids at high pressures. The expansion of the petroleum chemical industry added further impetus to the work on hydrogenation–dehydrogenation reactions. The industrial catalysts include various preparations[16] of nickel (especially Raney nickel and supported nickel), platinum, palladium, copper chromite and sulphides of transition metals for olefins and aromatics; and nickel, platinum and palladium for acetylenes. In fundamental studies of the mechanisms, metals have been used as powders, foils, wires, supported films and evaporated films, and single crystals. There is an especially bewildering array of experimental work on the hydrogenation of ethylene although, as Eley points out in a recent review[17], its behaviour is not typical of olefins and should not be considered in isolation. There has been less fundamental work on acetylene and its derivatives although their hydrogenation is extremely interesting[18]; this is partly because the hydrogenations are rather less important industrially, and partly because they are complicated by side reactions, especially polymerizations.

In spite of all the work on these hydrogenation–dehydrogenation reactions (especially on the hydrogenation of ethylene) and the early (1935–40) use made of parallel studies of the exchange reaction with deuterium, some of the biggest advances in our knowledge of the reaction have been made only recently, thanks to wider use of two experimental techniques. The older, and more explored, is the use of mass-spectrometers[19] to investigate the products of chemisorption of the hydrocarbons and the products of the exchange and hydrogenation reactions, and the other is the application of infra-red techniques[20] to the exploration of the structure of the chemisorbed fragments derived from saturated and unsaturated hydrocarbons. These points will be emphasized in the discussion of the hydrogenation of ethylene.

In general, the olefins hydrogenate easily to the alkanes with some concurrent migration of the double bond and hydrogen shift; the exchange reaction with deuterium has a higher activation energy and proceeds more slowly at lower temperatures, but may be relatively faster at higher temperatures—above 60°C with ethylene on nickel, for instance. The acetylenes can be hydrogenated to alkanes, but there is considerable polymerization of the acetylene too, especially over copper; the hydrogenation over many catalysts proceeds in two stages and the acetylene is converted to the olefin before this is reduced. This is in spite of the fact that the hydrogenation of ethylene by itself is faster than that of acetylene; apparently the acetylene is adsorbed far more strongly on the surface and the ethylene is cast into the gas phase until practically all the acetylene has been reduced and removed from the surface. Similarly, butadiene can be selectively hydrogenated to butylene, and methyl-acetylene gives propylene, in spite of a *decreasing* rate of hydrogenation of the isolated substances, according to the sequence

ethylene > propylene > butylene > acetylene ~ methylacetylene > benzene

The acetylenes are poisons for the catalysed hydrogenation of the olefins for a similar reason. These examples show that it is not easy to construct any 'reactivity series'. Experiments on isolated catalysts will not give the same order as competitive hydrogenation in a mixture. Experiments over different catalysts will often give different orders. Corson[16] gives many examples of

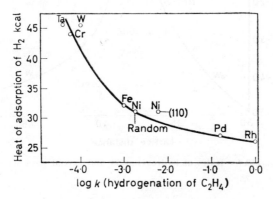

Figure 8.3. Rates of hydrogenation and heats of chemisorption[26]

this behaviour. The kinetics of hydrogenation of the simplest members of each type (ethylene, benzene and acetylene) are very similar[17,18], and over many catalysts can be represented by a rate proportional to p_{H_2} and independent of the substrate, although there are reports of inverse powers of the substrate concentration for ethylene over reduced copper[21] and over platinum[22], and for acetylene over reduced nickel[23] and over platinum[24].

It is very remarkable that over evaporated films[25,26] of various transition metals the hydrogenation of ethylene always has an activation energy of about 10 kcal, in spite of great changes in the rate from metal to metal. The rate increases as the heat of chemisorption of hydrogen or ethylene decreases (*Figure 8.3*)[26]. The hydrogenation of acetylene shows similar behaviour with an activation energy of about 6 to 7 kcal. The variation of the rate seems to depend upon changes in the pre-exponential factor, and this has been linked to changes in some geometric factor like the size of the unit crystal (*Figure 8.4*)[25,26].

The higher olefins show slower rate of hydrogenation, but also decreasing activation energies, in the sequence shown above, and there is more variation in the order of reaction.

8.2.1. Hydrogenation and exchange reactions with ethylene[17]

The hydrogenation which has been most investigated is that of ethylene, and the salient points governing the selection of a mechanism will be mentioned:

(i) The selection must be linked with that of the exchange reaction, for that has the same kinetics (rate $\propto p_{H_2}^1 \, p_{Et}^0$) with a higher activation energy

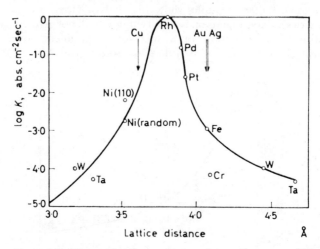

Figure 8.4. Rates of hydrogenation and crystal parameters[26]

(18·7 kcal compared with 10·7 kcal). The hydrogenation is faster below 60°C, the exchange above that temperature. With comparable conditions, rhodium is the most active hydrogenation catalyst (*Figure 8.4*).

(ii) The adsorption of the ethylene is strong on all transition metals, with high heats of adsorption; the adsorption of hydrogen (or deuterium) is not so strong (*Table 6.4*, page 146). Ethane is weakly adsorbed. If hydrogen is admitted to a nickel surface, and then ethylene, much hydrogenation occurs, but if the gases are admitted in the opposite sense, very little ethane appears in the gas phase[26]. Over rhodium, hydrogen can remove ethylene more easily.

(iii) There has been much controversy over the nature of the chemisorbed fragments. In some early isotope studies, Morikawa, Benedict and Taylor[27] found CH_4 and CD_4 exchanged to give mixed methanes over nickel at 184°C, and suggested a 'dissociative adsorption' of saturated hydrocarbons. This has been amply verified by Kemball's work[19,28] on the exchange between CH_4 and D_2 and on the cracking of ethane[29] over nickel. The important point here is that the release of ethane to the gas phase after the hydrogenation of ethylene is more likely to be from an ethyl radical and a hydrogen atom than from an adsorbed molecule.

The adsorption of ethylene may be dissociative, like that of methane, or associative, by the opening of the double bond

$$
\begin{array}{cc}
\mathrm{CH_2} & \\
\parallel & \\
\mathrm{CH \quad H} & \mathrm{H_2C{-}CH_2} \\
| \quad\ | & | \quad\ | \\
\mathrm{S \quad S} & \mathrm{S \quad S} \\
(I) & (II)
\end{array}
$$

The early attempts to decide which of these possibilities occurred were based on tests for isotopic mixing; it was found [30] that no mixed ethylenes could be detected by infra-red examination of the gases in a mixture of C_2H_4 and C_2D_4 after exposure to nickel surfaces. It was concluded that the associative chemisorption occurred, and as a result, much effort was put into relating the atomic spacings in the crystal faces of active catalysts to the likely structure of the adsorbed molecule [31].

Later work has considerably altered our ideas about the chemisorption. Mass spectrometer studies have shown: (a) there is some mixing of C_2D_4 and C_2H_4, and so some dissociative adsorption must occur [32], and (b) when ethylene is admitted to clean metal surfaces, some ethane appears in the gas phase [26]; when ethylene and deuterium are admitted together, light ethane appears immediately in the gas phase [33]. There is probably some dissociative adsorption, with self-hydrogenation of the ethylene, although the results with $C_2H_4 + D_2$ could be interpreted in another way, as indicated on page 205. Beeck termed this dissociative form an 'acetylenic complex' and it may have the structure (III) or (IV):

$$
\begin{array}{cc}
 & \mathrm{S \quad S} \\
 & | \quad\ | \\
\mathrm{HC{=}CH} & \mathrm{H{-}C{-}C{-}H} \\
| \quad\ | & | \quad\ | \\
\mathrm{S \quad S} & \mathrm{S \quad S} \\
(III) & (IV)
\end{array}
$$

Beeck suggested that most of the surface is covered with this complex, leaving a small area on which the reaction occurs—perhaps through the associative form (II) [26]. Infra-red studies, discussed later in this section, have shown that the species (I)–(IV) can each be present under different conditions of temperature and pressure of hydrogen. These studies emphasize that results obtained with chemisorption of one substance alone must be applied with caution when other substances are present.

(iv) There have been many suggestions about possible mechanisms, and all types have been explored. One of the difficulties is to know how much weight to put on the results that show a rate inversely dependent on the ethylene pressure (over copper and platinum). Laidler has emphasized this feature in his calculation of the rate of hydrogenation by the theory of absolute reaction rates [34]. He uses Langmuir isotherms to obtain the concentration of the species which react to give the transition complex, which is a partly desorbed ethane molecule; in other words, the rate-determining step is the rate of desorption of the product! The treatment suggests that the large steric factor found for the hydrogenation of ethylene on nickel may be due to the loss of entropy on

203

forming the adsorbed activated complex. The greater activity of certain metals such as rhodium, compared to nickel, must then be attributed to more mobile surface fragments; certainly this may be favoured by the smaller heat of adsorption (*Figure 8.3*). However, the formulation of 'adsorbed pairs of ethylene and hydrogen molecules' to give the correct rate law seems rather artificial.

Beeck[26] postulated that the surface is largely covered with acetylenic complexes, and that the reaction occurs by reaction between two chemisorbed hydrogen atoms and a gas-phase ethylene molecule—that is, by a VCI mechanism with hydrogen on the small area of surface left by the acetylenic complexes. The kinetics of the hydrogenation reaction follow successfully, but Eley[17] points out that the scheme cannot explain the kinetics of the exchange reaction and that the poisoning of the orthohydrogen–parahydrogen reaction by ethylene means that there is little chemisorbed hydrogen as atoms. Trapnell[35] has produced evidence that the ethylene completely blocks the surface of a tungsten wire, but some caution is necessary in carrying this over to nickel and other metals.

There have been several suggestions that the exchange and hydrogenation reactions need not go through the same mechanisms. Farkas[36] has maintained this view. It is perhaps relevant to note that in some of the most careful and extensive investigations of the exchange reactions of *saturated hydrocarbons* different mechanisms may be operating for different stages of a given deuteration (e.g. CH_4 and D_2) or for the early stages of deuteration of ethane over different catalysts.

However, if the exchange and hydrogenation reactions are linked and pass through the same transition state, they should have the same activation energy. As they do not, at any rate on most metals, the products must be formed from the same intermediates but through different transition states. This led Twigg to propose the following scheme[37]:

$$C_2H_4 \underset{k_{-1}}{\overset{k_1}{\rightleftharpoons}} \begin{matrix} H_2C-CH_2 \\ | \quad | \\ S \quad S \end{matrix} \quad ; \quad \begin{matrix} H_2C-CH_2 \\ | \quad | \\ S \quad S \end{matrix} \quad \begin{matrix} D_2 \\ | \\ | \\ S \end{matrix} \underset{k_{-2}}{\overset{k_2}{\rightleftharpoons}} \begin{matrix} CH_2D \\ | \\ CH_2 \\ | \\ S \end{matrix} \overset{D \quad k_3}{\underset{S}{\big|}} \longrightarrow C_2H_5D$$

$$\theta_1 \qquad\qquad \theta_1 \qquad\qquad \theta_2 \qquad \theta_3$$

Hydrogenation thus goes via k_1 (fast), k_2 (fast) and k_3 (slow), and exchange via k_1 (fast), k_2 (fast) and k_{-2} (slow). By applying a stationary-state treatment, Twigg showed that the two rates were

$$\text{Hydrogenation rate} = \frac{k_2 k_3}{k_{-2}+k_3}\, \theta_1 p_{H_2}$$

$$\text{Exchange rate} = \frac{k_{-2} k_2}{k_3+k_{-2}}\, \theta_1 p_{H_2}$$

If it is assumed that the adsorption of ethylene is strong and that θ_1 is constant, the observed rates follow. Twigg derived activation energies for the steps with nickel as catalyst as follows: $E_2 = 11$, $E_{-2} = 18$ to 22, $E_3 = 9$ to 13 kcal. The hydrogenation rate depends on a rate of desorption (k_3) and inspection of the thermochemical cycle given by Eley[17] (Figure 2) will show that the minimum value he allocates to the activation energy of a surface reaction (7·5 kcal) could equally well be applied to that of desorption (and this may be very similar on several metals at high coverages).

If parahydrogen were used in place of deuterium, conversion would occur by the exchange mechanism k_{-2}. This is negligible at low temperatures where some of the 'poisoning' effects of ethylene on the conversion were examined, and so the mechanism is satisfactory on this count; but the test of equality of rates at higher temperatures does not seem to have been made.

In order to account for the production of hydrogen and light ethane (C_2H_6) immediately ethylene is admitted to a nickel catalyst pretreated with deuterium, Twigg has to introduce the additional fast reactions

$$\begin{array}{c} CH_2D \\ | \\ CH_2 \\ | \\ S \end{array} \underset{k_{-4}}{\overset{k_4}{\rightleftharpoons}} \begin{array}{c} H_2C-CHD \\ | \quad | \\ S \quad S \end{array} \begin{array}{c} H \\ | \\ S \end{array} \text{ and } \begin{array}{c} H_2C-CH_2 \\ | \quad | \\ S \quad S \end{array} \begin{array}{c} D \\ | \\ S \end{array}$$

so that the ethyl radicals present are mainly C_2H_5 and with chemisorbed hydrogen atoms can give the 'light' gases. However, nobody seems to have commented on the fact that such fast reactions would remove any need for reaction k_{-2} as far as the deuteroethylenes are concerned, and their rate of appearance in the gas phase would depend on the rate of reaction k_{-1}. This would not be objectionable as far as activation energy is concerned, for the activation energy of desorption would certainly be no more than the heat of adsorption, which is probably quite low at the full coverages in the reaction, and it may be less, as explained in the last section. But the deuteration is now indistinguishable kinetically from the scheme proposed by Polanyi and Greenhalgh

$$\begin{array}{c} \quad \quad \quad \quad CH_2D \\ \quad \quad \quad \quad | \\ D+D+H_2C-CH_2 \underset{k'_{-1}}{\overset{k'_1}{\rightleftharpoons}} CH \quad \quad D \overset{k'_2}{\longrightarrow} C_2H_4D_2 \\ | \quad | \quad | \quad | \quad \quad \quad | \quad \quad \quad | \\ S \quad S \quad S \quad S \quad \quad \quad S \quad \quad \quad S \end{array}$$

and on either treatment the concentration of ethyl radicals is proportional to $D_2^{1/2}$. Nor will it do to put k_2 as the rate-determining step, in Twigg's scheme, as far as deuteration is concerned. This would get the kinetics correct for the deuteration, but because k_4, etc., are faster than k_3 this would require the deuteration to be faster than the hydrogenation, which is not correct at low temperatures.

There seems to be evidence for the occurrence of reaction k_4, k_{-4} in other work. Anderson and Kemball[38] have called the process 'repeated double point adsorption' and used it in discussing the exchange of deuterium and ethane over a variety of transition metal catalysts. Wilson, Otvos, Stevenson and Wagner[39] report a similar reaction in the exchange reaction of cis-2-butene and deuterium over nickel at $-78°C$, when the surface species give a random distribution of hydrogen and deuterium atoms very rapidly. Some quite independent work[20] on the infra-red absorption spectra of the adsorbed species shows that rapid reversible processes like k_4, k_{-4} do occur with ethylene on nickel.

The infra-red studies have shown that ethylene can be adsorbed on a nickel surface in a variety of ways, and the state of the surface affects the proportions of each chemisorbed form. On a surface reduced in hydrogen and evacuated at 350 °C before cooling to 35 °C, the adsorption of ethylene is mainly dissociative, and the adsorption peaks corresponding to the stretching and bending frequencies of the C—H bonds show that the dissociation complex has the formula (IV) rather than (III). Moreover, this complex is readily and reversibly hydrogenated by moderate pressures of hydrogen; this is in contrast with earlier views, although Beeck proposed a slow hydrogenation of the acetylenic complex. On a surface that has been reduced and evacuated at 35 °C, thus retaining a chemisorbed layer of hydrogen atoms, the adsorption of the ethylene seems to be in the form (II) with a small contribution from (I). This form is also readily reduced to ethyl radicals and reformed when the hydrogen is pumped off, thus giving excellent proof of the 'double point adsorption' k_4, k_{-4}. Unfortunately, the fate of the chemisorbed hydrogen atoms on admitting the ethylene is not known, for the metal—H bond is not easily identified in infra-red absorption.

It would thus appear that none of the theories advanced so far is adequate to explain the kinetics of both hydrogenation and exchange reactions, and that the spectroscopic evidence may help in the formulation of more adequate theories. It seems certain, however, that all surface reactions are fast (as postulated in Twigg's mechanism) and that adsorption or desorption steps are likely to be rate-determining. Further information on the heat of adsorption of ethylene and of ethane on nearly-filled surfaces would be most valuable here but may be very difficult to obtain. It may be that the kinetics of the exchange reaction of ethylene have been over-simplified; as mentioned, other exchange reactions show fractional orders[38], and perhaps further work on the kinetics of the ethylene exchange with infra-red techniques to identify surface species would be profitable. Possibly the *exchange* occurs via the acetylenic complexes. It would also be interesting to find the proportion of the acetylenic complexes on different metals. Is it much less on rhodium, for example, and does this account for the high rates over rhodium? Or is the complex more readily reduced over rhodium?

8.2.2. *Hydrogenation and dehydrogenation of cyclic compounds*

In these reactions, the hydrogenations are often carried out in solution but there is a large volume of experimental work on the gas-phase catalysis as well[16]. Over nickel catalysts at high temperatures and pressures the ease of hydrogenation of the separate reactants is

(open chain olefins) > cyclo-olefins > naphthalene > benzene > alkyl-benzenes > aryl-benzenes

Unsaturated side chains of cyclic hydrocarbons are hydrogenated before any ring double or aromatic bonds. In solution, under comparable conditions, the relative rates are in a similar order, for example with platinum in acetic acid the relative rates cyclohexane :: 1,4-cyclohexadiene :: 1,3-cyclohexadiene :: cyclohexene are as 1 :: 4·6 :: 6·6 :: 6·6 :: 8·1. In addition, hydrogen transfer occurs quite readily under catalytic conditions, and cyclohexene and cyclohexadienes disproportionate to benzene and cyclohexane:

Corson[16] has listed relative rates for several palladium-catalysed hydrogen transfer reactions.

One of the most interesting aspects of catalytic hydrogenation and dehydrogenation reactions is the attempt to correlate the activity of the catalysts for a particular reaction with the structure of the catalyst. Balandin[40,41] pointed out that cyclohexane and substances with similar six-membered rings (decalin, piperidine, cyclohexenes) could be dehydrogenated on certain metals that could expose atoms in octahedral faces with suitable spacings between the atoms, as shown by the enclosed metals in *Table 8.1*. Body-centred lattices cannot show octahedral faces. Balandin considered that the cyclic molecule was adsorbed by physical forces on the surface in particular relation to several metal atoms, so that the hydrogen atoms could be attracted to certain metal atoms and the C—H bonds strained. This was the 'multiplet' theory of adsorption. The reverse reaction, the hydrogenation of benzene, has been studied by Long, Frazer and Ott[42] and by Emmett and Skau[43]. Long, Frazer and Ott[42] studied the hydrogenation over iron, cobalt, nickel and copper, and over binary alloys of these metals, and concluded from x-ray examination of the metals that only catalysts capable of exposing octahedral faces were active. Emmett and Skau[43] showed that in addition to exposing an octahedral face, the lattice spacing must lie between certain limits, as shown in *Table 8.1*. Thus silver and iron are inactive, while cobalt, nickel and

Table 8.1. Structure and atomic radii (Å) of the metals and some non-metals[44]

Body-centred cubic lattices		Face-centred cubic lattices		Close-packed hexagonal lattices	
K	2·31	Sr	2·15	Mg	1·60
Ba	2·17	Ca	1·97	Zr	1·56
Na	1·86	Ce	1·82	Cd	1·49
Li	1·52	Th	1·80	Ti	1·46
Ta	1·43	Pb	1·75		
W	1·36	Ag	1·44	Os	1·35
Mo	1·36	Au	1·44	Zn	1·33
V	1·30	Al	1·43	Ru	1·33
α Cr	1·25			β Co	1·26
α Fe	1·24	Pt	1·38		
		Pd	1·37	Be	1·12
Diamond type	*cubic lattices*	Ir	1·35		
Sn	1·40	Rh	1·34	*Arsenic-type hexagonal*	
(grey)		Cu	1·28	*lattices*	
Ge	1·22	α Co	1·26	Bi	1·55
Si	1·17	Ni	1·24	Sb	1·45
C	0·76			As	1·25
(diamond)				C	0·71
		Tetragonal lattices		(graphite)	
		In	1·62	*Other lattices*	
		Sn	1·51	Mn	1·18
		(white)			

palladium are active, and alloys show intermediate activities (*Table 8.2*). There have been reports that iron films can catalyse the hydrogenations. Trapnell[44] has examined the possibility that the fit of the benzene molecule on the (110) plane of iron is near enough to an 'octahedral fit' to suit the theory. However, the inactivity of pure copper, in spite of suitable faces and spacings, points to the necessity of something more than the correct surface geometry. This inactivity was also found by Ipatieff, Corson and Kurbatov[45] in an examination

Table 8.2. Structure of pure and mixed metal catalysts and their activity in hydrogenating benzene[44]

Catalyst	Surface area m²	Space velocity in test	Temperature for producing C_6H_{12} °C		Structure†
			10%	50%	
Co	26·8	3,290	37	43	F
Fe–Co I (25·4%/74·6%)	29·2	3,430	43	55	F+B
Fe–Co II (59·9%/40·1%)	31·2	3,430	74	90	F+B
Fe–Co III (78·4%/21·6%)	25·2	3,430	190	214	F+B
Fe	27·1	3,430	Inactive		B
Cu VII (0·0006% Ni)	16·8	55	1·6% at 225		F
Ni I	5·4	2,600	117	131	F
Pd	2·9	3,020	82	101	F
Ag–Pd I (20%/80%)	7·7	1,850	110	138	F
Ag–Pd II (55%/45%)	8·6	1,850	120	—	F
Ag	9·6	58	Inactive		F

† F=face-centred cubic lattice; B=body-centred cubic lattice

of the effect of nickel on copper catalysts. They found that pure copper is a poor catalyst for the hydrogenation of benzene, but small proportions of nickel improve the activity greatly. Some of their results on the rate of hydrogenation of benzene at 225°C, with a 1:7 mixture of benzene to hydrogen were as follows:

Per cent nickel in copper	Per cent hydrogen in 12 sec
1·0	79
0·1	10
0·01	1·5
0·002	0

With a contact time of 180 sec, 0·005 per cent nickel shows no conversion, but 0·007 per cent shows 8 per cent conversion; the latter composition corresponds to one nickel atom/13,000 copper atoms. Nickel is an effective hydrogenation catalyst, but the amount of nickel present in any of the above experiments is small, and it is not very likely to be concentrated in the surface of the copper because nickel and copper readily form solid solutions. It appears that the nickel in some way activates the copper; it will be recalled that the addition of palladium to gold considerably reduces the activation energy for the ortho-hydrogen–parahydrogen conversion (section 8.1).

The problem of the relative activity of various metals in hydrogenation is a very intriguing one. Halpern[46] has recently shown that the order of activity of various metals is very similar for different hydrogenations or exchanges:

H_2D_2 exchange: Pt, Rh, Ru > Ni, Co > Fe, Cu[47]

Hydrogenation C_2H_4:   Rh > Pd > Pt > Ni > Fe > W > Cr > Ta[25,26]

          C_2H_2:   Pd > Pt > Ni, Rh > Fe, Cu, Co, Ir, > Ru, Os[48]

          C_6H_6:   Pt > Rh > Ru > Pd > Co > Ni > Fe[49]

D_2–NH_3 exchange: Pt > Rh > Pd > Ni > W > Fe > Cu > Ag[50]

The order is, however, very different for the exchange between deuterium and higher hydrocarbons[51]. Apart from this, the similar order of activity suggests that some property of the catalyst affects the rates of the hydrogenations or exchanges similarly. The work described earlier in this section shows that crystal spacings of the metals are important, perhaps affecting the interaction of species adsorbed on the surface sites. There has been a tendency recently to regard the crystal spacing as less important than the properties that determine the bond strength. The general relation between rate of reaction and

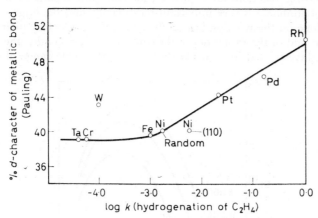

Figure 8.5. Rates of hydrogenation and percentage d-character[26]

heats of chemisorption of the reactants is well established—the greater the heats of chemisorption of reactants or products the slower the rate, as shown in *Figure 8.3*—but the problem then is to relate heats of chemisorption to atomic or co-operative properties of the metals. This problem has been discussed in section 6.4. The formation of bonds is concerned particularly with the electronic properties of the metal, and some correlations have been found between work functions and activities, and between Pauling's percentage d-character and activity (as shown in *Figures 8.5* and *8.6*) but these are rather simple and tentative measures of the bonding capacity and strength[52]. Moreover, it is really necessary to compare the effectiveness of various metals for the same molecular process (such as rate of adsorption or desorption, or rates of surface reaction). Far too little is known about the mechanisms to do this properly at present.

14—c.   209

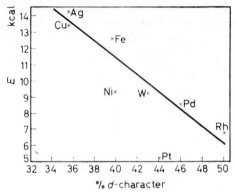

Figure 8.6. Activation energies of the deuterium–ammonia exchange and percentage
d-character[50]

8.3. SYNTHESIS AND DECOMPOSITION OF AMMONIA

These reversible reactions are of interest for two quite separate reasons. The synthesis of ammonia is very important industrially, and the large amount of research done on the reaction has produced a very satisfactory picture of the mechanism and of the properties of the catalysts[53–55]. Secondly, the reactions have been investigated in many laboratories over a wide range of pressures

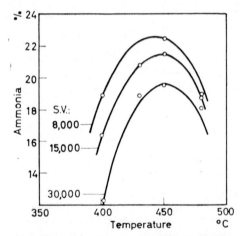

Figure 8.7. Percentage conversion to ammonia
for given flow rates and temperatures[55]
(Catalyst E; 330 atm; $H_2:N_2 = 3:1$)

and temperatures, and it is clear that different mechanisms operate under different conditions. At very high temperatures the decomposition seems to follow Langmuir–Hinshelwood mechanisms; at lower temperatures and higher pressures, the desorption of nitrogen seems to be the rate-determining step. In the synthesis of ammonia, carried out at high pressures and moderate temperatures, the adsorption of nitrogen is the rate-determining step.

In the synthesis reaction, it is well known that the equilibrium constant decreases as the temperature is increased[55,56], so that the conversion at equilibrium is greater at lower temperatures for any given pressure. On the other hand, the rate of synthesis over a catalyst increases with increase of temperature, so that a balance has to be struck. *Figure 8.7* shows results for a triply promoted catalyst (K_2O, CaO, Al_2O_3) obtained by Nielsen[55]. In practice, the temperature used is about 400 to 600°C. The percentage yield is increased if the pressure is increased, as shown in *Table 8.3* for three commercial processes, all of them using iron-based catalysts; however, the ratio actual conversion/theoretical conversion at equilibrium often *decreases* slightly as the pressure is raised.

Table 8.3[53]

Process	Temperature °C	Pressure atm	Conversion/pass % by weight
Mont Cenis	400–425	100	5–12
Haber–Bosch	550	200–250	15–20
Claude	500–650	900–1,000	40–80

The thermal combination of hydrogen and nitrogen in the absence of catalysts has never been observed, and the homogeneous decomposition of ammonia is also very slow at temperatures below 1,200°C. When hydrogen atoms are prepared in a discharge tube and streamed into nitrogen, no ammonia is formed; but if nitrogen atoms are streamed into hydrogen, ammonia is formed. Thus the need is for a catalyst which will break up the nitrogen molecule rather than for a hydrogenation catalyst; indeed, some good hydrogenation catalysts are ineffective in the ammonia synthesis. However, metals that form nitrides with gaseous nitrogen are ineffective as catalysts for the synthesis, presumably because of the stable ionic structure of the nitrides; other metals that form nitrides with ammonia but not with nitrogen, such as iron and nickel, or only absorb nitrogen weakly, such as manganese, or do not form bulk nitrides at all, such as osmium, are active; it is clear that there is little correlation between bulk nitride formation and catalytic activity. Magnetic and x-ray investigations have shown that there is no bulk nitride formed under the synthesis conditions with two of the most active catalysts, iron and osmium, and that little is formed even with tungsten, uranium and molybdenum, all of which retain some nitrogen after prolonged use as catalysts. The nitrogen that is active in the synthesis must be chemisorbed on the metal surface. The metals osmium and molybdenum are active and stable under synthesis conditions, while iron is as active initially but loses its activity rapidly. The addition of low percentages of alumina, or acidic oxides such as silica or zirconia with oxides of alkali metals and alkaline earths, increases the activity of these metals, and in addition considerably prolongs the life of the iron catalysts, so that they can compete favourably with the more active but more expensive metals. Promoted iron catalysts are more widely used than other catalysts, and there has been far more research into the way they function[56].

These iron catalysts were successful only after it was realized how essential it is to reduce the iron surface completely, even with the promoted catalysts. Any oxygen left on the iron surface will poison the reaction. The promoted iron catalysts are usually prepared by fusion in an oxygen atmosphere of mixtures of magnetite (Fe_3O_4) and the promoting oxides such as alumina and potassium oxide, followed by reduction with hydrogen under the same conditions as used in the synthesis. Other methods involve the coprecipitation of the hydroxides or the oxides from aqueous solution, and their calcination and reduction, or the addition of promoters by impregnation. Nielsen[55] states that a ferrous–ferric ratio of 0·5 in the oxides before reduction produces catalysts of maximum activity. The presence of traces of water vapour or oxygen in the hydrogen used for the reduction—or for the synthesis—can result in the formation of a surface oxide of iron which spoils the catalyst. As little as 0·016 per cent of water vapour has a definite effect, and 0·32 per cent strongly

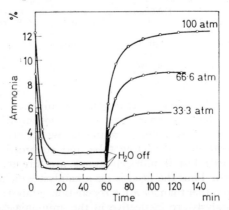

Figure 8.8. Effect of 0·32 per cent water vapour on the activity of catalyst 922 at various pressures[57a]

inhibits the synthesis. *Figure 8.8*, from Emmett and Brunauer[57a], illustrates this. The effect of the amount of oxygen retained by the surface is shown[57b] below; 5 mg of oxygen with 13 g of iron corresponds to 1 oxygen atom with about 800 iron atoms:

Oxygen retained by 13 g of catalyst (mg):	0	6·6	14·5
Ammonia formed/pass (%):	0·22	0·17	0·07

(Equilibrium concentrations for these conditions give 0·23 per cent/pass).

It was found by McGeer and Taylor[58] that the exchange reaction over iron

$$^{14}N_2 + {}^{15}N_2 \rightleftharpoons 2^{14}N^{15}N$$

was inhibited by oxygen; 0·15 per cent of oxygen in the gases reduced the rate of exchange by a factor of 100. These poisoning experiments together provide evidence that the adsorption of nitrogen as atoms is essential to the success of the synthesis, and are in keeping with earlier work of Taylor and Joris[59] showing that the same exchange was very slow below 600°C in the absence of hydrogen, and very slow below 400°C in its presence—presumably the hydrogen ensures reduction of the surface.

The chemisorption of nitrogen on iron catalysts or on evaporated films of iron is a slow activated process. The activation energy on an iron catalyst was found to vary from 10 kcal at low coverage to about 21·5 kcal on a full surface, while the heat of chemisorption varied from 44 to 30 kcal over the same range[60]. The activation energy of desorption is therefore nearly constant at 54 to 52 kcal. The chemisorptions on tungsten and on osmium are also activated, that on tungsten being very strong and on osmium very weak compared with iron.

In contrast, hydrogen and ammonia chemisorb and desorb rapidly on these ammonia catalysts. Moreover, ammonia and deuterium exchange readily over iron and other ammonia catalysts. Semiquantitative information about the exchange was obtained by Taylor and Jungers[61], who showed that exchange took place over a doubly promoted catalyst at room temperature in a matter of hours for the NH_2D stage, and in a few days the equilibrium proportions were obtained; the isotopic forms were detected by ultra-violet absorption spectroscopy. Later work by Laidler and Weber[62] on the exchange over a singly promoted catalyst gave the half-life of the NH_3 species as about 100 minutes at 120°C, and the activation energy as 13 kcal; this means a half-life of about 1 sec at 420°C at the same low concentrations. Evidently the surface reactions between H, N, NH, NH_2 and NH_3 are very rapidly equilibrated at the synthesis temperatures. Laidler and Weber's results and some others on the exchange reaction over metal films are discussed later in this section.

By the time of Taylor and Junger's work, however, it was realized that there was a close connection between the rate of the synthesis and the rate of adsorption of nitrogen. Emmett and Brunauer[63] showed that the rate of adsorption of nitrogen was always equal to the rate of formation of ($2HN_3$) for equivalent conditions on a number of catalysts and with a variety of conditions. It proved rather complicated to relate this idea to the actual kinetics, which can be described[64,65] by the general equation

$$\frac{dp_{NH_3}}{dt} = k_f p_{N_2} \left(\frac{p_{H_2}^3}{p_{NH_3}^2} \right)^{1-\beta} - k_b \left(\frac{p_{NH_3}^2}{p_{H_2}^3} \right)^{\beta} \tag{8.1}$$

where β lies between 0·3 and 0·5 and depends on the composition of the catalyst, while k_f and k_b depend on the catalyst and on the temperature. Clearly the first term relates to the forward and the second to the back reaction of the reversible pair

$$N_2 + 3H_2 \underset{k_b}{\overset{k_f}{\rightleftharpoons}} 2NH_3$$

Temkin and Pyzhev have given more complicated equations for the rate at very high pressures where the equilibrium must be expressed in terms of fugacities. The simple equation leads to some useful predictions for lower pressures, however. If the decomposition is neglected and $\beta = 0·5$, the equation becomes

$$\frac{dp_{NH_3}}{dt} = k_f p_{N_2} \left(\frac{p_{H_2}^{1.5}}{p_{NH_3}} \right) \tag{8.2}$$

If the proportion of ammonia does not vary very much with the ratio $r = p_{H_2}/p_{N_2}$, then the conversion rate is proportional to $p_{N_2} \cdot p_{H_2}^{1.5}$. Now $p_{H_2} + p_{N_2} = $ constant, so that the rate is proportional to $r^{1.5}/(1+r)^{2.5}$. This is a maximum when $r = 1.5$. Hence the maximum conversion rate should be at a ratio well below the stoichiometric value 3. Nielsen[55] gives several examples for the conversion over doubly or triply promoted catalysts which agree well at low conversion pressures with this prediction.

The problem was solved by Temkin and Pyzhev[64], and their equations were related to the experimental results mentioned above by Brunauer, Love and Keenan[60]. The assumptions made can be illustrated by considering the derivation of that part of the equation which relates to the decomposition. The assumptions are:

(i) The rate of the forward reaction is controlled by the rate of adsorption of nitrogen, and of the back reaction by the desorption of the nitrogen.

(ii) All the other adsorption–desorption steps, and the surface steps, are effectively in equilibrium.

(iii) The adsorption of the nitrogen, when in equilibrium, obeys a Freundlich isotherm.

This is in keeping with the pressures used and with the decline in the heat of adsorption as the coverage increases (Appendix II).

During a decomposition when the forward reaction can be ignored, these assumptions lead to the situation depicted below, where the double arrows denote species in equilibrium:

$$\begin{array}{ccc}
\mathrm{NH_3} & & \tfrac{3}{2}\mathrm{H_2} \\
\Updownarrow & & \Updownarrow \\
\overbrace{\mathrm{NH_2 + H}} \rightleftharpoons & \overbrace{\mathrm{H + H + H}} + \mathrm{N} & \xrightarrow[\text{R.D.S.}]{} \tfrac{1}{2}\mathrm{N_2} \\
\;\big|\quad\;\big| & \big|\quad\big|\quad\big|\quad\big| & \\
\;\mathrm{S}\quad\mathrm{S} & \mathrm{S}\quad\mathrm{S}\quad\mathrm{S}\quad\mathrm{S} &
\end{array}$$

The ammonia and the hydrogen can be immagined in equilibrium with a fictitious or 'virtual' concentration of nitrogen $[\mathrm{N_2^*}]$, much higher than the actual concentration of nitrogen because of the slowness of the desorption step. Then, because the nitrogen atom concentration is in equilibrium with the hydrogen and ammonia through the steps shown by double arrows above, it must also be in equilibrium with the virtual pressure of nitrogen, so that $[\mathrm{H_{ads}}]$ and $[\mathrm{N_2^*}]$ obey the Freundlich isotherm. These relationships allow the nitrogen atom concentration $[\mathrm{N_{ads}}]$ to be expressed in terms of the ammonia and the hydrogen concentrations. The rate of reaction is then put equal to $k[\mathrm{N_{ads}}]^2$. An example will clarify the derivation.

Emmett and Love[66] showed experimentally that for a particular doubly-promoted catalyst the adsorption of nitrogen fitted the Freundlich isotherm:

$$[\mathrm{N_{ads}}] \propto [\mathrm{N_2}]^{0.16}$$

and that the rate of decomposition followed the equation

$$-\frac{d[\mathrm{NH_3}]}{dt} = k' \frac{[\mathrm{NH_3}]^{0.6}}{[\mathrm{H_2}]^{1.0}} \tag{8.3}$$

(that is, β in equation (8.1) is $\tfrac{1}{3}$).

The proposed mechanism suggests that

$$\text{Rate} = k[\mathrm{N_{ads}}]^2 \quad \text{and} \quad [\mathrm{N_{ads}}] = \alpha[\mathrm{N_2^*}]^{0.16} \quad \text{and} \quad \frac{[\mathrm{N_2^*}]^{1/2}[\mathrm{H_2}]^{3.2}}{[\mathrm{NH_3}]} = K_{eq} \tag{8.4}$$

Therefore:

$$\text{Rate} = k[\text{N}_{\text{ads}}]^2 = k\alpha^2[\text{N}_2^*]^{0.32}$$

$$= k\alpha^2\left\{\frac{K_{\text{eq}}^2[\text{NH}_3]^2}{[\text{H}_2]^3}\right\}^{0.32}$$

$$= k'\frac{[\text{NH}_3]^{0.64}}{[\text{H}_2]^{0.96}} \tag{8.5}$$

and this is in reasonably good agreement with the experimental equation (8.3). Similar agreement was found in other cases, and there is now little doubt that the mechanism is sound.

It should be mentioned that the concentration $[\text{N}_{\text{ads}}]$ could also be calculated if the adsorption isotherm of ammonia in the presence of hydrogen could be determined, because of the equilibrium set up.

In general, therefore, the rate of the decomposition is proportional to $\{[\text{NH}_3]^2/[\text{H}_2]^3\}^\beta$ where β is twice the exponent n in the Freundlich isotherm $[\text{N}_{\text{ads}}] \propto [\text{N}_2]^n$.

If the rate-determining step for the forward reaction is the rate of adsorption of nitrogen, it is proportional to p_{N_2} and to the fraction of surface left bare by hydrogen and ammonia, i.e. to $f(\text{NH}_3,\text{H}_2)$. Then at equilibrium

$$k_f[\text{N}_2]f(\text{NH}_3,\text{H}_2) = k_b\left\{\frac{[\text{NH}_3]^2}{[\text{H}_2]^3}\right\}^\beta$$

and from this it can readily be shown that $f(\text{NH}_3,\text{H}_2)$ is $\{[\text{H}_2]^3/[\text{NH}_3]^2\}^{1-\beta}$. Thus if the same kinetic mechanism holds throughout the reaction, the rate law must be of the form

$$\frac{d[\text{NH}_3]}{dt} = k_f[\text{N}_2]\left\{\frac{[\text{H}_2]^3}{[\text{NH}_3]^2}\right\}^{1-\beta} - k_b\left\{\frac{[\text{NH}_3]^2}{[\text{H}_2]^3}\right\}^\beta$$

as suggested by equation (8.1).

Scholten, Konvalinka and Zwietering[67] have recently shown that the rate of chemisorption of nitrogen on a singly promoted iron catalyst is equal to the rate of synthesis at the same coverage of nitrogen. The rate of chemisorption during synthesis was measured gravimetrically, and checks were made with the coverage calculated from the adsorption isotherm. The authors report that the rate of adsorption appeared to be less when more hydrogen was present. This observation may be connected with the formation on the surface of NH rather than N, as suggested by the following investigation. Ozaki, Taylor and Boudart[68] compared the rates of synthesis of NH_3 and ND_3 on two normally active, doubly promoted iron catalysts at one atmosphere pressure and temperatures between 218 and 302°C. They concluded that the kinetic data show that the rate-determining step is the chemisorption of nitrogen, but the species mainly present on the surface is NH and not N. The evidence rests mainly on comparison of the observed rate law and those predicted if the equilibrium is: $\text{N}_a + 1.5\,\text{H}_2 \rightleftharpoons \text{NH}_3$ or $\text{NH} + \text{H}_2 \rightleftharpoons \text{NH}_3$. Reference to equation (8.4) in the derivation of equation (8.5) shows that the two equilibria will produce quite different rate laws for the effect of hydrogen pressure. The experimental rate law agrees with the equation calculated for $\text{NH} + \text{H}_2 \rightleftharpoons \text{NH}_3$. There is another important piece of evidence, however. The coefficient $(1-\beta)$ (which the authors denote as α) can be determined for H_2 and for D_2. The *ratio* of the coefficients is related to the ratio of the chemisorption equilibrium constants, and this second ratio can be calculated from the gas-phase partition functions of H_2, D_2, NH_3 and ND_3, for each of the adsorption equilibria. For $N_a + 1.5H_2 \rightleftharpoons NH_3$ the ratio should be 4·3 at 300°C and 5·4 at 250°C. For $NH_a + H_2 \rightleftharpoons NH_3$ the ratio should be 2·4 and 2·7, respectively. The observed value was 2·7, independent of temperature. This investigation of relative rates of isotopic species seems most important and will lead to significant changes in our ideas of the detailed mechanism.

There has been some very interesting work on the effect of promoters[55,56]. X-ray investigations have shown how the promoters are incorporated into the lattice of the oxides before reduction, and that the non-reducible oxides tend to concentrate on the surface of the crystallites of the reduced metal, the interior

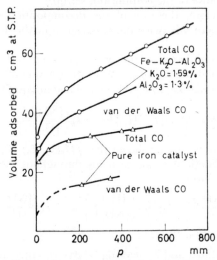

Figure 8.9. Comparison of the isotherms for total carbon monoxide adsorption at −183°C and for the physical adsorption on about 45 g of pure iron synthetic ammonia catalyst and on a similar quantity of a doubly promoted iron catalyst[69]

being almost pure α-iron. The iron as a whole is very porous, with densities below 3 g cm⁻³. The crystallites are small but grow as the catalyst ages with loss of area and of activity. The presence of promoter seems to keep the crystallite size smaller during reduction and to stabilize the area; more promoter generally means more resistance to severe conditions but a decreased performance at less severe conditions of temperature and pressure.

The concentration of promoters in the surface was confirmed by Brunauer and Emmett[69] by combining measurements of chemisorption and van der Waals adsorption for several gases. At −183°C, a 'pure iron' catalyst (which actually contained a trace of alumina) was exposed to various pressures of carbon monoxide, and the total adsorption (which included chemisorption with a van der Waals layer on top) was measured. On heating each system to 0°C, the van der Waals layer stripped, leaving the chemisorbed layer, so that on cooling again to $-183°C$ and readsorbing, the amount of gas taken up measured the van der Waals adsorption. The difference of the total and the van der Waals adsorption (see *Figure 8.9*, the two lower curves) gave the chemisorption. There were thus two estimates of v_m, the volume of gas required to fill the monolayer (pages 119–29), and these agreed, so it was assumed that all the surface atoms of iron chemisorbed the carbon mon-oxide. However, when singly or doubly promoted catalyst was used, the chemisorbed area (iron) was less than the total although both were greater

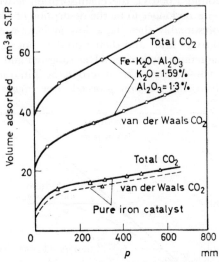

Figure 8.10. Comparison of the isotherms for the total and the van der Waals ad-sorption of carbon dioxide at $-78°C$ on 45-g samples of pure iron catalyst and a doubly promoted iron synthetic ammonia catalyst[69]

than for the unpromoted catalyst (*Table 8.4*). About 60 per cent of the surface appeared to be promoter, and only 40 per cent iron. This was checked by using carbon dioxide at $-78°C$, for on pure iron this was not chemisorbed, but on promoted iron showed both types of adsorption (*Figure 8.10*) and the chemisorbed area then corresponded to the *promoter* area. It will be seen from *Table 8.4* that the catalyst with greatest specific area is not that of greatest

Table 8.4. Areas of some iron catalysts[55]

Catalyst	Activity NH₃ under given conditions %	Total surface area m²g⁻¹	Iron area m²g⁻¹
A. 0·15% Al₂O₃ as impurity	3·3	1	1
B. 10·2% Al₂O₃	8·2	13·2	5·1
C. 1·59% K₂O and 1·3% Al₂O₃	12·3	3·72	1·5

activity. It is usually found that the doubly or triply promoted iron catalysts are much more active than the singly promoted catalysts for the synthesis of ammonia, although the reverse may be true if they are used as 'cracking' catalysts. Frankenburg[53] suggested that the singly promoted catalysts contained some acid centres that made them active in cracking, and that these centres are neutralized in the doubly promoted catalysts.

The decomposition of ammonia over metals such as tungsten, platinum and molybdenum at low pressures (less than 1 atm) has often been studied. At temperatures around 1,000°C, the chemisorption is weak, and the rate-determining step seems no longer to be the desorption of nitrogen but some of the surface steps; presumably these have low activation energies (exchange reactions suggest 13 to 20 kcal) and their rate does not increase in step with the desorption as the temperature rises. Over tungsten and over molybdenum the reaction is of very low order—almost zero in the initial stages, although the rate falls off slightly as the reaction proceeds (see *Figure 8.11*)[70] and there

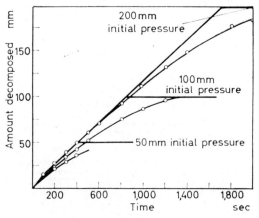

Figure 8.11. Decomposition of ammonia over tungsten[70]

have been some reports of retardation of the decomposition by nitrogen; perhaps it is significant that these two catalysts are also 'synthesis' catalysts. On platinum, on the other hand, which is a hydrogenation but not a synthesis catalyst, the reaction is definitely retarded by hydrogen. Hinshelwood and Burk[71] showed that the addition of hydrogen to 100 mm of ammonia greatly reduced the rate which appeared to be nearly inversely proportional to the hydrogen pressure. Schwab and Schmidt[72] followed the decomposition in the absence of added hydrogen, and showed that the rate was given by

$$-\frac{\mathrm{d}p_{\mathrm{NH_3}}}{\mathrm{d}t} = k\,\frac{p_{\mathrm{NH_3}}}{p_{\mathrm{H_2}}}$$

If p is the total pressure at time t (p_0 at zero time) the rate equation integrates to give

$$p + p_0 \ln (2p_0 - p) = -kt + \text{constant}$$

The plot of the left-hand side of this equation against time is a straight line, as shown in *Figure 8.12*, confirming the rate equation.

As mentioned earlier in this section, Laidler and Weber[62] investigated the exchange reaction between ammonia and deuterium over a singly promoted iron catalyst, using a microwave method to follow the disappearance of ammonia. They considered that their results fitted a LH mechanism with ammonia adsorbed as a molecule and deuterium as atoms, giving a rate law

$$-\frac{dp_{NH_3}}{dt} = k \frac{p_{D_2}^{1/2} p_{NH_3}}{(1+p_{NH_3})^2}$$

However, it would appear that their results could also be fitted by a mechanism that assumes dissociative adsorption of the ammonia. In contrast to these

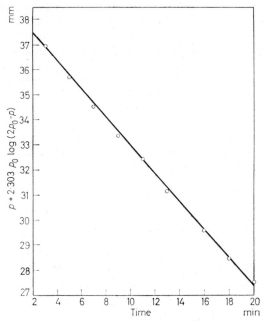

Figure 8.12. Decomposition of ammonia over platinum[72]

kinetics, Singleton, Roberts and Winter[73] find that the rate of the exchange over sintered films of tungsten, nickel and iron is proportional to the deuterium pressure and independent of the ammonia pressure over the first two catalysts but decreasing at high ammonia pressures over iron films. Kemball[50,74] has made a very detailed study of the exchange over evaporated films of various metals and has found an inverse correlation between the activation energies and the work function of the metal, with practically constant frequency factors.

The later work on this exchange reaction agrees with that of Taylor and Jungers[61] in showing that the exchange over iron films or over promoted iron catalysts is fairly rapid at low temperatures; in addition, it shows that the activation energy is fairly high (Laidler and Weber[62] give 13 kcal, Singleton, Roberts and Winter[73] 20 kcal and Kemball[50,74] 12·5 kcal) so that the reaction will be very fast at synthesis temperatures. However, there is obviously considerable variety of kinetics, depending on the conditions used for the reaction and for the preparation of the catalysts, and it will be some time before the mechanisms are agreed upon.

8.4. FISCHER–TROPSCH AND RELATED SYNTHESES

Many different and useful reactions between carbon monoxide and hydrogen can occur in the presence of suitable catalysts to yield hydrocarbons, alcohols, aldehydes and other oxygenated organic compounds. The main patterns of products for various catalysts, temperatures and pressures are reasonably established[75,76]. Although plausible reaction mechanisms have been suggested to account for these patterns, it has proved very difficult to devise kinetic tests of some of these mechanisms because of the number and complexity of the reactions involved. Only in the synthesis of methanol, with few side products, have the kinetic measurements been made with precision and related to a kinetic scheme[77]; this synthesis is discussed in section 8.5. In the present section, the 'Fischer–Tropsch'[78] syntheses of hydrocarbons and oxygenated derivatives over certain metal catalysts, the 'isosyntheses' of higher alcohols and hydrocarbons over oxide catalysts[79], and the 'oxo-reactions' which include hydrogenations and hydroformylations[80], are discussed together. In these syntheses, any kinetic studies that have been made are not easy to interpret, and evidence about the mechanisms is drawn from studies of product distributions, the fate of 'labelled' molecules that can be incorporated during the syntheses, and the structure of the catalyst before and after the syntheses as revealed by x-ray, electron diffraction and magnetic measurements.

The variety of products obtained with different catalysts and with different conditions of temperature, pressure and contact time indicate that true equilibrium is not reached in the syntheses. The standard free energy changes of typical reactions forming paraffins, olefins and alcohols from appropriate amounts of carbon monoxide and hydrogen have been summarized by Anderson et al.[76]. The changes are negative at low temperatures and positive at high, as shown in *Figure 8.13* for $n = 1$ and $n = 2$ in the general reactions

$$(2n+1)H_2 + nCO \rightarrow C_nH_{2n+2} + nH_2O$$
$$2nH_2 + nCO \rightarrow C_nH_{2n} + nH_2O$$
$$2nH_2 + nCO \rightarrow C_nH_{2n+1}OH + (n-1)H_2O$$

The general trend with longer times of contact or higher temperatures will be to yield saturated hydrocarbons. It is apparent that low temperatures would give the highest yield of any type of product, but some efficiency of conversion has usually to be sacrificed to speed of conversion, especially if the intermediate products are wanted. Other reactions, such as incorporation of some products, homologenation (represented by the reaction $-CH_2OH + CO + 2H_2 \rightarrow -CH_2CH_2OH + H_2O$), hydrocracking and isomerization complicate the patterns of products. The distribution of isomers, for example straight- or branched-chain, is rarely the same as the equilibrium distribution.

The principal catalysts and operating conditions and the type of product have been tabulated by Anderson, Feldman and Storch[79] as shown in *Table 8.5* for the Fischer–Tropsch syntheses and in *Table 8.6* for the alcohol and

Table 8.5. Variations of the Fischer–Tropsch synthesis[79]

Active constituent	Promoters	Pressure atm	Temp. °C	Products
Nickel	ThO_2, MgO	1	170–200	Gaseous and liquid paraffinic hydrocarbons
	ThO_2, MgO	1	250–450	Chiefly methane
Cobalt	ThO_2, MgO, MnO, K_2O	1–15	170–210	Chiefly paraffinic hydrocarbons plus small yields of alcohols and other oxygenated molecules
Ruthenium	—	10–100	170–200	Chief solid paraffinic hydrocarbons of very high molecular weight
Iron Conventional	Cu, MgO, Al_2O_3, CaO, ZrO_2, TiO_2, K_2O, K_2CO_3	10–30	200–270	Predominantly olefinic hydrocarbons; about 10% oxygenated products, chiefly alcohols
Fluidized catalyst†	—	15–50	290–400	Predominantly olefinic hydrocarbons; 10–25% oxygenated products, chiefly alcohols
Synol†	—	20	190–220	Olefinic hydrocarbons and more than 50% oxygenated products, chiefly alcohols
Nitrided†	—	7–30‡	190–200	Paraffinic and olefinic hydrocarbons and more than 60% oxygenated products, chiefly alcohols

† Same promoters used as for the conventional iron.
‡ Upper limit of pressure has not been fully investigated.

Table 8.6. Alcohol syntheses [79]

| Synthesis | Catalysts | | Pressure atm | Temp. °C | Products |
	Main constituents	Promoters			
Methanol	ZnO, Cu, Cr_2O_3, MnO	—	100–500	250–400	Largely methanol
Higher alcohol	ZnO, Cu, Cr_2O_3, MnO	Alkali oxides or carbonates	100–500	300–400	Methanol, isobutyl alcohol and other branched-chain alcohols
Iso	ThO_2	Al_2O_3, K_2CO_3	100–500	350–400	Alcohols, as with higher alcohols, and small yields of branched hydrocarbons
Iso	ThO_2	Al_2O_3, K_2CO_3	100–500	400–475	Branched hydrocarbons and small yields of alcohols

isosyntheses. It will be seen that the catalysts for the Fischer–Tropsch reactions are metals or promoted metals. The earliest catalysts used were cobalt and osmium with alkaline oxides as promoters; cobalt, nickel, iron and ruthenium are now used with oxides of thorium, magnesium or zirconium as promoters. Cobalt and nickel produce mainly straight-chain hydrocarbons of low or moderate molecular weight; ruthenium can be used with high pressures

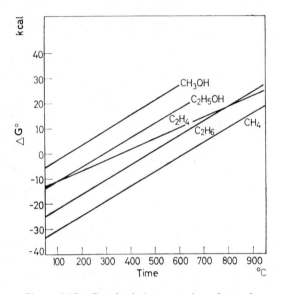

Figure 8.13. Standard free energies of reactions per C atom per mole of products

to give solid paraffins of high molecular weight. Iron can be used to give olefins, particularly if copper is present as promoter, or alcohols if lower temperatures are used. Iron nitrides are also effective catalysts; they are resistant to oxidation and to carbon deposition, and they usually produce shorter chains and more oxygenated products[81]. The chief catalysts for the alcohol and isosyntheses are oxides that are difficult to reduce, especially ThO_2. The pressures are much higher than for the metal catalysts, partly because the equilibrium constants for the reactions are small and high pressures increase the yield for any given equilibrium constant as well as increasing the rate of production. At the higher temperature range (400°C and higher) the products are chiefly hydrocarbons. There are much higher proportions of branched-chain molecules among the products of these syntheses, and the distribution of products is usually much nearer to equilibrium than with the metal catalysts.

The other useful synthesis is the oxo-synthesis. This consists of a hydroformulation[82–84] of suitable double bonds

$$R—CH{=}CH_2 + CO + H_2 \rightarrow R\cdot CH_2\cdot CH_2\cdot CHO \text{ and } R\cdot CH\Big\langle {\text{CHO} \atop \text{CH}_3}$$

The catalyst used in earlier work was metallic cobalt with thoria as promoter, at 130 to 160°C and pressures around 200 atm. All aliphatic olefins and many unsaturated esters can be hydroformylated. Other reactions that can occur are hydrogenations, homologenations and hydrogenolyses of aliphatic alcohols (expecially tertiary alcohols).

Homologenation: $R \cdot CH_2OH + CO + 2H_2 \rightarrow R \cdot CH_2CH_2OH + H_2O$

Hydrogenolysis: $CHOH + H_2 \rightarrow CH_2 + H_2O$

Hydrogenation: $C = C + H_2 \rightarrow CH \cdot CH$

There is a very curious pattern of hydrogenation as the proportion of carbon monoxide is increased[85]. In the absence of carbon monoxide the double bond is usually hydrogenated over cobalt. Relatively small partial pressures of carbon monoxide will stop the hydrogenation by poisoning the catalyst; but at high pressures the hydrogenation will begin again. It shows some features of the Friedel–Crafts or carbonium ion reactions at these higher pressures, in the sense that changes in the substrate molecule (e.g. substitution in an aromatic nucleus) produce changes in the rate that are consistent with carbonium ion intermediates. Moreover, cobalt and carbon monoxide at the pressures involved are known to form dicobalt octacarbonyl[82], and this with hydrogen can form a hydrocarbonyl which acts as an acid[86-88]

$$2Co + 8CO \rightleftharpoons (Co(CO)_4)_2 \overset{H_2}{\rightleftharpoons} 2HCo(CO)_4$$

Thus in the hydrogenations at higher pressures of carbon monoxide it may be that the intermediates are not surface compounds but the gegen-ions as in the Friedel–Crafts reactions; for example, for hydrogenolysis

$$(C_6H_5)_2CHOH + HCo(CO)_4 \rightleftharpoons (C_6H_5)_2CHOH_2^+ \cdot Co(CO)_4^-$$

and this reaction may be followed by stages which sum to give

$$(C_6H_5)_2CHOH_2^+ \cdot Co(CO)_4^- + Co(CO)_4 \rightarrow (C_6H_5)_2CH_2 + H_2O + (Co(CO)_4)_2$$

There is evidence from infra-red studies of the $HCo(CO)_4$ molecule that the hydrogen is not attached to one oxygen to form a OH group, as would be thought from the acid properties[89,90]. The hydrogen seems very weakly bonded to at least three of the CO groups, in a bridge structure. Weakly bonded hydrogen would be very active catalytically.

Adkins and Kršek[82,83] found evidence that the hydroformylations are probably homogeneous reactions. Dicobalt octacarbonyl dissolves in many organic solvents such as benzene, acetone or ether to give solutions that are quite effective catalysts for the oxo-reaction with a wide range of substrates. These solutions of the catalyst are not poisoned by sulphur compounds, nor are the solid oxo-catalysts, although in many heterogeneous reactions cobalt surfaces are poisoned by sulphur compounds. Wender and co-workers have shown that olefins will react with preformed $HCo(CO)_4$ to give aldehydes[91], and that $HCo(CO)_4$ is formed under reaction conditions in the absence of the olefin but cannot be detected when the olefin is present[92]. They conclude that the reaction proceeds by the formation of $HCo(CO)_4$ and its reaction with the olefin.

Natta has studied the kinetics of the hydroformylation reaction[93]. The rate is not altered appreciably in benzene, heptane or alcohol. The rate is proportional to the olefin concentration and approximately proportional to the total concentration of cobalt; it passes through a maximum as the pressure of carbon monoxide is increased, but increases as the pressure of hydrogen is increased. Martin[94] has suggested the following mechanism for the hydroformylation of di-isobutene (the initial steps are *not* equilibrated):

$$C_8H_{16} + Co_2(CO)_8 \rightleftharpoons Co_2(CO)_7 \cdot C_8H_{16} + CO$$

$$Co_2(CO)_7 \cdot C_8H_{16} + H_2 \rightarrow Co_2(CO)_6 + C_8H_{17}CHO \qquad \text{(slow reaction)}$$

$$Co_2(CO)_6 + 2CO \rightarrow Co_2(CO)_8 \qquad \text{(fast reaction)}$$

which leads to a rate law of the correct form. The structure of the olefin–cobalt carbonyl complex is possibly

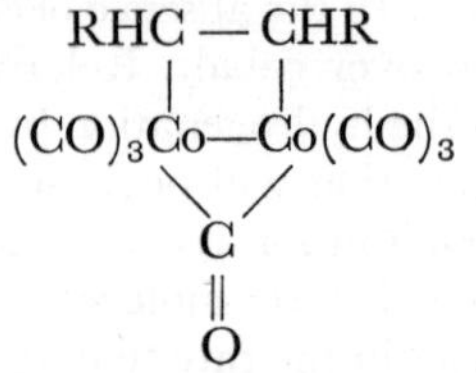

$$
\begin{array}{c}
\text{RHC} - \text{CHR} \\
| \qquad | \\
(CO)_3Co - Co(CO)_3 \\
\diagdown \quad \diagup \\
C \\
\| \\
O
\end{array}
$$

and the transition complex in the slow reaction (or possibly another intermediate) may be

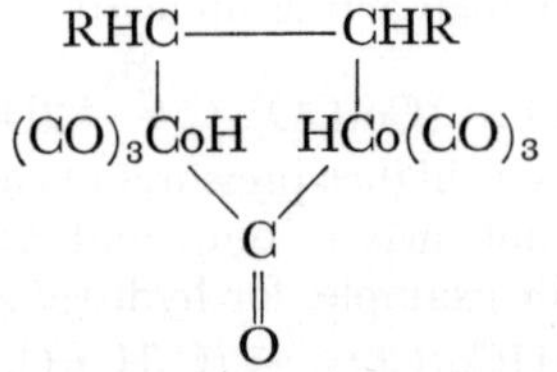

$$
\begin{array}{c}
\text{RHC} \underline{\qquad} \text{CHR} \\
| \qquad | \\
(CO)_3CoH \quad HCo(CO)_3 \\
\diagdown \quad \diagup \\
C \\
\| \\
O
\end{array}
$$

Halpern[46] has discussed these reactions and points out that the above scheme does not account for the observations of the formation of the hydrocarbonyl under reaction conditions and its known reaction with olefins. If the hydrocarbonyl is an intermediate, however, it is difficult to see how the hydroformylation can be retarded by carbon monoxide, unless the intermediate is formed in a termolecular reaction

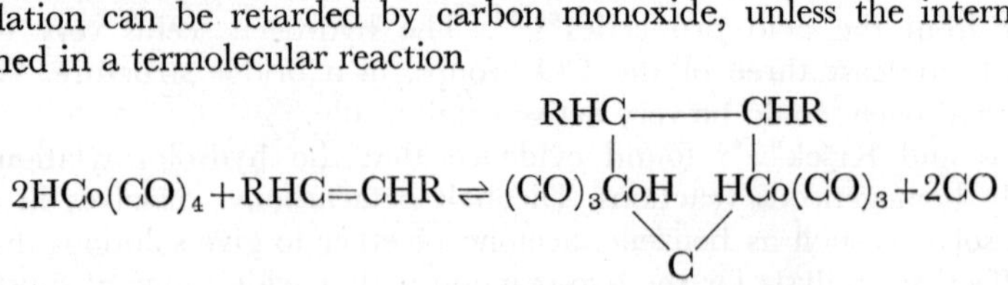

$$
\begin{array}{c}
\text{RHC} \underline{\qquad} \text{CHR} \\
| \qquad | \\
2HCo(CO)_4 + RHC{=}CHR \rightleftharpoons (CO)_3CoH \quad HCo(CO)_3 + 2CO \\
\diagdown \quad \diagup \\
C \\
\| \\
O
\end{array}
$$

and the slow step is its breakdown. It would also be necessary to assume that the equilibrium

$$Co_2(CO)_8 + H_2 \rightleftharpoons 2HCo(CO)_4$$

lay well to the left. Heterogeneous mechanisms have also been suggested for the oxo-reactions[95].

In the Fischer–Tropsch syntheses it seems certain that the intermediates are surface compounds[75]. It has been known for some time that the metals that are effective catalysts form carbides when heated in carbon monoxide at synthesis temperatures[96]. Somewhat earlier Fischer and Tropsch[97] had suggested that surface carbides might be the intermediates, and after the identification of the formation of metal carbides they developed the idea that the carbidic carbon was reduced to CH, CH_2 and CH_3 radicals which combined in various ways to form the higher hydrocarbons. This view was supported by the work of Craxford and Rideal[98] who postulated the steps:

$$Co + CO \rightarrow \text{chemisorbed } CO \xrightarrow{CO} CoC + CO_2$$

$$CoC + H_2 \rightarrow CoCH_2 \rightarrow \text{higher hydrocarbons}$$

One of the weaknesses of this theory is that carbided cobalt is markedly less active than cobalt, although iron carbides [Haegg or hexagonal carbide (Fe_2C) or cementite (Fe_3C)] are about as active as iron[99]. If the proportion of carbon monoxide is increased so that carburization occurs, the catalyst becomes less active, but it can be reactivated by reduction in hydrogen. In an active synthesis, very little cobalt carbide is formed. The chemisorption of carbon monoxide on a catalyst which had been used in the synthesis was much more like the chemisorption on a reduced than on a carbided cobalt surface.

There are two other types of investigation that suggest the carbide theory is inadequate. X-ray studies of cobalt which has been carburized show the pattern attributed to Co_2C; during synthesis on the carburized catalyst the pattern does not disappear nor does it form during the faster synthesis on the reduced catalyst[99,100]. X-ray studies also show that the cobalt in active reduced catalysts is cubic, and this cubic form is found at the end of the synthesis on uncarbided cobalt. However, if cobalt is carbided and reduced, as postulated in the carbide theory, the cobalt is hexagonal. Rather similar evidence was found in x-ray and electron diffraction studies of iron catalysts[101]. The electron diffraction experiments showed the same phases as the x-ray pattern diffraction studies for the freshly prepared catalysts; but after synthesis and extraction with a solvent to remove surface wax, the electron diffraction studies showed only patterns corresponding to magnetite, or to magnetite plus promoter, when the x-ray patterns showed that some carbides are present in the bulk catalyst after synthesis. The evidence is not conclusive[102] but it strongly suggests that cobalt carbide is not the true intermediate with cobalt catalysts and that iron carbides are not present in the surface of active iron catalysts.

A separate type of investigation also suggests that carbide is not the intermediate. With a catalyst prepared with a surface layer of ^{14}C carbide, the carbide theory suggests that the rate of appearance of ^{14}C in the gas phase should be related to the rate of synthesis, provided that little direct exchange occurs between the carbide and any gases containing carbon. Experiments showed that very little of the surface carbon appeared in the higher hydrocarbons ($C_3 + C_4$) during synthesis, although rather more appeared as methane[103]. However, the investigators pointed out that these results could be interpreted in different ways, depending on the assumptions made about the fraction of the surface of carbide that was active. If all the surface were active, then the results do not support the carbide theory. But if only a small fraction of the carbided surface is active, it may be depleted rapidly of ^{14}C which would be replaced by ^{12}C from carbon monoxide: thereafter there would be little ^{14}C put into the gas phase because the reaction would proceed through the newly formed carbide rather than the remaining carbide containing ^{14}C.

It is plain that the weight of evidence is against the carbide theory for the synthesis of molecules of moderate chain length, but it is not definitely disproved. However, methane may be formed through carbide as intermediate.

The sequence of free energy changes suggests that oxygenated molecules may be the intermediates in the hydrocarbon syntheses, especially as higher proportions of alcohols and aldehydes can be obtained if milder conditions that favour the isolation of intermediates are used. Anderson, Friedel and Storch[104] assumed that stepwise addition of carbon atoms occurred within an oxygenated surface intermediate, and Storch, Golumbic and Anderson[75] developed this scheme in more detail to account for the observed distributions of straight- and branched-chain products. By making simple assumptions about the points that could add a carbon atom, very close agreement between predicted and observed patterns was obtained[104]. Addition can occur at only one end of a growing chain on only one carbon atom if there are two at the end of the chain, or on the adjacent-to-end carbon if this is not attached to three carbons. They consider that the group added comes from an intermediate HCOH radical attached to the surface through the carbon atom, thus:

(*i*) Initiation:

$$\underset{M}{\overset{O}{\underset{\|}{\overset{\|}{C}}}} \quad \xrightarrow{2H} \quad \underset{M}{\overset{H \diagdown \diagup OH}{\underset{\|}{C}}}$$

(*ii*) Addition at end carbon atom to give straight-chain 'primary' intermediate:

$$\underset{M}{\overset{R \diagdown \diagup OH}{\underset{\|}{C}}} \; + \; \underset{M}{\overset{H \diagdown \diagup OH}{\underset{\|}{C}}} \; \longrightarrow \; \underset{M\;\;M}{\overset{R \diagdown \diagup OH}{\underset{\|\;\;\|}{C-C}}} \; (+H_2O) \xrightarrow{2H} \underset{M\;\;M}{\overset{R\cdot CH_2 \diagdown \diagup OH}{\underset{\|}{C}}}$$

(*iii*) Addition at end carbon to give straight-chain 'secondary' intermediate:

$$\underset{M}{\overset{R \diagdown \diagup OH}{\underset{\|}{C}}} \xrightarrow{H} \underset{M}{\overset{R \diagdown \diagup OH}{\underset{|}{CH}}} \longrightarrow \underset{M\;\;M}{\overset{R \diagdown \diagup OH}{\underset{|\;\;\|}{C--CH}}} (+H_2O) \xrightarrow{2H} \underset{M\;\;M}{\overset{R \diagdown \diagup OH}{\underset{|}{C-CH_3}}}$$

(*iv*) Addition to next-to-end carbon to give branched chain:

$$\underset{M}{\overset{\overset{\displaystyle CH_3}{|}}{\underset{\|}{\overset{R \diagdown \;|\; \diagup OH}{C}}}} \; + \; \underset{M}{\overset{H \diagdown \diagup OH}{\underset{\|}{C}}} \; \xrightarrow[+3H]{-H_2O} \; \underset{|}{\overset{CH_3}{R-CH-CH_2-OH}}$$

Other rather similar sequences[105] have been suggested with the intermediates attached to the surface by methylene carbons rather than by carbinol carbons. However, the scheme outlined above has received considerable backing from experiments with labelled alcohols, aldehydes, and with ketene. The first experiments[106] were with labelled ethyl alcohol, with the methyl and methylene carbon in turn labelled with ^{14}C. The alcohol is incorporated into the products in the presence of synthesis gas, and the labelled carbon can be followed into the products. The first important point is that with either carbon labelled there is a constant amount of radioactivity per product molecule and not an amount proportional to the chain length. Thus the molecule of alcohol is incorporated as a whole and not split into CH_3, CH_2 and so on. Also, the alcohol serves as an intermediate, one per molecule of product that has incorporated any alcohol. The distribution of methyl and methylene labelled carbon in the products shows that extra carbon-containing groups are added chiefly at the α-carbon of the alcohol, as indicated in the steps (ii), (iii) and (iv). Methyl alcohol is not effective in building chains. Higher alcohols are effective[107], and when present in very low proportions relative to the synthesis gas a strikingly high proportion of product molecules is formed with the alcohols as intermediates. Ketene is also very effective[108], the radioactivity per cubic centimetre of products from C_3 to C_8 being the same as for ketene when iron is the catalyst, and one-third of it when cobalt is the catalyst.

However, there are some difficulties with the theory of oxygenated intermediates as used in the scheme above. When carbon monoxide and hydrogen are admitted to iron or nickel catalyst prepared as films, there is evidence[20] from infra-red studies of the surface species that some carbon monoxide is adsorbed as shown in (i) but some is adsorbed as

In mixtures of carbon monoxide and hydrogen, there is no evidence of hydrogeneration to the form $\underset{\underset{M}{\|}}{HCOH}$; this is curious, for it has been known for some

time (and has been confirmed recently[109]) that more hydrogen is adsorbed after carbon monoxide has been pre-adsorbed. Of course, the infra-red conditions are much milder (lower pressures and temperatures) than the synthesis conditions, and it may not be possible to check the actual operating surface intermediates by infra-red techniques. It is also rather difficult to explain why all the added carbon does not go on to the carbinol carbon[107], at least in the first stage, say $C_2 \rightarrow C_3$. On balance, however, the schemes put forward by Storch, Anderson and colleagues are able to explain the majority of the observed phenomena.

8.5. THE SYNTHESIS OF METHANOL

In terms of production the catalytic synthesis of methanol from carbon monoxide and hydrogen is an important industrial process. The thermodynamics of the reaction, and the working conditions of temperature and pressure for the catalysed reaction, bear some interesting resemblances[77] to those of the synthesis of ammonia. Both reactions are exothermic, and both are accompanied by a decrease in the number of molecules present. The best conditions for efficient conversion if equilibrium could be reached would be low temperatures and high pressures. However, even the most active catalysts require operating temperatures as high as 400 to 500°C for ammonia and 300 to 450°C for methanol. At these temperatures, the free energy changes of both reactions are positive and large, so that the equilibrium constants are small. It is therefore essential to use high pressures between 100 and 500 atm to get good yields. There are some interesting contrasts between the reactions, too. The methanol synthesis is somewhat more complicated because of possible side reactions of the reactants and further reactions of the methanol. Over some catalysts, higher hydrocarbons or alcohols or aldehydes can appear from Fischer–Tropsch reactions, particularly at lower temperatures and pressures. Other catalysts, especially metals, can catalyse the formation of carbon dioxide and water by the reactions

$$2CO \rightarrow CO_2 + C$$
$$CO_2 + H_2 \rightarrow H_2O + CO$$

However, catalysts have been found that favour the methanol synthesis and by using these with high flow rates and keeping the conversion per pass low, the side reactions can be avoided.

The most effective catalysts are mixed oxides based on zinc oxide or cupric oxide. Neither of these oxides is very effective by itself, although certain preparations of zinc oxide are very selective, giving almost pure methanol at temperatures below 380°C. Also, some preparations of zinc oxide from minerals such as smithsonite are comparatively active[110], perhaps because of small proportions of promoters such as magnesium oxide or cupric oxide present in the mineral. The activity of the zinc oxide can be increased and the lifetime of the catalyst also increased by adding suitable promoters, which are usually high-melting-point oxides that are not easily reduced. The effective promoters for zinc oxide are chromic, ferrous and magnesium oxides; aluminium, thorium, zirconium and vanadium oxides have been used but are much less effective. Natta has pointed out[77] that some of these promoters, such as ferrous oxide, form solid solutions with zinc oxide, whereas others such as chromic oxide are not incorporated into the zinc oxide lattice. Chromic oxide, itself a poor catalyst for the synthesis, is the promoter most used. The effect of different proportions of the two components varies with the method of preparation and, as shown in *Figure 8.14*[111], with the operating temperature. The mixed catalysts have been prepared by mechanical mixing with good results, and also by co-precipitation of the hydroxides or the acetates of the metals and calcination, and by reduction of zinc chromate.

One of the principal functions of the promoter seems to be to keep the size of the crystallites low[112]; the size of these crystallites may affect the surface area and it may also affect the proportion of the faces exposed. Zinc oxide (and cupric oxide) crystallize in the hexagonal system, and some planes of its lattice contain only oxide ions, others contain only zinc ions. Another possible function of the promoters is to alter the surface concentrations of the crystal defects. There is clear evidence about the size of the crystallites from x-ray diffraction experiments of Natta and Corradini[112]. With the single oxide catalysts prepared from different minerals, the smallest crystallite size runs with the most active catalyst, and as the size grows, the activity decreases.

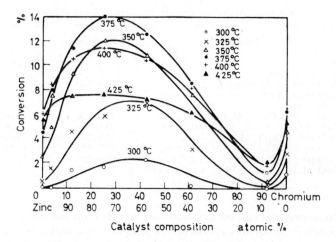

Figure 8.14. Percentage conversion of entering carbon monoxide to methanol during standard testing procedure at 178 atm[111]

Also, the crystallite sizes of mixed catalysts are much smaller than those of single catalysts and this holds true after prolonged heating, especially at higher temperatures. Schwab and Marhenkel[113] have also studied the effect of different methods of preparation and of different temperatures of drying of zinc oxide particles on the surface area, measured by the BET method or by isotopic exchange, and have shown that there is a considerable drop in area on heating the oxide (*Figure 5.3*). However, there does not appear to be any experimental evidence that the activity is correlated to the area, or whether the activity of unit area can change with the treatment. Natta has shown[114] that the activation energy of the synthesis is the same on pure zinc oxide and on the oxide promoted with chromic oxide, as shown in *Table 8.7*. This argues strongly that the same surface reaction with the same centres occurs on the simple and on the promoted catalyst. This could lead to increased rates if there were simply more area of the same sort and distribution of active centre on each unit area, or if there were more active centres per unit area and relatively little loss of area, in going from simple to promoted catalyst. As long as one thinks of the ions as the sites of adsorption, the first picture is attractive; but in view of the behaviour of these oxide catalysts in oxidation and similar reactions, it would be interesting to have measurements of the electrical conductivities of various catalysts under operating conditions.

It is significant that cupric oxide catalysts give much lower activation energies, as shown in *Table 8.7* for some doubly promoted catalysts. Catalysts based on copper oxide are more active initially than those based on zinc oxide, but this superiority is lost quite rapidly in operation. The copper oxide is reduced to copper too easily, and the metal is inactive as a synthesis catalyst. The best promoter for copper oxide is zinc oxide. It would appear that the mechanism on copper oxide catalysts involves a different rate-determining step.

Table 8.7. Activation energies for methanol synthesis[114]

Catalyst	Temperature °C	E cal mole^{-1}
Pure ZnO catalysts		
ZnO from smithsonite	325–370	27,000
ZnO from zinc acetate	330–353	30,000
Mixed catalysts		
CuO 34·6%–Cr$_2$O$_3$ 65·4%	292–326	14,000
ZnO 90%; Cr$_2$O$_3$ 5%; imbibed Cr$_2$O$_3$ 5%	331–365	28,000
ZnO 89%; Cr$_2$O$_3$ 11%	325–380	30,000
ZnO 80·8%; CuO 9·9%; Cr$_2$O$_3$ 9·3%	307–325	17,000
ZnO 60·9%; CuO 29·8%; Cr$_2$O$_3$ 9·3%	280–320	18,000
ZnO 51·3%; CuO 25·1%; Cr$_2$O$_3$ 23·6%	300–330	18,000

Both hydrogen and carbon monoxide are adsorbed on zinc oxide[115]. There is a weak reversible chemisorption at low temperatures, and a slow activated chemisorption at higher temperatures which is not reversible, the hydrogen being evolved as water and the carbon as carbon dioxide. This irreversible chemisorption almost certainly occurs by the formation of ions in each case. The chemisorption is increased by the addition of chromic oxide, but it is not certain whether this is due to increased area or to an increase in the sites for chemisorption per unit area; even if the adsorption starts on defects, however, the formation of positive ions on zinc oxide surfaces should lead to cumulative adsorption and reaction with the oxide ions.

The mechanisms advanced for the reaction over zinc oxide under synthesis conditions of high pressure have followed a Langmuir–Hinshelwood treatment without specifying the nature of the chemisorbed species. The treatment by Natta and his co-workers[116] has been extraordinarily successful in predicting rates from equations based on the assumptions that: (i) adsorption equilibria are established between all species and the surface, controlled by the fugacities F of gaseous species, and (ii) the rate-determining step on the surface is the termolecular forward step

$$CO(ads) + 2H_2(ads) \rightleftharpoons CH_3OH(ads)$$

and the unimolecular reverse reaction, with equilibrium constant K_{eq}. The rate of reaction, r, can then be expressed as

$$r = \frac{F_{CO}F_{H_2}^2 - (F_{CH_3OH}/K_{eq})}{(A + B.F_{CO} + C.F_{H_2} + D.F_{CH_3OH})^3}$$

By taking initial rates when F_{CH_3OH} can be put equal to zero, the constants A, B and C can be determined; by substituting them in the rate expression during a run, D can be evaluated. In this way, the constants were evaluated for temperatures from 320 to 390°C for various catalysts. The excellent agreement between predicted amount of methanol formed during runs at various temperatures and the amount found experimentally is shown in *Figure 8.15*. From the values of A, B, C and D, it is possible to calculate the equilibrium constants for the adsorption of the three gases at different temperatures, assuming that the concentration of adsorbing sites is independent of temperature. The results show that the methanol is the most strongly and the hydrogen

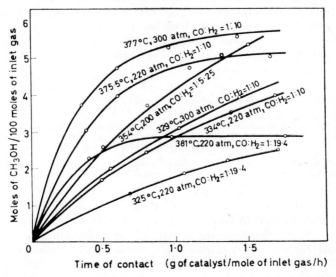

Figure 8.15. Calculated (lines) and experimental (points) conversions[117]

the least strongly adsorbed. If the amounts adsorbed during a run are in the same sequence, some explanation is found of the need for high partial pressures of hydrogen in the inlet mixtures. In experiments at low pressures, the amounts of the two reactant gases adsorbed are much more nearly equal for equal pressures, provided that long times are given for the attainment of adsorption equilibria. The kinetic estimates are therefore in part controlled by the short times of contact, giving estimates of the adsorption equilibrium constant that do not allow for the slow later adsorption of hydrogen.

8.6. HETEROGENEOUS CATALYSIS OF OXIDATIONS

Many oxidations are catalysed by metals or by oxides of metals. Some of these reactions have been investigated in great detail because they are important industrial processes, while some have in addition given us information about the mechanisms of oxidation catalysts[118]. In the first category are the oxidations of ammonia to nitric oxide and hence to nitric acid[119], of ammonia to nitrous oxide[120], of sulphur dioxide to sulphur trioxide[121], of carbon monoxide to carbon dioxide[122] and of various hydrocarbons to more valuable oxygenated products[118]. In the second category are the oxidations of ammonia and of carbon dioxide over oxide catalysts, of ethylene to ethylene oxide over silver catalysts[118] and of o-xylene to phthalic anhydride over vanadium pentoxide[123] which is a very versatile oxidation catalyst.

The oxides that are active in oxidation catalysis are nearly all semiconductor oxides with metals of variable valency. The chemisorption of gases on these oxides has been discussed in section 6.3, and it will be recalled that changes in the conductivity during adsorption indicate whether electrons move from the oxide to the chemisorbed species or vice versa. The decomposition of nitrous oxide on these catalysts can be thought of as the reverse of an oxidation, and it provides interesting evidence about the mechanism of catalysis by these oxides. Stone[124] has presented an 'activity series' showing the temperature at which the decomposition first becomes detectable, over various catalysts (*Figure 8.16*). There is a clear division into three groups: the *p*-type oxides are most active, the insulator oxides occupy a middle range, and the *n*-type

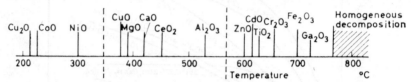

Figure 8.16. Relative activity of oxides for the decomposition of nitrous oxide, showing the temperature at which reaction first becomes appreciable[124]

oxides are least active. Moreover, with a typical *p*-type oxide the addition of an oxide with a cation of lower valency increases the activity in parallel with an increase in the electrical conductivity of the oxide, while the addition of oxides with higher valency cations produces exactly the opposite effect. Thus the addition of small quantities of lithium oxide (Li_2O) to nickel oxide (NiO) increases the activity for decomposition of nitrous oxide, while addition of indium oxide (In_2O_3) reduces it. The first additive increases the number of positive holes, with an increase in the conductivity and in the capacity of the surface to accept electrons. The increase in catalytic activity can be explained if the slow step is the loss of an electron to the surface oxide: a possible mechanism is the fast adsorption step $N_2O + e \rightarrow N_2 + O_{ads}^-$, while the slow step is one or both of the reactions

$$O_{ads}^- \rightarrow \tfrac{1}{2}O_2 + e$$

$$N_2O + O_{ads}^- \rightarrow O_2 + N_2 + e$$

Stone[124] and Winter[125] have recently discussed the mechanisms of this reaction and its relation to oxidations, and have emphasized the need for parallel studies of rates and the physical properties of the catalysts. Similar mechanisms of other oxidations will be discussed below.

8.6.1. *Oxidation of ammonia*

The thermal oxidation of ammonia, which is a complex chain reaction proceeding with measurable velocity only at high temperatures, produces mainly[126] water and nitrogen with traces of nitric oxide[127] in nearly stoichiometric mixtures and some hydrogen[128] with mixtures rich in ammonia. Ammonia can be burnt in air with difficulty, but the spectra of the flames show that the ammonia is first decomposed to NH_2 and NH and that these radicals react with oxygen[129]. Ammonia reacts fairly rapidly with nitric oxide or nitrogen dioxide at lower temperatures[130,131], yielding nitrogen and water by reactions such as

$$4NH_3 + 6NO \rightarrow 5N_2 + 6H_2O \tag{1}$$

$$2NH_3 + NO + NO_2 \rightarrow 2N_2 + 3H_2O \tag{2}$$

However, in the presence of certain catalysts, the oxidation can be controlled by suitable choice of temperature and flow rate to give either nitrous oxide or nitric oxide in very good yields. The behaviour of the surfaces of the catalysts suggest that they act through chemisorbing oxygen, either as atoms on the metals or ions on the effective oxides. There has naturally been much controversy over the course of these selective oxidations, and it must be admitted that satisfactory mechanisms have not yet been devised. It may be that studies of the high-temperature reactions of NH_2, NH and OH with NO_2, NO and O_2 in flames[129,132], and studies of the atomic reactions between H, N and O and these radicals, may help to discriminate between various proposals.

It has been known for a long time[133] that high yields of nitric oxide could be obtained if lean mixtures (say 8 per cent) of ammonia in air were passed at fairly high linear velocities over platinum gauze maintained by the heat of the exothermic oxidation at temperatures between 750 and 950°C. Yields of 80 to 100 per cent can be obtained, and they are not very sensitive to moderate changes in the temperature or the flow rate[134]. The catalyst is usually prepared in the form of successive layers of gauze, but with contact times of about 10^{-4} sec on each gauze more than 80 per cent conversion appears to occur on the first gauze; the succeeding layers take over as the first is destroyed during the reaction. It is remarkable that there is so little effect from side reactions such as

$$2NH_3 \rightarrow N_2 + 3H_2 \tag{3}$$

$$2NO \rightarrow N_2 + O_2 \tag{4}$$

which are known to occur on platinum surfaces[135] (and also on the surface of steel containers[119]). Perhaps the second reaction is inhibited by the oxygen present; the behaviour of the catalyst surface suggests that it is largely occupied by a chemisorbed layer of oxygen. The reaction of ammonia with this layer must be the cause of the production of nitric oxide rather than nitrogen which is formed over platinum in the absence of oxygen. Only at substantially lower temperatures or flow rates is there appreciable diminution of the yield of nitric oxide, due to reaction 4. At very high flow rates there may be loss due to reactions 1 and 2.

It has also been known[136] since 1930 that ammonia could be oxidized to nitrous oxide over oxides of bismuth and iron at temperatures around 300°C. Much more recently, Zawadzki[120] showed that many oxides or oxide mixtures give appreciable yields of nitrous oxide. The oxides that readily give lower oxides are particularly effective. Thus barium peroxide which readily decomposes to barium oxide gives nitrous oxide as the major product even if no gaseous oxygen is present; mixed catalysts containing manganese dioxide and either ferric oxide or cupric oxide are also very effective, as is nickelous oxide with oxygen presorbed in the lattice[137]. On the other hand, even platinum can give[120] appreciable proportions of nitrous oxide at temperatures below 450°C. Comparison of *Figures 8.17* and *8.18* shows that there is a similar pattern of product formation over platinum and over a mixed oxide, the yield of nitrous oxide passing through a maximum at 350 to 400°C, and the yield of

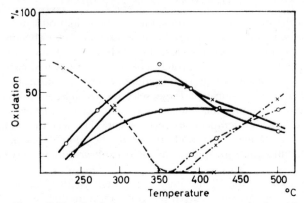

Figure 8.17. Oxidation of ammonia over a mixed oxide catalyst[120]
Catalyst: 45% CuO + 45% MnO$_2$ + 10% CaCO$_3$. Incoming gases: 10% NH$_3$+90% O$_2$.
—— N$_2$O, —·— NO, – – – NH$_3$. o 5 l./h, × 10 l./h

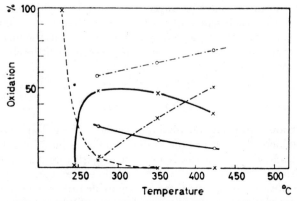

Figure 8.18. Oxidation of ammonia over platinum gauze[120]
Catalyst: platinum gauze 1039 mesh cm^{-2}, triple folded. Incoming gases: 10% NH$_3$+ 90% O$_2$. —— N$_2$O, —·— NO, – – – NH$_3$. × 4 l./h, o 16 l./h

nitric oxide rising with higher temperatures, although it is always higher on the metal. All this suggests that the chemisorbed oxygen on the platinum plays an important role although it cannot function quite like the oxygen ions in the oxides.

Many intermediates have been proposed in these oxidations. Bodenstein[138a] and Andrussov[135] carried out many careful investigations of the effects of temperature, contact time, reactant composition and possible side reactions. They formulated reaction schemes based on nitroxyl (HNO) or hydroxylamine (NH$_3$O) as the primary intermediates; in these schemes, nitrous oxide was formed by the reaction of two HNO groups, and nitric oxide was formed by the reaction of two HNO_2 molecules, themselves formed by oxidation of HNO. Krauss[138b] proposed similar intermediates. Lately, Zawadzki[120] has revived interest in the radical NH as intermediate; this was first suggested by Raschig[139]. Zawadzki again postulates the formation of nitric oxide from HNO_2 and nitrous oxide from HNO, and suggests a variety of reactions which could form nitrogen under conditions of slow flow and so on.

There is no certainty which radicals are adsorbed on the surface and which are desorbed into the gas phase. There is some evidence from thermocouple measurements that heat is released downstream from the catalyst as well as on its surface. It would be most helpful if it were known whether NH_2 or NH radicals were attached to the platinum directly or through the chemisorbed oxygen, and whether the relative proportions so adsorbed change much with the temperature and so cause the change in the product distributions.

It seems likely that the first reaction is removal of one or more hydrogen atoms from the ammonia by chemisorbed oxygen, to give NH_2 or NH radicals. If the nitrogen of these radicals is attached to surface oxygen at lower temperatures, then HNO may desorb to react in the gas phase with NH:

$$HNO + NH \rightarrow N_2O + H_2$$

or two HNO radicals might form a surface complex

$$H—N—O—Pt$$
$$|$$
$$N—N—O—Pt$$

which breaks down to give hydrogen, nitrous oxide and a partially covered surface which is rapidly oxidized by the oxygen. Such complexes are far more acceptable in face of the infra-red evidence about multiple bonding to the surface of metals. At higher temperatures, it seems possible that NH is oxidized to nitric oxide and OH radicals, either on the surface or in the gas phase, the nitric oxide desorbing rapidly and the OH radicals giving water and a partially oxidized surface. The principal effect of temperature is then to alter the lifetime of the chemisorbed HNO, low temperatures favouring longer life and increased chance of formation of the N—N bond. It does not seem necessary to suppose that nitrous acid is formed as an intermediate before nitric oxide appears. Also, it would appear that the most likely reaction of any HNO radicals that escaped into the gas phase was with oxygen to give OH radicals and nitrogen dioxide.

It would appear that infra-red absorption experiments on this system, if they could be carried out at high temperatures, might provide some crucial information.

8.6.2. *Oxidation of sulphur dioxide*

The annual production of sulphuric acid is very large, and much of the acid is made by the oxidation of sulphur dioxide to sulphur trioxide over platinum or vanadium pentoxide catalysts[121]. Other transition metals such as tungsten, palladium, gold and chromium are active catalysts, but not as active nor as durable as platinum. Other catalysts have been grouped[140] into low-temperature catalysts like platinum (especially the vanadates of sodium, potassium, barium, silver, rubidium, caesium, copper and tin) and high-temperature catalysts like vanadium pentoxide (especially the oxides of tungsten, titanium, iron, tin, chromium and arsenic). However, only platinum and vanadium pentoxide, alone or promoted with alkali sulphates or pyro-sulphates, are widely used for industrial processes. The use of platinized asbestos as a catalyst was proposed as long ago as 1831, when a patent was granted to Phillips for the process. For a long time the method was not success-ful commercially because dust, unoxidized sulphur and traces of mercury, arsenic and phosphorus (derived from the pyrites used as the source of sulphur) rapidly poison the platinum catalyst. The researches of Winkler at Freiburg, and of Kneitsch and other chemists of Badische Anilin- und Sodafabrik showed that sulphur dioxide and air could be purified sufficiently by injection of steam and thorough washing through filters drenched with sulphuric acid.

The platinum catalyst is usually supported on asbestos or on magnesium sulphate granules or on silica gel[141]. The vanadium catalysts consist of pellets of the supporting material impregnated with the pentoxide or an alkali-metal vanadate; some of these catalysts are calcined in an atmosphere of sulphur dioxide and contain K_2SO_4 and $K_2S_2O_7$ on their surfaces[141].

The vanadium catalysts which have been sulphated present complex sur-faces to the reactant gases. Boreskov[142] used chemical, thermal and x-ray analyses to show that V_2O_5 and K_2SO_4 form a compound which with K_2SO_4 gives a eutectic mixture; $K_2S_2O_7$ similarly gives low melting point mixtures with V_2O_5. It is likely that some of the promoted catalysts have a melt on their surfaces under operating conditions when the temperature may be be-tween 500 and 600°C[143]. The activation energy of conversion on these surfaces is lower than those reported for the surfaces of pure V_2O_5 catalysts, as shown in *Table 8.8*. This table also shows that various rate laws have been found by different investigators, without any very clear pattern emerging. It is thought that the rates of chemisorption of the three gases sulphur dioxide, sulphur trioxide and oxygen on the commercial catalysts at temperatures just below the operating temperatures decrease in the order $SO_2 > SO_3 > O_2$. Calder-bank[144] considers that a gas-phase oxygen molecule reacts with a chemisorbed sulphur dioxide molecule, in a slow rate-determining step:

$$SO_2 + 2e \rightarrow SO_2^{2-} \text{ (chemisorbed)}$$

$$SO_2^{2-} + O_2 \rightarrow SO_3 + O^{2-} \text{ (both chemisorbed)}$$

$$O^{2-} \rightarrow \tfrac{1}{2}O_2 + 2e$$

However, most of the active oxides are *n*-type semiconductor oxides, with excess electrons, and there is some evidence that increasing the electron density will increase the activity[140]. Thus with ferric oxide, the addition of oxides of Sn^{4+} or As^{5+} will increase the activity, whereas addition of K^+ or Cu^{2+} decreases it. This seems to suggest that some reaction with electrons passing from the catalyst is rate-determining. It is not easy to accept the reac-tion with sulphur dioxide as rate-determining, for this appears to be fast; if it is reaction with oxygen, the rate of reaction should, as pointed out by Clark and Berets[123] for this reaction and the oxidation of xylene, be proportional to $P_{O_2}^{\cdot 5}$. The other terms that appear in the rate expressions in *Table 8.8* are then due to the limitation of the surface available for chemisorption of oxygen because of the preferred chemisorption of sulphur dioxide and sulphur trioxide.

Table 8.8. Kinetics of the oxidation of sulphur dioxide on platinum and vanadium pentoxide catalysts[118]

Catalyst	Activation energy kcal mole^{-1}	Kinetics	Reference
Pt	10	$k[SO_2]/[SO_3]^{0.5}$	145
Pt	—	$\dfrac{k\,(\text{distance from equilibrium})}{[SO_3]^{0.5}}$	146
Pt or Pt on SiO$_2$	23	—	147
V$_2$O$_5$	38	—	148
V$_2$O$_5$ promoted	23–27	$k[O_2][SO_2]^{0.8}/[SO_3]^{0.8}$	147, 148
V$_2$O$_5$	34	$\dfrac{k_1[SO_2]^{0.5}[O]^{0.5}}{[SO_3]^{0.5}} - \dfrac{k_2[SO_3]^{0.5}}{[SO_2]^{0.5}}$	149
V$_2$O$_5$ promoted	29–31	$k[SO_2]^{0.4}[O_2]^{0.8}$	144

Very different mechanisms have been proposed for the reaction on the promoted catalysts. For example, Frazer and Kirkpatrick[150] proposed that compounds are formed in the surface 'melt' involving catalyst, reactants, promoter and support:

$$K_2S_2O_7 + V_2O_5 + 2SO_2 \rightarrow 2KV(SO_4)_2$$

$$2KV(SO_4)_2 + 2SiO_2 \rightarrow V_2Si_2O_7 + K_2S_2O_7 + 2SO_3$$

$$V_2Si_2O_7 + O_2 \rightarrow V_2O_5 + 2SiO_2$$

Mars and van Krevelen[151] showed that the rates in flow systems followed a rate law that could be fitted to the mechanism

$$SO_2 + Cat\!-\!O \rightleftharpoons SO_3 + Cat \qquad \text{(fast reaction)}$$

$$Cat + O_2 \rightarrow Cat\!-\!O \qquad \text{(slow reaction)}$$

A basic pattern like the last simplified scheme would appear to fit the evidence so far available from the correlation of rates and semiconducting properties of the catalysts discussed above.

The rate laws found for the reaction over metal catalysts are scarcely less complicated. It has generally been found that the rates are nearly independent of the oxygen pressure, however, and they are often nearly proportional to the first power of the sulphur dioxide concentration and inversely proportional to a power of the sulphur trioxide concentration which is near to one-half. Taylor and Lenher[146] have suggested that an equation which takes account of the back reaction can be fitted to their data on rates; the equation they propose is

$$\text{Rate} = \frac{k \text{ (distance from equilibrium)}}{[SO_3]^{0.5}}$$

More complicated equations have been suggested by Lewis and Ries[152]. Bodenstein and Fink[145] found a rate law which they explained by a mechanism involving the reaction of gaseous sulphur dioxide molecules with chemisorbed oxygen, with sulphur trioxide so strongly adsorbed that it inhibited the chemisorption of the oxygen. Surface reactions between chemisorbed sulphur dioxide and chemisorbed oxygen atoms have also been proposed as the rate-determining step. Boreskov[147] has proposed that many of the data can be fitted to an expression not unlike that proposed for the synthesis of ammonia (page 213), k_1 and k_2 being the velocity constants for the formation and the decomposition of the sulphur trioxide:

$$\text{Rate} = \frac{k_1[SO_2][O_2]^{0.25}}{[SO_3]^{0.5}} - \frac{k_2[SO_3]^{0.5}}{[O_2]^{0.25}}$$

This equation is very like that proposed by Krichevskaya[149] for the catalysed reaction on pure vanadium pentoxide, with different exponents of the concentrations of oxygen (see *Table 8.8*).

8.6.3. Oxidation of carbon monoxide

The catalytic oxidation of carbon monoxide is important in any attempts to extract the maximum amount of heat from the combustion of any carbon-containing compounds (especially in restricted supplies of oxygen) and in the removal of this poisonous and inflammable gas from air. The reaction has also been used extensively to study the behaviour of catalyst surfaces in chemisorption and reaction, because the over-all reaction is simple. The detailed mechanism of the catalysed reaction over any catalyst has unexpected complexities, however, and relatively few firm conclusions about detailed mechanisms have been reached[118,122,153,154].

It has been known for many years that the transition metals catalyse the oxidation, and that some promoted metals are especially effective. Colloidal platinum and platinum black[155], and copper promoted with palladium[156] have been used, for example to combust carbon monoxide in gas analyses, at moderate temperatures around 150 to 200°C. Silver oxide[157] is an effective catalyst around 200°C, and silver permanganate[158] is very active when promoted by a wide variety of weakly basic or weakly acidic oxides and especially by manganese dioxide; these silver catalysts are not poisoned by water vapour and are active under conditions of high relative humidity.

The most active catalysts, however, are those containing mixtures of manganese dioxide, cupric oxide, cobaltous oxide or nickelous oxide with other oxides[159]. These oxides have been characterized[160] by interatomic distances in the crystals of 1·75 to 1·85 Å; less importance is now attached to this, especially as other oxides with this spacing are not active. The mixed oxide catalysts based on manganese dioxide are known as Hopcalites. They are active with dry gases at temperatures as low as $-20°C$, but they are poisoned by water vapour; this poisoning is reversible and the catalysts can be reactivated by heating to moderate temperatures[122]. The most robust and active Hopcalites are: (*i*) a binary mixture of 60 per cent manganese dioxide and 40 per cent cupric oxide, and (*ii*) a four-component mixture of 50 per cent manganese dioxide, 30 per cent cupric oxide, 15 per cent cobaltic oxide and 5 per cent silver oxide. Different methods of preparation lead to different activities, however, partly because they yield crystallites of different sizes and so give different surface areas per gramme. The rate of oxidation on these mixed catalysts is usually independent of the pressure of carbon monoxide.

It has been found that the surfaces of these active oxides are reduced by carbon monoxide. It is therefore possible that the catalysis proceeds by alternate reduction and oxidation of the surface. This mechanism was suggested by Benton[161] for the oxidation over manganese dioxide. Both the reduction and the catalysed oxidation have rates which are proportional to the pressure of carbon monoxide over the single catalyst. In view of later evidence, this mechanism seems unlikely; by using ^{18}O, it has been shown[162] that the rate of reduction of the surface is slower by a factor of 10 than the rate of catalytic oxidation. It is difficult to see how the addition of oxygen could alter the rate of reduction of the surface, especially as it has been shown that carbon monoxide in air extracts relatively little ^{18}O from the surface[163].

The alternative mechanisms involve reaction between the gases chemisorbed on the oxide surfaces, or reaction between gas-phase carbon monoxide and oxygen chemisorbed in some form on the surface. Stone[164] has examined the results of investigations by many workers, including those at Bristol, and has shown that there is a qualitative connection between the activities of a variety of oxides and their semiconducting properties. The most active oxides are the *p*-type oxides which give measurable rates of oxidation at low temperatures— in some cases below $50°C$. These include manganese dioxide and some oxides used in Hopcalites. The next most effective are *n*-type oxides, such as ferric oxide, zinc oxide and titanium dioxide, which are active between 150 and $400°C$, but some intrinsic semiconductors like cupric and chromic oxides are also active. Stone considers that oxygen is chemisorbed on the surface of the *p*-types oxides at low temperatures, and that gas-phase carbon monoxide reacts with this chemisorbed oxygen:

$$O_2 + 2e \rightleftharpoons O_2^{2-} \quad \text{or} \quad 2O^- \text{ (chemisorbed)}$$

$$CO(gas) + O_2^{2-} \text{ (chemisorbed)} \rightarrow CO_3^{2-} \text{ (chemisorbed)}$$

$$\rightarrow O^{2-} + CO_2(gas)$$

Alternatively, on some oxides such as cuprous oxide the surface complex CO_3^{2-} may be decomposed by excess carbon monoxide[165]. At higher temperatures, 150 to $200°C$, carbon monoxide attacks the surface of these *p*-type oxides to form CO_3^{2-} with the surface ions, creating an anion vacancy which is filled with oxygen. A substantial change in activation energy from 2 to 3 kcal mole^{-1} at low temperatures to about 14 kcal at high has been observed[166]. On *n*-type oxides, chemisorption of oxygen would be depletive and so is very slight and the low-temperature mechanism is not effective; the high-temperature mechanism proceeds as on *p*-type oxides.

These simple schemes may require modification, because there are many differences in the observed behaviour with various oxides, various methods of preparation or pretreatment, and with different temperatures. Winter[167,168] has studied the exchange reactions of oxygen, carbon monoxide and carbon dioxide with oxide catalysts using ^{18}O, and formulates reactions different from those given above. He considers that the rate-determining step on nickelous oxide and chromic oxide is the reaction of oxygen with the surface to give O^{2-} and an oxygen atom, which subsequently forms the ion, followed by reaction of carbon monoxide from the gas phase with the ions to give CO_3^{2-}. He also showed that the reaction takes place on a few sites and not over the surface. Vainshtein and Turovskii[163] found that very little exchange took place with ^{18}O in chromic oxide surfaces, and concluded that the reaction did not take place by alternate reduction and oxidation. However, these studies do not give unequivocal evidence unless it is known what fraction of the surface sites are active in the catalysis, for an intense reaction on a few sites would appear to give little exchange whereas the same intensity of reaction spread over many sites would give much exchange.

Parravano and Boudart[154], and Schwab and Block[169], studied the effect on the oxidation over nickelous oxide of incorporating oxides of metals with singly and triply charged cations. Working in different temperature ranges, they found almost diametrically opposed results. Parravano and Boudart found that the additives have little effect on the low-temperature reaction, although the rate of this reaction is not very reproducible. With the high-temperature reaction, oxides with M^{1+} raise the activation energy from about 14 to about 17 kcal mole^{-1}, whereas M^{3+} oxides lowered it to about 8 kcal. As explained on page 142, the addition of M^{3+} oxides to p-type semiconductor oxides makes it easier to chemisorb oxygen whereas M^{1+} oxides should make it more difficult; hence the changes of activation energy point to a chemisorption of oxygen as rate-determining, as Winter suggests. However, as mentioned, Schwab and Block found the opposite change in activation energy at higher temperatures. Stone[164] and Parravano and Boudart[154] have attempted to rationalize these different and apparently conflicting results, but it appears that further work is necessary to check the experimental data and the interpretations.

The infra-red studies[170] of carbon monoxide and dioxide chemisorption on mixed nickel–nickelous oxide catalysts have introduced further difficulties, suggesting that the chemisorbed species depends upon the sequence of admission of gases as well as the pretreatment of the catalyst. If oxygen is admitted before carbon monoxide, then the spectrum of the bicarbonate ion CO_3^- is found, whereas if both gases are admitted together, the spectrum observed is attributed to Ni—O—C—O. Of course, the species observed may not be those active in the catalysis, and if this proceeds on a few sites, as Winter suggests, the active species may not be detected spectroscopically.

8.6.4. Oxidation of hydrocarbons

The controlled oxidation of hydrocarbons in the vapour phase over selected catalysts provides valuable methods of preparing oxygenated derivatives such as quinones, aldehydes, acids and acid anhydrides on a large scale. These derivatives are only moderately stable towards oxidation under the conditions used to prepare them, and the catalyst and the conditions of temperature and mixture composition must be carefully selected. Dixon and Longfield have given an excellent summary[171] of the work done on these selective oxidations. They deal in particular with the oxidation of aromatic derivatives to simpler structures and the oxidation of olefins. The oxidation of benzene to give maleic anhydride is important commercially, and so are those of naphthalene and of o-xylene to phthalic anhydride. With aliphatics, the oxidation of ethylene to ethylene oxide is useful and very interesting mechanistically.

Benzene can be oxidized to a variety of products. With high pressures and a high proportion of benzene it is possible to get phenol and hydroquinone, and quinone can also be prepared; but the biggest application is in the preparation of maleic anhydride using as catalyst vanadium pentoxide or mixtures of this oxide, silver oxide and other oxides. Low pressures of air-rich mixtures are used at 325 to 530°C.

In a similar manner, naphthalene can be oxidized to phthalic anhydride and to naphthaquinone simultaneously, although the naphthaquinone is further oxidized to phthalic anhydride and both these products are slowly oxidized to maleic anhydride. The oxidation of o-xylene to phthalic anhydride proceeds readily over vanadium pentoxide catalysts[172], and there have been some fundamental studies of the kinetics and of the behaviour of the catalyst. The catalyst is considerably reduced under normal conditions of oxidation[173]; thus with as little as 1 per cent of o-xylene in air, much V_2O_4 (which is catalytically inactive) is produced, while with 3 per cent of o-xylene V_2O_3 is found. The reaction seems to involve reduction of the surface and reoxidation by the oxygen; it would be interesting to check this using ^{18}O. Some confirmation is provided by studies[123] of the changes of electrical conductivity and thermoelectric e.m.f. with the presence of xylene or the oxidation mixtures. The catalyst is an n-type semiconductor, with anion vacancies under the normal pressure of oxygen. Oxygen is chemisorbed to only a limited extent, as the chemisorption is depletive. On exposure to the hydrocarbon, the surface conductivity increases; either the hydrocarbon gives a positive ion and electrons, or removes oxygen ions and releases electrons:

$$Xy + O^{2-} \rightarrow \text{oxidation product} + 2e$$

$$Xy \rightarrow Xy^+ + e$$

The oxygen then replaces the ion:

$$\tfrac{1}{2}O_2 + 2e \rightarrow O^{2-}$$

There is some evidence that the oxidation takes place at grain boundaries, with some sintering of the crystallites; this has also been observed in the oxidation of ethylene over silver. There is also evidence that the anion defects are mobile in the surface at comparatively low temperatures around 150° and in the bulk around 350°C. This change of mobility may account for the occurrence of minimum temperatures for catalytic activity in oxides.

o-Xylene can also be selectively oxidized[172] to give tolualdehyde if the oxides of zirconium, molybdenum or tungsten are used as catalysts, especially if the air–xylene ratio is kept below 5. The mechanisms of the alternative routes are not clear.

16—c.

The oxidation of o-xylene to phthalic anhydride appears to be controlled by the rate of oxygen chemisorption, for the rate of oxidation is independent of the ethylene pressure and proportional to the square root of the oxygen pressure[123]. As there is evidence of electron transfer in the reaction, it appears that the rate depends upon some step such as

$$O_{ads} + e \rightarrow O^- \qquad \text{(slow reaction)}$$

which follows

$$\tfrac{1}{2}O_2 \rightleftharpoons O_{ads}$$

and is followed by the fast reaction

$$Xy + O^- \rightarrow \text{oxidation product} + e$$

However, doubly charged ions of oxygen may also be involved.

There has been a great deal of work on the oxidation of ethylene to ethylene oxide. This is an unusual type of oxidation as an oxygen atom is added across the π-bond:

$$C_2H_4 + \tfrac{1}{2}O_2 \rightarrow C_2H_4O$$

The best catalyst is silver, alone or promoted with other metals such as gold, copper, iron or manganese or with oxides such as barium peroxide. The metal has been used in various forms, including studies of films and of single crystal faces, but for large-scale operations it is usually spread on to alumina as a support[174]. When high air–ethylene ratios (10 to 20) are used, the yields are generally about 50 per cent with a gentle maximum at about 260°C. Various rate laws have been proposed, some of the simple form

$$\frac{d[C_2H_4O]}{dt} = k[C_2H_4]^a[O_2]^b$$

with a about 1/3 and b about 2/3 and an activation energy of 19 kcal[175], and others[176] of the form

$$\frac{d[C_2H_4O]}{dt} = k[C_2H_4]/([C_2H_4][O_2] + c[C_2H_4] + d[O_2])[O_2]$$

Lower values[177, 178] of the activation energy, around 10 or 12 kcal, have been reported. It is generally agreed that the carbon dioxide which is formed in parallel comes partly from oxidation of the ethylene oxide, but also by an alternative route from ethylene[177]. This has been confirmed by using ^{14}C in the ethylene[179]. There are reports[180] that the carbon dioxide can reduce the rate of production of the ethylene oxide, whereas acetaldehyde or chlorinated ethylenes[174,181] increase the yield. Over oxides of copper and chromium the ethylene oxide is oxidized very rapidly and similar results have been found[182] for magnesium oxide–chromic oxide. On single crystals of silver, Kummer[183] reports that the reaction proceeds with different initial velocities on different faces, but that the rates soon become equal on these different faces because some process of sintering takes place. It also appears that the velocity is the same on films with different faces exposed initially[184]. Twigg[177] examined the chemisorption of the reactants on silver and found that ethylene is scarcely chemisorbed and that the chemisorption of oxygen is slow and activated. He also examined the rate of reaction between ethylene and the oxygen chemisorbed, showing that the rate of production of ethylene oxide is proportional to the fraction θ_O of surface covered with oxygen, but the rate of production of carbon dioxide is proportional to θ_O^2; he considered that the rate of reaction was determined by a reaction between the chemisorbed oxygen and a molecule of ethylene in a physically adsorbed layer. In the normal oxidation, with a mixture of oxygen and ethylene, he considered, as others have done, that the rate was determined by the rate of chemisorption of oxygen. Lyubarskii[185] has measured the electrical conductivity of films of silver on glass filaments, showing that chemisorption of oxygen causes transfer of electrons from the silver to the chemisorbed species so that the conductivity of the film decreases. Under the conditions of the reaction producing ethylene oxide, however, the conductivity is close to that of the reduced film, supporting the chemisorption of oxygen as the slow step. Lastly, some measurements of the rate of chemisorption show that there is a change in the rate at about $\theta = 0\cdot5$, and this has been attributed to the formation of double bonds to two surface atoms of silver in the early stages of the chemisorption.

Dixon and Longfield[171] have suggested that the oxidation of ethylene over silver is a reaction worthy of further study, using a variety of techniques including the measurement of electrical conductivity, under reaction conditions. Probably an examination of the chemisorption of ethylene by infrared spectroscopy would also be valuable. Very little is known about the mechanism of action of promoters nor about the reasons for the improved yields when chlorinated hydrocarbons are added in small quantities.

8.7. CATALYTIC CRACKING AND RELATED REACTIONS

The need to husband the oil resources of the world and the increasing use of petroleum as a source of chemicals have led to the introduction of many catalysed reactions in the refining and treatment of petroleums. The emphasis has changed in different decades[186-8]. There was first the demand for purification of the oils, particularly from sulphur; then came the need for motor and aviation fuel of better quality; and this in turn led to a search for methods of using the low-boiling fractions produced from the refining and breakdown of the crude petroleums; later still, the preparation of monomers like styrene and butadiene for rubbers and other polymers became important. While it is generally accepted that most of the reactions involve the formation (as intermediates) of carbonium ions and their subsequent isomerization, addition and exchange reactions, little is known of the details of the mechanisms. Thanks to extensive research, the best conditions for the operation of useful catalysts have been discovered empirically, and reasonably satisfactory rules for predicting the distribution of products are known. There is need for much more exploratory work on the kinetics and mechanisms of the various reactions.

The principal reactions are now grouped as (1) *cracking* reactions, in which lower-boiling point hydrocarbons are produced from 'heavier' petroleum fractions; (2) *catalytic reforming*, which involves hydrogenation–dehydrogenation and isomerization reactions and ring opening and closing; (3) *hydro-treating*, that is the catalytic hydrogenation of unsaturated compounds and the breakdown of compounds containing sulphur and nitrogen with the formation and removal of hydrogen sulphide and ammonia; and (4) *alkylation* and *polymerization* reactions which are often the reverse of the cracking reactions. Alkylations have been discussed in section 2.11, and polymerization reactions are the subject of Chapter 10.

8.7.1. Cracking and reforming reactions

The first cracking processes, used in 1920–30, were uncatalysed thermal reactions. In these reactions, large paraffin molecules or the side chains of substituted aromatic molecules are broken into smaller saturated hydrocarbons and olefins with, it is thought, uncharged free radicals as intermediates. The major final products are C_1 to C_3 hydrocarbons from paraffins and olefins and the side chains of aromatics. It was soon discovered, however, that better fuels could be prepared by catalytic decomposition, and uncatalysed thermal cracking has been substantially replaced by catalysed cracking over charcoal or platinum, over various acidic catalysts, such as acid-treated clays or silica–alumina mixtures, or over 'dual-purpose' catalysts of platinum, nickel or molybdenum on alumina. The acid catalysts are thought to function like Friedel–Crafts catalysts by giving from olefins carbonium ions which react in various ways to produce a pattern of products very different from that found in thermal cracking, with larger yields of C_3 and C_4 hydrocarbons, branched olefins and isoparaffins and aromatic compounds which are particularly useful in motor fuels or as starting points of the synthesis of other chemicals. The reactions over metal catalysts are probably free radical in character, but again the products are more useful than with thermal cracking, for there is more isomerization to branched chains, dehydrogenation of C_5 and C_6 naphthenes to aromatics and cyclization of paraffins; these are often classed apart from cracking reactions as 'reforming' reactions. The principal differences in the products of thermal and acid-catalysed reactions are shown in *Table 8.9*.

Table 8.9. Products of thermal and acid-catalysed reactions

Nature of reactant	Thermal cracking	Acid-catalysed cracking
Aliphatics	major products: C_2 hydrocarbons, with considerable amounts of CH_4 and C_3 hydrocarbons olefins: mainly $C_4 - C_{15}$ branching: little amount of aromatics: very small	C_3-C_6 hydrocarbons few above C_4 much large
Olefins	very little rearrangement split at about same rate as paraffins	much skeletal isomerization crack faster: much hydrogen shift
Aromatics	side chains split like paraffins, with one C group often left on ring ⬡—C ┆ C—C ┆ C—C—C substituted and unsubstituted aromatics crack at slower rate than paraffins	split off whole side chain and replace by H ⬡ ┆ C—C—C—C—C substituted aromatics crack at faster rate than paraffins, unsubstituted at slower

The first acid catalyst used was anhydrous $AlCl_3$, and other Friedel–Crafts catalysts like BF_3 have been used. However, the majority of processes use acid-treated clays, bentonite or kaolin, or synthetic silica–alumina or silica–alumina–zirconia catalysts. Several investigations have shown parallels between their surface acidity and the rate of cracking. The acidity has been determined by suspending the catalyst in benzene and titrating with n-butylamine using *p*-dimethylaminoazobenzene as indicator; by the evolution of CO_2 from a carbonate or of CH_4 from methylmagnesium bromide; by the

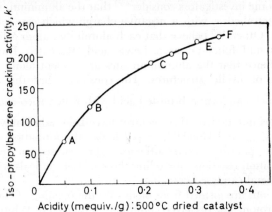

Figure 8.19. Dependence of isopropylbenzene cracking activity at 500° on acidity for a series of alumina–silica catalysts[189]

Catalyst	A	B	C	D	E	F
Al_2O_3 per cent	0·12	0·32	1·04	2·05	3·56	10·3

rate of hydrolysis of sucrose; and by adsorption of ammonia or quinoline from the vapour. Tamele, Schlaffer and Johnson[189] investigated the cracking of isopropyl benzene at 500°C and the polymerization of propylene at 200°C over a series of alumina–silica catalysts and found the activity to increase with the surface acidity (*Figure 8.19*). Milliken, Mills and Oblad[190-1] found a

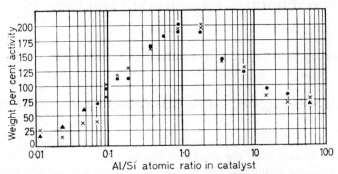

Figure 8.20. Comparison of observed activity (X) with the activity calculated from acidity (●) or composition (▲)[192]

similar effect for cracking of oils over various catalysts. Thomas[192] observed a correlation between acidity and activity of mixed silica–alumina catalysts which he was able to explain quantitatively. *Figure 8.20* shows the relation between the measured activity (weight per cent change in 1 h for a given flow rate) and that calculated from the acidity, making some simple assumptions about the contribution to it from each component.

245

Thomas considered also the activity of other binary mixtures of insulator and acidic oxides (MgO, Zr_2O_3, B_2O_3, TiO_2) and related it to the coordination numbers of the two metallic elements.

There is still considerable doubt whether the acid centres are Brönsted or Lewis acids. Some investigators consider[192] that the aluminium is coordinated to four silica tetrahedra, with a negative charge which can retain adsorbed hydrogen ions. Others[190] believe that each aluminium atom is linked to three oxygen atoms and functions as a Lewis acid. Recently, Danforth[193] has described evidence that the aluminium sites are present along the edge of a double chain of cyclic structures. He considers that the active site is

$>$Al—OH which can form a Brönsted acid with water as co-catalyst.

The reactions initiated by these centres have been admirably discussed by Greensfelder, Voge and Good[194], in particular the formation of carbonium ions from olefins, paraffins and naphthenes and the subsequent rearrangement, fission and addition reactions, including those of free radicals which occur in thermal and metal-catalysed cracking.

Carbonium ions are formed from olefins by the opening of the π-bond and addition of a proton. The preferred combination is given by Whitmore's rule[195] —the ion is formed which has most alkyl groups attached to the carbonium carbon—which was given some quantitative backing by the calculation of the proton affinities of primary, secondary and tertiary carbon atoms[196]. The method of formation from saturated aliphatics or naphthenes is less certain: it may be through the prior formation of an olefin or by extraction of a hydride ion

$$RH + H^+ \rightarrow R^+ + H_2$$

The carbonium ions can rearrange by reactions such as

$$CH_3 \cdot CH_2 \cdot \overset{+}{C}H_2 \rightarrow CH_3—CH{=}CH_2 \rightarrow CH_3—\overset{+}{C}H—CH_3$$
$$\underset{H^+}{|}$$

or by splitting (β to the carbonium carbon) and re-alkylation

$$CH_3 \cdot \overset{+}{C}H \cdot CH_2 \cdot CH_3 \rightarrow CH_3 \cdot CH{=}CH_2 + CH_3^+ \rightarrow \quad \overset{CH_3}{\underset{CH_3}{\diagdown\!\!\diagup}} CH \cdot CH_2^+$$

The olefin formed from the β-scission can in turn form a carbonium ion, and the cracking continues. The primary carbonium ion can also rearrange; the isomers can then crack to lower olefins and primary carbonium ions, and so on.

Although isomerizations occur spontaneously in all cracking and reforming processes, they are especially important in the conversion of n-C_4 and n-C_5 hydrocarbons to isoparaffins, for example for the production from n-butane of the isobutane used in the alkylation of olefins to branched octanes. Aluminium chloride with HCl has been used as catalyst, either as a complex of $AlCl_3$ with a hydrocarbon in solution or adsorbed on a carrier for vapour-phase reactions.

Very pure hydrocarbons such as n-butane cannot be isomerized by these acid catalysts[197-8], but isomerization occurs upon the addition of traces of olefin or substances which might react with the paraffin to form carbonium ions. Silica–alumina catalysts are also used, but the most effective are the dual-purpose or bifunctional catalysts, especially those containing platinum and silica–alumina or activated alumina.

8.7.2. *Bifunctional reforming catalysts*[199]

It has been found that the dehydrogenation and isomerization of straight-chain paraffins and of naphthenes, to give branched-chain paraffins or aromatics, proceed very effectively on bifunctional catalysts consisting of a metal and an acidic oxide. The metal appears to catalyse the hydrogenation–dehydrogenation reactions, and the acidic oxide to assist the isomerization reactions and the formation of aromatics.

The catalysts, which usually contain less than 1 per cent (sometimes 0·1 per cent) of metal, can be prepared[200] by impregnating a γ-alumina (or silica–alumina) catalyst with a solution of chloroplatinic acid, drying and calcining, or by co-gelling a suitable oxide sol with chloroplatinic acid and ammonia. It has also been shown[201] that mechanical mixing of platinum and the oxides produced an effective catalyst, and this has led to much discussion about the distribution of the metal in the impregnated and gelled catalysts. A combination of chemisorption and x-ray studies on these catalysts has shown that any metal crystals or crystallites are very small. The chemisorption of hydrogen[202-3] showed that, in fresh catalysts, nearly all the platinum atoms might be exposed in the surface. On aging or on heat treatment, the proportions of platinum atoms in the surface decreased, suggesting that sintering had occurred, and the average size of the crystallites (assuming simple geometrical shapes and the exposure of the common surface planes of the lattice) increased to about 250 to 300 Å. X-ray studies[202-3] also revealed this increase; in fresh catalysts, very few crystallites above the lower limit (50 Å) of the line-broadening technique were found, but on sintering the number of larger crystallites increased, in good agreement with the chemisorption studies.

The mechanisms of the reforming reactions have been discussed by Keulemans and Schuit[199]. For methylcyclopentane as reactant, they favour the following sequence: 'Dehydrogenation of methylcyclopentane over the metal (Pt) to give methylcyclopentene—migration of the olefin to an acid site—addition of a proton to form a carbonium ion—carbon skeleton rearrangement of the ion—release of a new olefin (cyclohexene) and migration to the metal—dehydrogenation of cyclohexene to benzene'.

Keulemans and Schuit agree with previous suggestions that the initial and final steps of this sequence are rapid, so that the rate is determined by that of isomerization at the acid sites, or possibly by the rate of migration in the mechanically mixed catalysts if the particle size is large. In general, the isomerization was found to provide evidence for the slow step by Weisz and Prater[204] who examined the relation between the rates of naphtha reforming and of (*a*) dehydrogenation of cyclohexane, which was only affected by the metal, and (*b*) isomerization of cumene, which was only affected by the acid sites, under standard test conditions over selected catalysts. The rate of reforming became independent of the rate of dehydrogenation above a comparatively low dehydrogenation activity, but it paralleled the rate of cumene isomerization over a wide range of catalyst activity. In another study of the isomerization of n-pentane over platinum–alumina, Sinfelt, Hunwitz and Rohrer[205] showed that the kinetics fit the mechanism

$$\text{n-pentane} \overset{\text{Pt}}{\rightleftharpoons} \text{n-pentene} + H_2 \qquad \text{(fast equilibrium)}$$

$$\text{n-pentene} \overset{\text{acid}}{\underset{\text{site}}{\longrightarrow}} \text{iso-pentene} \qquad \text{(slow step)}$$

$$H_2 + \text{iso-pentene} \underset{\text{Pt}}{\rightleftharpoons} \text{iso-pentane} \qquad \text{(fast equilibrium)}$$

The 'slow step' on the acid site is assumed to involve several carbonium ion reactions.

Other bifunctional catalysts that have been used in reforming reactions include oxides and sulphides of transition elements such as chromium, molybdenum and tungsten; the activity of $MoO_2/SiO_2/Al_2O_3$ approaches[199] that of $Pt/SiO_2/Al_2O_3$. Some of these catalysts have also been used in hydro-treating reactions, in which the charge is mixed with hydrogen and passed over the catalysts. The aromatics are reduced to naphthenes—changes which, for example, assist the production of lubricating oils with viscosities not too sensitive to changes of temperature, or improve the burning quality of diesel fuels. Hydro-treating also removes sulphur from sulphides and mercaptans, arsenic from arsines and nitrogen from amines as H_2S, AsH_3 and NH_3, respectively; this provides a most important method of purification before catalytic reforming.

In conclusion, it must be pointed out that, despite the success of the carbonium ion mechanisms in predicting the proportions of various products, there is no direct evidence at present of their existence in the gas phase near the catalysts. The justification for postulating their existence rests on indirect evidence—the different pattern of reactions in thermal, metal-catalysed and acid-catalysed reactions, the connections between cracking activity and acidity of the catalyst and the analogy of acid-base catalysed reactions and Friedel–Crafts reactions, where the existence of ionic mechanisms and carbonium ion intermediates is firmly established.

REFERENCES

[1] TRAPNELL, B. M. W. *Catalysis* (Ed. P. H. EMMETT) Vol. III: Reinhold, New York, 1955, p. 9

[2] ELEY, D. D. and ROSSINGTON, D. R. *Chemisorption* (Ed. W. E. Garner): Butterworth, London, 1957, p. 137

[3] BONHOEFFER, K. F. and FARKAS, A. *Z. phys. Chem. (Leipzig)* 1931, **B12**, 231

[4] FRANKENBURGER, W. and HODLER, A. *Trans. Faraday Soc.* 1932, **28**, 229

[5] ROBERTS, J. K. *Proc. R. Soc. A* 1935, **152**, 445, 464, 477

[6] FRANKENBURG, W. G. *J. Amer. chem. Soc.* 1944, **66**, 1827, 1838

[7] RIDEAL, E. K. *Proc. Camb. phil. Soc.* 1939, **35**, 130; *J. Soc. chem. Ind., Lond.* 1943, **62**, 335

[8] RIDEAL, E. K. and TRAPNELL, B. M. W. *J. Chim. phys.* 1950, **47**, 126; TRAPNELL, B. M. W. *Proc. R. Soc. A* 1951, **206**, 39

[9] LAIDLER, K. J. *J. phys. Chem.* 1953, **57**, 318, 320

[10] COUPER, A. and ELEY, D. D. *Disc. Faraday Soc.* 1950, **8**, 172

REFERENCES

[11] KUMMER, J. T. and EMMETT, P. H. *J. phys. Chem.* 1952, **56**, 258

[12] CREMER, E. *Advanc. Catalys.* 1956, **7**, 75; CREMER, E. and KERBER, K. *Z. Electrochem.* 1953, **57**, 757

[13] RIENÄCKER, G. *et al.*, *Z. anorg. Chem.* 1948, **257**, 41; 1950, **283**, 287

[14] MIKOVSKY, R. J., BOUDART, M. and TAYLOR, H. S. *J. Amer. chem. Soc.* 1954, **76**, 3818

[15] COUPER, A. Thesis, University of Bristol, 1949

[16] CORSON, B. B. *Catalysis* (Ed. P. H. Emmett) Vol. III: Reinhold, New York, 1955, Chapter 3

[17] ELEY, D. D., *Catalysis* (Ed. P. H. Emmett) Vol. III, Reinhold, New York, 1955, Chapter 2

[18] BOND, G. C., *Catalysis* (Ed. P. H. Emmett, Vol. III, Reinhold, New York, 1955, Chapter 4

[19] KEMBALL, C. *Proc. R. Soc. A* 1951, **207**, 539; *Tilden Lecture, Proc. chem. Soc., Lond.* 1961, p. 264

[20] EISCHENS, R. P. and PLISKIN, W. A. *Advanc. Catalys.* 1958, **10**, 1

[21] PEASE, R. N. *J. Amer. chem. Soc.* 1923, **45**, 1196, 2296
PEASE, R. N. and HARRIS, C. A. *J. Amer. chem. Soc.* 1927, **49**, 2503

[22] FARKAS, A. and FARKAS, L. *J. Amer. chem. Soc.* 1938, **60**, 22

[23] DE PAUW, F. and JUNGERS, J. C. *Bull. Soc. chim. belg.* 1948, **57**, 618

[24] SHERIDAN, J. *J. chem. Soc.* 1945, 305

[25] BEECK, O. *Rev. mod. Phys.* 1945, **17**, 61

[26] BEECK, O. *Disc. Faraday Soc.* 1950, **8**, 118

[27] MORIKAWA, K., BENEDICT, W. S. and TAYLOR, H. S. *J. Amer. chem. Soc.* 1936, **58**, 1445, 1795

[28] KEMBALL, C. *Proc. R. Soc. A* 1953, **217**, 376

[29] KEMBALL, C. and TAYLOR, H. S. *J. Amer. chem. Soc.* 1948, **70**, 345

[30] CONN, G. K. T. and TWIGG, G. H. *Proc. R. Soc. A* 1939, **171**, 70

[31] TWIGG, G. H. and RIDEAL, E. K. *Trans. Faraday Soc.* 1940, **36**, 533

[32] DOUGLAS, J. E. and RABINOVITCH, B. S. *J. Amer. chem. Soc.* 1952, **74**, 2486

[33] TURKEVICH, J., SCHISSLER, D. O. and IRSA, P. *J. phys. Chem.* 1951, **55**, 1078

[34] LAIDLER, K. J. *Catalysis* (Ed. P. H. Emmett) Vol. I: Reinhold, New York, 1954, Chapter 5

[35] TRAPNELL, B. M. W. *Trans. Faraday Soc.* 1952, **48**, 160

[36] FARKAS, A. *Trans. Faraday Soc.* 1939, **35**, 906, 941

[37] TWIGG, G. H. *Disc. Faraday Soc.* 1950, **8**, 152

[38] ANDERSON, J. R. and KEMBALL, C. *Proc. R. Soc. A* 1954, **223**, 361

[39] WILSON, J. N., OTVOS, J. W., STEVENSON, D. P. and WAGNER, C. D. *Industr. Engng Chem. (Industr.)* 1953, **45**, 1480

[40] BALANDIN, A. A. *Z. phys. Chem. (Leipzig)* 1929, **B2**, 289; 1929, **B3**, 167; for summary see Trapnell [44]

[41] BALANDIN, A. A. *Advanc. Catalys.* 1958, **10**, 96

[42] LONG, J. H., FRAZER, J. C. W. and OTT, E. *J. Amer. chem. Soc.* 1934, **56**, 1101

[43] EMMETT, P. H. and SKAU, N. *J. Amer. chem. Soc.* 1943, **65**, 1029

[44] TRAPNELL, B. M. W. *Advanc. Catalys.* 1951, **3**, 1

[45] IPATIEFF, V. N., CORSON, B. B. and KURBATOV, I. D. *J. phys. Chem.* 1939, **43**, 589; CORSON, B. B. and IPATIEFF, V. N. *J. phys. Chem.* 1941, **45**, 431

[46] HALPERN, J. *Advanc. Catalys.* 1959, **11**, 301

[47] SCHUIT, G. C. A., DE BOER, N. H., DORGELO, G. J. H. and VAN REIJEN, L. L. *Chemisorption* (Ed. W. E. Garner): Butterworth, London, 1957, p. 39

[48] SHERIDAN, J. and REID, W. D. *J. chem. Soc.* 1952, p. 2962

[49] SCHUIT, G. C. A. and VAN REIJEN, L. L. *Advanc. Catalys.* 1958, **10**, 242

[50] KEMBALL, C. *Proc. R. Soc. A* 1952, **214**, 413

[51] ANDERSON, J. R. *Rev. pure appl. Chem. (Australia)* 1957, **7**, 166

[52] For summaries see: BAKER, M. McD. and JENKINS, G. I. *Advanc. Catalys.* 1955, **7**, 1; DOWDEN, D. A. *J. chem. Soc.* 1950, p. 242

[53] FRANKENBURG, W. G. *Catalysis* (Ed. P. H. Emmett) Vol. III: Reinhold, New York, 1955, Chapter 6

[54] BOKHOVEN, C., VAN HEERDEN, C., WESTRIK, R. and ZWIETERING, P. *Catalysis* (Ed. P. H. Emmett) Vol. III: Reinhold, New York, 1955, Chapter 7

[55] NIELSEN, A. *Advanc. Catalys.* 1953, **5**, 1

[56] NIELSEN, A. *An Investigation on Promoted Iron Catalysts for the Synthesis of Ammonia*: Gjellerups, Copenhagen, 1950

[57a] EMMETT, P. H. and BRUNAUER, S. *J. Amer. chem. Soc.* 1930, **52**, 2682

[57b] ALMQUIST, J. A. and BLACK, C. A. *J. Amer. chem. Soc.* 1926, **48**, 2814

[58] McGEER, J. P. and TAYLOR, H. S. *J. Amer. chem. Soc.* 1951, **73**, 2743

[59] TAYLOR, H. S. and JORIS, G. G. *J. chem. Phys.* 1939, **7**, 893

[60] BRUNAUER, S., LOVE, K. S. and KEENAN, R. G. *J. Amer. chem. Soc.* 1942, **64**, 751

[61] TAYLOR, H. S. and JUNGERS, J. C. *J. Amer. chem. Soc.* 1935, **57**, 660

[62] LAIDLER, K. J. and WEBER, J. *J. chem. Phys.* 1951, **19**, 381, 1089

[63] EMMETT, P. H. and BRUNAUER, S. *J. Amer. chem. Soc.* 1934, **56**, 35

[64] TEMKIN, M. and PYZHEV, V. *Acta phys.-chim. U.R.S.S.* 1940, **12**, 327; *Zh. fiz. Khim.* 1939, **13**, 851

[65] BRILL, R. *J. chem. Phys.* 1951, **19**, 1047

[66] EMMETT, P. H. and LOVE, K. S. *J. Amer. chem. Soc.* 1941, **63**, 3297

[67] SCHOLTEN, J. J. F., KONVALINKA, J. A. and ZWIETERING, P. *Trans. Faraday Soc.* 1960, **56**, 262

[68] OZAKI, A., TAYLOR, H. S. and BOUDART, M. *Proc. R. Soc. A* 1960, **258**, 47

[69] BRUNAUER, S. and EMMETT, P. H. *J. Amer. chem. Soc.* 1937, **59**, 310, 1553; 1940, **62**, 1732

[70] HINSHELWOOD, C. N. *The Kinetics of Chemical Change*: Clarendon Press, Oxford, 1940, p. 189

[71] HINSHELWOOD, C. N. and BURK, R. E. *J. chem. Soc.* 1925, p. 1105

[72] SCHWAB, G. M. and SCHMIDT, H. *Z. phys. Chem. (Leipzig)* 1929, **B3**, 337

[73] SINGLETON, J. H., ROBERTS, E. R. and WINTER, E. R. S. *Trans. Faraday Soc.* 1951, **47**, 1318

[74] KEMBALL, C. *Trans. Faraday Soc.* 1952, **48**, 254

[75] STORCH, H. H., GOLUMBIC, N. and ANDERSON, R. B. *The Fischer–Tropsch and Related Syntheses*: Wiley, New York, 1951

[76] ANDERSON, R. B., HOFER, L. J. E. and COHN, E. M. *Catalysis* (Ed. P. H. Emmett) Vol. IV: Reinhold, New York, 1956, Chapters 1–5

[77] NATTA, G. *Catalysis* Vol. III: Reinhold, New York, 1955, Chapter 8

[78] FISCHER, F. and TROPSCH, H. *BrennstChemie* 1923, **4**, 276; 1924, **5**, 201, 217

[79] ANDERSON, R. B., FELDMAN, J. and STORCH, H. H. *Industr. Engng Chem. (Industr.)* 1952, 44, 2418

[80] ORCHIN, M. *Advanc. Catalys.* 1953, **5**, 385

[81] ANDERSON, R. B. *Advanc. Catalys.* 1953, **5**, 355

[82] ADKINS, H. and KRŠEK, G. *J. Amer. chem. Soc.* 1948, **70**, 383

[83] ADKINS, H. and KRŠEK, G. *J. Amer. chem. Soc.* 1949, **71**, 3051

[84] ROELEN, O. *German Patent No. 103,362*, 1938

[85] WENDER, I., ORCHIN, M. and STORCH, H. H. *J. Amer. chem. Soc.* 1950, **72**, 4842

[86] WENDER, I., LEVINE, R. and ORCHIN, M. *J. Amer. chem. Soc.* 1949, **71**, 4160

[87] WENDER, I., METHINE, S. and ORCHIN, M. *J. Amer. chem. Soc.* 1951, **73**, 5704

[88] STERNBERG, H. W., WENDER, I., FRIEDEL, R. A. and ORCHIN, M. *J. Amer. chem. Soc.* 1953, **75**, 2717

[89] FRIEDEL, R. A., WENDER, I., SCHUFLER, S. L. and STERNBERG, H. W. *J. Amer. chem Soc.* 1956, **77**, 3951

REFERENCES

[90] EDGELL, W. F., MAGEE, C. and GALLUP, G. *J. Amer. chem. Soc.* 1956, **78**, 4185, 4188

[91] WENDER, I., STERNBERG, H. W. and ORCHIN, M. *J. Amer. chem. Soc.* 1953, **75**, 3042

[92] ORCHIN, M., KIRCH, L. and GOLDFARB, I. *J. Amer. chem. Soc.* 1956, **78**, 5450

[93] NATTA, G., ERCOLI, R., CASTELLANO, S. and BARBIERI, F. H., *J. Amer. chem. Soc.* 1954, **76**, 4049

[94] MARTIN, A. R., *Chem. & Ind.* 1954, p. 1536

[95] ALDRIDGE, C. L., FASCE, E. V. and JONASSEN, H. B. *J. phys. Chem.* 1958, **62**, 869

[96] BÄHR, H. A. *et al.*, *Ber. dtsch. chem. Ges.* 1928, **61**, 2177; 1930, **63**, 2226

[97] FISCHER, F. and TROPSCH, H. *BrennstChemie* 1926, **7**, 299

[98] CRAXFORD, S. R. and RIDEAL, E. K. *J. chem. Soc.* 1939, p. 1604

[99] WELLER, S., HOFER, L. J. E. and ANDERSON, R. B. *J. Amer. chem. Soc.* 1948, **70**, 799

[100] HOFER, L. J. E. and PEEBLES, W. C. *J. Amer. chem. Soc.* 1947, **69**, 893

[101] McCARTNEY, J. T. *et al.*, *J. phys. Chem.* 1953, **57**, 730

[102] ANDERSON, R. B., HOFER, J. E. and COHN, E. M. *Catalysis* (Ed. P. H. Emmett) Vol. IV: Reinhold, New York, 1956, p. 331

[103] KUMMER, J. T., DEWITT, T. W. and EMMETT, P. H. *J. Amer. chem. Soc.* 1948, **70**, 3632

[104] ANDERSON, R. B., FRIEDEL, R. A. and STORCH, H. H. *J. chem. Phys.* 1951, **19**, 313

[105] GALL, D., GIBSON, E. J. and HALL, C. C. *J. appl. Chem.* (*Lond.*) 1952, **2**, 371

[106] KUMMER, J. T. and EMMETT, P. H. *J. Amer. chem. Soc.* 1951, **73**, 564

[107] KUMMER, J. T., EMMETT, P. H. *et al.*, *J. Amer. chem. Soc.* 1953, **75**, 5177

[108] BLYHOLDER, G. and EMMETT, P. H. *J. phys. Chem.* 1959, **63**, 962

[109] SASTRI, M. V. C. and VISWANATHAN, T. S. *J. Amer. chem. Soc.* 1955, **77**, 3967

[110] NATTA, G. *G. Chim. industr.* 1930, **12**, 13

[111] MOLSTAD, M. C. and DODGE, B. F. *Industr. Engng Chem.* (*Industr.*) 1935, **27**, 134

[112] NATTA, G. and CORRADINI, P. *Proceedings of the International Symposium on the Reactivity of Solids* 1952: Elander, Gothenburg, 1954, p. 619

[113] SCHWAB, G. M. and MARHENKEL, H. *Solid–Gas Interface*, Proceedings of the Second International Congress of Surface Activity (Ed. J. H. Schulman) Vol. II: Butterworth, London; Academic Press, New York, 1957, p. 64

[114] NATTA, G. *Catalysis* (Ed. P. H. Emmett) Vol. III: Reinhold, New York, 1955, p. 402

[115] TAYLOR, H. S. and KISTIAKOWSKY, G. B. *J. Amer. chem. Soc.* 1927, **49**, 2468

[116] NATTA, G., PINO, P., MAZZANTI, G. and PASQUON, I. *Chim. e Industr.* 1953, **35**, 705

[117] NATTA, G. *Catalysis* (Ed. P. H. Emmett) Vol. III: Reinhold, New York, 1955, p. 394

[118] DIXON, J. K. and LONGFIELD, J. E. *Catalysis* (Ed. P. H. Emmett) Vol. VII: Reinhold, New York, 1960, Chapters 3–6

[119] SPRATT, D. A. *Spec. Publ. chem. Soc.* (*Lond.*) No. 10, 1957, p. 53

[120] ZAWADZKI, J. *Disc. Faraday Soc.* 1950, **8**, 140

[121] DUECKER, W. W. and WEST, J. R. *Sulfuric Acid*: American Chemical Society Monograph, Reinhold, New York, 1959

[122] KATZ, M. *Advanc. Catalys.* 1953, **5**, 177

[123] CLARK, H. and BERETS, D. J. *Advanc. Catalys.* 1957, **9**, 204

[124] STONE, F. S. *Chemistry of the Solid State* (Ed. W. E. Garner): Butterworth, London, 1955, Chapter 15

[125] WINTER, *Advanc. Catalys.* 1958, **10**, 196 (see p. 232)

[126] STEPHENS, E. R. and PEASE, R. N. *J. Amer. chem. Soc.* 1950, **72**, 1188; 1952, **74**, 3480

VAN TIGGELEN, A. *et al.*, *Bull. Soc. chim. belg.* 1953, **62**, 205; 1954, **63**, 542

[127] WALSH, A. D. and DAVIS, A.—private communication

[128] WISE, H. and FRECH, M. F. *J. chem. Phys.* 1953, **21**, 948

[129] GAYDON, A. G. and WOLFHARD, H. G. *Flames*: Chapman & Hall, London, 1960, pp. 150, 326

[130] WISE, H. and FRECH, M. F. *J. chem. Phys.* 1954, **22**, 1463; 1955, **23**, 1374

[131] ROSSER, W. A. and WISE, H. *J. chem. Phys.* 1956, **25**, 1078

[132] SUGDEN, T. M. and BULEWICZ, E. M. *Chemical Reactions in Lower and Upper Atmosphere*: Conference, San Francisco, April 1961

[133] OSTWALD, W. *Chemikerztg* 1903, **27**, 457

[134] DIXON, J. K. and LONGFIELD, J. E. *Catalysis* (Ed. P. H. Emmett) Vol. VII: Reinhold, New York, 1960, p. 283

[135] ANDRUSSOW, L. *Angew. Chem.* 1926, **39**, 321; 1935, **48**, 593

[136] NAGEL, A. VON Z. *Elektrochem.* 1930, **36**, 754

[137] KRAUSS, W. Z. *Electrochem.* 1949, **53**, 320

[138a] BODENSTEIN, M. Z. *Elektrochem.* 1944, **47**, 501

[138b] KRAUSS, W. Z. *Elektrochem.* 1950, **54**, 264

[139] RASCHIG, F. *Angew. Chem.* 1927, **40**, 1183; 1928, **41**, 207

[140] KAWAGUCHI, T. *J. chem. Soc. Japan* 1954, **75**, 835; 1955, **76**, 1112

[141] DIXON, J. K. and LONGFIELD, J. E. *Catalysis* (Ed. P. H. Emmett) Vol. VII: Reinhold, New York, 1960, p. 325

[142] BORESKOV, G. K. *et al.*, *J. gen. Chem. U.S.S.R.* 1954, **24**, 21

[143] TOPSOE, H. and NIELSEN, A. *Trans. Danish Acad. tech. Sci.* 1948, **1**, 3, 8

[144] CALDERBANK, P. H. *J. appl. Chem.* (*Lond.*) 1952, **2**, 482; *Chem. Engng Progr.* 1953, **49**, 585

[145] BODENSTEIN, M. and FINK, C. G. Z. *phys. Chem.* (*Leipzig*) 1907, **60**, 1, 46

[146] TAYLOR, G. B. and LENHER, S. Z. *phys. Chem.* (*Leipzig*) 1931, Bodenstein Testband, p. 30

[147] BORESKOV, G. K. *et al.*, *Zh. fiz. Khim.* 1945, **19**, 535; 1956, **30**, 2560

[148] BORESKOV, G. K. *J. appl. Chem. U.S.S.R.* 1940, **13**, 329, 653

[149] KRISHEVSKAYA, E. L. *Zh. fiz. Khim.* 1947, **21**, 287

[150] FRAZER, J. H. and KILPATRICK, W. *J. J. Amer. chem. Soc.* 1940, **62**, 1659

[151] MARS, P. and KREVELEN, D. W. VAN *Chem. Engng Sci.* 1954, **3**, Supplement, 41

[152] LEWIS, W. K. and RIES, E. D. *Industr. Engng Chem.* (*Industr.*) 1925, **17**, 593

[153] HAUFFE, K. *Advanc. Catalys.* 1955, **7**, 213

[154] PARRAVANO, G. and BOUDART, M. *Advanc. Catalys.* 1955, **7**, 50

[155] TAYLOR, G. B. *et al.*, *J. phys. Chem.* 1930, **34**, 748

[156] HURST, W. W. and RIDEAL, E. K. *J. chem. Soc.* 1924, pp. 685, 694

[157] BENTON, A. F. and BELL, R. T. *J. Amer. chem. Soc.* 1934, **56**, 501

[158] KATZ, M. *Advanc. Catalys.* 1953, **5**, 177, see p. 191

[159] FRAZER, J. C. W. *Chem. Abstr.* 1920, **14**, 2533

[160] KATZ, M. *Advanc. Catalys.* 1953, **5**, 177, see p. 188

[161] BENTON, A. F. *J. Amer. chem. Soc.* 1923, **45**, 887, 900

[162] VASIL'EV, V. N., ELOVICH, S. Y. and MARGOLIS, L. Y. *Dokl. Akad. Nauk S.S.S.R.* 1955, **101**, 703

[163] VAINSHTEIN, F. M. and TUROVSKII, G. Y. *Dokl. Akad. Nauk S.S.S.R.* 1950, **72**, 297; 1951, **78**, 1173

[164] STONE, F. S. *Chemistry of the Solid State* (Ed. W. E. Garner): Butterworth, London, 1955, p. 397

[165] GARNER, W. E., STONE, F. S. and TILEY, P. F. *Proc. R. Soc. A* 1952, **211**, 472

REFERENCES

[166] PARRAVANO, G. *J. Amer. chem. Soc.* 1953, **75**, 1448, 1452
[167] WINTER, E. R. S. *Chemisorption* (Ed. W. E. Garner): Butterworth, London, 1957, p. 189
[168] WINTER, E. R. S. *Advanc. Catalys.* 1958, **10**, 196
[169] SCHWAB, G. B. and BLOCK, J. *Z. phys. Chem.* (*Frankfurt*) *N.S.* 1954, **1**, 42; *Z. Elektrochem.* 1954, **58**, 756
[170] EISCHENS, R. P. and PLISKIN, W. A. *Advanc. Catalys.* 1957, **9**, 662
[171] DIXON, J. K. and LONGFIELD, J. E. *Catalysis* (Ed. P. H. Emmett) Vol. VII: Reinhold, New York, 1960, p. 183
[172] PARKS, W. G. and ALLARD, C. E. *Industr. Engng Chem.* (*Industr.*) 1939, **31**, 1162
[173] SIMARD, G. L., STEGER, J. F., ARNOTT, R. J. and SIEGEL, L. A. *Industr. Engng Chem.* (*Industr.*) 1955, **47**, 1424
[174] McBEE, E. T., HASS, H. B. and WISEMAN, P. A. *Industr. Engng Chem.* (*Industr.*) 1945, **37**, 432
[175] WAN, S. *Industr. Engng Chem.* (*Industr.*) 1953, **45**, 234
[176] ORZECHOWSKI, A. and MACCORMACK, K. E. *Canad. J. Chem.* 1954, **32**, 388, 415, 432, 443
[177] TWIGG, G. H. *Proc. R. Soc. A* 1946, **88**, 92, 105, 123
[178] MURRAY, K. E. *Aust. J. sci. Res. A* 1950, **3**, 433
[179] MARGOLIS, L. Y. and ROGINSKII, S. Z. *Izv. Akad. Nauk S.S.S.R., Otdel. Khim. Nauk* 1956, **3**, 282
[180] KURILENKO, A. I., KUL'KOVA, N. V., RYBAKOV, N. A. and TEMKIN, M. I. *Zh. fiz. Khim.* 1958, **32**, 1043
[181] LAW, G. H. and CHITWOOD, H. C. *Chem. Abstr.* 1941, **35**, 7414
[182] MARGOLIS, L. Y. and TODES, O. M. *Izv. Akad. Nauk S.S.S.R., Otdel. Khim. Nauk* 1952, 52
[183] KUMMER, J. T. *J. phys. Chem.* 1956, **60**, 666
[184] WILSON, J. N., VOGE, H. H., STEVENSON, D. P., SMITH, A. E. and ATKINS, L. T. *J. phys. Chem.* 1959, **63**, 463
[185] LYUBANSKII, G. D. *Dokl. Akad. Nauk S.S.S.R.* 1956, **110**, 112
[186] OBLAD, A. G., SHALIT, H. and TADD, H. T. *Advanc. Catalys.* 1957, **9**, 510
[187] RYLAND, L. B., TAMELE, M. W. and WILSON, J. N. *Catalysis* (Ed. P. H. Emmett) Vol. VII: Reinhold, New York, 1960, Chapter 1
[188] *Catalysis* (Ed. P. H. Emmett) Vol. VI: Reinhold, New York, 1958
[189] TAMELE, M. W. *Disc. Faraday Soc.* 1950, **8**, 270
[190] MILLIKEN, T. H., MILLS, G. A. and OBLAD, A. G. *Disc. Faraday Soc.* 1950, **8**, 279
[191] OBLAD, A. G., MILLIKEN, T. H. and MILLS, G. A. *Advanc. Catalys.* 1951, **3**, 236
[192] THOMAS, C. L. *Industr. Engng Chem.* 1949, **41**, 2564
[193] DANFORTH, J. D. *Advanc. Catalys.* 1957, **9**, 558
[194] GREENSFELDER, B. S., VOGE, H. H. and GOOD, G. M. *Industr. Engng Chem.* (*Indust.*) 1949, **41**, 2573
[195] WHITMORE, F. C. *Industr. Engng Chem.* (*Indust.*) 1934, **26**, 94
[196] EVANS, A. G. and POLANYI, M. *J. chem. Soc.* 1947, p. 252
[197] PINES, H. and WACKLER, R. C. *J. Amer. chem. Soc.* 1946, **68**, 595
[198] OBLAD, A. G. and GORIN, M. H. *Industr. Engng Chem.* (*Indust.*) 1946, **38**, 822
[199] KEULEMANS, A. I. M. and SCHUIT, G. C. A. *The Mechanism of Heterogeneous Catalysis*: Elsevier, Amsterdam, 1960, p. 159
[200] CIAPETTA, F. G. and PLANK, C. J. *Catalysis* (Ed. P. H. Emmett) Vol. I: Reinhold, New York, 1954, Chapter 7
[201] HINDIN, S. G., WELLER, S. W. and MILLS, G. A. *J. phys. Chem.* 1958, **62**, 244
[202] SPENADEL, L. and BOUDART, M. *J. phys. Chem.* 1960, **64**, 204
[203] ADLER, S. F. and KEAVNEY, J. J. *J. phys. Chem.* 1960, **64**, 208
[204] WEISZ, P. B. and PRATER, C. D. *Advanc. Catalys.* 1959, **9**, 575
[205] SINFELT, J. H., HURWITZ, H. and ROHRER, J. C. *J. phys. Chem.* 1960, **64**, 892

PART IV

CATALYSIS AND INHIBITION OF
CHAIN REACTIONS

9

THE RATES OF CHAIN REACTIONS

9.1. INTRODUCTION

THE CHARACTERISTIC features of simple chain reactions were outlined in Chapter 1, where expressions were obtained for the rates of reaction in terms of the velocities of the initiating, propagating and terminating steps. In the derivation, only one type of reactive chain centre, X, was used, and it is necessary to consider whether this simple pattern of reaction needs modifying when the catalysis and inhibition of chain reactions are considered in more detail[1-3].

It is unusual for there to be only one chemical intermediate acting as a centre in a chain reaction, whether this proceeds by a free atom or radical or by an ionic chain mechanism. More often, there are two chemically distinct chain centres which react in alternate propagation steps. This almost always occurs when the chain reaction involves two reactants, as in the combination of hydrogen and chlorine when chlorine and hydrogen atoms alternate as chain centres:

$$Cl* + H_2 \rightarrow HCl + H*$$
$$H* + Cl_2 \rightarrow HCl + Cl*$$

In many oxidations in the liquid phase two free radicals alternate, such as the radicals RCO and RCO·OO in the oxidation of liquid aldehydes

$$RCO* + O_2 \rightarrow RCO·OO*$$

$$RCO·OO* + RCHO \rightarrow RCO* + RC\overset{\displaystyle OOH}{\underset{\displaystyle O}{\diagup}}$$

Alternation of centres usually occurs, too, in unimolecular decompositions such as that of phosgene, where the $COCl_2$ molecule reacts with one centre

$$Cl* + COCl_2 \rightarrow COCl* + Cl_2$$

and the other centre decomposes to yield the other product and the chloride atom by the reversible reaction

$$COCl* \rightleftharpoons CO + Cl*$$

In many cases where there are two centres, however, it has been shown that their stationary-state concentrations are often quite different. In the hydrogen–chlorine reaction, for instance, the hydrogen atoms react much more rapidly with the chlorine molecules (bond energy 59 kcal mole^{-1}) than the chlorine atoms react with hydrogen molecules (bond energy 104 kcal mole^{-1}). Any inhibitor which reacts with hydrogen atoms and chlorine atoms at about the same rate finds far fewer hydrogen atoms to react with in an equimolar mixture of hydrogen and chlorine; it meets about one hydrogen atom for every 600 encounters with chlorine atoms at room temperature, and one to 25 at about 300°C and so the removal of centres is almost entirely removal of chlorine atoms. The practical effect of this is that the two propagation steps can be telescoped into one, involving chlorine atoms, which will compete with the effective terminating steps. A similar simplification can be made for the auto-oxidation reactions:

$$Cl* + H_2 + Cl_2 \rightarrow 2HCl + Cl*$$

$$RCO \cdot OO* + RCHO + O_2 \rightarrow RCO \cdot OO* + RC \overset{\displaystyle OOH}{\underset{\displaystyle O}{\diagdown}}$$

Again, in addition polymerization, the monomer m combines with a growing polymer radical of j units, m_j^*, to give a new chain centre m_{j+1}^*. However, it has been shown[4] that the reactivities of the two centres are so similar, provided that j is greater than about 5 or 6, that the polymerization can be regarded as occurring by one type of propagation step with one velocity constant

$$m + m_j^* \overset{k_p}{\longrightarrow} m_{j+1}^*$$

Particularly in the last case, the representation by a single propagating step produces a great simplification in the kinetic expression relating the over-all rate to the velocity constants of the initiation, propagation and termination steps, as in cases (i) and (ii) (see p. 260).

Another type of reaction which occurs in some chain reactions must be mentioned. This is *chain transfer*. It is of particular importance in addition polymerization of certain monomers, e.g. styrene. In it, a growing polymer radical becomes saturated by donating or extracting a labile group—usually a hydrogen atom—to or from a transfer agent which may be the solvent or the monomer or the initiator. The effect is to terminate the growth of that particular polymer, but to start another, or at least to provide a radical capable of starting another; with transfer, the rate of polymerization is not altered, but the average degree of polymerization (which is the average number of monomer units in the polymer molecules) is decreased.

The over-all rate of a chain reaction consisting of initiation, propagation and termination steps is readily derived, as was shown in section 1.4, if it is assumed that the chain centres are very reactive and do not accumulate in the system after a short period. In this short period, the rate of termination is increasing as the chain centres are formed by the initiating reaction, until the two processes become equal. Thereafter the chain centre concentration is determined by equating the two rates, and the over-all rate of reaction is obtained by substituting this concentration in the expression for the velocity of the propagating step. The propagating step does not affect the chain centre concentration unless more than one centre is formed for each centre consumed in that step. When this occurs, the chain is said to 'branch'. In some cases the *branching reaction* is different from the propagation reaction. For example, in the thermal reaction between hydrogen and oxygen, the propagation step is

$$OH* + H_2 \rightarrow H_2O + H*$$

and the branching steps are

$$O* + H_2 \rightarrow OH* + H*$$
$$H* + O_2 \rightarrow OH* + O*$$

Whenever branching occurs, the expression for the rate of change of centre concentration becomes

$$\frac{d[X]}{dt} = I + F[X] - G[X] - M[X]^2 \tag{9.1}$$

where I represents the rate of formation of centres in the initiation reaction, $F[X]$ the rate (net) of production of centres in the branching step, $G[X]$ the rate of termination by reaction of X with the wall or with an inhibitor, and $M[X]^2$ the rate of removal of centres by mutual combination or disproportionation. Quadratic branching where two centres react to give three or more centres has sometimes been postulated, but it seems to be very rare and will be ignored here.

A stationary state for [X] can be reached if, at some value of [X]

$$I + (F - G)[X] - M[X]^2 \leqslant 0 \tag{9.2}$$

Whenever $G > F$, a value of [X] can be reached at which this condition is satisfied, even if $M[X]^2$ is zero; this inequality $G > F$ leads to rate equations

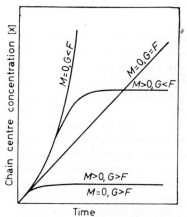

Figure 9.1. Growth of chain centres according to the equation d[X]/dt= $I + (F - G)[X] - M[X]^2$ for different values of F, G and M

of the type considered in section 1.4. If $G < F$, however, the chains are linearly branched; in this case, and when $G = F$, a stationary state cannot be achieved unless M is real and positive; provided M is real and positive, and I, F, G and M, which are likely to be functions of the reactant concentrations and the temperature, are not changing, a stationary level of [X] is always

259

obtainable in principle. The changes in centre concentration with time for the three principal situations, each with I, F, G and M invariant, are shown in *Figure 9.1*. The rate of the main reaction at any moment is equal to the rate of the propagation step and so proportional to the appropriate centre concentrations shown in *Figure 9.1*. In practice, high centre concentrations may lead to so rapid a rate that I, F, G and M are substantially changed by changes of temperature or reactant concentration, so that the curves of *Figure 9.1* refer to idealized conditions.

9.2. STATIONARY-STATE RATES

Where a stationary state is achieved, comparatively simple general equations for the rates can be written down, and the following cases are of most interest for considering the role of catalysts and of inhibitors in chain reactions; more comprehensive treatments have been given by Semenov[1,2] and by Dainton[3].

(*i*) Non-branching chains with linear termination predominant:

$$\text{Rate} = k_p[\text{R}][\text{X}] = k_p[\text{R}]\frac{I}{G} \ (\equiv V_i V_p/V_t) \tag{9.3}$$

(*ii*) Non-branching chains with mutual termination predominant:

$$\text{Rate} = k_p[\text{R}][\text{X}] = k_p[\text{R}]\sqrt{\frac{I}{M}} \ (\equiv V_p(V_i/V_m)^{1/2}) \tag{9.4}$$

(*iii*) Branching chains with mutual termination and with $I \ll (F-G)[\text{X}]$:

$$\text{Rate} = k_p[\text{R}][\text{X}] = k_p[\text{R}]\frac{F-G}{M} \tag{9.5}$$

The equations (9.3) and (9.4) will be recognized as alternative statements of the equations (1.19) and (1.20) derived in section 1.4.

Thus in general terms, for a given value of [R] at a fixed temperature, the rate of a non-branching chain reaction can be increased by increasing k_p or I or by decreasing G or M, and decreased by the opposite means. The rate of a branching chain in a steady-state region can be increased by increasing k_p or F or by decreasing G or M, and decreased by the opposite changes. These possibilities provide the key to the catalysis and inhibition of chain reactions. A catalyst will usually act by increasing I or F, and rather rarely by decreasing G; it is difficult to visualize any ways in which it could decrease M unless one includes electrostatic effects such as changes in the dielectric constant of the solvent medium (see page 319). In some polymerizations which give stereo-regulated polymers the catalyst does alter the nature of the propagation step, but it probably affects the rate of initiation as well; and in a few ionic reactions the catalyst (or a species derived from it) takes part in a propagation step. An inhibitor will usually act by increasing G or M, and rather more rarely by decreasing F or I; it may be noted that with branched-chain reactions, it is often extremely difficult to distinguish between a decrease of F or an increase in G, as each produces the same kinetic effect. An example of these problems is discussed in detail in section 11.4. For non-branching chains, there are many examples of reactions whose rates conform to the general equations (9.3) and (9.4). For example, in the catalysis of many addition polymerizations, the rate is accurately proportional to the square root of the catalyst concentration, as shown in *Figure 10.2*. In these reactions, the kinetics are clearly of type (*ii*), and the termination of chains is mutual. In the ionic polymerization of styrene catalysed by stannic chloride, the rate is proportional to the catalyst concentration, as shown in *Figure 10.14*. That the stannic chloride is altering the rate of initiation, but not the remaining steps, is confirmed by the constancy of the molecular weight of the polymer. In addition polymerization, the mean molecular weight when measured as the *number* average (and not the weight average) is equal to the number of monomer units multiplied by the molecular weight of the monomer; thus a constant molecular weight means a constant degree of polymerization. This in turn means a constant value for the *chain length*, i.e. the ratio

$$\frac{\text{Rate of propagation}}{\text{Rate of termination}}$$

The most likely explanation of this is that neither rate is changed. In photochemical reactions, the intensity of light absorbed takes the place of the catalyst concentration; in the absence of inhibitors, the high radical concentration in these reactions often leads to mutual termination. In the presence of an inhibitor, however, the rate is proportional to the intensity of the light absorbed, as shown in *Figure 9.8* for the effect of nitrosyl chloride on the formation of phosgene, so the termination is linear; it is probably due to the reaction

$$Cl^* + NOCl \rightarrow NO + Cl_2$$

These examples show that catalysts can often be used to give useful information about the chain mechanism, and some examples where quantitative information has been obtained are given in later sections of this book.

In many chain reactions, the chain centres may be removed by reaction with the walls of the vessel, or formed by some heterogeneous reaction on the walls. If only one of these reactions is occurring, a change of the surface area–volume ratio of the vessel will cause a change in the rate of reaction. If the rate increases with increase of surface, the chains are probably starting on the walls; if the rate decreases with increase of surface, then the chain centres are being removed by the walls. If changing the surface area has no effect on the rate, then either the walls are ineffective in *both* initiating and in terminating reactions or else they are acting in both. A distinction is possible if a homogeneous catalyst or inhibitor is found for the reaction. The addition of the catalyst in amounts large enough to dominate the initiation will allow the effects of the surface on the terminating steps to be investigated, while the use of an effective homogeneous inhibitor will allow the effect of the surface on the initiating steps to be investigated. The second method was used by Pease[5] to show that the thermal reaction between hydrogen and chlorine both starts and is terminated on the walls.

9.3. INHIBITORS AND INDUCTION PERIODS

Inhibitors have been very useful in deciding the mechanisms of many reactions. The presence of a chain reaction can be confirmed if an inhibitor can be found which acts independently of the rate and mode of initiation. It is not sufficient to show a slowing or even suppression of the rate without reference to the

261

method of initiation, for a slowing may be due to the poisoning of a hetero-geneous or an enzyme catalyst. If it can be established that no catalyst is present, then inhibition of the rate by small proportions of an additive is diagnostic of a chain reaction. If the inhibitor has the same *relative* effect on the rate with different rates of initiation—perhaps with different methods or different catalysts—then the evidence is stronger. If different inhibitors can be found, and it can be shown that the rate of removal of these inhibitors is the same for a given rate of initiation, then a chain reaction is certain.

These methods were brilliantly exploited by Bäckström[6,7] to show that the thermal oxidation of aldehydes and of sulphites in solution are chain reactions. The photochemical reactions have large quantum yields, and it was accepted that they were chain reactions, initiated photochemically, with chain lengths in the absence of inhibitors as high as 10^4. Bäckström showed that the thermal and the photochemical oxidations were inhibited in the same way by alcohols, and identified the oxidation products of these alcohols and measured the rate of removal of the alcohols during the photochemical oxidation of sulphite. He showed that the rate of removal increased to a constant value as the inhibitor concentration was increased, and that this rate was very nearly the same for three alcohols (butyl, isopropyl and benzyl) and very nearly equal to the rate of photochemical initiation. Moreover, the chain length appeared to be the same for a given amount of inhibitor in the thermal and in the photochemical oxidations. This demonstrated clearly the independence of the action of the inhibitor and the rate of initiation.

Later work has supported this interpretation of the behaviour of inhibitors in many non-branching chain reactions, and many quantitative tests have been made. An excellent demonstration of the inverse dependence of the rate upon the concentration of the inhibitor nitrosyl chloride in the photochemical reaction between chlorine and carbon monoxide is shown in *Figure 9.9*. The effect of increasing the concentration of inhibitor (benzoquinone) on the thermal polymerization of methylmethacrylate, catalysed by benzoyl peroxide, is shown in *Figure 10.7*. If the inhibitor is very effective, relative to the propa-gation step, it may blot out the reaction completely; but as the inhibitor is used up, the action will revive. This behaviour is shown for the thermal reac-tion between hydrogen and chlorine, inhibited by nitrosyl chloride, in *Figure 9.2*, and for the thermal polymerization of styrene, inhibited by benzoquinone, in *Figure 10.8*. In such cases, the length of time that the reaction is inhibited is called the *induction period*, and the induction period is often proportional to the amount of inhibitor added, as in *Figure 10.10*. At one time, a distinction was made between the complete suppression of reaction, which was called inhibition, and the slowing, which was called retardation. It is now realized that there is a continuous change from one to the other, for example, the inhi-bition of the hydrogen–chlorine reaction by nitrosyl chloride becomes a retar-dation if the reaction is catalysed by the addition of nitric oxide, as shown in *Figure 9.2*. Similar transition has often been shown for polymerization reactions, and for oxidations.

The only mechanistic justification[3,4] for a distinction between retarders and inhibitors would arise if it could be shown (for example) that inhibitors removed some radical, formed from the catalyst, *before* the radical could form a proper chain centre with the reactant, and that the inhibitor did not react with the chain centre proper, and that retarders removed only chain centres, or vice versa. It is almost certain that such selectivity is unknown in free-radical chains, but the specific functions of cocatalysts in initiating ionic chains suggest that selective inhibitors for catalyst suppression or chain centre removal may be possible.

There are two important conclusions to be drawn when results like those in *Figures 9.2* and *10.8* are obtained. The first is that all the reaction concerned normally proceeds through a chain mechanism. The second is that a detailed study of the end of the induction period, and the way the rate builds up, is likely to yield useful information about the kinetics of the chain reaction, although the detailed treatment will be different in each case; some examples are given in sections 10.2 and 11.2.

There is no general agreement about the precise criterion for the end of the induction period[3]. Some investigators have used the point at which the *extent* of reaction reaches the minimum detectable amount; others have used the point at which the *rate of reaction* first becomes measurable; others have used the point at which the rate reaches its *maximum* value. There is little reason, other than convenience, for preferring one choice to the others. If the induction periods are to be related to a kinetic scheme, however, it is important that the same criterion should be applied to the kinetic analysis and the experimental measurements, especially when the induction periods are short relative to the period of acceleration.

There can be induction periods in chain reactions even when no inhibitor is present. In all chain reactions that are started by mixing stable reactants and catalysts, as distinct from the injection of centres prepared apart from the reactants, the centre concentration takes a finite time to build up to a level which gives an appreciable rate or extent of reaction, and even longer to reach the level corresponding to the 'stationary state' and a steady rate of reaction in non-branching chain reactions[8-11]. It is instructive to examine these times for a simplified system in which the rates of various reaction steps can be estimated reasonably accurately[8, 9]:

$$\text{Initiation:} \qquad M + Cl_2 \xrightarrow{k_i} 2Cl + M$$

$$\text{Propagation:} \qquad Cl + R \xrightarrow{k_p} P + Cl$$

$$\text{Termination:} \qquad M + 2Cl \xrightarrow{k_t} Cl_2 + M$$

The rate of growth of the centre concentration is given by the equation

$$\frac{d[Cl]}{dt} = 2k_i[M][Cl_2] - 2k_t[M][Cl]^2$$

If it is assumed that the changes in $[M]$ and $[Cl_2]$ during the time taken to establish the stationary concentration $[Cl]_s$ can be neglected, and $[Cl]$ is expressed by $[Cl] = \alpha[Cl]_s$, then it can be shown (following Benson[8,9]) that

$$\ln \frac{(1+\alpha)}{(1-\alpha)} = 4M_t(k_i k_t[Cl_2])^{1/2} \tag{9.6}$$

Now k_i/k_t is equal to the dissociation constant of the reaction

$$Cl_2 \rightleftharpoons 2Cl$$

and this is known accurately although it varies rapidly with temperature. The termination constant has not been determined, but by analogy with the similar reactions in iodine and bromine, a value of 10^{17} cc^2 mole^{-2} sec^{-1} seems quite reasonable; it is independent of temperature within the accuracy required here. In a typical mixture of reactants with about 0·1 atm (2×10^{-6} mole cm^{-3}) of chlorine at 600°K, it is found that the time taken to establish a centre concentration equal to 90 per cent of the stationary value is about 50 seconds. This would mean that the steady reaction rate is not achieved for this time. In actual chlorination reactions, the time is far shorter than this. The contradiction is easily explained, for there is definite evidence that the chain centres are formed in catalysed reactions on the walls of the reaction vessels[5,12].

It can also be shown that the fraction of reaction, F, that occurs in the time taken for [X] to reach the fraction α of the stationary-state value in the simple scheme just discussed is given by

$$\ln (1-F) = [\ln (1-\alpha^2)]k_p/4Mk_t$$

If R is hydrogen, then the value of k_p is known and it can be shown that the time taken for F to equal 0·01 in equimolar mixture at 600°K and 1 atm pressure is about 3 seconds. Thus the induction period, measured as the time taken to achieve the fraction 0·01 of reaction, is small compared with the time taken to reach $\alpha = 0\cdot90$. Similarly, the time taken to reach $F = 0\cdot01$ in the presence of wall reactions must be much smaller than the time taken to reach a steady value of [X] and a steady rate. An exception to this occurs when conditions are chosen so that the maximum rate is extremely slow, as this means k_p is small; this condition is sometimes found in polymerizations[8,9]. Other induction periods have been reported in pyrolyses[10,11].

9.4. INDUCTION PERIODS IN BRANCHED-CHAIN REACTIONS

In branched-chain reactions, however, lengthy induction periods, terminated quite abruptly, can be found. The theory of branching chains has been extensively developed by Semenov[1,2], beginning in the decade 1920–30. Using the nomenclature introduced earlier in this chapter, and considering first reactions in which M is so small that $M[X]^2$ can be neglected for all practical values of [X]:

$$\frac{d[X]}{dt} = I + (F-G)[X] \tag{9.7}$$

If $F-G$ is independent of time, the equation can be integrated. Writing $F-G=\phi$, and assuming [X]=0 at $t=0$, integration gives:

$$[X] = \frac{I}{\phi}(e^{\phi t}-1) \tag{9.8}$$

If $\phi < 0$, $e^{\phi t}$ rapidly becomes very small compared with unity as t increases, and the chain centre concentration reaches a steady value $I/(-\phi)$. Correspondingly, the rate of reaction is constant, and the reaction is identical with a non-branching chain reaction. If $\phi > 0$, $e^{\phi t}$ rapidly becomes very large compared with unity as t increases. The chain centre concentration then increases exponentially with time, according to

$$[X] = \frac{I}{\phi} e^{\phi t} \tag{9.9}$$

The rate of reaction is that of the propagation step, i.e. $k_p[X] \times f[\text{reactants}]$. Writing this as $A[X]$, there results

$$\text{Rate} = \frac{AI}{\phi} e^{\phi t} \tag{9.10}$$

Integrating, assuming again that ϕ is independent of time, the total amount reacted after time t is

$$\Delta(\text{products}) = \frac{AI}{\phi^2} e^{\phi t} \tag{9.11}$$

By differentiating equation (9.11), or by comparing equations (9.10) and (9.11), it follows that

$$\frac{d\Delta(\text{products})}{dt} = \phi\Delta(\text{products}) \tag{9.12}$$

and hence

$$\ln \Delta(\text{products}) = \phi t + \text{constant} \tag{9.13}$$

These two equations are very useful for testing whether a reaction proceeds by branched chains and for determining ϕ from experimental results, especially where the amount of product formed can be determined from changes in some simple physical property such as pressure of reactants.

Semenov[13] has demonstrated that the exponential growth can result in a long quiescent period followed by an abrupt acceleration. For example, in a gas at 0·01 mm pressure, if I equals 10 molecules sec^{-1}, ϕ equals 5 sec^{-1} and A is 500 sec^{-1}, then after 4 seconds 0·10 per cent has reacted, after 5 seconds 14 per cent has reacted, but after 5·35 seconds 80 per cent has reacted. Hence branched-chain reactions can result in appreciable induction periods, the length being controlled by ϕ, the *acceleration constant* or *net branching factor*. Of course, if ϕ is negative, the reaction reaches a steady rate; if ϕ is positive, acceleration will occur. When this is rapid (ϕ large), as it appears to be in many gas-phase oxidations such as those of hydrogen or phosphorus, ignition may occur. If it is slow (ϕ close to 0), slow autocatalysis occurs, as in the oxidation of many liquid or gaseous hydrocarbons. In specific kinetic studies, the aim is to evaluate ϕ and to relate the measurements to variables such as the concentrations of reactants, the size of the reaction vessel and the temperature. Now the end of the induction period τ (during which A, I and ϕ are assumed to be constant) is defined by the rate or the amount of product reaching specified values. In either case, the simple expressions given above show that $\phi\tau$ is a constant. Thus some very useful information about ϕ can be obtained from studies of τ. Considerable efforts have been made to evaluate both long and short induction periods, and a particular example is given in section 11.4 on the hydrogen–oxygen reaction.

Another cause of long induction periods was described by Semenov. In a very slow reaction, one of the products may not be very stable and may decompose slowly to give radicals that can augment the rate of the initial reaction. Examples are known in thermal oxidations, as detailed in sections 11.2 and 11.3, when hydroperoxides or aldehydes may be the intermediates, and in some thermal decompositions. The process is quite reasonably called autocatalysis, but the similarity of mechanism and of behaviour (on a different time basis) to branched-chain reactions has led to the adoption of Semenov's phrase—degenerate chain branching.

9.5. CATALYSIS AND INHIBITION OF SOME CHAIN REACTIONS OF CHLORINE

9.5.1. *Introduction*

The reaction of chlorine with hydrogen, and the substitution of hydrogen by chlorine in saturated organic compounds, are typical chain reactions[14,15]. They appear to fit the following mechanism:

Initiation   (1) $Cl_2 \longrightarrow 2Cl^*$ (thermal, photochemical or catalysed)

Propagation (2) $Cl^* + RH \longrightarrow R^* + HCl$

            (3) $R^* + Cl_2 \longrightarrow RCl + Cl^*$

Termination (4) $2Cl^* \xrightarrow{M} Cl_2$

            (5) $Cl^* + inhibitor \longrightarrow end$

            (6) $Cl^* + wall \longrightarrow end$

Unless impurities are present or inhibitors are added, the chains are long, for the propagation steps (2) and (3) are fast. The homogeneous thermal initiation by (1) is slow, however, as mentioned in section 9.3, and it appears that the thermal reactions are often initiated by reaction of chlorine with the walls. The termination is also often on the wall. The reactions are inhibited by oxygen, by phenols, by nitrogen-containing substances such as ammonia, amines, nitrogen trichloride and nitrosyl chloride, and sometimes by the products of the reaction.

The addition of chlorine to carbon monoxide to yield phosgene, and the addition of chlorine to olefins, are also chain reactions. They seem to have a common pattern of initiation and propagation which can be written (with Y

as CO or $\diagdown C{=}C \diagup$) as:

          Initiation   (1) $Cl_2 \longrightarrow 2Cl^*$

          Propagation   (8) $Cl^* + Y \longrightarrow YCl^*$

                      (9) $YCl^* + Cl_2 \longrightarrow YCl_2 + Cl^*$

          Termination (4) $2Cl \xrightarrow{M} Cl_2$

                      (6) $Cl^* + wall \longrightarrow end$

                      (10) $Cl^* + YCl^* \longrightarrow Cl_2 + Y$

                      (11) $YC^*l + YCl^* \longrightarrow Cl_2 + 2Y$

There are, however, considerable differences from one reactant Y to another in the importance of the reverse reactions (-8) and (-9) and in the dominant terminating step. The most common terminating step, apart from (6) at low pressures, seems to be (11), but (10) also occurs; (4) is probably less important because it requires a third body, M.

These reactions form the basis of many successful preparations of substituted or addition compounds of chlorine with saturated or unsaturated hydrocarbons. In these preparations, photochemical initiation is often used, allowing reasonable rates at low temperatures where the products are stable. In other preparations, 'halogen carriers' such as ferric chloride or iodine are used as catalysts, but it is not certain that their action involves the homolytic splitting of chlorine. The reactions with hydrogen and with carbon monoxide provide some typical examples of the catalysis and inhibition of non-branching chain reactions.

9.5.2. *Hydrogen and chlorine*

The combination of hydrogen and chlorine was the first reaction to be identified as a chain reaction. Most of the kinetic investigations have been carried out on the photochemical reaction. Chlorine absorbs light of wavelength less than 5,500 Å. The quantum yield is rather variable, but with light of wave-length less than 4,785 Å it indicates a chain length of 10^4 or 10^5 in normal vessels at room temperature. In the absence of impurities, the principal chain-terminating step appears to involve reaction of the chain centres at the wall of the vessel. Convincing evidence for this was found by Trifonov[16]. He showed that the rate of reaction was greater in vessels of larger diameter when the reaction was initiated near the axis of the vessel. At moderate pressures, the rate of termination would depend upon the rate of diffusion to the wall, which is proportional to D/d^2, where D is the diffusion coefficient of the centres and d is the diameter of the vessel. The rate of a non-branching chain reaction, with termination on the walls, is proportional to 1/rate of termination (cf. equation (9.3)), and hence in this example the rate is proportional to d^2.

Traces of foreign gases have a marked effect on the velocity of the photochemical reaction[15]. Small proportions of oxygen, ammonia, nitrogen trichloride, nitric oxide, chlorine dioxide, nitrosyl chloride and ozone can greatly reduce the rate. There is also evidence[17] that the product, HCl, inhibits the reaction, just as HBr inhibits the hydrogen–bromine reaction, but the effect of HCl molecules is not so pronounced[14]. All the inhibiting gases except oxygen can cause an induction period during which the hydrogen–chlorine reaction does not proceed. The inhibitors may be removed during the induction period, either thermally or photochemically or by photosensitized reaction with the chlorine atoms, and a dramatic increase in the rate of the main reaction occurs when the inhibitor is finally destroyed.

The thermal reaction proceeds rapidly about 250 to 300°C and is almost certainly a chain reaction. The rate is sensitive to the presence of impurities, to the diameter of the vessel and to the nature of the vessel walls. The addition of nitrosyl chloride produces an induction period during which any combination of hydrogen and chlorine is quite negligible, as shown in *Figure 9.2*. This demonstrates that any possible molecular reaction is negligible at these temperatures. Oxygen also inhibits the thermal reaction, but not nearly as effectively as it inhibits the photochemical reaction; probably the products of the termination reactions, HO_2 and ClO_2, are much less stable at the higher temperatures of the thermal reaction.

The inhibition by oxygen was used by Pease[5] and by Morris and Pease[19] to show that the thermal reaction is initiated on the walls. With oxygen present, the rate of reaction was increased when the surface/volume ratio was increased. In the absence of oxygen, however, the rate of reaction is independent of the surface/volume ratio. These facts demonstrate that the thermal reaction in the absence of impurities is initiated *and* terminated on the walls. The experiments with added oxygen showed that clean Pyrex vessels are more active initiators than vessels coated with potassium chloride, but their activity decreases more rapidly.

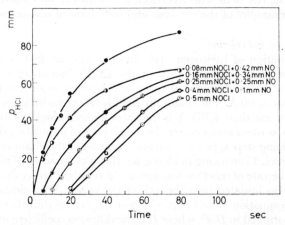

Figure 9.2. Effect of mixtures of nitric oxide and nitrosyl chloride on the reaction between 70 mm hydrogen and 70 mm chlorine at 300°C. ● no additives[18]

An interesting point arises from consideration of the reactions that make nitrosyl chloride such an effective inhibitor. The work on the phosgene synthesis, described in the next section, shows that the effective reaction is

$$NOCl + Cl^* \rightarrow NO + Cl_2 \qquad (9.14)$$

The N—Cl bond is weak, and reaction (9.14) is strongly exothermic. However, at higher temperatures not only can the nitrosyl chloride decompose to yield chlorine atoms

$$NOCl + M \rightarrow NO + Cl^* + M$$

but the reverse of reaction (9.14) can, in the presence of excess of nitric oxide, become a useful source of chlorine atoms. Thus at moderate temperatures the inhibiting reaction (9.14) produces a catalyst, nitric oxide. This is the reason for the sudden increase in the velocity of the reaction, as shown by the right-hand curve of *Figure 9.2*, at the end of the induction period. The figure also shows that the induction periods are shortened if some nitrosyl chloride is replaced by nitric oxide, until it ultimately vanishes. When different amounts of nitrosyl chloride are added, the induction period increases with increase in the amount of nitrosyl chloride, but the rate at the end of the induction period is very nearly constant, as shown in *Figure 9.2*. If the following simple scheme is adopted, these results can be explained[18].

Initiation (1) $NO + Cl_2 \xrightarrow{k_1} NOCl + Cl*$

Propagation (2) $Cl* + H_2 \xrightarrow{k_2} HCl + H*$

$H* + Cl_2 \longrightarrow HCl + Cl*$

Termination (3) $Cl* + NOCl \xrightarrow{k_3} NO + Cl_2$

Applying equation (9.3), it is found that

$$\frac{d[HCl]}{dt} = \frac{2k_1 k_2 [H_2][Cl_2][NO]}{k_3[NOCl]} \tag{9.15}$$

Now the amount of nitrosyl chloride together with nitric oxide is very small compared with the initial amount of chlorine, and the relative amounts of nitric oxide and nitrosyl chloride at the end of the induction periods are controlled by the balanced reactions

$$2NOCl \rightleftharpoons 2NO + Cl_2$$

so that the ratio $[NO]/[NOCl]$ is nearly independent of the initial amount of nitrosyl chloride. Thus the rate of the main reaction is nearly independent of the initial amount of nitrosyl chloride. It is also sustained, during each run, because as hydrogen and chlorine are consumed, the ratio $[NO]/[NOCl]$ increases. It can be seen from *Figure 9.3* that the rate does not fall off very rapidly.

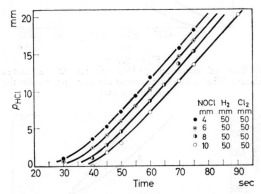

Figure 9.3. Induction periods and rates of the hydrogen–chlorine reaction for the mixtures shown[18]

The rate equation (9.15) is a very good fit to the experimental results at 250°C. In *Figure 9.4(a)*, rate $\times [NOCl]/[NO]$ is plotted against $[H_2] \times [Cl_2]$ and the points are a close fit to a straight line. From the slope of this line, $k_1 k_2/k_3$ can be determined, and as the ratio k_1/k_3 can be calculated from known equilibrium constants, k_2 can be evaluated[18].

At higher temperatures, mixtures of hydrogen and chlorine ignite spontaneously as soon as they are admitted to a heated reaction vessel. These

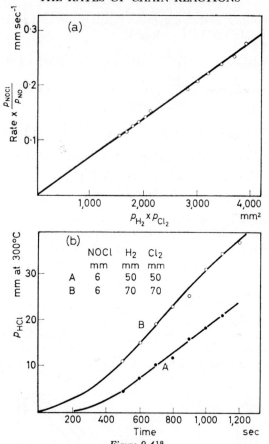

Figure 9.4[18]
(*a*) Test of equation (9.15). (*b*) Fit of calculated amount (line) and experimental amount (points) for the mixtures shown

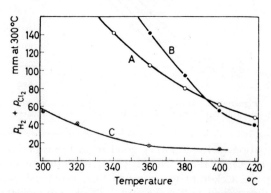

Figure 9.5. Ignition boundaries of hydrogen–chlorine mixtures[18]
A, $H_2 + Cl_2$; B, $H_2 + Cl_2 + 0.1$ mm NOCl; C, $H_2 + Cl_2 + 0.1$ mm NO. Ignition occurs above each boundary

270

ignitions appear to be thermal and to depend upon the self-heating of the reacting mixture. There is a simple boundary of pressure and temperature above which ignitions occur (curve A, *Figure 9.5* for equimolar mixtures in a cylindrical Pyrex vessel of diameter 28 mm) [18]. If the rate law for the slow reaction just outside the boundary were known, the assumption of thermal ignitions could be tested by an equation due to Frank–Kamenetskii. This states that

$$\frac{QEr^2(\text{rate})}{LRT^2} = \text{constant} \qquad (9.16)$$

where Q is the heat evolved in the reaction concerned, E is the activation energy of the reaction, L the thermal conductivity of the mixture, R the gas constant and r the radius of the vessel; the constant takes the value 3·32 for a spherical vessel, and 2·00 for a cylindrical vessel. The rate of reaction is related to the concentrations of the reactants, and this connects the concentrations (or pressures) at the boundary to the temperature T. There is a critical rate for each temperature for given reaction and vessel. Unfortunately, the rate is not

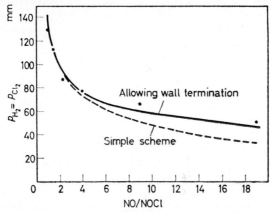

Figure 9.6. Ignition boundary for hydrogen–chlorine mixture with 1 mm of (NO+NOCl) in the proportions shown. The points are experimental and the line calculated from theory

very reproducible in the absence of additives, as the wall controls the initiation and the termination reactions. However, when a mixture of nitric oxide and nitrosyl chloride is added, the reactions are all in the gas phase and the rates become reproducible and at low temperatures ($\sim 300°C$) follow the rate law (9.15). It is therefore interesting to examine the ignition boundaries in the presence of these additives.

When nitric oxide is added, the boundary is lowered to curve C (*Figure 9.5*). When nitrosyl chloride is added, there is a short induction period before ignition, and the boundary moves to curve B. It is almost independent of the amount of nitrosyl chloride added, provided this is above a low minimum amount. These two features are in keeping with the assumption of thermal ignitions depending upon a critical rate at each temperature, and the observation of the induction periods followed by a rate of reaction which is independent of the initial concentration of nitrosyl chloride at lower temperatures.

271

When the thermal conductivities of the mixtures are calculated, using the formulae of Lindsay and Bromley[20], and the rate law (9.15) is put into the Frank–Kamenetskii equation (9.16), an excellent description of the boundary at different concentrations of nitric oxide and nitrosyl chloride is obtained. *Figure 9.6* shows how the predicted line from the simple scheme fits the experimental points at 300°C. If a small contribution to the termination is assigned to the wall at *low* concentrations of nitrosyl chloride, an even better description results. It must be emphasized that the predictions give the absolute values and not just the relative values of the boundary.

It is also possible to show that the rate law (9.15) and the Frank–Kamenetskii equation (9.16) combine to give an equation for the boundary C in *Figure 9.5* that predicts the correct activation energy for the reaction in the presence of nitric oxide and nitrosyl chloride. It can be seen from the two equations that

$$[H_2][Cl_2]e^{-E/RT} = \text{constant} \times T^2$$

where $E = E_1 + E_2 - E_3$. From a plot of $\log [H_2][Cl_2]/T^2$ against $1/T$ E is predicted as 25 ± 2 kcal. Now reactions 1 and 3 are reversible, and so $E_1 - E_3$ is equal to ΔE^0 for reaction 1, having a value of 19·2 kcal. E_2 has been determined as 5·5 kcal, so that E is 24·7 kcal, in excellent agreement with the predicted value.

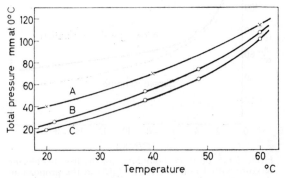

Figure 9.7. Variation of the upper limit of ignition with temperature in hydrogen–chlorine mixtures[21]
A, Apin's values[22] for nitrogen trichloride alone; B, equimolar hydrogen and chlorine, each with about 1 per cent nitrogen trichloride; C, equimolar nitrogen and chlorine

It is interesting that nitrogen trichloride which acts as a very powerful inhibitor of the photochemical reaction at room temperature and high pressures[23], can act as an initiator of ignitions of mixtures of hydrogen and chlorine at lower pressures[21]. It is known that nitrogen trichloride decomposes explosively if its pressure is below a critical value[22]; this critical value changes with temperature in much the same way as does the second limit of ignition in hydrogen–oxygen mixtures, as shown in curve A, *Figure 9.7*. The pressure of nitrogen trichloride can be lowered, however, if other gases are present, as shown by Apin, and the lower curve shows the explosion boundary for 1 per cent of nitrogen trichloride in nitrogen. If the other gases can react, however, the explosion of the nitrogen trichloride can cause ignition of these gases; curve B shows the boundary for equimolar mixtures of hydrogen and chlorine (with 1 per cent nitrogen trichloride) which combine explosively at pressures below the boundary. The explosion of the nitrogen trichloride undoubtedly involves branched-chain reactions and provides enough centres, which may be Cl or NCl₂ or NCl, to initiate thermal explosion of the non-branching chains in the hydrogen–chlorine system.

9.5.3. Carbon monoxide and chlorine

The reaction between carbon monoxide and chlorine is also a typical chain reaction. The kinetics of the thermal and the photochemical reactions have been studied extensively by Rollefson and his co-workers[24], by Bodenstein and his co-workers[25] and later by Burns and Dainton[26]. The earlier investigations have been summarized by Leighton and Noyes[27] and by Steacie[28]. There is general agreement between all the investigators about the experimental results, but slightly different mechanisms have been advanced to explain them. Rollefson included a step in which COCl* is formed in a third-order reaction

$$Cl^* + CO + M \rightarrow COCl^* + M$$

and suggested that Cl_2 is particularly effective as M, perhaps because of the formation of Cl_3. However, there is now considerable evidence that the above reactions are balanced for the particular pressures of carbon monoxide and chlorine present at any moment, and it is not necessary to include M in the rate equations. For this reason, Bodenstein's reaction scheme is at present preferred:

Initiation	(1)	$Cl_2 \rightarrow 2Cl^*$
Propagation	(2)	$Cl^* + CO \rightarrow COCl^*$
	(3)	$COCl^* \rightarrow CO + Cl^*$
	(4)	$COCl^* + Cl_2 \rightarrow COCl_2 + Cl^*$
Termination	(5)	$Cl^* + COCl \rightarrow CO + Cl_2$

This scheme, with thermal or photochemical initiation, can account for the observed rate laws. The other possible termination reactions, $2Cl + Cl_2$ and $2COCl \rightarrow 2CO + Cl_2$ are less important than reaction 5, the first because it needs a third body and the second because COCl is very much less than Cl. By combining the results of photochemical and thermal reactions, Bodenstein and co-workers[25] were able to estimate k_4, k_5 and K_{COCl} at various temperatures. However, there is always some difficulty in combining photochemical and thermal results, and it was therefore very helpful when the sector method was applied to the photochemical reaction to evaluate these constants[26,29]. In the more recent determinations, Burns and Dainton[26] found their results fitted the law predicted from Bodenstein's scheme for the photochemical reaction:

$$\frac{d[COCl_2]}{dt} = k_4 \left(\frac{I_{abs}}{k_5 K_{COCl}} \right)^{1/2} [CO]^{1/2} [Cl_2] \tag{9.17}$$

They were also able to evaluate k_4, k_5 and K_{COCl}, and found activation energies $E_4 = 2 \cdot 69$ kcal and $E_5 = 0 \cdot 83$ kcal, in reasonable agreement with Bodenstein's estimates (2·6 and 1·9, respectively).

18—c.

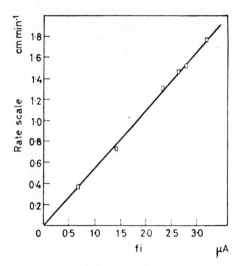

Figure 9.8. Dependence of rate on I_{abs} in the inhibited photochemical carbon monoxide–chlorine reaction[26]
$P_{OC} = P_{Cl_2} = 300$ mm; $p_{NOCl} = 0.0028$ mm; temperature: 25°C; 100 scale mm $\equiv$ 10·5 mm Hg

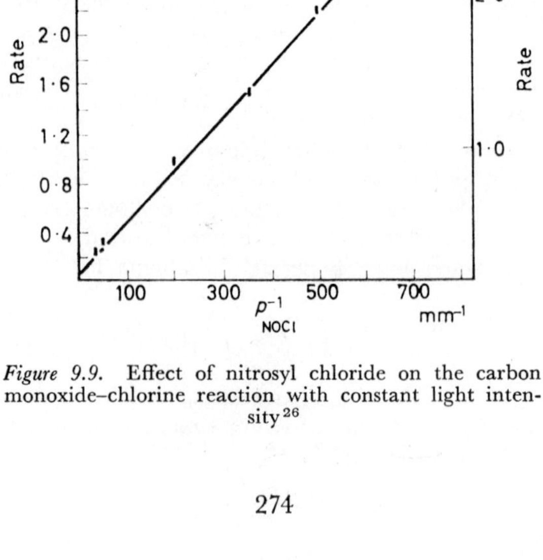

Figure 9.9. Effect of nitrosyl chloride on the carbon monoxide–chlorine reaction with constant light intensity[26]

Burns and Dainton[26] also continued Dainton's work[30] on the inhibition of the photochemical reaction by nitrosyl chloride. Nitrosyl chloride introduces the termination reactions

$$(6) \quad Cl* + NOCl \rightarrow NO + Cl_2$$

$$(7) \quad COCl* + NOCl \rightarrow NO + CO + Cl_2$$

and the rate law becomes

$$\frac{d[COCl_2]}{dt} = \frac{2I_{abs}k_1k_4[CO][Cl_2]}{[NOCl](k_6K_{COCl} + k_7[CO])} \tag{9.18}$$

Figure 9.8 shows that the rate is proportional to I_{abs}, and *Figure 9.9* shows that the rate is inversely proportional to [NOCl]. Burns and Dainton were able to evaluate k_6 and k_7 at several temperatures and found that the reactions have low activation energies, near to 1 kcal.

9.5.4. *Chlorination of hydrocarbons and their derivatives*

There has been a lot of work on the photochemical and thermal chlorination of hydrocarbons and their derivatives[28,31,32], but relatively little work on

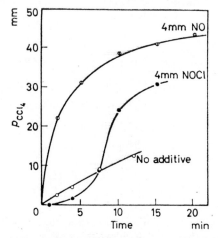

Figure 9.10. Effects of nitric oxide and nitrosyl chloride on the thermal reaction between chloroform and chlorine[33] $P_{CHCl_3} = 50$ mm; $P_{Cl} = 50$ mm; temperature 272°C

the catalysis and inhibition of these reactions. Saturated aliphatic hydrocarbons give chlorinated substitution products, and the partially chlorinated products usually chlorinate more rapidly than the parent hydrocarbon. Olefins form addition products more readily than substitution products. Aromatic hydrocarbons can form either or both types of chlorine derivative.

The chain character of the substitution reactions is shown by the inhibiting effects of oxygen, phenol, amines, nitrosyl chloride and so on. Two examples may be quoted:

(*i*) The thermal chlorination of chloroform is inhibited strongly by nitrosyl chloride, which is decomposed during an induction period. This can be seen by comparing the two lower curves in *Figure 9.10*. On the other hand, nitric oxide increases the rate, as shown by the upper curve. The reactions introduced by the nitric oxide and the nitrosyl chloride are almost certainly similar to those they introduce into the hydrogen–chlorine reaction. An unusual feature of the catalysis by nitric oxide is that the rate of the catalysed reaction is independent of the concentration of nitric oxide as soon as this is above a low minimum[33].

(*ii*) The thermal and photochemical chlorinations of olefins are inhibited by oxygen[34]. For example, Chaikin[35] studied the thermal chlorination of ethylene in the gas phase at $227°C$ and found a rate law

$$\text{Rate} = w_0 + \frac{a[\text{Cl}_2][\text{C}_2\text{H}_4]}{b + c[\text{O}_2]} \tag{9.19}$$

Chaikin showed that the products of the chlorination are themselves inhibitors, quite independently of the oxygen, and they contribute to the term b in the expression (9.19). The walls also inhibit the reaction, but chains are started at the surface. This was demonstrated by the radial distribution of temperature in the reaction vessel during the experiment[35,36]. Chaikin's results[35] fit the mechanism

Initiation	(1)	$\text{Cl}_2 \xrightarrow{\text{surface}} 2\text{Cl}*$
Propagation	(2)	$\text{Cl}* + \text{C}_2\text{H}_4 \rightarrow \text{C}_2\text{H}_4\text{Cl}*$
	(3)	$\text{C}_2\text{H}_4\text{Cl}* + \text{Cl}_2 \rightarrow \text{C}_2\text{H}_4\text{Cl}_2 + \text{Cl}*$
Termination	(4)	$\text{Cl}* + \text{reaction product} \rightarrow \text{end}$
	(5)	$\text{Cl}* + \text{surface} \rightarrow \text{end}$
	(6)	$\text{Cl}* + \text{O}_2 \rightarrow \text{end}$

$$\text{Rate} = \frac{2k_1 k_2 [\text{Cl}_2][\text{C}_2\text{H}_4]}{k_4[\text{product}] + k_5 + k_6[\text{O}_2]} \tag{9.20}$$

Presumably the product of reaction 4 is a free radical which is less reactive towards the ethylene than is the chlorine atom. k_1 and k_5 each contain a surface/volume factor.

There do not seem to have been any direct quantitative measurements of the rate of attack by chlorine molecules or chlorine atoms on various surfaces, in spite of the importance of these reactions in the thermal chlorinations and in photochemical chlorinations at low pressures. Some indirect evidence of the rate of chlorine atom attack on Pyrex surfaces was obtained by Ashmore and Spenser[37] during the study of the decomposition of nitrosyl chloride and its formation from chlorine and nitric oxide. There have also been measurements of the rate of recombination of halogen atoms on various surfaces[38].

There is an interesting link between the inhibition by oxygen of the chlorination of hydrocarbons and the catalysis by chlorine of the auto-oxidations of chlorinated derivatives of hydrocarbons[28,39]. It seems likely[39] that a chlorine atom adds to a chloroethylene, or extracts a hydrogen atom from a partially chlorinated paraffin, to give a radical which readily adds on oxygen. This peroxy radical is not easily attacked by chlorine, so the chlorination chain is stopped, but probably two of the peroxy radicals react to give an acid chloride and oxygen:

$$CCl_2:CCl_2 + Cl^* \rightarrow CCl_3 \cdot CCl_2^*$$

or

$$CCl_3 \cdot CHCl_2 + Cl^* \rightarrow CCl_3 \cdot CCl_2^* + HCl$$

$$CCl_3 \cdot CCl_2^* + O_2 \rightarrow CCl_3 \cdot CCl_2 \cdot O_2^*$$

$$2CCl_3 \cdot CCl_2 \cdot O_2^* \rightarrow 2CCl_3 \cdot COCl + 2Cl^* + O_2$$

The last reaction may consist of two steps.

By similar reactions, trichloroethylene gives dichloroacetyl chloride, $CHCl_2 \cdot COCl$, while chloral gives phosgene, carbon monoxide and hydrogen chloride. Phosgene is frequently a side-product of the auto-oxidations of many chloro-derivatives.

9.6. CATALYSIS AND INHIBITION OF (CHAIN) THERMAL DECOMPOSITIONS

9.6.1. Introduction

Hydrocarbons and their derivatives decompose in the gas phase at moderately high temperatures. Perhaps the best known of these decompositions is the 'cracking' of higher hydrocarbons, because of its importance in petroleum chemistry. However, the thermal decompositions of lower hydrocarbons, of alkyl halides, of aldehydes, ketones and ethers have been of great interest to kineticists from 1920 onwards. In the early investigations, the decompositions were treated as simple unimolecular processes, and studies of the decompositions were used to test theories of unimolecular reactions, for example the Lindemann theory. Later work has shown that many of the reactions are complex. Some of these complex pyrolyses proceed almost exclusively by chain reactions; in others, it has been suggested that chain and molecular reactions occur in parallel.

Thus acetaldehyde can decompose by a simple unimolecular, exothermic step

$$CH_3 \cdot CHO \rightarrow CH_4 + CO \qquad \Delta H = -5 \text{ kcal}$$

or by a chain reaction with steps as follows [40,41]

Initiation: $CH_3 \cdot CHO \rightarrow CH_3^* + CHO^*$

Propagation: $CH_3^* + CH_3 \cdot CHO \rightarrow CH_4 + CH_3 \cdot CO^*$

$CH_3 \cdot CO^* \rightarrow CH_3^* + CO$

Termination: $CH_3^* + CH_3^* \rightarrow C_2H_6$

Experimentally, the general chain character of the reaction is confirmed by the acceleration produced by traces of oxygen, diacetyl, di-t-butyl peroxide or halogens, and by the inhibition by nitric oxide (in small proportions—larger proportions produce catalysis) and by propylene.

277

Similarly, dimethyl ether decomposes very largely by a chain mechanism which may be[40]

Initiation: $\qquad$ $CH_3—O—CH_3 \xrightarrow{k_0} CH_3O* + CH_3^*$

Propagation: $\quad CH_3^* + CH_3OCH_3 \xrightarrow{k_1} CH_4 + CH_2OCH_3^*$

$$CH_2OCH_3^* \xrightarrow{k_2} CH_2O + CH_3^*$$

$$CH_2O \xrightarrow{k_2} CO + H_2$$

Termination: $\quad CH_3^* + CH_2OCH_3^* \xrightarrow{k_3} CH_2O + C_2H_6$

The rate law given by this scheme is

$$w = \left(\frac{k_0 k_1 k_2}{k_3}\right)^{1/2} [CH_3OCH_3] \tag{9.21}$$

Almost all the decompositions can be accelerated if a catalyst is present to supply free radicals by decomposition or by reaction with the substrate. Thus alkyl peroxides or oxygen can catalyse many of the decompositions. Halogens will catalyse the decompositions of most alkyl halides, of ethers and of aldehydes, because they dissociate readily. Metal alkyls and the azo-compounds used to initiate polymerizations are also effective. Photolysis of added ketones or aldehydes can also initiate other decompositions. However, the decompositions of a few alkyl chlorides such as n-propyl chloride are not accelerated by catalysts which produce free radicals and so are assumed to decompose only by molecular eliminations, directly to olefins and hydrogen chloride. On the whole, studies of the catalysis of decompositions have not been much help in deciding the mechanism of the decomposition. The existence of catalysis by free radicals provides evidence that the reaction *can* proceed by a chain reaction but not that it does so in the absence of the catalyst.

Inhibitors have been more useful than catalysts in deciding whether the decomposition proceeds by a chain mechanism. Thus the decompositions of certain alkyl chlorides, in vessels which have been extensively used and so 'conditioned', are retarded by propylene or n-hexane. These decompositions are thought to proceed by chain reactions. On the other hand, those decompositions of chlorides that are insensitive to oxygen as a catalyst are not inhibited by propylene, and the decompositions are assumed to be molecular eliminations[42-44].

In the first group, the propagation reactions may be, for example

$$Cl* + CH_2Cl—CH_2Cl \rightarrow HCl + *CHCl—CH_2Cl$$
$$*CHCl—CH_2Cl \rightarrow Cl + CHCl{=}CH_2$$

The hydrogen atom removed in the first step leaves a radical that can form an olefin by loss of a chlorine atom. If, however, the radical cannot form an olefin by losing a chlorine atom, the chain cannot continue. The radical is not likely to decompose by losing a hydrogen atom.

In ethyl chloride, for example, the first step may be

$\qquad$ (a) $\quad CH_3 \cdot CH_2Cl + Cl* \rightarrow CH_3 \cdot CHCl* + HCl$

or

$\qquad$ (b) $\quad CH_3 \cdot CH_2Cl + Cl* \rightarrow *CH_2 \cdot CH_2Cl + HCl$

The radical $*CH_2 \cdot CH_2Cl$ *could* form an olefin by loss of a chlorine atom, but $CH_3 \cdot *CHCl$ *could not*. Thus if reaction a is preferred to reaction b for energetic reasons, the chains will not propagate. This appears to be so for many mono-chloro-derivatives besides ethyl chloride and, as would be expected, for 1,1-dichloroethane but not for 1,2-dichloroethane. Thus the identification of chain reactions in some of these decompositions, by use of inhibitors, can be linked systematically with the structure and reactivity of the molecule[45].

9.6.2. Inhibitors of decompositions

The decompositions of ethers and of alkanes have been studied extensively. In 1933 Dintzes and Frost found[46] that the decomposition of hydrocarbons was auto-inhibited, and also that the initial rate could be lowered by adding propylene. Hinshelwood and Stubbs[47,48] showed that nitric oxide inhibited many

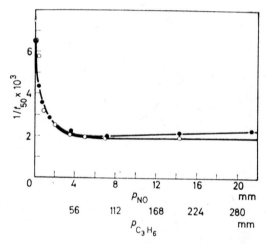

Figure 9.11. Inhibition of ether decomposition by nitric oxide ($\bigcirc$) and by prophylene ($\bullet$)[47b]. Initial pressure of ether: 100 mm at 550°C

decompositions and that the rate reached some limiting value at higher concentrations of nitric oxide. When it was shown that propylene in larger proportions (about 12 parts propylene : 1 part nitric oxide) produced the *same limiting rate* (measured by dp/dt, or by a fractional life, t_{50}; see *Figure 9.11*) it was concluded that the limiting rate was that of a molecular reaction which would proceed in parallel with a chain reaction in the absence of the inhibitor. Stepukhovich and Chaikin[49] showed that isobutylene and propylene produced the same limiting rate of decomposition. Voevodsky and Poltora[50] showed that the inhibited and the uninhibited reactions tend to the same rates at higher percentage decompositions.

The most serious difficulty with this interpretation of the results is that the composition of the products is the same in the uninhibited and in the inhibited reaction, for many decompositions. Moreover, Wall and Moore[51,52] showed that exchange occurred between C_2H_6 and C_2D_6 in the presence of 2·5 per cent nitric oxide at 610°C, and that H_2, HD and D_2 were formed. Later, Rice and Varnerin[53] found that when a mixture of C_2D_6 and CH_4 was decomposed, in the absence or presence of nitric oxide, the CH_3D/CH_4 ratio was proportional to the extent of decomposition.

Rice and Polly[54] proposed that the 'inhibitors' can also initiate chains, so that at high concentrations of inhibitor the rate of pyrolysis becomes

$$\text{Rate} = \frac{R_i R_p}{R_t} = \frac{k_p k_i I \cdot f [\text{reactant}]}{k_t I} \tag{9.22}$$

which is independent of I. However, k_i/k_t would have to be the same for, say, nitric oxide and propylene, in order to produce the same limiting rate, and it is difficult to see why this should be. (However, see page 281.)

Yet another possibility is that the residual reaction simply represents the rate of initiation of chains. If the chains are normally short, but many in

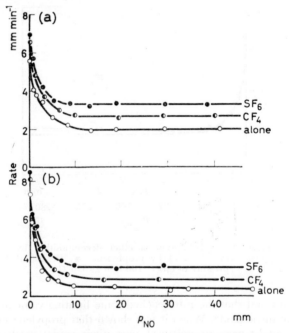

Figure 9.12. Inhibition curves for (a) n-butane (150 mm, 550°C) and (b) n-pentane (150 mm, 540°C) with and without added inert gases[48b]

number, this might lead to similar products for the inhibited and the uninhibited reactions: it would explain why the limiting rate is the same with different inhibitors. However, Jach and Hinshelwood[55] found some strong experimental evidence against this suggestion. The initiation step is probably a unimolecular decomposition of the molecule being pyrolysed. Thus if the limiting rate is the rate of initiation, it should be increased if sufficient inert gas is added. The rate of initiation in the *uninhibited* reaction should similarly be increased by adding inert gases, but the total rate of uninhibited decomposition, being equal to ($R_i \times$ chain length), should be increased by a greater

280

factor than is the limiting rate. As shown in *Figure 9.12*, however, the *actual* increase in rate for a given addition is independent of the amount of nitric oxide used. This evidence strongly indicates that the limiting rate and the chain portion of the reaction are independent.

Voevodsky[56] has drawn attention to the possibility that chains are initiated and terminated on the walls, so accounting for the observation that the rate of decomposition at high pressures is independent of the ratio S/V. At low pressures (e.g. 25 cm propane at 610°C) he finds that the initial rate of decomposition decreases as S/V is increased from 1 to 10. He also finds that pretreatment of the vessel walls affects the initial rate of the uninhibited reaction, and also the final limiting rate. Voevodsky postulates that there are reversible and irreversible processes of initiation on the wall, the irreversible initiative being poisoned by inhibitors or by the products of reaction. However, as pointed out by Laidler and Wojciechowski[57], Voevodsky's theory requires that the amount of nitric oxide required for inhibition should depend on the S/V ratio, and there is no evidence for this. In addition, the fully inhibited reaction often shows a well-defined induction period.

Laidler and Wojciechowski[57] have returned to the idea that the nitric oxide can initiate reactions (by abstraction of a hydrogen atom to give HNO and a hydrocarbon radical) as well as terminating them. With propylene, they suppose that the stable[58] allyl radical, C_3H_5, acts as does the nitric oxide. With ethane decomposition their scheme is

$$\text{Initiation} \qquad C_2H_6 + NO \xrightarrow{k_1} C_2H_5^* + HNO$$

$$\text{Propagation} \left\{ \begin{array}{l} C_2H_5^* \xrightarrow{k_2} C_2H_4 + H^* \\[2mm] H^* + C_2H_6 \xrightarrow{k_3} C_2H_5^* + H_2 \end{array} \right.$$

$$\text{(Equilibrium)} \qquad H^* + NO \underset{k_{-4}}{\overset{k_4}{\rightleftharpoons}} HNO$$

$$\text{Termination} \quad C_2H_5^* + HNO \xrightarrow{k_{-1}} C_2H_6 + NO$$

This scheme leads to

$$\text{Rate of decomposition} = \left(\frac{k_1 k_2 k_3 k_{-4}}{k_{-1} k_4} \right)^{1/2} [C_2H_6] \qquad (9.23)$$

The inhibitor is involved in k_1, k_{-1}, k_4, k_{-4}, which occur in the ratio $k_1 k_{-4}/k_{-1} k_4$. Now

$$\frac{k_1}{k_{-1}} = \frac{[C_2H_5]_e [HNO]_e}{[C_2H_6]_e [NO]_e}$$

and

$$\frac{k_{-4}}{k_4} = \frac{[H]_e [NO]_e}{[HNO]_e}$$

and hence

$$\frac{k_1}{k_{-1}} \cdot \frac{k_{-4}}{k_4} = \frac{[C_2H_5]_e [H]_e}{[C_2H_6]_e} = \text{constant}$$

281

the equilibrium constant of the reversible reaction $C_2H_6 \rightleftharpoons C_2H_5^* + H^*$. Thus the velocity constants involving the inhibitor have no effect on the rate—in other words, the limiting rate is independent of the amount and *nature* of the inhibitor. Their mechanism also accounts for the experimental observation that the degree of inhibition is found to be less at higher ethane concentrations in the partially inhibited reaction, for nitric oxide and ethane compete in reactions 4 and 3 for hydrogen atoms.

The same authors treat other decompositions similarly, and broadly speaking, their theory seems to account for most of the observed facts. It is not immediately obvious, however, whether this theory can explain the results obtained by Jach, Stubbs and Hinshelwood[48b].

Purnell and Quinn[59] have studied the decomposition of n-butane in the absence and presence of propylene. They have studied the distribution of products in the *very early stages* of the reaction, finding the same products in the inhibited and the uninhibited reaction. However, they find a significant linear increase in the ratio ethylene/ethane with the pressure of propylene added, even when the rate of production of ethylene together with propane has reached its limiting value. In conjunction with other observations, they find this quite incompatible with the idea that the limiting rate is a molecular reaction.

Although the evidence is not conclusive, it now appears unlikely that the residual 'inhibited' reactions in the pyrolyses of hydrocarbons and the derivation are molecular reactions. It follows from this that 'mixed' chain and molecular reactions are not as common as they were once thought to be. The reactions proceed either by molecular elimination, as with some alkyl chlorides and bromides, or by chain reactions. Lastly, the suggestion that inhibitors can under some circumstances become 'catalysts' is in keeping with similar behaviour of inhibitors in polymerization and in chlorination reactions.

9.6.3. *Decomposition of organic peroxides, hydroperoxides and other chain initiators*

The compounds ROOH and ROOR', where R and R' may be alkyl, acyl, aryl or aroyl groups, or their derivatives, form an interesting series of hydroperoxides and peroxides which have been recognized for many years but isolated and investigated only recently[60]. They are important intermediates in the oxidation of some hydrocarbons, and those that are stable at room temperature but decompose readily at higher temperatures or in the presence of catalysts have proved very useful for initiating free radical polymerizations or oxidations.

The thermal stability of the hydroperoxides and the peroxides varies greatly with the chemical nature of the groups R and R'. Thus methyl hydroperoxide and dimethyl peroxide are extremely unstable, whereas di-t-butyl peroxide can be distilled at atmospheric pressure; acetyl peroxide explodes very easily, whereas benzoyl peroxide is stable. The types of products vary greatly with the conditions and with the nature of R and R'. Thus n-butyl and isobutyl hydroperoxides at about 90 to 100°C yield acids and hydrogen, whereas t-butyl hydroperoxide gives oxygen and t-butanol. In the vapour phase at about 300°C, t-butyl hydroperoxide gives, *inter alia*, t-butanol, methanol, acetone, formaldehyde, methane and water.

In the vapour phase or in solution in non-acidic solvents, the hydroperoxides and peroxides decompose by homolytic fission of the —O—O— bond to give alkoxyl or similar radicals; these radicals can undergo some or all of various possible reactions which may set up a chain decomposition of the parent reactant. Gray and Williams[61] have summarized the possible reactions as follows:

(i) association with another radical, dimerization or disproportionation, (ii) loss of hydrogen atom by decomposition or by reaction with another radical, (iii) loss of a smaller radical by decomposition or by reaction with another radical, (iv) hydrogen abstraction from solvent or from parent molecule, (v) rearrangement by migration, and (vi) addition to unsaturated molecule. Reasonable combinations of these reactions are found to account for most of the reported product distributions. For example, the decomposition of di-t-butyl peroxide in the vapour or in solution gives initially t-butoxy radicals Me_3CO*; these can decompose to give acetone and methyl radicals, or extract hydrogen atoms from the peroxide or from a solvent molecule, or disproportionate to butanol and isobutene epoxide[62,63]:

$$Me_3COH + *CH_2CMe_2O* \rightarrow \overset{\displaystyle O}{\overset{\displaystyle /\!\!\setminus}{CH_2CMe_2}}$$

$$\underset{\underset{Me_3COH + R*}{RH\downarrow}}{\uparrow}$$

$$Me_3COOCMe_3 \rightarrow 2Me_3CO* \rightarrow 2Me_2CO + 2Me* \rightarrow C_2H_6$$

$$\underset{CH_4 + R*}{RH\downarrow}$$

There is a similar free-radical decomposition of hydroperoxides. Thus cumene hydroperoxide decomposes in hydrocarbon solvents to give principally methane, acetophenone and dimethylphenylcarbinol[64]:

$$PhMe_2COOH \rightarrow PhMe_2CO* + OH*$$

$$PhMe_2CO* + RH \rightarrow PhMe_2COH + R*$$

$$PhMe_2CO* \rightarrow PhMeCO + Me*$$

$$Me* + RH \rightarrow CH_4 + R*$$

$$R*(or\ Me*) + PhMe_2COOH \rightarrow ROH(MeOH) + PhMe_2CO*$$

$$2R*(or\ Me*) \rightarrow RR(C_2H_6)$$

It is clear that chain decompositions are set up. Many of these decompositions appear to be first-order reactions, and the activation energies and pre-exponential factors of some of them have been assembled by Kirk and Knox[65], as shown in *Table 9.1*. Gray and Williams[61] have also tabulated activation energies for the decomposition of peroxidic compounds.

The free-radical nature of these decompositions makes the hydroperoxides and peroxides very useful catalysts for auto-oxidation reactions and for polymerizations; many examples of their use are discussed in the next two chapters. At this point, attention may be drawn to two features: (i) The decomposition of hydroperoxides and peroxides can be catalysed by the redox systems considered in section 3.1, and the combination produces some very powerful sources of free radicals for initiating polymerizations. (ii) When hydroperoxides or peroxides are used as catalysts, their decomposition may be accelerated by reaction with the chain centres; some caution is necessary in attempts to correlate the rate of initiation by these catalysts with their 'normal' rate of decomposition.

283

Besides decomposing by free-radical mechanisms, some cycloalkyl and aralkyl hydroperoxides can apparently decompose by an ionic mechanism to give a different set of products[64,66]. For example, cumene hydroperoxide decomposes in acidic solvents, or in the presence of typical acid catalysts including heavy metal ions, to give good yields of phenol and acetone, with some cumene peroxide, instead of methane, acetophenone and dimethylphenylcarbinol. Carbonium ion mechanisms have been proposed to account for such products.

Table 9.1[65]

R	*Dialkyl peroxides*† ROOR		*Alkyl hydroperoxides* ROOH			
	E kcal mole^{-1}	log A sec^{-1}	E_{hom} kcal mole^{-1}	log A_{hom} sec^{-1}	E_{het} kcal mole^{-1}	log A_{het} sec^{-1}
Hydrogen‡			48·0	12·0	20	
Methyl	36·1	15·4	—	—	—	—
Ethyl§	34·1	14·2	37·7±0·7	13·4±0·3	18	6
Isopropyl	—	—	40·0±0·7	15·2±0·3	17	6
n-Propyl	36·5	15·4	—	—	—	—
t-Butyl	37·5	15·6	37·8±0·7	13·7±0·3	25	8
Mean‖	36·2	15·2	38·5	14·1		

† Values from Hanst, P. L. and Calvert, J. G. *J. phys. Chem.* 1959, **63**, 104.
‡ *A* factor for H_2O_2 is calculated for a pressure of 15 mm Hg of H_2O_2 from data in Hoare, D. E., Protheroe, J. B. and Walsh, A. D. *Trans. Faraday Soc.* 1959, **55**, 548.
§ Error limits are standard errors.
‖ Mean values are the average for organic peroxides.

The decomposition of benzoyl peroxide, which is widely used as an initiator for polymerizations, has been studied extensively. It turns out to be very complex. At low concentrations, the decomposition is apparently unimolecular, but the rate of decomposition is accelerated by the addition of sources of free radicals. At higher concentrations, the apparent first-order constant increases; this increase can be prevented by the addition of typical inhibitors such as quinones, amines, iodine or oxygen. It thus appears that the free radicals formed by the decomposition initiate or induce further decomposition through chain reactions. Hammond and Soffer[67] examined the decomposition in dry carbon tetrachloride with iodine present and also in moist carbon tetrachloride with iodine present. In the dry solvent, principally iodobenzene was formed, and in the moist, benzoic acid almost quantitatively. Both these are probably formed from benzoyl hypoiodite, itself formed from iodine and the benzoate radicals that are the primary product of the decomposition of the peroxide

$$Ph \cdot CO \cdot O \cdot O \cdot CO \cdot Ph \to 2Ph \cdot CO \cdot O*$$

$$Ph \cdot CO \cdot O* + I_2 \to Ph \cdot CO \cdot OI + I* \quad (\to PhI + CO_2)$$

$$Ph \cdot CO \cdot OI + H_2O \to Ph \cdot CO \cdot OH + HOI$$

In the presence of suitable monomers, the benzoate radicals initiate polymerization and have been identified in the polymer molecules. In some solvents, especially those in which there are C—H links, the decomposition is very fast.

This is because there are chain steps set up:

$$Ph \cdot CO \cdot O^* + RH \rightarrow Ph \cdot CO \cdot OH + R^*$$

$$R^* + Ph \cdot CO \cdot O \cdot O \cdot CO \cdot Ph \rightarrow RO \cdot CO \cdot Ph + Ph \cdot CO \cdot O^*$$

This induced decomposition is very fast in primary or secondary alcohols, in ethers and in some hydrocarbons.

In less active solvents, the benzoate radical decomposes before reacting with the solvent, to give phenyl radicals and carbon dioxide. By using radioactive carbon in the carbonyl group[68], the rate of decomposition can be counted from the carbon dioxide evolved. The phenyl radical can then attack the peroxide, or the solvent, or products of the benzoate attack. The products are therefore many and the kinetics complicated. Walling[69] has given a full account of the investigations up to 1957. Recently, attention has been given to determining the primary and the induced decomposition under polymerization conditions, and an account of some investigations is given in section 10.22.

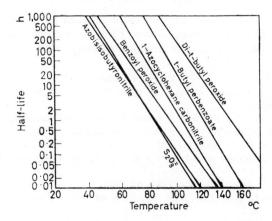

Figure 9.13. Half-lives of some common initiators[69]

The thermal decompositions of many azo-compounds have been used as sources of free radicals. The simple di-alkyl or di-aryl azo-compounds only slowly yield radicals by fission of the —N=N— bonds, and these radicals are not very effective initiators. Diazo-compounds such as ArN=N—NRR′ initiate more readily, and so does nitrosoacetanilide. The most useful initiators are the azo-compounds with complex groups such as disubstituted aceto-nitriles. The decomposition rates of a variety of these compounds at 80°C have been tabulated by Walling[69]. Azobisisobutyronitrile is a good example. It decomposes at a convenient rate in a first-order reaction which is scarcely affected by the solvent, evolving nitrogen which can be used to follow the rate of decomposition and hence, with some assumptions, the rate of initiation of chains.

Figure 9.13, taken from Walling[69], shows the half-life of some common initiators at different temperatures. It will be clear that the lines for peroxy-compounds are only approximate, for their position will vary somewhat with the solvent used. The figure includes a line for the persulphate ion, which decomposes by fission of an —O—O— bond, as do the peroxides:

$$S_2O_8^{2-} \rightarrow 2 \ {}^*SO_4^-$$

If no suitable substrate is present, the sulphate ion radicals react with the solvent water. The oxygen evolved comes from the water, as demonstrated by using ^{18}O in the water:

$${}^*SO_4^- + H_2O \rightarrow HSO_4^- + OH^*$$

$$2OH^* \rightarrow H_2O + \tfrac{1}{2}O_2$$

In the presence of suitable monomers, the sulphate ion-radical can initiate polymerizations, and sulphur can be detected in the polymer molecules. In the presence of substrates such as methanol, or reducing agents such as thio-sulphates or sulphites, chain reactions can be set up:

$${}^*SO_4^- + CH_3OH \rightarrow HSO_4^- + CH_2OH^*$$

$$CH_2OH^* + S_2O_8^{2-} \rightarrow CH_2O + HSO_4^- + {}^*SO_4^-$$

Because of these chain reactions, the combination of persulphate ion with a reducing agent provides a ready source of free radicals, and redox initiators are extensively used, especially in emulsion polymerizations.

REFERENCES

[1] SEMENOV, N. N. *Chemical Kinetics and Chain Reactions*: Oxford University Press, London, 1935

[2] SEMENOV, N. N. *Some Problems of Chemical Kinetics and Reactivity* Vol. I and II (Trans. J. E. S. Bradley): Pergamon Press, London, 1958

[3] DAINTON, F. S. *Chain Reactions*: Methuen, London, 1956

[4] FLORY, P. J. *Principles of Polymer Chemistry*: Cornell University Press, Ithaca, N.Y., 1953

[5] PEASE, R. N. *J. Amer. chem. Soc.* 1934, **56**, 2388

[6] BÄCKSTRÖM, H. L. J. *J. Amer. chem. Soc.* 1927, **49**, 1460; *Trans. Faraday Soc.* 1928, **24**, 601

[7] For a summary of Bäckström's work see: AMIS, E. S. *Kinetics of Chemical Change in Solution*: Macmillan, London, 1949, p. 219 *et seq.*

[8] BENSON, S. W. *Foundations of Chemical Kinetics*: McGraw-Hill, New York, 1960

[9] BENSON, S. W. *J. chem. Phys.* 1952, **20**, 1605

[10] HOWLETT, K. E. *Trans. Faraday Soc.* 1952, **48**, 35

[11] GOODALL, A. M. *Trans. Faraday Soc.* 1958, **54**, 195

[12] SEMENOV, N. N. *Some Problems of Chemical Kinetics and Reactivity* Vol. I (Trans. J. E. S. Bradley): Pergamon Press, London, 1958, Chapter 6

[13] SEMENOV, N. N. *Some Problems of Chemical Kinetics and Reactivity* Vol. II (Trans. J. E. S. Bradley): Pergamon Press, London, 1958, p. 23

[14] TROTMAN-DICKENSON, A. F. *Gas Kinetics*: Butterworth, London, 1955, p. 181 *et seq.*

[15] SEMENOV, N. N. *Some Problems of Chemical Kinetics and Reactivity* Vol. I (Trans. J. E. S. Bradley): Pergamon Press, London, 1958, pp. 160, 264

[16] TRIFONOV, A. *Z. phys. Chem. (Leipzig)* 1929, **B3**, 195

[17] NORRISH, R. G. W. and RITCHIE, M. *Proc. R. Soc. A* 1933, **140**, 99, 112, 713

[18] ASHMORE, P. G. and CHANMUGAM, J. C. *Trans. Faraday Soc.* 1953, **49**, 254

[19] MORRIS, J. C. and PEASE, R. N. *J. Amer. chem. Soc.* 1939, **61**, 391, 396

[20] LINDSAY, A. L. and BROMLEY, L. A. *Industr. Engng Chem. (Industr.)* 1950, **42**, 1508

REFERENCES

21 ASHMORE, P. G. *Nature, Lond.* 1953, **172**, 449

22 APIN, A. Y. *Zh. fiz. Khim.* 1940, **14**, 494

23 GRIFFITHS, J. G. A. and NORRISH, R. G. W. *Proc. R. Soc. A* 1934, **147**, 140

24 See ROLLEFSON, G. K. and BURTON, M. *Photochemistry and the Mechanism of Chemical Reactions*: Prentice Hall, New York, 1946, p. 317

25 BODENSTEIN, M., BRENSCHEDE, W. and SCHUMACHER, H.-J. *Z. phys. Chem. (Leipzig)* 1938, **B40**, 121

26 BURNS, W. G. and DAINTON, F. S. *Trans. Faraday Soc.* 1952, **48**, 39, 52

27 NOYES, W. A. and LEIGHTON, P. A. *The Photochemistry of Gases*: Reinhold, New York, 1941, p. 277

28 STEACIE, E. W. R. *Atomic and Free Radical Reactions* Vol. I and II: Reinhold, New York, 1954

29 BODENSTEIN, M., BRENSCHEDE, W. and SCHUMAKER, H.-J. *Z. phys. Chem. (Leipzig)* 1937, **B35**, 382

30 DAINTON, F. S. *Trans. Faraday Soc.* 1947, **43**, 365

31 DAINTON, F. S., LOMAX, D. A. and WESTON, M. *Trans. Faraday Soc.* 1957, **53**, 460
DAINTON, F. S. *et al. Trans. Faraday Soc.* 1962, **58**, 284, 295, 308, 318

32 GOLDFINGER, P. *et al.*, *Trans. Faraday Soc.* 1961, **57**, 2197, 2210, 2220

33 SPENCER, M. S. Thesis, University of Cambridge, 1956

34 SCHUMACHER, H.-J. *et al.*, *Z. phys. Chem. (Leipzig)* 1941, **B51**, 281; 1942, **B52**, 72

35 CHAIKIN, A. M. Thesis, University of Moscow, 1955. See SEMENOV, N. N. *Some Problems of Chemical Kinetics and Reactivity* Vol. I (Trans. J. E. S. Bradley): Pergamon Press, London, 1958, p. 220

36 MARKEVICH, A. M. *Zh. fiz. Khim.* 1948, **22**, 941

37 ASHMORE, P. G. and SPENCER, M. S. *Trans. Faraday Soc.* 1959, **55**, 1868

38 OGRYZLO, E. A. *J. phys. Chem.* 1961, **65**, 191

39 WALLING, C. *Free Radicals in Solution*: Wiley, New York, 1957, p. 447

40 SEMENOV, N. N. *Some Problems of Chemical Kinetics and Reactivity* Vol. I (Trans. J. E. S. Bradley): Pergamon Press, London, 1958, p. 223

41 MACCOLL, A. *Rates and Mechanisms of Reactions* (Ed. S. L. Friess and A. Weissberger): Interscience, New York, 1961, Part I, p. 483

42 BARTON, D. H. R. *et al.*, *J. chem. Soc.* 1951, pp. 2033, 2039

43 HOWLETT, K. E. *Trans. Faraday Soc.* 1952, **48**, 25; *J. chem. Soc.* 1935, p. 945

44 GOODALL, A. M. and HOWLETT, K. E. *J. chem. Soc.* 1956, pp. 2640, 3092

45 SEMENOV, N. N. (Ed.) *Some Problems of Chemical Kinetics and Reactivity* Vol. I (Trans. J. E. S. Bradley): Pergamon Press, London, 1958, p. 240

46 DINTZES, A. I. and FROST, A. V. *Zh. obshchei Khim.* 1933, **3**, 747

47a HINSHELWOOD, C. N. *The Kinetics of Chemical Change*: Clarendon Press, Oxford, 1940, p. 92

47b SMITH, J. R. E. and HINSHELWOOD, C. N. *Proc. R. Soc. A* 1942, **180**, 1237

48a STUBBS, J. J. and HINSHELWOOD, C. N. *Disc. Faraday Soc.* 1951, **10**, 129; *Proc. R. Soc. A* 1950, **200**, 458

48b JACH, J., STUBBS, F. J. and HINSHELWOOD, C. N. *Proc. R. Soc. A* 1954, **224**, 283

49 STEPUKHOVICH, A. D. and CHAIKIN, A. M. *Zh. fiz. Khim.* 1953, **27**, 1013, 1737

50 SEMENOV, N. N. *Some Problems of Chemical Kinetics and Reactivity* Vol. I (Trans. J. E. S. Bradley): Pergamon Press, London, 1958, p. 244

51 WALL, L. A. and MOORE, W. J. *J. Amer. chem. Soc.* 1951, **73**, 2840

52 WALL, L. A. and MOORE, W. J. *J. phys. Chem.* 1951, **55**, 965

53 RICE, F. O. and VARNERIN, R. E. *J. Amer. chem. Soc.* 1954, **76**, 324

54 RICE, F. O. and POLLY, O. L. *J. chem. Phys.* 1938, **6**, 273

55 JACH, J. and HINSHELWOOD, C. N. *Proc. R. Soc. A* 1955, **229**, 143; 1955, **231**, 145

56 VOEVODSKY, V. V. *Trans. Faraday Soc.* 1959, **55**, 65

[57] WOJCIECHOWSKI, B. W. and LAIDLER, K. J. *Canad. J. Chem.* 1960, **38**, 1027

[58] BRICE, W. A. and RUZICKA, D. J. *Canad. J. Chem.* 1960, **38**, 835

[59] PURNELL, J. H. and QUINN, C. P. *Nature, Lond.* 1961, **189**, 656

[60] HAWKINS, E. G. E. *Organic Peroxides*: Spon, London, 1961

[61] GRAY, P. and WILLIAMS, A. *Chem. Rev.* 1959, **59**, 239

[62] RALEY, J. H., RUST, F. F. and VAUGHAN, W. E. *J. Amer. chem. Soc.* 1948, **70**, 88

[63] RUSSELL, G. A. *J. org. Chem.* 1959, **24**, 300

[64] KARASCH, M. S., FONO, A. and NUDENBERG, W. *J. org. Chem.* 1951, **16**, 113

[65] KIRK, A. D. and KNOX, J. H. *Trans. Faraday Soc.* 1960, **56**, 1296

[66] HOCK, H. and LANG, S. *Ber. dtsch. chem. Ges.* 1944, **77**, 257
HOCK, H. and KROPF, H. *Angew. Chem.* 1957, **69**, 313

[67] HAMMOND, G. S. and SOFFER, L. M. *J. Amer. chem. Soc.* 1950, **72**, 4711

[68] BARSON, C. A. and BEVINGTON, J. C. *J. Polym. Sci.* 1956, **20**, 133

[69] WALLING, C. *Free Radicals in Solution*: Wiley, New York, 1957, Chapter 10

CATALYSIS, INITIATION AND INHIBITION
OF POLYMERIZATION REACTIONS

10.1 INTRODUCTION

THE FORMATION of polymeric molecules can occur by condensation or by addition reactions[1]. In a condensation polymer, the repeating units lack some of the atoms of the monomer from which it was formed, whereas in an addition polymer the molecular formula of the repeating unit is that of the monomer. Both types of polymer have end groups which are different from the repeating units.

In simple condensation reactions, as discussed in Chapter 2, two molecules react with the elimination of a small molecule such as water. The formation of an ester $R \cdot CO \cdot OR'$ is typical of simple condensation reactions between monofunctional acids and bases. If the reacting molecules are at least bifunctional, active groups remain in the molecule of product, and it can undergo further condensation reactions. The result is often a linear polymer, as with the polyesters of dibasic acids and glycols, which have a definite repeating unit and definite interunit links of formula —CO—O—. With higher functionality, as with polyesters of glycerol, or phenol–formaldehyde polymers, the product is often a non-linear polymer. Upon superficial inspection, these repeated linear and non-linear condensations look like non-branching and branching chain reactions, respectively, but they are not chain reactions. They proceed by a succession of similar reactions between the original reactants and, as the reaction proceeds, the products of the earlier reactions. First some 'dimers' are formed, then these react with 'monomers' and other 'dimers' to form larger molecules, and so on. The average degree of polymerization gets larger with time, first slowly and then with increasing rapidity, until there are a few very large polymers. There is rarely complete polymerization, of course, and the final degree of polymerization is much lower if there is a slight excess of one of the bifunctional reactants. It can also be kept low if small quantities of a monofunctional reagent are added (a result very like inhibition), and these reagents are called *stabilizers*. There are some other interesting features of condensation reactions, which resemble certain steps in chain reactions. For example, there is the possibility of formation of cyclic compounds or linear polymers, depending upon an intramolecular rather than an intermolecular condensation; this looks like mutual termination competing with propagation steps. Indeed, the formation of linear polymers from cyclic monomers is often a chain process, giving addition polymers; it is arguable in some cases, however, that the cyclic compounds are themselves condensation products and not true monomers. Nevertheless, it remains true that condensation polymerization has no initiating step, no characteristic active centres and, perhaps more important, no termination step in the absence of stabilizers. Each successive reaction is like all the others in type, but between different-sized reactants, rather than an exact repetition of all the steps that went before and that come after.

The kinetics of condensation polymerization can be expressed conveniently in terms of the equivalents of the functional groups, e.g. in polyesterification with pure reactants it is often found that the rate follows the equation

$$\frac{d[COOH]}{dt} = k[COOH]^2[OH]$$

In the presence of a small quantity of a strong acid, however, the rate law is often

$$\frac{d[COOH]}{dt} = k[acid][COOH][OH]$$

It is concluded that in the first case the acid reactant is itself acting as a catalyst. These simple kinetics appear to hold better in the later stages of polymerization than in the earlier stages[2].

Addition polymerization, on the other hand, has all the characteristics of a chain reaction. At present it is largely concerned with reactions of the double bond in olefins or substituted olefins or in dienes, but aldehydes and cyclic oxides or esters or imines can form addition polymers. The cyclic compounds can be made bifunctional by opening the ring, the olefins by change of the π-electrons; but these processes are not spontaneous at useful temperatures and the monomer must be activated by reaction with a catalyst, or some part of it, in an initiating mechanism which yields a monofunctional centre. The chain centres can be free radicals or carbonium ions or carbanions. Each of these centres can attack another monomer molecule, amongst other possible reactions, and add to it with the formation of another centre of higher molecular weight but almost identical reactivity—indeed, after a few additions, the centres can be treated as identical in this propagating step. The characteristic feature of chain mechanisms (a relatively slow initiation followed by a rapid propagation step) is very well shown in addition polymerization, for the local burst of activity upon initiation is 'frozen' in each polymer molecule; at any time after the reaction has started nearly all the material is present as monomer or as complete polymer, with extremely little as molecules of intermediate size.

There is thus a contrast in the changes of the molecular weights of condensation and addition polymers during the course of polymerization. In condensation polymerization, there is a steady transition from monomers through molecules of increasing size to the final large polymers. In addition polymerization, there are monomers and completed polymers, with no substantial amount of material ever in an intermediate stage. This difference in growth is illustrated in *Figure 10.1*[3] which shows results for the 'polycondensation' of benzyl chloride catalysed by stannic chloride. The reaction appears to be a condensation:

$$(PhCH_2Cl)_n \rightarrow \text{~~}CH—CH—CH\text{~~}$$
$$\underset{\text{Ph}}{|} \quad \underset{\text{Ph}}{|} \quad \underset{\text{Ph}}{|}$$

or
$$\rightarrow \text{~~}C_6H_4—CH_2—C_6H_4—CH_2\text{~~} + (n-1)HCl$$

but the kinetics suggest a chain reaction. The molecular weight at various stages of the reaction (upper curve) also supports an addition rather than a condensation reaction (lower curve).

Many unsaturated monomers can be polymerized by either a free radical or an ionic mechanism, depending upon the catalyst, the temperature and the solvent used. Substituted ethylenes with the substituents on both carbon atoms will not polymerize readily; those with structures $CH_2:CXY$ prefer to add

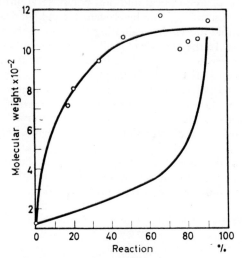

Figure 10.1. Molecular weights during polymerization of benzyl chloride catalysed by stannic chloride (0·165M). Upper curve, experimental; lower curve, expected for condensation polymerization[3]

tail-to-tail. If a substituent in an olefin is strongly electrophilic, polymerization proceeds more readily by free radical or carbanion mechanisms, whereas nucleophilic substituents favour a carbonium ion mechanism. Thus certain substituents lead to ready catalysis by free radical or by basic initiators, and others by acidic initiators. Pepper[4] has given the following range of qualitative susceptibilities to these catalysts for the vinyl monomers:

$$CH_2{=}CHY:$$

	CN	
	$CO_2 \cdot Me$	Free radical
	OA·	or
	CH$=$CH$_2$	basic
	C_6H_4Cl	
Acidic	C_6H_5	
	CH_3	
	OAlk	
	$C_6H_4 \cdot OCH_3$	

The type of catalyst used, the optimum temperature range for reaction, and the method of termination are each so different that it is best to consider each type of polymerization mechanism separately. In addition, it is necessary to

291

consider separately emulsion polymerization, which has many unique characteristics, and the production of stereoregulated polymers in the presence of an interface or of an ionic complex capable of orienting molecules of monomer in the propagation step.

10.2.   FREE-RADICAL POLYMERIZATION

10.2.1. Introduction

The mechanisms of free-radical addition polymerizations are much better understood than those of ionic or heterogeneous polymerizations, and there has been considerable success in evaluating the velocity constants of some of the individual steps. In the absence of inhibitors, the termination is by mutual reaction of the centres, to the virtual exclusion of linear termination, and this makes conditions very favourable for applying the rotating sector technique to the photoinitiated polymerizations of many vinyl monomers. There is not complete agreement between different groups of workers about the absolute value of the velocity constants of propagation and mutual termination, but the values obtained for the activation energies are not very different. It is agreed that values of the velocity constants for propagation and termination are independent of the rate of initiation when this is changed by quite large factors. Some of the values collected by Flory[1] are given in *Table 10.1*, with a few other results to indicate the range of values reported.

Table 10.1. Frequency factors and energies of activation for propagation and termination

Monomer	Propagation		Termination		Reference
	E_p kcal mole^{-1}	A_p l. mole^{-1} sec^{-1}	E_m kcal mole^{-1}	A_m l. mole^{-1} sec^{-1}	
Vinyl acetate	7·3	$2·4 \times 10^8$	5·2	$2·1 \times 10^{11}$	5, 6
	4·4	$2·1 \times 10^6$	0	$3·0 \times 10^9$	7
Styrene	7·8	$2·2 \times 10^7$	2·4	$1·3 \times 10^9$	8
	6·5	$1·0 \times 10^6$	2·8	$3·0 \times 10^8$	9
Methyl methacrylate	6·3	$5·1 \times 10^6$	2·8	$7·0 \times 10^8$	10
	4·4	$5·0 \times 10^5$	0	$1·0 \times 10^8$	11

It will be seen that the frequency factors of the propagation steps are low. This is in agreement with prediction from the transition state theory of velocity constants for reactions of this type, where large reactant molecules are accumulated in the transition complex[12]. In the absence of catalysts, free radicals are not readily formed thermally from the monomers, neither when pure nor when dissolved in common solvents. The rates of the thermal polymerizations are low and erratic. A great variety of catalysts—or more properly initiators—are known, however, and they fall naturally into two groups:

(*i*) The first group consists of unstable organic compounds which decompose thermally or photochemically into two free radicals capable of starting polymerizations. Members of this group are particularly useful for polymerization of the bulk monomers or of the monomers diluted with organic solvents. Here they will be called *homolytic initiators*.

(*ii*) Catalysts of the second group consist of combinations of oxidizing and reducing reagents, now known as *redox initiators*, which generate free radicals by suitable electron transfer with a corresponding change of charge on some ion. These initiators are particularly useful with water-soluble monomers and for emulsion polymerization.

Although some of the problems encountered in using these initiators are common to both groups, it will be convenient to discuss the groups separately.

10.2.2. *Homolytic initiators*

Perhaps the best known of these initiators are various compounds containing peroxy- or azo-groups, such as peroxides and hydroperoxides, aromatic azo- or diazo-compounds and aliphatic azobisnitriles[13,14]. These compounds generally decompose in several stages:

$$(C_6H_5 \cdot COO)_2 \rightarrow 2C_6H_5 \cdot COO^* \rightarrow 2C_6H_5 + 2CO_2^*$$

$$(C_6H_5)_3C—N{=}N—C_6H_5 \rightarrow (C_6H_5)_3C^* + N_2 + C_6H_5^*$$

$$(CH_3)_2C—N{=}N—C(CH_3)_2 \rightarrow (CH_3)_2C—N{=}N^* + {}^*C(CH_3)_2$$

$$\underset{\displaystyle CN \qquad NC}{} \qquad \underset{\displaystyle CN \qquad NC}{}$$

$$\rightarrow 2(CH_3)_2C(CN)^* + N_2$$

A few other compounds, such as aldehydes and ketones, have been used for photochemical initiation in solution. These compounds, and metal alkyls, alkyl iodides and diazomethane have also been used to initiate gas-phase polymerizations. In simple solutions of the catalysts in inert solvents, the primary free radicals formed from the catalysts can recombine, or attack their parent molecules, or react together to give more stable products. The activation energy of the decompositions seems to be about 30 kcal in many cases, and the initiators are effective (see section 9.6.3) at temperatures between room temperature and 100°C. Substituents like —OCH_3 seem to lead to faster decomposition of peroxides, whereas —CN or —NO_2 leads to slower rates. The order of the decomposition is often greater than one, perhaps because of the secondary decomposition produced by the primary radicals. In some solvents, the radicals may react preferentially with the solvent; this will usually produce another radical, and this may be less or more reactive than the primary radicals. Azo-compounds seem to be freer from secondary reactions than peroxides, particularly in the presence of monomer, and their use as catalysts has increased.

In the presence of monomer, the primary radicals add to the double bond. This is in contrast with the initiation of ionic polymerization, where the donation of a proton is very common. In free-radical polymerizations, there is ample evidence that the primary radicals are incorporated in the final polymer molecules. Thus polystyrene and poly(methyl methacrylate), prepared with bromobenzoyl peroxide, contain both bromobenzoate and bromophenyl groups, showing that both of the radicals initiate chains[15]. Polymers initiated with azo-compounds containing ^{14}C are radioactive[16], as are[17] polymers initiated with persulphates containing ^{35}S. It is rather more difficult to determine how many such groups are present in each polymer molecule, however.

The most direct method is obviously to analyse the given yield of polymer for the group, either chemically or radiochemically, and to calculate the number of polymer molecules present from the measured molecular weight. It is necessary to have accurate information about the molecular weight distribution in order to do this. Unfortunately, polymer fractions of low molecular weight may be lost in manipulation, and this greatly affects the count of molecules.

An accurate count of groups per molecule would give useful information about the termination of chains. In the absence of transfer reactions, there would be one group per polymer if the chains were terminated linearly, one if they were terminated mutually with disproportionation, and two groups if they were terminated by mutual combination. Now the kinetics can distinguish reliably between linear and mutual combination, for the two possibilities lead to the different rate laws (equations (9.3) and (9.4))[13,18]. The kinetics show

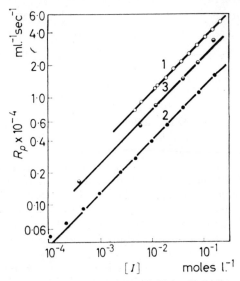

Figure 10.2. Log–log plots of initial polymerization rates R_p against initiator concentration[19]. Line 1, methyl methacrylate using azobisisobutyronitrile at 50°C; line 2, styrene with benzoyl peroxide at 60°C; line 3, methyl methacrylate with benzoyl peroxide at 50°C

that in the majority of free-radical polymerizations without added inhibitors the predominant termination is by mutual reaction of centres. This leads, as explained, to a rate law

$$\text{Rate} = k_p[\text{m}](k_i[\text{cat}]/k_m \text{ (or } k_d))^{1/2}$$

where k_m, k_d are the velocity constants for termination by combination and by disproportionation, respectively.

$$\text{Xm}_j + \text{Xm}_j \rightarrow \text{Xm}_j\text{m}_j\text{X} \qquad\qquad k_m[\text{Xm}_j]^2$$

$$\text{Xm}_j + \text{Xm}_j \rightarrow \text{Xm}_{j-1}\text{m}' + \text{Xm}_{j-1}\text{m}'' \qquad k_d(\text{Xm}_j]^2$$

Thus in *Figure 10.2* the plots of log (rate) versus log [cat] ([I]) are linear with slope equal to one-half, for three systems of monomers and initiators[19]. It is also found that the rate is proportional to the concentration of monomer, with some exceptions at low monomer concentrations which will be discussed later. There is thus good evidence that either k_m or k_d are operating, or both, and it would appear that the relative proportions of each could be determined from knowledge of the average number of X groups per polymer molecule. This has, in fact, often been done; for example, Arnett and Peterson[16] determined the molecular weight of poly(methyl methacrylate) by osmotic measurements and by counting the radioactive end groups from the initiator 2,2'-azobisiso-butyronitrile labelled with ^{14}C. Assuming *two* end groups per molecule, the radioactive method gave 390,500 for the number average molecular weight. The osmotic method gave 390,000. Thus the assumption of mutual termination by combination seems to be correct for this polymerization.

When this method of termination is exclusively mutual, the count of molecules, n, from the molecular weight gives the number of chains started, $2n$. Thus the rate of initiation of chains can be estimated. It can also be esti-mated, of course, from determinations of the total number of initiator frag-ments incorporated in the polymer in a given time.

From the number of chains started, it is easy to calculate the efficiency of initiation of the chains by the catalyst if the rate of decomposition of the initiator is known. Thus, for the initiator used by Arnett and Peterson[16], the ratio of the radicals which initiate chains to the total radicals generated by initiator decomposition was found to vary with the monomer:

	Methyl methacrylate	Styrene	Acrylonitrile	Vinyl acetate	Vinyl chloride
Monomer efficiency	0·52–0·59	0·66–0·82	1·02	0·68–0·82	0·70–0·77

Various interpretations of these fractional efficiencies are possible. The primary radicals may recombine, or the radicals A—N=N and A may initiate at different rates with various monomers, or one of these radicals may be quite ineffective. In addition, there are two other serious complications which may invalidate the somewhat idealized treatment of efficiencies of initiation which has so far been given. These complications are due to the possibilities of (*i*) chain transfer, which affects the molecular weight and also the average number of initiator groups per polymer molecule, and (*ii*) induced decomposi-tion of the initiator.

Transfer reactions of the active centres with molecules of the monomer do not usually affect the rate of reaction, for one reactive centre is immediately replaced by another of comparable activity. They are often hydrogen abstrac-tion reactions such as

$$Xm_j^* + m \xrightarrow{k_{t,m}} Xm_{j-1}m' + Hm^*$$

Transfers of this type will increase the proportion of polymers with one initiator fragment and will invalidate any attempt to distinguish between dispropor-tionation and combination of chain centres in the terminating process. Also, a count of molecules from the molecular weight would not give the number of chains started. On the other hand, the count of initiator fragments still gives the rate of initiation of chain centres, and the efficiency of initiation can be calculated from this.

Transfer with the solvent is also possible, for instance

$$Xm_j^* + HS \xrightarrow{k_{T.HS}} Xm_{j-1}m'' + S^*$$

Unless the solvent radicals S^* are unusually reactive or unusually unreactive, this process will not affect the rate unless the concentration of monomer is low. If the concentration of monomer is high, almost all solvent radicals react with monomer molecules to form chain centres of the same reactivity as Xm_j^*. If the concentration of monomers is low, S^* may combine with polymer radicals and alter the rate of termination; this point is discussed in more detail later. At all concentrations of monomer, transfer with the solvent will alter the number of initiator fragments per polymer molecule, and so make it impossible to distinguish between disproportionation and combination. Again, the molecular weight does not lead to a reliable figure for the number of chains started, although a count of initiator fragments will still do so.

Chain transfer with the solvent has one other interesting aspect which may be emphasized here. As explained, it leads to little change in the rate of polymerization but to a decrease in the average molecular weight of the product. This curtailment of the molecular weight by transfer reactions is an inhibition of size, even if not an inhibition in the rate of consumption of monomer, and substances which readily 'transfer' are often used as 'regulators' or 'modifiers' to control the molecular weight during polymerization. The ratio of the velocity constant of the transfer reaction to that of the normal propagation step is called the *transfer constant*, C_T, and it can be determined from the change in the degree of polymerization (the average number of monomer units per polymer molecule) upon dilution of the monomer with the transfer agent. It can readily be shown that the degree of polymerization, $\overline{DP}$, is given by

$$\frac{1}{\overline{DP}} = \frac{(k_i k_d)^{1/2} [cat]^{1/2}}{k_p} + \frac{k_{T.m}}{k_p} + \frac{k_{T.HS}[SH]}{k_p[m]}$$

when termination is by disproportionation; for termination by combination, the first term becomes

$$\frac{(k_i k_m)^{1/2} [cat]^{1/2}}{2k_p}$$

Thus a plot of $1/\overline{DP}$ against the ratio [solvent]/[monomer] when [cat] is kept constant, should give a straight line of slope C_T. Some plots are shown in *Figure 10.3*[20]. Analysis of the variations of the intercept of the graph with [cat] should give the velocity constants for transfer with monomer. Early values of the transfer constants for various radicals and solvents were summarized by Flory[21]. Some values are:

Monomer	Transfer constant $C_T \times 10^4$ at 80°C		
	Benzene	Toluene	Carbon tetrachloride
Styrene	0·059	0·31	130
Methyl methacrylate	0·075	0·52	2·39
Vinyl acetate	—	92	—

There has been some interesting work recently on the preparation of block copolymers of acrylonitrile by transfer reactions. Bamford and White[22] have indicated the methods used to prepare block copolymers and have described the use of preformed polymers of monomer A, with a terminal amine group, as macromolecular transfer agents during the polymerization of monomer B. The amine group, preferably a tertiary amine, is formed during the polymerization of A by using a tertiary amine as transfer agent. Monomer B is then

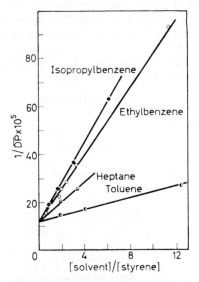

Figure 10.3. Chain transfer by solvent[20]. $\overline{DP}^{-1}$ for polystyrene in various solvents plotted against the solvent/monomer ratio.

polymerized under conditions leading to long chains and to high rates of transfer. Acrylonitrile and methyl methacrylate polymerize readily to form block copolymers in this way. Bamford, Jenkins and White[23] describe the advantages of carrying out this copolymerization under heterogeneous conditions and develop the kinetics of heterogeneous polymerizations in detail. They also consider the kinetics of formation of graft copolymers, starting with a polymer of methyl methacrylate with terminal double bonds and copolymerizing with acrylonitrile.

It is also possible for the growing polymer molecule to react with the initiator, and so 'induce' its decomposition. Normally, the primary radicals do not induce further (chain) decomposition because they are collected by a molecule of monomer before they collide a sufficient number of times with the (dilute) initiator. Reaction can occur between a growing polymer radical and a molecule of initiator, however, giving a small dead polymer and another initiating radical. Now the effect of induced decomposition of the initiator is the opposite of transfer to monomer or solvent, as far as the count of fragments per polymer molecule is concerned. This can be illustrated as follows, with an initiator X_2:

$$Xm_j^* + cat \rightarrow Xm_jX + X^*$$

$$X^* + m \rightarrow Xm^*, \text{etc.}$$

Thus the small dead polymer contains two fragments of initiator, and if it is counted it will increase the fragments per average polymer. If this induced decomposition is rapid, it greatly increases the rate of decomposition of the initiator and the rate of initiation of chains. Bevington[24] has devised an ingenious way of measuring the induced decomposition of peroxides and of azo-compounds by isotopic dilution. The normal initiation and the transfer of X to the polymer radical lead to an apparent rate of incorporation of the initiator fragment—that is to an apparent rate of initiation

$$R_{i,a} = R_i + 2k'[Xm^*][cat]$$

The rate of propagation is still

$$R_p = k_p[m][Xm_j^*]$$

Therefore

$$R_{i,a} = R_i + 2k'[cat]R_p/k_p[m] \tag{10.1}$$

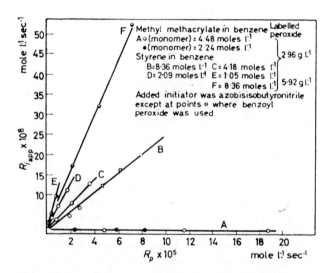

Figure 10.4. Apparent rate of initiation ($R_{i_{app}}$) by bis(3,5-di-bromo-4-methoxybenzoyl)peroxide for polymerizations of styrene and methyl methacrylate at 60°C as a function of total rate of polymerization (R_p)[24]

If the rates of polymerization are measured for a constant amount of labelled (^{14}C) initiator and of monomer, but with increasing amounts of unlabelled initiator, the analysis for fragments measures an increased $R_{i,a}$, and Bevington found that this is a linear function of R_p, as expected from equation (10.1): (*Figure 10.4*). From the slopes, the ratio k'/k_p can be determined. It

298

turned out to be zero for methyl methacrylate with bis(3,5-dibromo-4-meth-oxybenzoyl)peroxide with the methoxy groups labelled, but 1·34 at 60°C for styrene with the same initiator. Bevington shows that this is in agreement with other evidence of the relative reactivity of the polymer radicals towards peroxides which contain bromine.

If the rate of decomposition of the initiator is measured in the absence of the polymerization reaction, to obtain the efficiency of initiation of polymerization this rate of decomposition ought to be compared with R_i, determined by extrapolation of plots such as those of *Figure 10.4*. Otherwise the efficiency may *appear* to be extremely high, because of the induced decomposition.

There is another deviation from the expected rate laws (equations (9.3) or (9.4)) when solutions of styrene in benzene or toluene are polymerized at low concentrations of monomer. If a constant concentration of initiator is used, the rate of polymerization should be proportional to the monomer concentration, as indeed it is at high monomer concentrations. At low values, however, the rate is often slower than the linear relation predicts. Thus Flory[1] (page 116) presents data of Mayo, Gregg and Matheson[25], showing that the ratio initial rate/[monomer] is constant at high values of [monomer] but falls as [monomer] is decreased (benzoyl peroxide at 60°C):

[m] (moles l.$^{-1}$)	8·35	5·85	3·34	0·84	0·42
$10^4 \times$ rate/[m] (sec^{-1})	0·48	0·47	0·44	0·35	0·32

It seems significant that this type of deviation is greater with styrene than with other monomers. Several explanations have been offered, but a clear decision between them has not been made. Jenkins[26] has reviewed the three prinicpal suggestions†. Broadly speaking, they envisage either a decreased rate of initiation in more dilute solutions of monomer or an increased rate of termination due to chain transfer. In either case, the effects can be interpreted as leading to a higher order of the monomer concentration in the rate law at low concentrations of monomer.

The earliest suggestion put forward[28] to explain this apparent increase in the order proposed that the true initiating agent is a complex of the initiator and the monomer:

$$\text{initiator} + \text{m} \rightleftharpoons \text{complex} \xrightarrow{k_c} \text{initiates}$$

Suppose that the equilibrium constant of the reaction to form the complex is K. If the initial concentrations of the initiator and monomer are c and m, respectively, and the concentration of complex is x, then

$$K = x/(c-x)(m-x)$$

As x is presumably small compared with c or m, terms in x^2 can be ignored:

$$x = Kcm/(1+Km+Kc)$$

Thus in very dilute solutions of monomer, $x \propto m$, whereas in concentrated solutions x becomes independent of m and equal to c. Thus the 'complex' theory predicts a rate of initiation independent of [monomer] when [monomer]

† Another suggestion has been put forward by Dainton[27] to account for the high order of the ionic polymerization of styrene at low monomer concentration (see page 319). It could be developed into a general explanation for free-radical polymerizations.

is high, but proportional to [monomer] when [monomer] is low. When the chains are terminated mutually, the rate of polymerization will be proportional to [monomer] at high concentrations of monomer and to $[\text{monomer}]^{3/2}$ when [monomer] is low. Jenkins[26] develops the kinetics and shows that the following equation holds for several polymerizations where the deviations from first order kinetics are small:

$$[m]^3/R_p^2 = \frac{k_m}{k_p^2 k_c[\text{cat}]} ([m] + 1/K)$$

However, although the plots of $[m]^3/R_p^2$ against $[m]$ are linear, the values of K deduced from the plots are very similar for three different polymerizations analysed by Jenkins. In addition, the value of K seems to increase with temperature. It is generally agreed that these relationships make the complex theory untenable.

The second suggestion, emphasized by Matheson[29], is that the primary radicals recombine, or react together to give inert products, and that this process becomes more important when there are fewer monomer molecules to catch the radicals. Thus at low monomer concentrations the efficiency of initiation drops, and the ratio initial rate/[monomer] would fall if it were measured in the presence of a constant amount of initiator. However, Flory[30] has presented calculations which certainly suggest that the chance of recombination of primary radicals is very small at the dilutions used; nor would any 'cage effect' of the solvent used to dilute the monomer be important.

The third suggestion was originated by Burnett and Loan[31] and has been developed also by Jenkins[32]. It is that transfer occurs between polymer radical and solvent, and between polymer radical and initiator, and that the new radicals formed increase the rate of termination in pairs. The equations developed are very complex, but they can again be interpreted as leading to a first-order dependence of the rate of polymerization at high monomer concentrations and a higher (second) order at low concentrations. Bevington[24] has pointed out that it is incorrect to assume that the solvent radicals will always be less reactive than the primary radicals towards the monomer, for there is experimental evidence that this is not so for benzene and styrene. It might be thought that primary radical together with polymer radical combination is not much more likely than recombination of primary radicals and therefore should be rejected on the basis of Flory's calculations. But the concentration of polymer radicals is much greater than the concentration of free primary radicals; also there have been several reports of initiators acting as retarders at high concentrations. To put it another way, the lifetime of the primary radical and of any individual chain centre may be of the same order of magnitude, but the lifetime of a chain is very much greater and each regeneration of a centre prolongs the opportunity of capture of a primary radical. Thus besides chain transfer with the initiator, chain termination with the initiator fragments should not be ignored when the concentration of the monomer is low.

10.2.3. Redox initiators

Initiators of this group consist of mixtures of oxidizing and reducing substances; these mixtures are chosen so as to form free radicals, suitable for initiating polymerizations, by electron transfer or group transfer reactions similar to those discussed in Chapter 3. They are especially useful in aqueous solutions, but certain combinations have been devised for use in non-aqueous solvents. In 1946 Bacon[33] described the catalytic action of mixtures of persulphates with several reducing agents such as metals and their salts, hydrazine and hydroxylamine, thiols, sulphites, thiosulphates and polyhydric phenols. In the next few years, many investigations were reported, and the progress was summarized in 1955 by the same author[34]. He classified the initiators under their main oxidizing component, and discussed the behaviour of systems based on hydrogen peroxide, persulphates, diacyl peroxides, hydroperoxides, oxygen and some miscellaneous oxidizing agents. Rather more complex systems of three components have also been used[35,36]. These usually contain one of the oxidizing agents mentioned above, a heavy metal salt and a reducing agent such as a sugar, a thiol, a hydroyacid or ester, benzoin or a thiosulphate. By using a salt of the metal, such as a stearate or naphthenate, these three-component systems can be used for non-aqueous media, for example in hydrocarbons.

In redox polymerization, the free radical which initiates the chain is formed in a reaction which can be thought of as an electron transfer (see section 3.2). One of the earliest redox systems studied was the mixture of hydrogen and ferrous sulphate long known as 'Fenton's reagent'[37]. The redox reaction was formulated as

$$H_2O_2 + Fe^{2+} \rightarrow Fe^{3+} + OH^- + OH^*$$

The fate of the OH* radical depends upon the conditions of the experiment. In the absence of a suitable monomer or an oxidizable substance, the oxidation of the ferrous salt may go to completion or the hydrogen peroxide may be catalytically decomposed by a chain process[38], as described in section 3.1.2.

In the presence of suitable monomers such as acrylonitrile, methyl methacrylate or styrene, however, the OH* radical can initiate polymerization[37]. When the monomer concentration is increased, the number of ferrous ions oxidized per molecule of peroxide falls from two to one, and at high concentrations the molecular weight of the polymer, determined from osmotic pressure measurements, is in agreement with the degree of polymerization calculated from the rates of consumption of monomer and of hydrogen peroxide, if it is assumed that each peroxide molecule initiates one chain and that these are terminated by mutual combination. Bacon[34] has summarized the extensive evidence that the OH* radical initiates the chains.

If other organic substances are present, the redox system can oxidize them. For example, the ferrous peroxide system readily oxidizes aromatic compounds and aliphatic hydroxy-acids such as glycollic acid, and addition of hydroxyl groups to olefinic bonds can occur:

$$CH_2:CH \cdot CH_2OH + 2OH^* \rightarrow HO \cdot CH_2 \cdot CH(OH) \cdot CH_2 \cdot OH$$

There is thus an interesting connection between the polymerization and oxidation reactions, and the possibility of change from one reaction to the other as the concentration of reactants are varied.

This interplay is very evident in the three component mixtures, as can be seen from the notation used by Dolgoplosk and Tiniakova in a recent classification of redox systems[36]. They represent the action of mixtures of cumene

301

hydroperoxide (dimethyl benzyl hydroperoxide), a ferrous or cuprous salt and a reducing agent like dihydroxymaleic acid as follows:

$$Fe^{2+}(Cu^+) \underset{\underset{\overset{|}{-C-OH}}{\overset{|}{-C-OH}}}{\overset{ROOH}{\rightleftharpoons}} RO^* + OH^- + Fe^{3+}$$

Another way of representing the action of these systems is by a scheme similar to those used by biochemists to depict coupled systems, for instance[34]

Oxidizing sugar   Fe^{2+} ROOH   R·OM*

+e   −e   etc.

Reducing sugar   Fe^{3+} OH$^-$+ RO*   M

Dolgoplosk and Tiniakova[36] also discuss the rather rare redox systems which produce two radicals in one bimolecular step, and the more common redox initiators which react to produce one intermediate which dissociates, for example triazenes may decompose as follows:

$$C_6H_5 \cdot N \cdot NH : N \cdot CH_3 \xrightarrow{H_2O} C_6H_5 \cdot NH_2 + CH_3 \cdot N : N \cdot OH$$

$$CH^* + OH^* + N_2$$

The first step of this sequence seems to be rate-determining and is presumably the redox stage.

The three-component redox systems have been of great importance in the emulsion copolymerization of styrene and butadiene to produce synthetic rubbers. Simpler redox initiators give slow rates. Fast rates at quite low temperatures can be obtained by three-component systems such as cumene hydroperoxide–ferrous ion–reducing sugars or polyamines of the general formula $NH_2(CH_2 \cdot CH_2 \cdot NH)_nH$; persulphate ion–ferrous ion–sodium sulphite; and benzoyl peroxide–ferrous ion–α-ketols such as benzoin, sorbose or fructose. The lower temperatures result in polymers with less branching, apparently because there is more 1,4-linking and less of the 1,2-linking which can give branched polymers:

$$\sim CH_2 \cdot CH : CH \cdot CH_2 \sim \qquad \sim CH_2 \cdot CH \sim$$
$$| $$
$$CH$$
$$\|$$
$$CH_2$$

1,4-linking   1,2-linking

There are many variables with emulsion polymerization, and factors such as the type and concentrations of the various components of the initiator in the aqueous and in the disperse phases, the type and concentration of emulsifying agent and the value of the pH of the solution have usually been varied empirically to help to find conditions which give satisfactory rates and products.

The radicals RO* formed from peroxides and hydroperoxides are not very stable, and in the absence of monomer can break down to give simpler molecules. The decomposition of cumene hydroperoxide ($PhCMe_2 \cdot OOH$) has often been studied[39,40], and it is agreed that the RO* radical breaks down to acetophenone and a methyl radical, but there is some disagreement about the fate of the methyl radicals:

$$Fe^{2+} + ROOH \rightarrow Fe^{3+} + RO* + OH^-$$

$$RO* \rightarrow C_6H_5 \cdot CO \cdot CH_3 + CH_3*$$

$$CH_3^* + CH_3^* \rightarrow C_2H_6$$

$$Fe^{3+} + CH_3^* + H_2O \rightarrow Fe^{2+} + CH_3OH + H^+ \Bigg\} \text{(Kolthoff and Reynolds [39])}$$

$$CH_3^* + ROOH \rightarrow CH_3OH + RO* \quad \text{(Wise and Twigg [40])}$$

It is plain there are several possible radicals which can initiate polymerization chains in the presence of monomers, and that there may be complex behaviour at low concentrations of monomer.

Indeed the investigations of redox polymerizations subsequent to Bacon's review [34] have been more concerned with the possible complexities of the systems than with any new principles. It has been realized that all metal ions of interest are complexed with the whole or part of the solvent molecules and that many reactions written as electron transfer reactions could also be formulated as atom or group transfers involving part of the solvation molecules (see section 3.2). Thus the reaction for all but very acid solutions could be more properly written

$$Fe^{2+} + H_2O_2 \rightarrow FeOH^{2+} + OH$$

and thus regarded as the transfer of a hydroxyl group. The ferrous and the complex ferric ions are also complexed with H_2O molecules. Many similar examples have been given for oxidation–reduction, such as

$$Fe(H_2O)_6^{2+} + R* \rightarrow Fe(H_2O)_6^{3+} + R^-$$

$$\text{or} \rightarrow FeOH(H_2O)_5^{2+} + RH$$

as well as for isotopic exchange reactions (see section 3.2).

A particularly interesting variant of this behaviour is found with the photochemical electron transfer in the hydrated ions of certain of the transition metals. The reactions can be typified as

$$M(H_2O)_6^{2+} \rightarrow M(H_2O)_5OH^{2+} + H*$$

and result in the photoreduction of water. The hydrogen atoms have been shown to initiate the polymerization of water-soluble vinyl monomers [41]. Incidentally, the polymerization serves as a very sensitive test for free radicals, as the polymers may be insoluble and so produce opalescence when only $10^{-9} M$ hydrogen atoms have been formed. Dainton and James [41-43] have examined the ions ferrous, chromous, cobaltous, nickelous, vanadous and manganous, and have reported a linear relationship between the minimum value of the quantum necessary for the photoreaction and the standard redox potential of the couple $M_{Aq}^{2+} - M_{Aq}^{3+}$ in aqueous solution. By consideration of the potential energy curves for the reaction, they relate the quantum required to the ionization potential, I_M, of the reaction

$$M_{Aq}^{2+} \rightarrow M_{Aq}^{3+} + e^-$$

and this in turn to the redox potential, $E°$, by the equation [42]

$$h\nu = \text{constant} + I_M = E°F + T\Delta S + \text{constant}$$

This relation predicts that the linear plot (*Figure 10.5*) should have a slope of 23·06 kcal/V. The observed value is 23·5 kcal/V.

There is another complicating feature of redox polymerization which is not unlike the induced decomposition observed with the initiators which function by homolytic dissociation. The growing polymer radicals can act as oxidizing or reducing agents towards the complex cations and so lose their free-radical properties. Dainton and James[43] note two specific examples with polyacrylonitrile radicals; it appears that the chromous ion or ferrous ion catalyse the polymerization in low concentrations, but in higher concentrations the

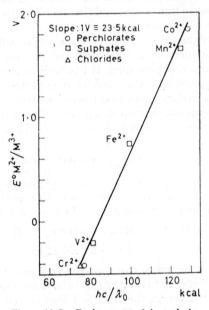

Figure 10.5. Redox potentials and the long-wave limits of the electron-transfer spectra of the bivalent ions of the transition elements[42]

initiators introduce termination steps so effective that the polymer cannot grow:

$$m_j^* + FeOH^{2+} \rightarrow m_jOH + Fe^{2+}$$
$$m_j^* + Cr(H_2O)_6^{2+} \rightarrow m_jH + CrOH(H_2O)_5^{2+}$$

10.2.4. Inhibitors and retarders

As explained in section 9.3, the enormous variation in the effectiveness of different substances in slowing the rate of polymerization led Foord[44] to suggest that there were two distinct classes of substances, *retarders* which slowed the rate of polymerization, and *inhibitors* which virtually stopped the polymerization for a lengthy period. Thus in the thermal polymerization of styrene, he found that mono- and diderivatives of aromatic compounds, and some nitroso compounds, slowed the rate, whereas amino derivatives, phenols, quinones and substituted quinones produced induction periods, the length of which was proportional to the initial concentration of inhibitor (*Figure 10.6*).

Further investigations, revealing examples of transition from inhibition to retardation as the experimental conditions were varied, have led to the belief that there is no fundamental difference between the two, but only a matter of degree[45].

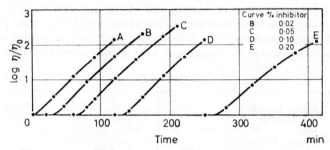

Curve	% inhibitor
B	0·02
C	0·05
D	0·10
E	0·20

Figure 10.6. Induction periods in polymerization of styrene in presence of benzoquinone (120°C)[44]

The polymerization of a number of vinyl monomers can be inhibited by the compounds mentioned above. A good deal is known about the kinetic behaviour of the inhibitors, but less about the chemical nature of the reactions by which they terminate chains. The identification of elements and groups from the inhibitor in the polymer shows that the termination is by reaction between the polymer radical and the inhibitor. Another piece of evidence in favour of reaction with the polymer radical rather than the primary radicals is that the molecular weight falls as the concentration of inhibitor is increased, whereas if there were fewer chains initiated the rate could fall without the molecular weight decreasing. Part of the decrease in molecular weight is due to a change in the mode of termination from mutual to linear:

$$m_j + m_j \rightarrow \text{end}$$
$$m_j + I \rightarrow \text{end} \tag{10.2}$$

and another effect is a steady decrease in the average value of j as the concentration of inhibitor is increased. It does not follow, however, that one molecule of inhibitor is used up for each chain terminated. If the inhibitor is a free radical, it may combine with the polymer radical to give a stable molecule, or a group or atom may be transferred to give two stable molecules. If it is a molecule, the reaction (10.2) may transfer a group to end the polymer, leaving a less reactive inhibitor radical which may capture another polymer radical. Another possibility is that two inhibitor radicals, after terminating two chains, may react to give one molecule of inhibitor and one other molecule; this is believed to happen with quinones in both polymerization and oxidation reactions. Thus there are several ways in which one inhibitor molecule can terminate two chains. On the other hand, it is quite possible for an inhibitor to undergo a chain transfer with the polymer radical, if the inhibitor radical is moderately reactive. Thus each case of inhibition has to be examined carefully to establish the number of polymer chains terminated by one inhibitor molecule. If this can be done, the maximum rate of removal of the inhibitor

20—c.   305

will be related simply to the number of chains started and can be used to estimate the rate of initiation.

This approach has been used by many investigators; the work of Melville and his colleagues and of Bartlett and his colleagues may be singled out as examples of the methods of kinetic analysis used.

Melville and Watson[46] examined the thermal and catalysed (benzoyl peroxide) polymerizations of styrene and of methyl methacrylate and the effect of quinone on these reactions. Considering first the catalysed polymerization of methyl methacrylate, their results, and also the earlier results of Norrish and Brookman[47], demonstrate that in the absence of inhibitor the

Table 10.2

Benzoyl peroxide concentration moles % × 10³	$c^{1/2}/rate$ (rate: %/h)	Ozone concentration moles % × 10³	$c^{1/2}/rate$ (rate: %/h)
2·6	8·90	6·50	2·67
4·2	8·65	13·20	2·40
7·0	9·42	29·60	2·40
8·9	8·30	67·30	2·53

termination of the chains is mutual, for the rate is proportional to the square root of the concentration of initiators such as benzoyl peroxide or ozone (*Table 10.2*). When quinone is added in increasing amounts, the rate of polymerization is slowed, as shown in *Figure 10.7*. Melville and Watson[46] analysed

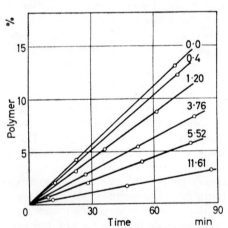

Figure 10.7. Effect of benzoquinone (mole/mole monomer) × 10⁴ on the peroxide-catalysed polymerization of methyl methacrylate (80°C)[46]

their results in the belief that there was a difference between retardation as shown in this figure and inhibition (as shown in *Figure 10.8*), suggesting that the retardation was due to chain transfer. However, a simple variation of their

306

scheme suggests that the termination is partly the mutual step occurring in the absence of inhibitor and partly linear due to the quinone. Thus the

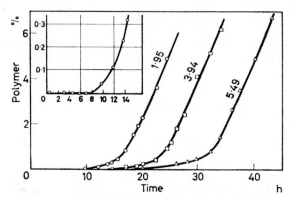

Figure 10.8. Effect of benzoquinone (mole/mole monomer) × 10⁴ on the thermal polymerization of styrene (80°C)[46]

following scheme, with the rates as shown, can be postulated:

$$\text{Catalyst} \rightarrow \text{initiation} \qquad R_i$$
$$m_j^* + m \rightarrow m_{j+1} \qquad k_p[m_j^*][m]$$
$$m_j^* + m_j^* \rightarrow \text{end} \qquad k_m[m_j^*]^2$$
$$m_j^* + Q \rightarrow \text{end} \qquad k_t[m_j^*][Q]$$

leading to an equation for the concentration of m_j

$$R_i = k_m[m_j^*]^2 + k_t[m_j^*][Q] \qquad (10.3)$$

The rate of polymerization is

$$R_p = k_p[m_j^*][m]$$

Substituting for m_j^* in the first expression

$$R_i k_p^2[m]^2 = k_m R_p^2 + k_t k_p[m][Q]R_p \qquad (10.4)$$

This can be cast into different forms to apply the results. If interest is in the more retarded rates, they can be tested against equation (10.4) in the form

$$\frac{R_i k_p^2}{r^2} = 10^4 k_m + \frac{k_t k_p 10^2[Q]}{r}$$

where r is the percentage rate of reaction ($100R_p/[m]$).

When the concentration of initiator is kept constant, a plot of $1/r^2$ against $[Q]/r$ should be linear. *Figure 10.9* (line A) shows the results of *Figure 10.7* plotted in this way.

Melville and Watson also give some results of the inhibition of the benzoyl peroxide-catalysed polymerization of styrene, which can be used to test the effect of changing R_i, assuming this to be proportional to the concentration of benzoyl peroxide, with a constant amount of benzoquinone present. The form of the equation tested in *Figure 10.9* (line B) is

$$\frac{k_i[\text{Bz}]k_p^2}{r} = 10^4 k_m r + \text{constant}$$

These plots therefore support a steady transition from predominantly mutual to predominantly linear termination, as the concentration of inhibitor is increased.

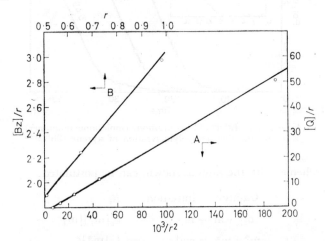

Figure 10.9. Line A, plot of $1/r^2$ against $[\text{Q}]/r$ for the benzoquinone (Q) inhibited polymerization of methyl methacrylate; Line B, plot of $[\text{B}_2]/r$ against r for the benzoyl peroxide (B$_2$) catalysed polymerization of styrene. Q = (moles benzoquinone/mole monomer) × 10^4. B$_2$ = (moles benzoyl peroxide/mole monomer) × 10^4. r = rate per cent/hour

In the thermal polymerization of styrene, in the absence of an initiator, the inhibition becomes very marked. Similar long induction periods in the polymerization of vinyl acetate were found by Bartlett and Kwart[48] when duroquinone or dinitrobenzene was added to the monomer in the presence of the initiator benzoyl peroxide. Analysing their results by a similar reaction scheme but ignoring the mutual termination reaction, they show that

$$-\frac{d[\text{Q}]}{dt} = k_t[\text{Q}][\text{m}_j^*] \quad \text{and} \quad -\frac{d[\text{m}]}{dt} = k_p[\text{m}][\text{m}_j^*] \qquad (10.5)$$

and hence

$$\ln\frac{[\text{Q}_0]}{[\text{Q}]} = \frac{k_t}{k_p}\ln\frac{[\text{m}_0]}{[\text{m}]}$$

Using the portions of the curves which show the acceleration in the rate of consumption of monomer, they were able to show that k_t/k_p was large for many inhibitors. Thus the ratio $[\text{Q}]/[\text{Q}_0]$ has to change very considerably before $[\text{m}]/[\text{m}_0]$ shows much change. This shows why the rate of reaction is hardly detectable until the inhibitor has been very substantially consumed,

and it is possible that a similar explanation accounts for the abrupt acceleration, as shown in *Figure 10.6*, found at the end of the induction periods in
polymerization†. The ratio $[Q]/[Q_0]$ is calculated from the time of reaction,
for the rate of consumption of the inhibitor will be constant if the rate of
initiation of chains is constant. If the inhibitor stops y chains per molecule
consumed, then

$$[Q] = [Q_0] - R_i t/y \qquad (10.6)$$

and the induction period τ is given by

$$\frac{y[Q_0]}{R_i} = \tau$$

This relationship is supported by the plot of the induction period against the
ratio of the initial concentration $[Q_0]$ of inhibitor to the concentration $[Bz]$
of the peroxide initiator (*Figure 10.10*). If y is known, the slope of the line can

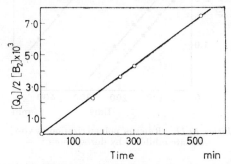

Figure 10.10. The induction period for the
duroquinone (Q_0) inhibited polymerization of
vinyl acetate catalysed by benzoyl peroxide
(B_2) [48]

be used to determine R_i, as explained earlier. Bartlett and Kwart[48] found that
the slopes with duroquinone and with the inhibitor 2,2-diphenylpicryl-
hydrazyl, a stable free radical, were equal. They consider that this shows y is
one in each case. Another way of determining R_i and the rates k_t/k_p is to use
the period of acceleration of the polymerization. By combining equation
(10.5) and the equation

$$R_i = k_t[Q][m_j^*]$$

it follows that

$$-\frac{d[m]}{d_t} = k_p[m]R_i/k_t[Q]$$

and therefore from equation (10.6)

$$-\frac{1}{\dfrac{d \ln [m]}{dt}} = \frac{k_t}{k_p R_i}\left([Q_0] - \frac{R_i t}{y}\right) = \frac{k_t}{k_p}\left(\frac{[Q_0]}{R_i} - \frac{t}{y}\right)$$

†It is important to realize that the acceleration is marked on the time scale shown, but
that changes in concentration of chain centres are linked to the concentrations of catalyst,
monomer and inhibitor by reactions which are very fast on that time scale. Thus it remains
permissible to use the stationary-state approximation for individual points on the curve
even where the slope is increasing.

Thus $-1/(\{d \ln [m]\}/\{dt\})$ should be a linear function of time. This relationship is tested in *Figure 10.11*, and the parallel lines show that the relationship holds very well.

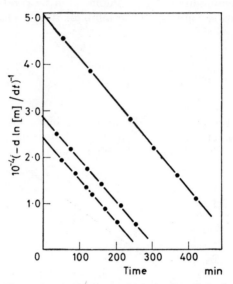

Figure 10.11. Rates of polymerization of vinyl acetate inhibited by duroquinone[48]

The values of k_t/k_p collected by Bartlett and Kwart[48] range widely:

Nitrodurene	1–1·5
Nitrobenzene, *p*-nitrotoluene	18–21
o-Dinitrobenzene	94–98
m-Dinitrobenzene	104–106
p-Dinitrobenzene	259–278

In the photoinitiated polymerization of methyl methacrylate, the relative efficiency of phenols and hydroquinones increases as the redox potential decreases[49]. It has been suggested that the hydroquinones give a hydroxyl-hydrogen to the polymer radical, and that two of the stable semiquinone radicals disproportionate to give quinone and hydroquinone. There does not seem to be a constant order of efficiencies of inhibition for all addition polymerizations, however, and it seems likely from other evidence that direct addition of the polymer radical to the inhibitor occurs in many cases. The extreme effectiveness of the free radical 2,2-diphenylpicrylhydrazyl for styrene, methyl methacrylate and vinyl acetate polymerizations is ascribed, however, to the extraction of a hydrogen atom from a polymer radical, leaving it with a double bond. Other free radicals, such as diphenylcyanomethyl, diphenyl nitrogen and triphenylmethyl have been used, but some of these seem to be used up by chain transfer or by initiation of chains as well as in termination reactions[50]. This is also true of oxygen, which can act as an inhibitor or transfer agent; there is also evidence that benzoquinone can undergo transfer reactions with styrene.

Rather similar problems can arise with redox initiators, which can act as terminators, as mentioned in the last section. Some interesting work on this dual function has been begun by Dainton and his collaborators[51]. They have investigated the reduction of the rate of polymerization of aqueous solutions of acrylamide by various oxidizing ions. The polymerization is initiated by γ-rays from ^{60}Co; these rays produce hydrogen atoms and hydroxyl radicals which start the chain. The metal ions can oxidize the hydrogen atoms or the polymer radicals:

$$H^* + m \rightarrow Hm^* \rightarrow Hm_j^* \rightarrow \text{polymer}$$

$$H^* + M^{3+} \rightarrow H^+ + M^{2+} \tag{10.7}$$

$$Hm_j^* + M^{3+} \rightarrow m_j + M^{2+} + H^* \tag{10.8}$$

The metal ions thus compete with monomer for H^* atoms. Reducing ions can similarly attack and reduce the hydroxyl or the polymer radicals. The investigators develop a mechanism for the action of oxidizing ions which predicts a linear relationship between R_p^2 and $R_p[M^{3+}]$, provided that the reaction

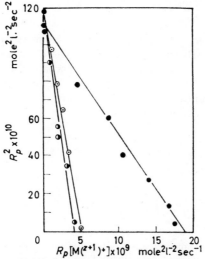

Figure 10.12. Effect of added ferric ($\odot$) and cupric ($\bullet$) perchlorates and equimolar mixtures of the two ($\circleddash$) on the rate of polymerization of 0·4M acrylamide solution in 0·1N perchloric acid solution at 25°C[51]. Dose rate $= 2·68 \times 10^{11}$ eVl.$^{-1}$ sec^{-1} for $\odot$ and slightly less for $\bullet$

(10.7) is negligible. Linear plots were found for ferric and cupric ions (*Figure 10.12*) and also for ceric ions after an induction period. From the linear portion, the velocity constant of reaction (10.8) can be determined. Dainton and co-workers found that argentous and mercuric ions react rapidly with hydrogen atoms, however, but slowly with the polymer radicals, and do not give simple linear plots of R_p^2 versus $R_p[M^{z+}]$. These investigations give the absolute values of the velocity constants of the reactions between the polyacrylamide radicals and various cations, and also allow the evaluation of the relative values of the primary yield of H* and OH* from the γ-radiation.

This inhibition of polymerization is shown by other components of the redox catalysts. For example, hydrogen atom transfer can occur between the polymer radical m_j and a reactive component HA of a redox couple, as shown in equation (10.9). Thiols used for 'activation' of persulphate initiators in butadiene–styrene copolymerization can also act as 'modifiers' or 'regulators' of the molecular weight by hydrogen transfer:

$$m_j^* + RSH \rightarrow m_jH + RS^*$$

There have also been studies of the reactions between polymer radicals and metal salts in non-aqueous solvents. These reactions are particularly useful in determining rates of initiation, for the salts are very effective inhibitors. Bamford, Jenkins and Johnston[52] have investigated the effect of ferric salts on the polymerization of acrylonitrile, methacrylonitrile and styrene in N,N-dimethylformamide as solvent.

10.2.5. Auto-acceleration

It is quite possible for vinyl and diene monomers to produce non-linear polymers that show structural branching. There are several ways in which this can be caused by transfer reactions. Perhaps the simplest is by chain transfer to a polymer radical m_j^* from one of the 'internal' carbons of a polymer molecule or radical, followed by the later addition of another polymer radical m_k^* to the activated carbon atom:

$$m_j^* + \overset{\backslash}{\underset{\backslash}{C}}H_2 \rightarrow m_jH + \overset{\backslash}{\underset{\backslash}{*}}CH$$

$$m_k^* + *\overset{\backslash}{\underset{\backslash}{C}}H \rightarrow m_k\!-\!\overset{\backslash}{\underset{\backslash}{C}}H$$

Another way is by transfer from a vinyl monomer to give a polymer radical which contains a terminal unsaturated bond; this radical can grow at the active end by normal propagation steps with monomer molecules, or act as a monomer itself and add another polymer radical to give a diradical:

$$m^* + CH_3 \cdot CH \vdots CH_2 \rightarrow m^*H + *CH_2 \cdot CH \vdots CH_2$$

$$CH_2 \vdots CH \cdot CH_2^* + ym \rightarrow CH_2 \vdots CH \cdot CH_2 \cdot m_y^*$$

$$m_z^* + CH_2 \vdots CH \cdot CH_2 \cdot m_y^* \rightarrow m_z \cdot CH_2 \cdot *CH \cdot CH_2 m_y^*$$

Clearly the diradical can grow into a branched polymer. Either of the above methods can be repeated to give a network polymer.

Polymer radicals can often be linked through reaction with a double bond in a polymer formed from a diene. Thus the following reactions lead to cross-linking of the radicals m_x^* and m_y^* through another molecule:

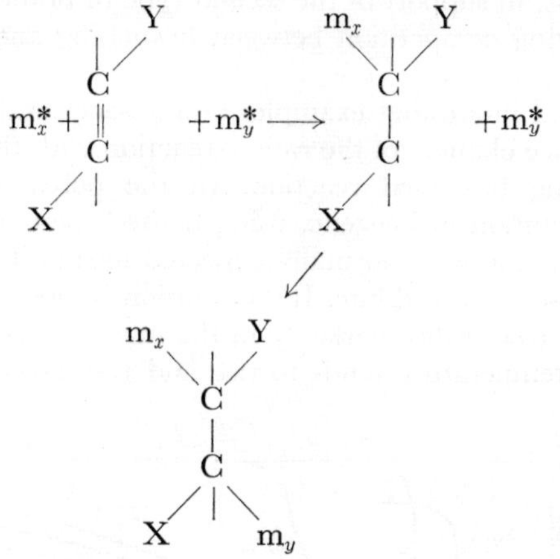

The result is a branched polymer, and if m_x, m_y and the linking molecule contain other double bonds, complicated networks can result from repetition of these reactions. However, in all the above reactions, the branching is *structural* and not *kinetic*. In none of the reactions does one reactive centre yield two. Indeed, kinetic branching in polymerization seems rare. Even where the phenomena appear to suggest branching reactions—as in ionic polymerizations, where almost explosively fast reactions and negative temperature co-efficients have been observed—very few branching mechanisms have been suggested [53].

The polymerization of formaldehyde vapour is catalysed by acids and by Friedel–Crafts catalysts† such as stannic chloride and boron trifluoride. The polymerization appears to start on the surface of the vessel when this is cooled below 90°C, and was found to follow a rate law which seemed to indicate kinetic branching:

$$\text{Rate} = \frac{[\text{aldehyde}][\text{catalyst}]}{k'[\text{aldehyde}] - k''[\text{catalyst}]}$$

The branching reaction proposed [54] for the first catalysts used, formic acid and acetic acid, involved the reaction of the terminal $—CH_2OH$ group of the polyoxymethylene with the acids

$$—CH_2OH + H \cdot COOH \rightarrow —CH_2 \cdot O \cdot CH_2(OH)_2$$

The two hydroxyl groups on the terminal carbon then lead to structural and kinetic branching. This is not possible with other catalysts such as hydrogen chloride, and it was proposed [55] that they split the polymer into *two* fragments, each with a hydroxyl group which could propagate the chain

$$—CH_2OH + H \cdot CH \cdot O \rightarrow —CH_2 \cdot O \cdot CH_2OH \rightarrow \quad \text{etc.}$$

† The term catalyst is preferred to initiator here.

The nature of the catalysts, and the conditions for initiating polymerization, suggest that the chains may be ionic. There is good evidence[53] that the poly-oxymethylenes can be depolymerized readily in the presence of acids by fission of the C—O bonds, in support of the second type of branching step. There is clearly an interesting competition between branching and depolymerization in these systems.

There are several interesting examples of auto-acceleration in polymeriza-tions. These produce changes of the rate of reaction with time which resemble a slowly-developing branched reaction. In the polymerization of methyl methacrylate in solution in benzene, using benzoyl peroxide as initiator, the progress of the reaction is as normally expected for addition polymerization, provided that the solution is dilute. If the solution is more concentrated, how-ever, the reaction accelerates markedly in the middle stages (*Figure 10.13*)[56]; concurrently the temperature tends to rise and the molecular weight of the

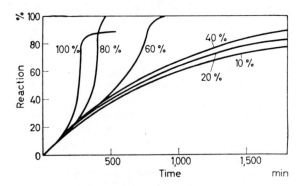

Figure 10.13. Accelerating rates of polymerization of methyl methacrylate in benzene solution at 50°C[56]. Cata-lyst = 10 g l.$^{-1}$ benzoyl peroxide; initial monomer concen-tration given on each curve

product to increase. Bengough and Norrish[57] found this acceleration in the polymerization of vinyl chloride, initiated by benzoyl peroxide, to be accom-panied by an increase in viscosity of the medium. The acceleration was sup-pressed by the addition of a good solvent for the polymer particles, as found earlier by Norrish and Smith[58] for the polymerization of methyl methacrylate. They suggested that the acceleration was due to a decrease in the rate of termination, rather than to any change in the rate of initiation. Bengough and Norrish[57] suggested that the growing polymer radicals underwent chain trans-fer with groups on the 'surface' of the precipitating polymer particles, and the adsorbed radicals were not terminated as readily as free radicals in true solution. However, it is not easy to see why the polymer has to precipitate before 'immobilizing' the radicals, nor why the mutual termination is greatly decreased once the radicals grow out from the surface.

Bamford and Barb[59] also ascribed the acceleration to a reduction in the rate of termination but suggested a different reason for the reduction. They consider that the polymer particles aggregate after precipitating and occlude growing polymer radicals together with monomer. With the polymers that

314

absorb monomer (and swell) the trapped radical can continue to grow, as in emulsion polymerization, and the chance of termination is greatly reduced.

Evidence for trapped radicals in the polymer particles has been found from electron spin resonance (ESR) studies[60]. Bamford and his colleagues[61] have used ESR techniques to measure the concentration of the occluded radicals in the particles. Bamford and Jenkins[62] used the reaction of the trapped radicals with the stable free radical, α,α'-diphenyl-β-picrylhydrazyl, to estimate the concentration of the occluded radicals and showed that the radicals could initiate very rapid polymerizations when the system was heated to about 60°C.

The effects of limited solubility on the rates of polymerizations, and on the determination of the velocity constants of the individual steps, have been the subject of much discussion. Dainton and his colleagues[63] have made a detailed study of the effect of polymer precipitation on the polymerization of acrylonitrile, in an attempt to resolve reported discrepancies in the rate laws with different methods of initiation. They conclude that the rate of polymerization is, in general, the sum of two propagating processes in these systems. One is the normal growth of polyacrylonitrile radicals, and the steps in this reaction can be studied by such methods as sector techniques. The other, slower propagation consists of the slow growth of radicals present in stable suspended polymer particles by addition of monomer adsorbed on them. These particles increase in number during the early growth stage and later remain constant in number (as indicated by electron microscope studies of their size and number[64]) but grow steadily in size. Some of the reported anomalies in the rates may be due to changes in the relative importance of these two paths at different monomer or initiator concentrations.

10.2.6. *Emulsion polymerization*

In emulsion polymerization, the monomer is usually dispersed in water with an emulsifying agent such as soap. Initiation occurs by reaction of the dispersed monomer with radicals generated in the water from an initiator (such as the redox initiators discussed in section 10.2.2), but it has been established that the propagation reaction does not occur in the polymer droplets. After the polymerization has proceeded to a reasonable extent, the droplets can be separated and are found to contain very little of the polymer formed. The site of polymerization in the early stages was identified by Harkins[65] as the soap micelles rather than the droplets of the monomer; after this early stage, the character of the emulsion has changed and polymerization occurs in particles of polymer swollen by dissolved monomer and stabilized by the soap. The qualitative picture of the early stages may be summarized as follows. Some of the soap stabilizes the monomer droplets and the rest forms soap micelles. Monomer diffuses out of the droplets and enters the micelles. The initiating radicals enter both the droplets and the micelles, but as there are many more micelles and they present a much greater surface, the rate of polymerization is greater in the micelles. Polymer grows rapidly in activated micelles and they absorb or dissolve more monomer and collect more soap on their surfaces at the expense of the other micelles and the droplets, which become less stable in dispersion. In the later stages these particles are the loci of polymerization; their number remains constant and so does the rate of polymerization from about 10 to 80 per cent conversion.

315

Smith and Ewart[66,67] developed Harkin's ideas into a very satisfactory quantitative theory and tested it rigorously. In the first place, they showed that the number of particles depends on the concentration of soap (c_s) and the rate of generation of primary radicals (ρ) according to the expression $N c_s^{3/5} \rho^{2/5}$. They showed experimentally that the rate of polymerization per particle is independent of the value of ρ. This led them to suggest that the polymerization goes on in a particle until the next primary radical enters and starts another polymer radical. The two radicals immediately combine, and the particle is inactive until the next primary radical enters and starts one chain, whereupon the cycle repeats. Thus on the average there will be one half of the particles with one growing polymer radical and the other half with none. The rate of polymerization is then obtained by substituting $N/2$ for the value of m_j^* in the usual expression, giving

$$R_p = k_p N[\mathrm{m}]/2$$

In each particle the rate of growth is constant at $k_p[\mathrm{m}]$ so long as one chain has been started, and the rate of termination is equal to ρ/N if all the primary radicals are captured by the particles. Hence the average degree of polymerization is $k_p N[\mathrm{m}]/\rho$.

One very important outcome of this analysis is the possibility of increasing the rate of reaction without simultaneously decreasing the degree of polymerization. In bulk polymerization, such an advantageous move is impossible because of the mutual termination of chains. The rate of polymerization is then given by the expression $R_p(R_i/R_m)^{1/2}$, and the degree of polymerization by

$$2R_p/(R_i R_m)^{1/2} = 2k_p[\mathrm{m}]/(k_t R_i)^{1/2}$$

Clearly, if the rate of polymerization is increased by the only means normally available, by increasing R_i, the degree of polymerization is lowered; longer polymers can only be obtained by slow rates that are perhaps uneconomical. But with emulsion polymerization, the concentration $(N/2)$ of radicals can be increased, for example by increasing the concentration of soap, without increasing ρ, and this will actually *increase* the degree of polymerization. However, ρ cannot be set at too low a level, for then N would be too low, unless it could be arranged that the value of ρ was kept high for the initial stages while the particles were being generated, and then decreased for the later stages.

The essential differences between the behaviour of catalysts in bulk and in emulsion polymerization thus arise from the isolation of each growing polymer radical during emulsion polymerization, so that the concentration of these radicals can be increased without the penalty of an increased rate of termination.

Flory[68] has pointed out that polymerizations in media in which the polymer has limited solubility show some characteristics of emulsion polymerization, in that the polymerization often occurs more favourably inside the precipitated polymer particles which are swollen by dissolved monomer (see the end of the previous section).

10.3.   IONIC POLYMERIZATION

There are many polymerization reactions which proceed by chain mechanisms with charged chain centres[4]. These may be carbonium ions or carbanions. Where comparison is impossible, as with various vinyl compounds, it appears[4] that monomers with electrophilic substitutes polymerize by free radical or carbanion centres, while nucleophilic substituents favour carbonium ion centres (see page 291). A charged centre can polarize a monomer more readily than can a free radical, however, so that the propagation reactions of charged centres may be more favourable energetically than those of free radicals[69]. Thus ionic polymerizations are likely to have lower activation energies for propagation, although they will have low frequency factors as well. The velocity constants of individual steps in ionic polymerizations have not been measured, but the over-all activation energy of many cationic polymerizations is quite low, as shown in *Table 10.3*. It will be seen that *negative* activation energies have been reported; this is in sharp contrast with free-radical polymerizations. There is also greater variety in the rate laws.

Many side reactions such as isomerations and alkylations often occur during ionic polymerizations. In fact, with some monomers such as alkenes it is not possible to obtain long polymers unless the temperature is lowered until the side reactions are too slow to compete, and with some monomers this may require temperatures as low as $-50°C$. The rates of these low-temperature polymerizations would be extremely slow with higher activation energies.

Table 10.3. Cationic polymerization

Monomer (m)	Catalyst (C)	Cocatalyst (Co)	Solvent	Rate expression	Activation energy kcal mole^{-1}	Reference
Styrene	$AlCl_3$	?	CCl_4	$k[m][C]$	1·2	70
	$TiCl_4$	Solvent	$(CH_2Cl)_2$	$k[m]^2[C]$	$-8·5$	71
	$SnCl_4$	H_2O?	CCl_4	$k[m]^3[C]$	3	72
	CCl_3COOH	—	$(CH_2Cl)_2$	$k[m]^2[C]^2$	8	73
	CCl_3COOH	—	CH_3NO_2	$k[m]^2[C]$	14	73
α-Methyl styrene	$SnCl_4$	H_2O	C_2H_5Cl	$k[m]^{1-2}[C]^{3/2}$	$-3·5$	74
n-Butylvinyl ether	$BF_3-(C_2H_5)_2O$	?	$(CH_2Cl)_2$	$k[m]([C]+k_2[m])$	$-ve$	75
	$BF_3-(C_2H_5)_2O$	?	$(CH_2Cl)_2$	$k[m]^2[C]$	6	76
Octylvinyl ether	I_2	?	$n-C_6H_{14}$	$k[m][C]^2$	10	77
Isobutene	$TiCl_4$	CCl_3COOH	$n-C_6H_{14}$	—	$-7·5$	78

Styrene polymerizes without side reactions at higher temperatures, however, and has often been used in kinetic studies.

The catalysts most used in *cationic* polymerizations are the typical Friedel–Crafts catalysts. Strong acids and acidic surfaces (similar to those used for cracking reactions of petroleums) have also been used. Pepper[4] has listed some twenty metal halides investigated as catalysts, among which boron trifluoride, aluminium chloride, aluminium bromide, titanium tetrachloride and stannic chloride have been used most often. The order of reactivity of these catalysts differs somewhat with conditions of experiment, and it is now generally accepted that the catalysts require 'activation' by a *cocatalyst* which apparently reacts with the catalyst to give the true initiator. In some systems the catalyst appears to be water or some other proton-yielding substance

$$BF_3 + HOR \rightarrow BF_3OR^- H^+$$

In other systems, the same function can be performed by the solvent, particularly if this contains halogen atoms

$$SnCl_4 + RCl \rightarrow SnCl_5^- R^+$$

317

In spite of much study of the initiation process, it is not certain whether the ions separate or remain as an ion pair. The almost total absence of results showing fractional powers of the catalyst concentration in the rate of expression has been used as an argument against separation, for the rate of initiation would then be proportional to the square root of the catalysed concentration; but this would not be valid if one ion of the pair initiated and the other reacted in a linear termination reaction. The rate expression would then be of the form $R_i R_p / R_t$ and the rate would be independent of the catalyst concentration. This is sometimes observed, and in these cases the kinetic evidence is inconclusive.

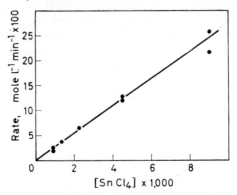

Figure 10.14. Rate of polymerization of α-styrene with stannic chloride as catalyst[79]

Expt.	[SnCl$_4$] $\times 10^3$	dh/dt mm min^{-1}	$\frac{1}{\Delta h_\infty} \times \frac{dh}{dt}$ $\times 10^2$	$-\frac{d[m]}{dt}$ $\times 10^2$	[η]	Mol. wt.
96	0·9	0·20	1·04	1·81	1·82	10,000
97	0·9	0·33	1·43	2·49	1·85	10,400
98	1·35	0·40	2·08	3·61	—	—
95	2·25	0·86	3·7	6·45	1·88	10,700
90	4·5	1·60	6·93	12·0	1·85	10,400
91	4·5	1·64	7·26	12·6	1·86	10,500
89	9·0	2·95	12·55	21·8	1·84	10,300
114	9·0	3·34	14·8	25·9	(1·22	5,500)

$[m] = 1.74$ (in ethylene dichloride). $T = 25°C$

In many cases the rate is directly proportional to the catalyst concentration, as shown in *Figure 10.14* for the polymerization of α-methyl styrene with stannic chloride as a catalyst. Most mechanisms of initiation are written rather cautiously as a proton (or carbonium ion) exchange between the catalyst–cocatalyst complex and the monomer, e.g.

$$BF_3OR^-H^+ + m \rightarrow HM_1^+ \cdot BF_3OR^-$$

with the anion (gegen-ion) in close attendance on the polymer radical. The propagation steps are then written as for free-radical polymerizations with the carbonium ion taking the place of the free radical. The order of the reaction in monomer concentration is often second, which would be expected from the initiation and propagation steps proposed if the termination is linear. How-

318

ever, higher orders have been observed at low monomer concentrations in the polymerizations of styrene, just as for free-radical polymerization (page 299). Dainton and his collaborators[80] have proposed an interesting scheme to account for this, different from the schemes proposed for free-radical polymerizations but apparently valid for them. He suggests that the primary radical Hm_1^+ may suffer termination more readily than larger radicals. If $k_{t,1}$ and $k_{t,j}$ are the velocity constants for linear termination of Hm_1^+ and of Hm_j^+, respectively (with similar notation for propagation) the rate of consumption of monomer is

$$-\frac{d[m]}{dt} = k_i[cat][cocat][m] \frac{k_{p,1}[m]}{k_{p,1}[m]+k_{t,1}} \cdot \frac{k_{p,j}[m]}{k_{t,j}}$$

The order can clearly rise from two when [m] is high to three when [m] is low.

There seems to be general agreement that many more polymer molecules are produced than catalyst molecules consumed. This has been taken to indicate that the termination process regenerates the catalyst, for example by reactions with the gegen-ion or with the cocatalyst†:

$$-CH_2 \cdot CHY^+ \cdot AlCl_4^- \rightarrow -CH:CHY + H^+ \cdot AlCl_4^-$$

$$-CH_2 \cdot CHY^+ \cdot AlCl_4^- \rightarrow -CH_2 \cdot CHYCl + AlCl_3$$

$$RX + -CH_2 \cdot CHY^+ \cdot AlCl_4^- \rightarrow -CH_2 \cdot CHYX + RCl + AlCl_3$$

However, in view of other reactions of isomerization, alkylation and so on, it seems very likely that the disparate ratio of polymer to catalyst molecules may indicate ready proton transfer to monomer molecules, as with hydrogen atom transfer in free-radical polymerization. In the polymerization of vinyl ethers and of 1-alkenes, in particular, the molecular weights are low. It is also possible that termination can occur by hydride extraction either from a dead polymer or from a carbonium ion, but this would not necessarily reduce the molecular weight and might produce branched molecules.

In some mechanisms the termination reaction is written as a spontaneous expulsion of a proton, although the same kinetic effect could be obtained by treating the carbonium ion together with the gegen-ion as an entity suffering unimolecular decomposition. Efforts have been made to distinguish the ionic nature of the species concerned in the termination reaction by the effect on the rate and degree of polymerization of altering the dielectric constant of the medium. Thus the experimental findings[79] that the rate and the degree of polymerization were both decreased by decrease in the dielectric constant was thought to show that the dielectric constant was affecting the termination reaction; the effect was required that the termination reaction, if bimolecular, is between two oppositely charged ions. However, it is not certain that this is the only explanation of the results; and if the ions concerned are the polymer carbonium ion and the gegen-ion, it would appear necessary to consider them as independent ions, in which case it is difficult to account for the linear dependence of the rate on the concentration of the catalyst.

It has been found that certain compounds, particularly aromatic hydrocarbons, can act as terminating agents and so keep the degree of polymerization low, just as do transfer agents in free-radical polymerizations. The

† This is the reason for preferring Friedel–Crafts 'catalysts' rather than initiators.

addition of an active terminating agent T reduces the number average of the molecular weight from $\overline{P_{n,0}}$ to $\overline{P_{n,T}}$ where

$$\frac{1}{\overline{P_{n,T}}} = \frac{1}{\overline{P_{n,0}}} + \frac{k_t}{k_p} \cdot \frac{[T]}{[m]}$$

where k_t is the velocity constant of the terminating step, k_p that of the propagation step, and $[T]$, $[m]$ are the concentrations of T and the monomer, respectively. It is therefore possible to determine the ratio of the velocity constants of the terminating and propagation steps, and hence the difference of activation energies, $E_p - E_t$. In the polymerization of styrene, catalysed by stannic chloride, the addition of p-xylene has a marked effect[81], and the value of $E_p - E_t$ is about -7 kcal mole^{-1}. This indicates that the terminating step has a considerable activation energy. By further studies[81] of the effect of changing the dielectric constant upon the activation energies, it has been concluded that the terminating step does not involve charge transfer.

10.4 HETEROGENEOUS CATALYSIS OF POLYMERIZATION

A variety of heterogeneous catalysts have been developed for the polymerization of unsaturated monomers, and some of the processes produce polymer molecules of very regular structure from monomers that are not readily polymerized by free-radical or ionic catalysts as well as from isobutene, butadiene, styrene and other commonly used monomers[82,83].

The catalysts that most resemble conventional heterogeneous catalysts are supported metal or oxide catalysts. They readily produce polymers of high molecular weight, but some of these have only small fractions of stereoregular molecules. For example, oxides of the transition metals, and especially of chromium supported on charcoal, silica, alumina or thoria, will produce highly crystalline polyethylene, whereas the polymers from other olefins or dienes have been reported to contain very little isotactic polymer, and styrene cannot be polymerized with these catalysts. The catalyst is used in a fixed bed or in a slurry with solvents such as aliphatic or aromatic hydrocarbons at temperatures of 120 to 180°C, and the monomer is passed in under pressures of 30 to 35 atm. Other important catalysts are nickel or cobalt on charcoal, prepared by reducing the oxides, and partially reduced oxides of metals of Groups V or VI on alumina or an oxide of Group IVA. Molybdena is the most used oxide, and it is activated by reduction with hydrogen and with promoters such as metal hydrides or metal aluminium hydrides; similar promoters are used with oxides, for instance vanadium oxide. The promoters reduce and activate fresh catalyst, reactivate spent catalyst and remove catalyst poisons, but they also seem to take a direct part in the polymerization. These supported catalysts produce products with a wide range of molecular weights, depending upon the conditions and varying from greases to tough resinous polymers. Rather high temperatures and pressures are necessary with these metal and reduced oxide catalysts.

Some novel and effective catalysts have emerged in recent years which give polymers of a very regular structure. The best known of these are the Ziegler catalysts, the Alfin catalysts and various organolithium compounds. The organolithium compounds[84] such as butyl- or amyl-lithium can be used in homogeneous solution to polymerize isoprene or butadiene at quite low temperatures, from 100°C to well below 0°C, and the polymers contain *cis*- and *trans*-forms of mixtures of 1,4-, 1,2- and 3,4-structures. With these catalysts in heterogeneous suspensions a much higher proportion of one or other of the linkings is produced, e.g. 91 per cent of *cis*-1,4-configurations in polyisoprene with butyllithium at 40°C. In addition, lithium metal or lithium metal plus a complex halide such as lithium aluminium chloride, suspended in hydrocarbon solvents such as petroleum jelly at 200°C, produce stereoregulated polydienes. It appears that polymers produced from metallic lithium or organolithium compounds are very similar, and that the metal may react with monomer to give a lithium alkyl which is the actual catalyst[85]. The Alfin[86] catalysts are complex mixtures, a common one consisting of a sodium salt of a methyl n-alkyl carbinol and the sodium adduct of an olefin in the presence of sodium chloride particles. The catalyst mixture must be prepared in an atmosphere of dry nitrogen. Other combinations of an alkali metal ion and halide ion are satisfactory, provided that the M–X distance lies between 2·81 and 3·29 Å. It has been shown that solid alkali metal halide is essential to the catalysis, and that the more finely divided particles are better catalysts than coarse particles. These factors point to the need for some critically spaced complex, perhaps adsorbed on the surface of the solid halide which controls the propagation step in the polymerization by presenting the diene in an incipient 1,4-form. Uelzmann[87] has suggested a scheme involving anionic propagation starting from an aggregate of ions:

$$
\begin{array}{ccc}
CH_2 & & R-CH_2 \\
\diagdown & & \diagdown \\
CH & & CH \\
| & & \| \\
{}^{+}CH & \longrightarrow & CH \\
\diagup\diagup & & \diagup \\
R^{-} \qquad {}^{-}CH_2 & & {}^{-}CH_2 \\
\diagdown & & \diagup \\
Na^{+} & & Na^{+} \\
\downarrow & & \\
\end{array}
$$

$$Na^{+} \quad Cl^{-} \quad Na^{+} \quad OR^{-}$$

The net effect is that a polarized diene molecule is inserted between a growing polymer carbanion and a sodium atom or ion on the surface and this process is repeated to form the propagation steps. However, other parts of the ionic surface may be required to polarize or to orient the diene, for the above mechanism would not seem to require any particular M–X distance, and no particular function is proposed for the isopropoxide ion. Morton and his co-workers[86] who developed the Alfin catalysts have proposed free-radical mechanisms. There has been very little work on the kinetics of these polymerizations.

The Ziegler catalysts are remarkable for the mild conditions of temperature and pressure under which they operate, and the control they give over the structure of the polymer molecules. They consist of mixtures of a metal alkyl and a metal halide, aluminium triethyl and titanium tetrachloride being a typical example. Although polymerization had been effected with similar catalysts before[88] Ziegler's work, he was the first to investigate systematically[89] the function of the metal alkyl and to show which metal halides promoted the growth of long polymer molecules and which appeared to restrict the growth. During attempts to prepare higher olefins by reacting them with aluminium hydride or with aluminium alkyls, Ziegler[90] found that the molecular weights of the products were variable and on the whole lower than might be expected. The discovery[91] that an almost quantitative dimerization of ethylene to 1-butene could be achieved if nickel salts were present led to an investigation of the effect of other transition metal compounds. It was found that compounds of metals of Groups IV, V and VI with triethylaluminium or diethylaluminium chloride gave a high yield of polyethylene. Rather later, Natta[92, 93] showed that these catalysts gave sterically differentiated polymers of propylene and other olefins. Natta proposed[92] that the transition metal compound be regarded as the catalyst and the metal alkyl as the cocatalyst. He showed that a lower oxidation state of the catalyst was necessary for activity, although the metal itself often resulted in dimerization rather than polymerization, just as did nickel. Also, the presence of a solid–liquid interface appeared to be necessary for stereoregulation of the structure of the polymer molecule. Since then, much has been written on the mechanism of these remarkable reactions, and free radical, cationic and anionic chains with a propagation step sterically regulated by the surface or by individual complex ions have been proposed. The mild conditions of polymerization point to an ionic mechanism, but it cannot be said that any particular scheme is completely satisfactory.

The components of Ziegler catalysts are: (i) an organometallic compound of a metal of Group II or III, especially alkyls of aluminium, zinc or magnesium, or an alkali metal hydride, or an alkyl metal hydride of the type R_nM—X, and (ii) a salt such as a halide or alcoholate or acetylacetonate of a metal of Groups IV, V and VI, especially of chromium, molybdenum, thorium, vanadium or zirconium. There appears to be a reaction between the two components in which the metal of component (ii) is partially alkylated and also is reduced, for example with titanium to an oxidation state of 3 or lower. Natta[92] considers that the best catalysts are the transition elements with lowest work functions and lowest ionization potentials. During operation, the effective catalyst is probably a solid or is present at the surface of a solid phase or the surface of colloidally dispersed particles, but there are differences in appearance and behaviour with different components. Many other mixtures have been investigated which start with salts and metals and probably give alkyl compounds with monomers. The monomers which can be polymerized include ethylene, most higher olefins including styrene, and conjugated dienes. With some catalysts, great structural regularity can be attained with polymers of α-olefins, especially if the trihalides of titanium, vanadium, chromium or zirconium are used with aluminium triethyl. On the other hand, linear crystalline polymers of butadiene in a 1,2-structure and of isoprene in a 3,4-structure are best obtained from the oxygen-containing salts of the same metals; halides lead to 1,4-addition with butadiene. The ratio of catalyst to cocatalyst and the size of the particles also affect the crystallinity—very fine particles produce more amorphous polymers. The optimum conditions can vary from room temperature and pressure, generally with a hydrocarbon solvent and the titannic chloride plus aluminium triethyl catalyst, to temperatures of 200°C with correspondingly high pressures.

In many cases there are conflicts between the most desirable conditions for one or other of the three variables, stereospecificity, molecular weight and speed of reaction. The main factors which can be used, albeit rather empirically, to control the specificity of the polymerization have been listed as: (*i*) the state of aggregation and degree of dispersion of the catalyst, (*ii*) the valency of the metal in the catalyst, and (*iii*) the nature of the substituent on the heavy metal and on the cocatalyst component. The molecular weight is sensitive to the total amount of catalyst used, the molar ratio of catalyst and cocatalyst and the presence of chain transfer agents including hydrogen, some metal alkyls which are partly ionic, hydrogen adsorbing metals and some alkyl halides. The rate of reaction is increased by increasing the weight of catalyst used and the olefin pressure as well as by raising the temperature.

Partly because of the variety of experimental conditions that have been rapidly explored, the theories of the mechanism are numerous and have not yet been so tested as to show reasons for preferring any one theory. Free-radical and ionic intermediates have been proposed, bound in various ways to the surface. Stemming from Ziegler's work on aluminium alkyls, and supported by evidence of the end groups incorporated in the polymer, Natta[94] considers that the monomer is inserted between the aluminium atom and the alkyl radical with a considerable degree of polarization of the metal alkyl and of the olefinic bonds. Friedlander and Oita[95] propose a similar propagation step but involving free radicals adsorbed on the surface. Gaylord and Mark[96] have proposed a 'reeling-off' mechanism of monomers co-ordinated around a titanium ion. While all these account for some end-to-end orientation of the monomer $CH_2 : CHR$ as it enters the growing polymer radical, it is not easy to see how the CHR group entering is orientated with respect to the CHR groups already in the polymer, unless the R groups are held in a particular relation to the sites which adsorb the —CH_2 groups in the monomer and polymer. Uelzmann has proposed[87] a scheme which in part satisfies this requirement by postulating hydrogen bonding between the methyl carbon of propylene and the chloride ions of the surface of the catalyst with the monomer activated on the titanium ion and the polymer held on the Al complex. It seems that some definite configuration of three centres at least is needed for the monomer to be fed into the polymer in such orientation that an isotactic structure results. This configuration may turn out to be a property of a complex between catalyst and cocatalyst, or one or both of these components adsorbed in a definite relationship on the surface of, say, the reduced metal halide crystal. As with all catalytically active surfaces, the adsorption must not be too strong and must be reversible.

All the propagation schemes that have been discussed above assume that the active sites are fixed on the catalyst surface, like active sites on enzymes, and Natta[97,98] has reported kinetic and radiochemical adsorption measurements of the concentration of these active sites on typical catalysts. The kinetic method consists of the determination of the ratio of the number of ethyl groups in the polymer to the number of monomer units polymerized. Natta shows that if one chain starts at each active centre, from an ethyl group, and ethyl groups can terminate the growing polymer by transfer from the catalyst, the ratio is equal to

$$\frac{\text{number of active centres} + \sum \text{rate of termination with Et} \times \text{time}}{\text{rate of propagation} \times \text{time}}$$

From this relationship, it was estimated that there were 6×10^{-3} active centres per molecule of titanium trichloride. The adsorption experiments are to some extent independent of the polymerization reaction and consist of measurements of the adsorption of aluminium alkyls, labelled with ^{14}C, on the catalyst; they suggest that there are about 3×10^{-3} sites per molecule of titanium trichloride. The difference may be connected with the observations[97] that the size of crystallite changes as the polymerization begins, so that the proportion of active centres changes during the 'settling' period. The length of this period depends upon the catalyst preparation and the concentration of monomer, and is a feature of stereospecific polymerization of styrene[99] as well as of ethylene and proplyene.

The termination step may consist of the transfer of a hydride ion or a hydrogen atom to the catalyst, which becomes ready for further activation by monomer. Natta has proposed, as mentioned above, that the catalyst complex may transfer an ethyl group to the polymer radical, and he has listed the possible initiation, propagation and termination processes in the polymerization of propylene in his Table III (Natta[97]). Similar transfer to or from the transfer agents has been proposed for the reactions that are used to control the molecular weight of the polymers. Gordon and Roe[100] have discussed the general effect on the molecular weight distribution of assuming that the termination step is the desorption of the growing chain end from the catalyst surface.

A different propagation mechanism has been proposed by Gilchrist[101]. In this, the monomer and the metal alkyl are adsorbed on the catalyst surface. An alkyl group is transferred from the metal alkyl to one end of the double bond of a monomer adsorbate, and the other (negative) end of the radical adds another adsorbed monomer in the propagation step. The growing end of the polymer radical moves over the surface, with a positive charge migrating under the surface. This mechanism is similar to a two-dimensional ionic polymerization with the gegen-ion moving in the titanium chloride, perhaps by change in the charge on the metal ions.

The kinetics of polymerization of butadiene in solution in heptane at $25\,^\circ\text{C}$, in the presence of heterogeneous catalysts prepared from titanium tetrachloride and $\text{Al(iso-C}_4\text{H}_9)_3$, have been investigated by Gaylord, Kwei and Mark[102]. They followed the rate by the rate of disappearance of gaseous butadiene. The rate is proportional to the amount of catalyst taken and depends upon the monomer pressure:

$$-\frac{dP}{dt} = aP + bP^2$$

With catalysts containing low ratios of aluminium to titanium (1·0 to 1·6), the first term predominates, but with ratios above 2·0 the second term predominates. At low aluminium/titanium ratios, the reaction is initially rapid and produces highly stereoregular polymers that are essentially all *trans*-1,4-

polybutadiene; but the rate soon slows down. The authors propose mechanisms that involve adsorption and reaction by Langmuir–Hinshelwood or VCI mechanisms (see Chapter 6). It is rather startling to find polymerization mechanisms without formal initiating, propagating or terminating steps in the scheme. Adsorption takes the place of initiation and desorption of the polymer ends the growing molecule, rather as chain transfer does in free-radical polymerization schemes, leaving the heterogeneous site free to start a new polymer. A succession of surface reactions, or VCI steps, act as the propagating reactions. Further investigations of the ways in which the two metals affect the kinetics and the production of stereoregular polymers would be valuable. The authors conclude that the aluminium alkyl must be present in the active catalyst, as well as acting as a reducing agent for the titanium.

Similar conclusions are emerging from recent studies of soluble Ziegler-like catalysts. Carrick[103] prepared soluble catalysts by dissolving vanadium tetrachloride in a solution of aluminium bromide and aluminium triphenyl in cyclohexane, and proposed that the polymer grows on the (reduced) vanadium ion in the complex

$$R \qquad X$$
$$\diagdown \qquad \cdots$$
$$Al \qquad V{-}R$$
$$\diagup \qquad \cdots$$
$$R \qquad X$$

Badin[104] has proposed similar structures for the complex formed in the reaction between titanium tetrachloride and aluminium triethyl. With *bis*-(cyclopentadienyl)-titanium dichloride and aluminium alkyls, spectrophotometric studies[105] have shown that complexes are immediately formed by reactions such as

$$(C_5H_5)_2TiCl_2 + (CH_3)_2AlCl \rightleftharpoons (C_5H_5)_2TiCl_2 \cdot (CH_3)_2AlCl$$

From these complexes, catalysts active for the linear polymerization of ethylene are slowly formed. Such catalysts are more active if traces of oxygen are present in the ethylene, suggesting that the oxidation of a lower valency form of titanium is necessary for a catalyst to be activated.

REFERENCES

[1] FLORY, P. J. *Principles of Polymer Chemistry*: Cornell University Press, Ithaca, N.Y., 1953

[2] FLORY, P. J. *J. Amer. chem. Soc.* 1939, **61**, 3334; 1940, **62**, 2261

[3] VALENTINE, L. and WINTER, R. W. *J. chem. Soc.* 1956, p. 4768

[4] PEPPER, D. C. *Quart. Rev. (Lond.)* 1954, **8**, 88

[5] MATHESON, M. S., AUER, E. E., BEVILACQUA, E. B. and HART, E. J. *J. Amer. chem. Soc.* 1949, **71**, 2610

[6] KWART, H., BROADBENT, H. S. and BARTLETT, P. D. *J. Amer. chem. Soc.* 1950, **72**, 1060

[7] BURNETT, G. M. and MELVILLE, H. W. *Proc. R. Soc. A* 1947, **189**, 456

[8] MATHESON, M. S., AUER, E. E., BEVILACQUA, E. B. and HART, E. J. *J. Amer. chem. Soc.* 1951, **73**, 1700

[9] BAMFORD, C. H. and DEWAR, M. J. S. *Proc. R. Soc. A* 1948, **192**, 309; 1949, **197**, 356

[10] MATHESON, M. S., AUER, E. E., BEVILACQUA, E. B. and HART, E. J. *J. Amer. chem. Soc.* 1949, **71**, 497

[11] MACKAY, M. H. and MELVILLE, H. W. *Trans. Faraday Soc.* 1949, **45**, 323

[12] DAINTON, F. S. *Chain Reactions*: Methuen, London, 1956, p. 53

[13] BURNETT, G. M. *Mechanism of Polymer Reactions*: Interscience, New York, 1954, Chapter IIIA

[14] BEVINGTON, J. C. *Rep. Progr. Chem.* 1958, **55**, 28

[15] PRICE, C. C., KELL, R. W. and KREBS, E. *J. Amer. chem. Soc.* 1942, **64**, 1103

[16] ARNETT, L. M. and PETERSON, J. H. *J. Amer. chem. Soc.* 1952, **74**, 2027, 2031

[17] SMITH, W. V. *J. Amer. chem. Soc.* 1949, **71**, 4077

[18] BAMFORD, C. H., BARB, W. G., JENKINS, A. D. and ONYON, P. F. *The Kinetics of Vinyl Polymerization by Radical Mechanisms*: Butterworth, London, 1958

[19] FLORY, P. J. *Principles of Polymer Chemistry*: Cornell University Press, Ithaca, N.Y., 1953, p. 115

[20] GREGG, R. A. and MAYO, F. R. *Disc. Faraday Soc.* 1947, **2**, 328

[21] FLORY, P. J. *Principles of Polymer Chemistry*: Cornell University Press, Ithaca, N.Y., 1953, p. 145

[22] BAMFORD, C. H. and WHITE, E. F. T. *Trans. Faraday Soc.* 1956, **52**, 716

[23] BAMFORD, C. H., JENKINS, A. D. and WHITE, E. F. T. *J. Polym. Sci.* 1959, **34**, 271

[24] BEVINGTON, J. C. and LEWIS, T. D. *Polymer* 1960, **1**, 1

[25] MAYO, F. R., GREGG, R. A. and MATHESON, M. S. *J. Amer. chem. Soc.* 1951, **73**, 1691

[26] JENKINS, A. D. *J. Polym. Sci.* 1958, **29**, 245

[27] DAINTON, F. S., TOMLINSON, R. H. and BATKE, T. L. *Cationic Polymerization and Related Complexes* (Ed. P. H. Plesch): Academic Press, New York, 1953, p. 82

[28] SCHULZ, G. V. and HUSEMANN, E. *Z. phys. Chem. (Leipzig)* 1938, **B39**, 246

[29] MATHESON, M. S. *J. chem. Phys.* 1945, **13**, 584

[30] FLORY, P. J. *Principles of Polymer Chemistry*: Cornell University Press, Ithaca, N.Y., 1953, p. 120

[31] BURNETT, G. M. and LOAN, L. D. *Trans. Faraday Soc.* 1955, **51**, 214, 219, 226

[32] JENKINS, A. D. *Trans. Faraday Soc.* 1958, **54**, 1885, 1895

[33] BACON, R. G. R. *Trans. Faraday Soc.* 1946, **42**, 140

[34] BACON, R. G. R. *Quart. Rev. (Lond.)* 1955, **9**, 287

[35] MORGAN, L. B. *Trans. Faraday Soc.* 1946, **42**, 169

[36] DOLGOPLOSK, B. A. and TINIAKOVA, E. T. *J. Polym. Sci.* 1958, **30**, 315

[37] BAXENDALE, J. H., EVANS, M. G. and PARK, G. S. *Trans. Faraday Soc.* 1946, **42**, 155

[38] BAXENDALE, J. H. *Advanc. Catalys.* 1952, **4**, 31

[39] REYNOLDS, W. L. and KOLTHOFF, I. M. *J. phys. Chem.* 1956, **60**, 969

[40] WISE, W. S. and TWIGG, G. H. *J. chem. Soc.* 1953, p. 2172

[41] DAINTON, F. S. and JAMES, D. G. L. *J. Chim. phys.* 1951, **48**, C17

[42] DAINTON, F. S. *Chem. Soc. spec. Publ.* 1954, **1**, 18

[43] DAINTON, F. S. and JAMES, D. G. L. *Trans. Faraday Soc.* 1958, **54**, 649

[44] FOORD, S. G. *J. chem. Soc.* 1940, p. 48

[45] BARTLETT, P. D., HAMMOND, G. S. and KWART, H. *Disc. Faraday Soc.* 1947, **2**, 342

[46] MELVILLE, H. W. and WATSON, W. F. *Trans. Faraday Soc.* 1948, **44**, 886

[47] NORRISH, R. G. W. and BROOKMAN, E. F. *Proc. R. Soc. A* 1939, **171**, 147

[48] BARTLETT, P. D. and KWART, H. *J. Amer. chem. Soc.* 1950, **72**, 1051

[49] CHINMAYANANDAM, B. R. and MELVILLE, H. W. *Trans. Faraday Soc.* 1954, **50**, 73

[50] MAYO, F. R. and GREGG, R. A. *J. Amer. chem. Soc.* 1948, **70**, 1284

REFERENCES

[51] COLLINSON, E., DAINTON, F. S., SMITH, D. R., TRUDEL, G. J. and TAZUKÉ, S. *Disc. Faraday Soc.* 1960, **29**, 188

[52] BAMFORD, C. A., JENKINS, A. D. and JOHNSTON, R. *Proc. R. Soc. A* 1957, **239**, 214

[53] BEVINGTON, J. C. *Quart. Rev. (London.)* 1952, **6**, 141

[54] CARRUTHERS, J. E. and NORRISH, R. G. W. *Trans. Faraday Soc.* 1936, **32**, 195

[55] BEVINGTON, J. C. and NORRISH, R. G. W. *Proc. R. Soc. A* 1951, **205**, 516

[56] SCHULZ, G. V. and HARBORTH, G. *Makromol. Chem.* 1947, **1**, 106

[57] BENGOUGH, W. I. and NORRISH, R. G. W. *Proc. R. Soc. A* 1950, **200**, 301

[58] NORRISH, R. G. W. and SMITH, R. R. *Nature, Lond.* 1942, **150**, 336

[59] BAMFORD, C. H. and BARB, W. G. *Disc. Faraday Soc.* 1953, **14**, 208

[60] FRAENKEL, G. K., HIRSHON, J. M. and WALLING, C. *J. Amer. chem. Soc.* 1954, **76**, 3606

[61] BAMFORD, C. H., JENKINS, A. D., SYMONS, M. C. R. and TOWNSEND, M. G. *J. Polym. Sci.* 1959, **34**, 181

[62] BAMFORD, C. H. and JENKINS, A. D. *Proc. R. Soc. A* 1955, **228**, 220

[63] DAINTON, F. S., SEAMAN, P. H., JAMES, D. G. L. and EATON, R. S. *J. Polym. Sci.* 1959, **34**, 209

[64] THOMAS, W. M., GLEASON, E. H. and MINO, G. *J. Polym. Sci.* 1957, **24**, 43

[65] HARKINS, W. D. *J. Amer. chem. Soc.* 1947, **69**, 1428

[66] SMITH, W. V. and EWART, R. H. *J. chem. Phys.* 1948, **16**, 592

[67] SMITH, W. V. *J. Amer. chem. Soc.* 1948, **70**, 3695

[68] FLORY, P. J. *Principles of Polymer Chemistry*: Cornell University Press, Ithaca, N.Y., 1953, p. 216

[69] DAINTON, F. S. *Chain Reactions*: Methuen, London, 1956, pp. 47, 147

[70] JORDAN, D. O. and MATHIESON, A. R. *J. chem. Soc.* 1952, pp. 611, 621

[71] PLESCH, P. H. *J. chem. Soc.* 1953, p. 1653

[72] WILLIAMS, G. *J. chem. Soc.* 1940, p. 775

[73] BROWN, C. P. and MATHIESON, A. R. *J. chem. Soc.* 1957, p. 3612

[74] DAINTON, F. S. and TOMLINSON, R. H. *J. chem. Soc.* 1953, 151

[75] WORSFIELD, D. J. and BYWATER, S. *J. Amer. chem. Soc.* 1957, **79**, 4917

[76] COOMBES, J. D. and ELEY, D. D. *J. chem. Soc.* 1957, p. 3700

[77] ELEY, D. D. and RICHARDS, A. W. *Trans. Faraday Soc.* 1949, **45**, 425

[78] PLESCH, P. H. *J. chem. Soc.* 1950, p. 543

[79] DAINTON, F. S., TOMLINSON, R. H. and BATKE, T. L. *Cationic Polymerization and Related Complexes* (Ed. P. H. Plesch): Academic Press, New York, 1953, p. 80

[80] PEPPER, D. C. *Trans. Faraday Soc.* 1949, **45**, 397, 404

[81] OVERBERGER, C. G., PEARCE, E. M. and WEI, L. C. K. *J. Polym. Sci.* 1958, **31**, 235

[82] STILLE, J. K. *Chem. Rev.* 1958, **58**, 541

[83] GAYLORD, N. G. and MARK, H. F. *Linear and Stereoregular Addition Polymers: Polymerization with Controlled Propagation* (Polymer Reviews, Vol. II): Interscience, London and New York, 1959

[84] GAYLORD, N. G. and MARK, H. F. *Linear and Stereoregular Addition Polymers: Polymerization with Controlled Propagation* (Polymer Reviews, Vol. II): Interscience, London and New York, 1959, p. 240

[85] TOBOLSKY, A. V., HSIEH, H. and KELLEY, D. J. *J. Polym. Sci.* 1957, **26**, 240

[86] MORTON, A. A. *et al.*, *J. Amer. chem. Soc.* 1950, **72**, 3785; 1952, **74**, 5434; *Industr. Engng Chem. (Industr.)* 1952, **44**, 3876

[87] UELZMANN, H. *J. Polym. Sci.* 1958, **32**, 457

[88] ELLIS, L. M. *Chem. Abstr.* 1941, **35**, 464
FISCHER, M. *Chem. Abstr.* 1957, **51**, 1024

[89] For full list of references, see [82]

[90] ZIEGLER, K. *Angew. Chem.* 1952, **64**, 323

[91] ZIEGLER, K. *et al.*, *Angew. Chem.* 1955, **67**, 426, 541; *Petroleum* 1955, **34**, No. 8, 111

[92] NATTA, G. *Angew. Chem.* 1956, **68**, 393

[93] NATTA, G. *Mod. Plast.* 1956, **34**, 169

[94] NATTA, G. *et al.*, *J. Polym. Sci.* 1957, **26**, 120

[95] FRIEDLANDER, H. N. and OITA, K. *Industr. Engng Chem. (Industr.)* 1957, **49**, 1885

[96] GAYLORD, N. G. and MARK, H. F. *Linear and Stereoregular Addition Polymers: Polymerization with Controlled Propagation* (Polymer Reviews, Vol. II): Interscience, London and New York, 1959, p. 178

[97] NATTA, G. *J. Polym. Sci.* 1959, **34**, 21

[98] NATTA, G. and PASQUON, I. *Advanc. Catalys.* 1959, **11**, 1

[99] BURNETT, G. M. and TAIT, P. J. T. *Polymer* 1960, **1**, 151

[100] GORDON, M. and ROE, R.-J. *Polymer* 1961, **2**, 41

[101] GILCHRIST, A. *J. Polym. Sci.* 1959, **34**, 49

[102] GAYLORD, N. G., KWEI, T. K. and MARK, H. F. *J. Polym. Sci.* 1960, **42**, 417

[103] CARRICK, W. L. *J. Amer. chem. Soc.* 1958, **80**, 6455

[104] BADIN, E. J. *J. phys. Chem.* 1959, **63**, 1791

[105] BRESLOW, D. S. and NEWBERG, N. R. *J. Amer. chem. Soc.* 1959, **81**, 81
CHIEN, J. C. W. *ibid.* 86

CATALYSIS AND INHIBITION OF SOME CHAIN REACTIONS OF OXYGEN

11.1. INTRODUCTION

OXIDATIONS in which atmospheric oxygen reacts with combustible gases and vapours are so familiar, and often occur so rapidly, that there is a natural tendency to look upon the oxygen molecule as very reactive. In fact, it is rather inert chemically towards other molecules, and the rapidity of combustion processes is due to reaction of oxygen with free radicals in the propagating steps of chain reactions[1]. Chain reactions also occur in the slow oxidation of saturated and unsaturated hydrocarbons and of their derivatives, and of some inorganic substances, either in solution or as pure liquids. The chain character of these *auto-oxidations* was first demonstrated by Bäckström by comparison of the photochemical and thermal oxidations of aldehydes and of sodium sulphite (see page 262). Like all chain reactions, their rates can be increased by the addition of catalysts which give suitable free radicals by thermal or by photochemical decomposition or by electron-transfer reactions, and they can be decreased by the addition of inhibitors which replace reactive radicals by inactive radicals or molecules. The uncatalysed auto-oxidations are usually slow, because the initial step between the reactants to give radicals is slow. However, in some circumstances these auto-oxidations show self-acceleration or *auto-catalysis* due to the diradical properties of the oxygen molecule or the oxygen atom. It is, therefore, interesting to discuss some of the common features of the auto-oxidations in relation to the reactivity of the oxygen molecule.

It is difficult to split the oxygen molecule with its high bond strength of 118 kcal/mole, and reactions in which this occurs are nearly always endothermic and occur slowly at low temperatures. It would appear reasonable, however, for the oxygen molecule, with its two unpaired electrons, to behave as a diradical and to react with a molecule XY to give the compound XOOY. This would require a 'square' transition complex:

$$\begin{array}{ccc} X\cdots O \\ \vdots \quad | \\ Y\cdots O \end{array}$$

Now most of the compounds of XY of interest contain short bonds such as C—H or C═O or H—H, and it is probably difficult to overlap the potential bond-forming orbitals to form the complex. It would be easier to form the linear complex $X\cdots Y\cdots O_2$, and a great many oxidations seem to proceed by reaction steps with this sort of transition complex. Thus many unsaturated and saturated hydrocarbons can give yields of hydroperoxides under mild conditions of temperature (0 to 100°C), the overall reaction being

$$RH + O_2 \rightarrow ROOH$$

There is experimental evidence[2] that these oxidations begin with a slow reaction which is the abstraction of a hydrogen atom from the hydrocarbon

$$RH + O_2 \rightleftharpoons R....H....O_2 \rightarrow R^* + HO_2^*$$

The HO_2^* radical does not appear to be very reactive, but the hydrocarbon radical R^* can combine with another oxygen molecule to give a radical RO_2^* which, like oxygen, can extract a hydrogen atom from the parent molecule RH:

$$R^* + O_2 \rightarrow RO_2^*$$
$$RO_2^* + RH \rightarrow ROOH + R^*$$

These reactions form the propagating steps of a chain reaction. Similar reactions have been postulated in the low-temperature oxidation of some saturated hydrocarbons and of many hydrocarbon derivatives[3,4].

At higher temperatures, the oxidation of hydrocarbons yields many compounds, including alcohols, aldehydes and acids as well as peroxidic compounds. It is certain that at some stage in these reactions the O—O bond is split. For example, in the oxidation of propane at about 300°C, very little peroxide can be detected but aldehydes and their oxidation products are found[5,6]. At lower temperatures, the reaction can be photoinitiated in the presence of mercury, and both aldehydes and hydroperoxides occur in comparable amounts. At about 25°C, only hydroperoxides are found[7].

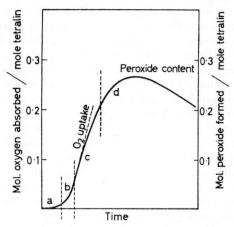

Figure 11.1. Course of oxidation of tetralin at 76°C[8]

Now the rates of the uncatalysed low- and high-temperature oxidations show very similar changes during the reactions. This is illustrated in *Figures 11.1* and *11.2*. *Figure 11.1* shows schematically the rate of consumption of oxygen during the oxidation of tetralin at 76°C[8]. Initially the reaction is slow, and very little oxygen is consumed until the end of the *induction period* (phase a). There is then a rapid acceleration to a maximum rate which is sustained for a substantial portion of the reaction. The product in the initial stages is almost exclusively tetralin hydroperoxide[9]. *Figure 11.2* shows the rates of consumption of reactants and the rates of production of various compounds during the oxidation of ethane[10]. Once again, there is an induction period, followed by an acceleration of the rate of removal of ethane or oxygen; the concentrations of the peroxides, aldehydes and (later) acids pass through a maximum, while those of final products such as carbon monoxide and carbon dioxide increase slowly.

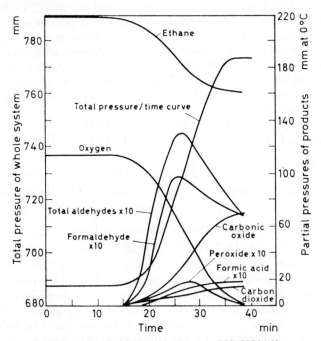

Figure 11.2. Oxidation of ethane at 303–305°C[10]

This auto-catalysis is attributed to a similar cause in each case, namely the breakdown of a fairly stable intermediate. In the low-temperature oxidations, this is almost certainly the hydroperoxide, known to decompose slowly. If the decomposition yields radicals, as in the reaction

$$ROOH \rightarrow RO* + OH*$$

new reaction chains will be initiated and the rate of oxidation will increase. The rate reaches a maximum either because the reactants are being consumed or because the hydroperoxide concentration increases to a maximum value. There have been suggestions that the auto-catalysis of the high-temperature oxidations is also due to the formation and decomposition of hydroperoxides. While this may be true for the higher hydrocarbons, there is considerable evidence against it for the lower hydrocarbons (C_1 to C_4). In the first place, the amounts of hydroperoxides formed during the oxidation of the lower hydrocarbons are small, and insufficient to cause the auto-catalysis. Norrish and Knox[5] and Shtern[6] have separately shown that the peroxy compounds formed in the oxidation of propane consist principally of hydrogen peroxide which is considerably more stable than alkyl peroxides. On the other hand, aldehydes are formed[11] in about the right amount to cause the auto-catalysis, as shown by direct addition of small amounts of formaldehyde[12–14] to methane–

331

oxygen mixtures or of acetaldehyde[5,6] to propane–oxygen mixtures during the induction periods. Furthermore, Kirk and Knox[15] have shown quantitatively that ethyl and propyl hydroperoxides decompose too rapidly to account for the length of the induction period and shape of the rate curve in the accelerating periods of the oxidations of ethane and propane[16]. There is a good deal of evidence too, that the aldehydes are formed in parallel with the hydroperoxides throughout the oxidations at intermediate temperatures, and that the relative proportions of hydroperoxides and aldehydes at different temperatures can be accounted for, if both are formed from the peroxy radicals. Thus Semenov and his colleagues[17] postulate that the radical C_3H_7OO* can react bimolecularly with the parent hydrocarbon, or decompose to give aldehydes and alkoxy radicals:

$$C_3H_8 + O_2 \rightarrow C_3H_7^* + HO_2^*$$

$$C_3H_7^* + O_2 \rightarrow C_3H_7OO* \longrightarrow CH_3O* + CH_3CHO \quad \text{or} \quad C_2H_5CHO + CH_2O$$

$$C_3H_8 \searrow$$

$$C_3H_7OOH + C_3H_7^*$$

The alkoxy radicals continue the chain by reacting with the hydrocarbon

$$RO* + C_3H_8 \rightarrow ROH + C_3H_7^*$$

while the aldehydes are oxidized in reactions such as

$$HCHO + O_2 \rightarrow HO_2^* + CHO* \tag{11.1}$$

which yield fresh centres to start new chains.

The rate of formation of the new chains depends upon the concentration of the intermediates, whether these be aldehydes or hydroperoxides, and this in turn depends upon the rate of certain chain steps of the main oxidation. The reactions forming new centres are, therefore, branching reactions, and Semenov and Norrish have preferred the term degenerate branching to auto-catalysis. They are distinguished from normal branching reactions, such as occur in the hydrogen-oxygen reaction

$$H* + O_2 \rightarrow HO* + *O*$$

$$*O* + H \rightarrow OH* + H*$$

because the intermediate which decomposes or is oxidized, does so long after the chain which produced it has ended. Thus the time scale of the acceleration is vastly greater for the hydrocarbon than for the hydrogen oxidation. Nevertheless, there is considerable advantage in treating all these branching reactions in the same formal way.

The true branching reactions in oxidations involve splitting the oxygen molecules directly, instead of the split occurring after a combination. Some of the branching reactions that have been proposed[1] are

(a) in the oxidation of phosphorus

$$P_4O_n^* + O_2 \rightarrow P_4O_{n+1} + *O* \qquad O < n \leqslant 9$$

(b) in the oxidation of sulphur

$$*S* + O_2 \rightarrow *SO* + *O*$$

(c) in the oxidation of hydrogen sulphide

$$HS* + O_2 \rightarrow *SO* + HO*$$

$$*SO* + O_2 \rightarrow SO_2 + *O*$$

In most of these reactions, the radical attaching the oxygen molecule is much more reactive than alkyl radicals. This can be seen from comparison of the two reactions (the heats of formation are from Semenov[1]):

$$H* + O_2 \rightarrow HO* + *O*$$

$$52 \quad 0 \quad \ 8 \quad 59{\cdot}2 \qquad \Delta H_{298} = 15{\cdot}2 \text{ kcal}$$

$$CH_3^* + O_2 \rightarrow CH_3O* + *O*$$

$$31{\cdot}5 \quad 0 \quad -0{\cdot}5 \quad 59{\cdot}2 \qquad \Delta H_{298} = 27{\cdot}2 \text{ kcal}$$

The second reaction will be vastly slower than the first for comparable concentrations and temperature, unless the A factors in the Arrhenius expression are very different. In the oxidation of methane, a much more likely reaction of the methyl radical on energetic grounds is the step

$$CH_3^* + O_2 \rightarrow CH_2O + OH* \qquad (11.2)$$

This is exothermic (37 kcal), but it does involve a four-centre transition complex; perhaps the formation of this is helped by the planar structure of the

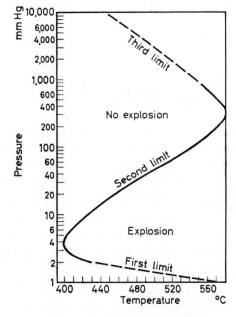

Figure 11.3. Boundary of ignition of mixtures of $2H_2 + O_2$ in a spherical vessel, 7·4 cm diam.[18]

CH_3 radical. If (11.2) occurs, then branching must wait upon further reactions of the formaldehyde molecule, such as (11.1).

The outstanding feature of the true branched-chain reactions is the abrupt way their rates change when comparatively small changes are made in the total pressure or composition or temperature of the reaction mixtures. For example, in the oxidation of hydrogen, ignitions occur to the right of a pressure–temperature boundary such as that shown in *Figure 11.3*[18]. To the left of the peninsula which lies at low pressures and temperatures, the reaction rate is extremely small; it increases sharply as the boundary is approached, and the transition to ignition occurs over small ranges of pressure or temperature. Ignition peninsulae with similar shapes, and rates that change in a similar way as the boundaries are approached, are found with the oxidations of phosphorus, sulphur, H_2S, PH_3, CS_2, CO, CH_4 and silane[19].

Referring again to *Figure 11.3*, ignitions above the high-pressure boundary are not of quite the same type as those in the low-pressure peninsula. They are probably thermal in nature, that is, they occur because the rate of production of heat by the reaction is greater than the rate at which it can be conducted

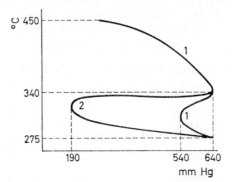

Figure 11.4. Ignition region (1) and cool flame region (2) for $C_3H_8 + O_2$ [2]

away to the surroundings. Below the boundary, the reaction rate is high some considerable distance away, and there is a steady increase in rate as the boundary is approached. Thermal ignitions occur above P, T boundaries of fairly simple shape in the oxidation of all hydrocarbons; in addition, in some oxidations a new phenomenon appears in the form of a 'cool-flame' region[20]. In *Figure 11.4*, boundary 1 encloses the region of thermal ignitions, boundary 2 the cool flames. Within 2, the combustion is incomplete, and several partial ignitions can follow the first. A full explanation of the reactions in this region is not possible at present. One suggestion is that they involve branching reactions between the peroxy radicals RO_2^* and the more stable intermediates, the upper temperature boundary being ascribed to some non-branching reaction of RO* with high activation energy, so that its rate increases more rapidly with temperature than that of the branching reaction. At pressures below the tip of the cool-flame region, the fast reactions show anomalous variation of rate with temperature. There is a region in which the rate actually *decreases* as the temperature rises, as shown in *Figure 11.5* for butane–oxygen mixtures[21]. This behaviour is almost certainly connected with the upper temperature limit of the cool-flame region and may be due to similar competition between branching and non-branching reactions.

This brief survey of some of the main features of auto-oxidation reactions shows the complexity of the reactions involved. Accepting the chain character of these oxidations, it is clear that any substance which can provide free radicals will be a potential catalyst, and any substance that can convert active radicals into inactive radicals or molecules will be a potential inhibitor. However, the variety of reactions possible, involving initiation and termination and interference with the branching reactions, true or degenerate, requires the detailed interpretation of each oxidation and makes generalizations difficult and probably misleading. Studies of the catalysis and inhibition of these oxidations have been directed to practical ends, as in the inhibition of un-wanted oxidation of materials in storage or in use or the catalysis of certain oxidative preparations, or else to the elucidation of kinetic measurements and the evaluation of certain rate constants. Both these aims will be illustrated by examples in the sections which follow.

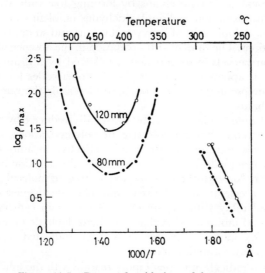

Figure 11.5. Rates of oxidation of butane at different temperatures (total reactant pressure shown)[21]

11.2. LOW-TEMPERATURE AUTO-OXIDATIONS

In this section, the reactions of molecular oxygen with unsaturated hydro-carbons, derivatives of hydrocarbons and some inorganic compounds at temperatures below 200°C will be considered in more detail.

Most of these auto-oxidations involve peroxy-derivatives as intermediates or even as the major product[22]. The primary products of auto-oxidations of mono-olefins, of 1,2- and 1,4-dienes and of hydroaromatic compounds are usually hydroperoxides; 1,3-dienes can form polymeric or intramolecular peroxides, and polynuclear aromatic hydrocarbons also form the latter. Bateman[23] has discussed the yield of hydroperoxides under various conditions. Secondary products such as aldehydes, ketones and acids are also formed even under mild conditions and are the major products in the presence of some catalysts such as heavy metal ions. Bawn[24] and Cooper and Melville[25] have produced evidence of peroxide intermediates in the oxidation of aldehydes. Vartanyan *et al.*[26] have shown that hydroperoxide is the primary product in the oxidation of n-decane at about 140°C, and that the rate of formation of

335

secondary products (alcohol, ketone and acid) is equal to that of decomposition of the hydroperoxide. Similarly, the rates of formation of cyclohexanone and cyclohexanol during the oxidation of liquid cyclohexane are proportional to the rate of decomposition of cyclohexyl hydroperoxide during the same oxidation. Hawkins[27] has discussed the evidence about the points of oxygen attack in alkanes, cycloalkanes, alkylaromatics and the corresponding alkene compounds.

As might be expected for chain reactions with free radicals as chain centres, the auto-oxidation reactions are slow, unless the reactants are photolysed or a catalyst is present to initiate chains by forming free radicals. The effective catalysts for the oxidation of liquid aldehydes or olefins are the peroxides, hydroperoxides, soluble salts of heavy metal ions and so on, that are effective in polymerizations. The rates of auto-oxidation in the absence of catalysts often show induction periods of several hours, followed by a dramatic increase in the rate. This is apparently because the hydroperoxides formed as primary products decompose to give free radicals, so increasing the rate of initiation of the reaction chains.

The rates of auto-oxidation can be drastically reduced by the addition of inhibitors, and those that are effective in polymerizations, such as hydro-quinones, phenols and amines, are usually effective in auto-oxidations. The inhibitors may react with the radicals R*, either by addition or by transfer of a hydrogen atom, or with the hydroperoxides to give molecular products and so prevent the acceleration of the reaction. The effectiveness of an inhibitor can vary considerably with the structure of the chain centres. Thus hydro-quinone is a good inhibitor of oxidation of benzaldehyde or sodium sulphite, but not of the oxidation of oils. Semenov[28] has indicated certain conditions which lead to large inhibition effects:

(1) The chain radicals must react more readily with the inhibitor than with the reactant or with themselves. Thus antioxidants such as di- or tri-hydroxy aromatics or aromatic amines are effective because the radical readily extracts H* from —OH or —NH$_2$. But with very high rates of initiation, in intense light or with powerful catalysts, the inhibitors may appear relatively less effective because of the high rate of radical termination processes.

(2) The products of interaction of inhibitor and radical must be inactive towards the reactant. Thus with a hydrogen-transfer inhibitor AH, the termination process may be either

$$R^* + AH \rightarrow RH + A^*$$

or

$$RO_2^* + AH \rightarrow RO_2H + A^*$$

but in either case it is necessary that the radical A* is either unreactive towards oxygen or, as seems more likely, reacts with oxygen to give a relatively stable radical AO$_2^*$.

(3) The hydrogen-transfer inhibitors are likely to lose a hydrogen atom by dissociation at high temperatures. Thus an inhibitor effective at low temperatures may become a catalyst at higher ones.

The kinetics of the oxidation of liquid olefins have been extensively investigated by Bolland[22] and by Bateman[23], and a good deal of data about the relative effectiveness of various inhibitors and about the velocity constants of elementary reaction steps are known.

Considering first the uninhibited reaction, Bateman *et al.*[29] develop the following reaction scheme to give a general rate equation:

$$\text{Production of R* or RO}_2^* \text{ radicals at rate } r_i \qquad \text{(initation)}$$

$$R* + O_2 \rightarrow RO_2^* \qquad\qquad k_2 \qquad \text{(propagation)}$$

$$RO_2^* + RH \rightarrow RO_2H + R* \qquad k_3$$

$$R* + R* \rightarrow \text{end} \qquad\qquad k_4 \qquad \text{(termination)}$$

$$R* + RO_2^* \rightarrow \text{end} \qquad\qquad k_5$$

$$RO_2^* + RO_2^* \rightarrow \text{end} \qquad\qquad k_6$$

If $r = -(\mathrm{d}[O_2]/\mathrm{d}t)$, and r_∞ is the rate at very high oxygen pressures, then

$$r^{-2} = r_i^{-1}\{k_2^{-2}k_4[O_2]^{-2} + 2k_2^{-1}k_3^{-1}k_5[RH]^{-1}[O_2]^{-1} + k_3^{-2}k_6[RH]^{-2}\} \quad (1)$$

$$r_\infty = r_i^{1/2}k_3k_6^{-1/2}[RH] \qquad (2)$$

and

$$\left\{\left(\frac{r_\infty}{r}\right)^2 - 1\right\}[O_2] = 2\phi k_2^{-1}k_4^{1/2}k_3k_6^{-1/2}[RH] + k_2^{-2}k_4k_3^2k_6^{-1}[RH]^2[O_2]^{-1} \quad (3)$$

where

$$\phi = k_5(k_4k_6)^{-1/2}$$

Experiment shows that eqn. (2) holds for the oxidation of most olefins when the oxygen pressure is above 100 mm, and if experiments are carried out with different olefins, the relative values of the ratios $r_\infty/[RH]$ allow the comparison of $k_3k_6^{-1/2}$. There is reason to believe that most of the variations between the ratios are due to variations in k_3 and so the relative ease of oxidation of various olefins has been estimated. Also, if different catalysts are investigated, eqn. (2) allows a comparison of their efficiencies from the relative rates of initiation, r_i.

Eq. (3) suggests that, at lower pressures of oxygen, a plot of $([(r\infty/r)^2 - 1][O_2]$ against $[O_2]^{-1}$ should be linear. From the slope and intercept of this plot, ϕ and the relative values of $k_2k_4^{-1/2}$ can be obtained, once those of $k_3k_6^{-1/2}$ are known through use of eqn. (2), for different olefins. The values of ϕ are usually between 10 and $\frac{1}{10}$. The drastic assumption that $\phi = 1$ has often been used to simplify eqn. (1); the influence of ϕ on the form of the rate equation has also been discussed by Bateman[23].

It has been found that the catalysts benzoyl peroxide and azoisobutyronitrile give reaction rates which are proportional to the square root of the catalyst concentration, as required by eqn. (1) and (2). In addition, the rate of photolysed oxidations is (in the absence of inhibitors) proportional to the square root of the light intensity, giving further support to eqn. (1) and (2).

In the accelerating portion of an auto-catalysed oxidation in the absence of a catalyst, the amount of hydroperoxide formed is proportional to the extent of reaction, i.e. to the amount of oxygen absorbed. In the light of the behaviour of peroxide catalysts, it might be expected that the rate of auto-oxidation should be proportional to [hydroperoxide]$^{1/2}$ and so to [oxygen absorbed]$^{1/2}$. Instead, the rate is usually found to be a linear function of the oxygen absorbed, as shown in *Figure 11.6.* This suggests that the rate of hydroperoxide decomposition is proportional to [hydroperoxide]^2. However, at very low concentrations the plots of [rate] against [oxygen absorbed] curve towards the origin, as shown in *Figure 11.7*, so that the intercept of *Figure 11.6* is not real. In this region, the rate of auto-oxidation is proportional to [hydroperoxide]$^{1/2}$, and the decomposition is a first-order reaction. It is possible that the decomposition

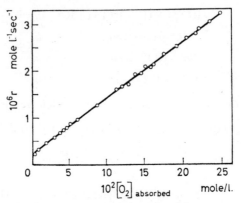

Figure 11.6. Auto-oxidation of cyclohexene at
45°C, 728 mm[23]

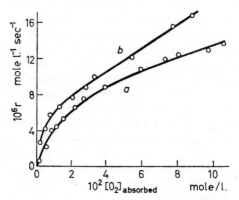

Figure 11.7. Auto-oxidation of (*a*) tetralin at
75°C, 180 mm; (*b*) 1-methylcyclohexene at
65°C and 350 mm; low extents of oxidation[23]

is a unimolecular reaction in both concentration ranges, but in the second-order stage where activation controls the rate of decomposition. If the reactant or solvent is the chief activator at low concentrations, and the hydroperoxide at higher, the rate laws would follow as

hydroperoxide + solvent → RO* + OH* + solvent

hydroperoxide + hydroperoxide → RO* + OH* + hydroperoxide

338

A more likely interpretation, however, is that the hydroperoxide is appreciably dimerized in concentrated solution, and that the monomer and the dimer can decompose independently

$$2\,ROOH \rightleftharpoons (ROOH)_2$$

$$2(RO* + OH*) \qquad RO_2* + H_2O + RO*$$

In the absence of oxygen, the products from decomposition of the dimer would be different from those of the monomer, but this would be difficult to test. There is evidence from infra-red spectroscopy of the existence of dimers in concentrated hydroperoxides[30].

Ions of metals with more than one valency state, such as iron, cobalt, nickel, copper and manganese, are active catalysts for auto-oxidations[27]. The effect of these ions on the oxidation of sodium sulphite has been known for a long time, but investigations of their effect on the oxidation of aldehydes and unsaturated compounds are more recent and have been helped by parallel studies of redox catalysts in polymerization reactions. The catalysts are added to these organic reactants as salts of organic acids like acetates, stearates and naphthenates. Thus cobaltous acetate in acetic acid catalyses the oxidation of benzenaldehyde and of olefins[31], and the stearates of cobalt, iron, copper and manganese catalyse that of liquid alkanes[8,9].

The oxidation of sulphites is probably initiated as follows in the presence of cupric ions[32]:

$$SO_3^{-} + Cu^{2+} \rightarrow *SO_3^{-} + Cu^{+}$$

Several schemes for the propagation steps have been suggested, with the ion radicals SO_3^{-} and SO_5^{-} or the corresponding acid radicals HSO_3 and HSO_5 as chain carriers, e.g.

$$*SO_3^{-} + O_2 \rightarrow *SO_5^{-} \qquad *SO_5^{-} + SO_3^{2-} \rightarrow SO_5^{2-} + *SO_3^{-}$$

followed by

$$SO_5^{2-} + SO_3^{2-} \rightarrow 2SO_4^{2-}$$

The cupric ion is reformed in terminating steps or by direct oxidation.

In detailed studies of the catalysis of the oxidation of benzaldehyde by cobaltous acetate in glacial acetic acid, Bawn[24] showed that the rate of reaction was

$$- \frac{d[O_2]}{dt} = k_6 [C_6H_5 \cdot CHO]^{3/2} [Co(CH_3 \cdot COO)_2]^{1/2}$$

The plot of *Figure 11.8* demonstrates that this rate expression holds. Bawn considers that the oxidation is initiated by the reaction (in which Co^{3+} is used without inferring that the ion is not complexed)

$$C_6H_5 \cdot CHO + Co^{3+} \rightarrow C_6H_5 \cdot CO* + H^{+} + Co^{2+} \qquad (11.3)$$

and propagated by the centres $C_6H_5 \cdot CO*$ and $C_6H_5 \cdot CO \cdot O_2^*$, as in the common pattern of auto-oxidations. The rate of the initiation reaction was measured from that of removal of an added inhibitor, β-naphthol, during the induction period (see *Figure 11.9*) and was found to correspond very closely with the reaction rate (11.3) measured directly in the absence of oxygen. Although, in the oxidation of benzaldehyde, the hydroperoxide formed does not react rapidly with the metal ion, in the catalysed oxidation of many hydrocarbons the hydroperoxides are rapidly attacked by the metal ions in in reactions such as

$$ROOH + Co^{2+} \rightarrow RO* + OH^- + Co^{3+}$$
$$ROOH + Co^{3+} \rightarrow RO_2^* + H^+ + Co^{2+}$$

As a result, the concentration of ROOH rapidly reaches a maximum value, and there is a corresponding maximum in the rate of oxidation of the hydro-

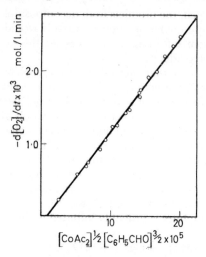

Figure 11.8. Oxidation of benzaldehyde catalysed by cobalt acetate[24]

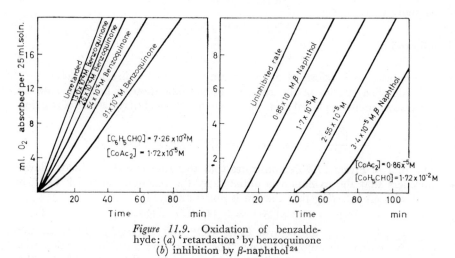

Figure 11.9. Oxidation of benzaldehyde: (*a*) 'retardation' by benzoquinone
(*b*) inhibition by β-naphthol[24]

carbon. Tobolsky, Metz and Mesrobian[33] discussed the kinetics of this maximum rate, using a simple scheme[34] with the usual propagation and termination steps and an initiation step

$$ROOH + Cat \rightarrow X + Y \rightarrow 2R* \qquad \text{(initiate)}$$

340

Under conditions where [RH] changes little, the maximum value of [ROOH] is proportional to $[RH]^2/[catalyst]$, and the maximum rate of oxidation is proportional to $[RH]^2$. In practice, dependence of the rate upon $[hydrocarbon]^2$ is often found, but the dependence upon the catalyst concentration is very variable. Thus Woodward and Mesrobian[35] found the oxidation rate of tetralin at 50°C, with cobaltous acetate, to be proportional to $[tetralin]^2$ and independent of [catalyst]. Bawn and his coworkers found that the rates of oxidation of trimethylethylene and of pentene-2 were dependent upon $[hydrocarbon]^2$ but that the dependence upon the catalyst concentration was different with each hydrocarbon and changed with the concentration. Brook and Matthews[36] determined the oxidation rate of paraffinic lubricating oils, catalysed with low concentrations of copper or iron stearates, as proportional to $[catalyst][O_2]^{1/2}[RH]^2$, but it became independent of the copper concentration at higher concentrations; they point out that a similar limiting rate has been observed for other systems. It is plain that several factors may contribute to the variation of the rate law under different conditions; solvation or complexing of the metal ions, ionization of the hydroperoxides as acids, possible catalysis of some of the steps by acids, and introduction of terminating steps by the metal ions have all been suggested. It may also be that the assumption of stationary-state conditions for the concentration of the hydroperoxide leads to oversimplification of the rate expression. Further experiments are needed before firm generalizations can be made about the behaviour of the metal ion catalysts in auto-oxidations.

The rate of initiation by the catalysts can be measured, as mentioned already for the oxidation of benzaldehyde, by the addition of inhibitors and measurement of their maximum rate of removal. However, assumptions about the number of radicals removed by each molecule of inhibitor have to be made, and perhaps because of this or of reactions similar to transfer reactions in polymerizations, there is disagreement between different investigators about the number of chains started by each molecule of catalyst decomposed.

Bolland and ten Have[37] studied the oxidation of the unsaturated compound ethyl linoleate, catalysed by the decomposition of benzoyl peroxide, in the presence of several inhibitors. They showed that the chain was propagated by the usual steps involving R^* and RO_2^*, and that the uninhibited reaction was terminated by the combination

$$RO_2^* + RO_2^* \rightarrow end \qquad (k_t)$$

and the inhibited by the reaction

$$RO_2^* + AH \rightarrow RO_2H + A \qquad (k'_t)$$

With the usual steady-state assumptions and propagation rate $k_3[RO_2^*][RH]$ the rates of the inhibited reaction, r_I, and of the uninhibited, r_U, are given by

$$r_I = r_i k_3[RH]/k_t[AH]$$
$$r_U^2 = r_i k_3^2[RH]^2/k'_t$$

Hence, by using different inhibitors and comparing the ratios of $r_I[AH]/[RH]$, the relative values of k_t can be determined. As shown in *Table 11.1*, the relative velocity constants for termination change systematically with the oxidation-reduction potential of the system A/AH, i.e. the more easily the hydroquinone is oxidized by the loss of hydrogen, the bigger the velocity constant of termination. This provides strong support for the termination reaction proposed for the inhibited reaction. Assuming that each molecule of hydroquinone reacts with two of the radicals RO_2^*, it was deduced that each

Table 11.1. Relative efficiency of various phenols and hydroquinones in inhibiting the oxidation of ethyl linoleate

Inhibitor	Relative efficiency per —OH group	Oxidation-reduction potential for A/AH V
Phenols		
Resorcinol	0·016	1·179
β-naphthol	0·077	1·153
p-methoxyphenol	0·170	1·984
α-naphthol	0·56	0·933
Pyrogallol	3·00	0·676
Hydroquinones		
Catechol	0·63	0·810
Hydroquinone	1·00	0·715
Toluhydroquinone	1·5	0·653
Trimethylhydroquinone	5·7	0·528
1,4-naphthohydroquinone	(40)	0·482

molecule of benzoyl peroxide starts one chain. However, a later investigation of the efficiency of azoisobutyronitrile in initiating the oxidation of various olefins gives results varying from two to 0·4 chains started per molecule of catalyst decomposed. The value with ethyl linoleate was 1·5. It is clear that the efficiencies of initiation may vary widely from catalyst to catalyst and from reactant to reactant, for reasons not yet obvious.

Hammond and co-workers[38] have suggested that the inhibition of the auto-oxidation of cumene, initiated by azobisisobutyronitrile, occurs by the successive steps

$$RO_2^* + I \rightleftharpoons complex$$

$$complex + RO_2^* \rightarrow inactive\ products$$

In the first place, with many inhibitors the rate of removal of inhibitor is one-half the rate of initiation of chains. The rate laws with *N*-methylaniline and diphenylamine are of the form

$$-\frac{d[O_2]}{dt} = kr_i^{1/2}/[I]^{1/2}$$

and this also indicates that each inhibitor molecule reacts with two peroxy radicals. Lastly, there is evidence of intermediate complexes between inhibitor and peroxy radicals; Walling[4] has discussed the nature of these complexes and the possibility that they occur with monofunctional inhibitors.

When the rate of initiation is high, an inhibitor may be destroyed so rapidly that the rate of oxidation increases noticeably in the course of the reaction, as in the autocatalytic oxidations. A careful study of the rate during this period can lead to the determination of the rate of initiation. Cooper and Melville[25] studied the rate of oxidation of n-decanal, inhibited by hydroquinone, in this way. They produced evidence that the hydroquinone was converted to quinone by reaction with the peroxy chain carriers, and proposed the reaction scheme

Initiation: $\qquad$ $R \cdot CHO + O_2 \rightarrow R \cdot CO^* + HO_2^*$ $\qquad$ (r_i)

Propagation: $\qquad$ $R \cdot CO^* + O_2 \rightarrow R \cdot CO \cdot O_2^*$ $\qquad$ (k_2)

$\qquad$ $R \cdot CO \cdot O_2^* + R \cdot CHO \rightarrow R \cdot CO \cdot O_2H + R \cdot CO^*$ $\qquad$ (k_3)

Termination: $\qquad$ $R \cdot CO \cdot O_2^* + QH_2 \rightarrow R \cdot CO \cdot O_2H + QH^*$ $\qquad$ (k_4)

$$\tfrac{1}{2}Q + \tfrac{1}{2}QH_2 \quad \overset{rapid}{\nwarrow}$$

Thus

$$-\frac{d[QH_2]}{dt} = \tfrac{1}{2}r_i \quad \text{and} \quad [QH_2]_t = [QH_2]_0 - {}^{1/2}r_i t$$

Also the rate of oxidation

$$r = \frac{r_i \cdot k_3 \cdot [R \cdot CHO]}{k_4 [QH]}$$

$$\frac{1}{r} = \frac{k_4}{k_3 [R \cdot CHO]} \left\{ \frac{[QH_2]_0}{r_i} - \frac{t}{2} \right\}$$

Figure 11.10, in which $1/r$ is plotted against t, shows that such an equation holds. From the slope and intercept, and the known value of $[QH_2]_0$, r_i can be calculated.

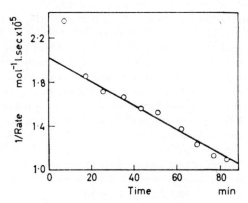

Figure 11.10. Removal of inhibitor in the oxidation of n-decanal[25]

There have not been many applications of these methods of comparing the efficiency of different catalysts for auto-oxidation reactions. It is unlikely that all the methods can be applied to all the oxidations, but very desirable that as many as possible should be applied to each oxidation as a check on the assumptions made in developing the reaction schemes.

The preparation of hydroperoxides and peroxides has been fully discussed by Hawkins[3]. The commercial preparation of cumene hydroperoxide and its utilization in further preparations offer some interesting examples of catalysed reactions. Cumene is prepared by that of propylene with benzene in the liquid or vapour phases; the catalysts used are acids or Friedel–Crafts catalysts such as BF_3. Oxidation of the cumene is carried out in emulsion or in solution at about 90 °C, in the presence of metal salts or mild alkalis, using low conversions to minimize decomposition of the product. Besides being used as a catalyst for polymerizations, cumene hydroperoxide is useful as an intermediate in the production of phenol and acetone. It decomposed readily in the presence of acid catalysts in aqueous or anhydrous solution, and both mineral and organic acids and metal salts (as discussed in section 3.8) are used.

Another important method of preparing hydroperoxides was found by Rust and Vaughan[39]. Hydrogen bromide acts as a catalyst for the auto-oxidation of the lower hydrocarbons in the gas phase at low temperatures. For example, isobutane is oxidized at 150 to 200 °C to give principally t-butyl hydroperoxide with small proportions of t-butyl alcohol and di-t-butyl peroxide. It has been suggested that the catalyst takes part in the propagation steps of a chain reaction

$$HBr + (CH_3)_3CO_2^* \rightarrow (CH_3)_3COOH + Br^*$$
$$Br^* + (CH_3)_3CH \rightarrow (CH_3)_3C^* + HBr$$
$$(CH_3)_3C^* + O_2 \rightarrow (CH_3)_3CO_2^*$$

Hydrogen bromide also catalyses other auto-oxidations, such as those of the side chains of alkylbenzenes to give ketones, acids or phenols.

11.3.   OXIDATION OF GASEOUS HYDROCARBONS

11.3.1.   Methane

The oxidation of the simplest hydrocarbon, methane, is of interest because the kinetics of the reaction have been studied extensively, and there is general agreement that formaldehyde is the intermediate responsible for autocatalysis or degenerate branching at high temperatures. Several rival kinetic schemes have been proposed which can explain the experimental results, however.

Following the discovery of Bone and Gardner[11] that formaldehyde is formed during the oxidation, its role has been established by Norrish and Foord[12]. In particular, they showed that formaldehyde reaches a maximum concentration when the rate of the methane oxidation is fastest, and that addition of this concentration to the original mixture eliminates the induction period, without altering the maximum rate of methane oxidation. Lower concentrations shortened the induction period but resulted in the same maximum rate. With greater concentrations, an enhanced initial rate was observed as soon as the mixture entered the vessel, but the rate soon fell to the steady 'maximum' rate observed after induction periods. In addition, photolysing the mixtures with wavelengths absorbed by formaldehyde (but not by methyl hydroperoxide†)

† Fok and Nalbandjan[7] isolated methyl hydroperoxide from the products of the photo-chemical oxidation at low temperatures. The propagation step (1) of the scheme which follows can be split into two stages

$$CH_3^* + O_2 \rightarrow CH_3O_2^* \qquad (1a)$$
$$CH_3O_2^* \rightarrow CH_2 + OH^* \qquad (1b)$$

but Semenov and Norrish have argued that (1b) is so fast that no other reaction is likely to occur.

led to a shortening of the induction period and an increased maximum rate[14]. It seems certain therefore that formaldehyde is the intermediate responsible for branching.

This view has been strikingly confirmed by quantitative treatment of the auto-catalysis by Karmilova, Enikolopyan and Nalbandjan[13] and by Enikolopyan[14]. They showed that acceleration followed the law

$$\text{rate} = ae^{\phi t}$$

established by Semenov for branching reactions. From their reaction scheme, assuming formaldehyde was the branching agent, they were able to predict a and ϕ and obtained predicted rate *versus* time curves which fitted the experimental results remarkably well. *Figure 11.11* shows the predicted curves for the consumption of methane (full line) and experimental points in the mixtures initially containing 0, 0·5, 1·0 and 12·6 per cent formaldehyde, at $T = 423°C$ and $p_{CH_4} = p_{O_2} = 118$ min. *Figure 11.12* shows how the relative concentrations of formaldehyde change for the same mixtures, the points

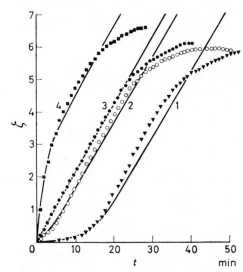

Figure 11.11. Oxidation of methane[2,14]

Points, experimental; lines, prediction

again being experimental and the lines predicted results (using one experimental point (not shown) to calibrate the predicted lines). They found the maximum rate to be given by

$$-\left(\frac{d[CH_4]}{dt}\right)_{max} = \frac{2k_2k_3}{k_6}\left(\frac{k_2k_5}{k_2'k_5'}\right)^{1/2}[CH_4]^2[O_2]$$

and the maximum formaldehyde concentration by

$$[CH_2O]_{max} = \left(\frac{k_2k_5}{k_2'k_5'}\right)^{1/2}[CH_4]$$

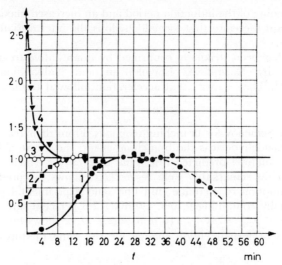

Figure 11.12. Calculated and experimental relative concentrations of formaldehyde during oxidation of methane[2,14]

The velocity constants refer to the reaction scheme (here slightly rearranged)

$$CH_4+O_2 \rightarrow CH_3^*+HO_2^* \qquad (0) \qquad \text{initiation}$$

$$CH_3^*+O_2 \rightarrow CH_2O+OH^* \qquad (1)$$
$$OH^*+CH_4 \rightarrow CH_3^*+H_2O \qquad (2)$$
propagation of main reaction

$$O_2+CH_2O \rightarrow HCO^*+HO_2^* \qquad (3) \qquad \text{branching reaction} \qquad (11.4)$$

$$HCO^*+O_2 \rightarrow CO+HO_2^* \qquad (4)$$
$$HO_2^*+CH_2O \rightarrow H_2O_2+HCO^* \qquad (5')$$
propagation of formaldehyde oxidation

$$HO_2^*+CH_4 \rightarrow CH_3^*+H_2O_2 \qquad (5) \qquad \text{induced oxidation of methane}$$

$$OH^*+CH_2O \rightarrow HCO^*+H_2O^* \qquad (2') \qquad \text{induced oxidation of formaldehyde}$$

$$OH^*+wall \rightarrow end \qquad (6) \qquad \text{termination}$$

The scheme proposed by Norrish[40] differs considerably from the above in the initiation and branching reactions. He considers that the degenerate branching steps at lower temperatures are

$$CH_2O+O_2 \rightarrow H_2CO_2+{}^*O^* \qquad (11.5)$$
$$^*O^*+CH_4 \rightarrow CH_3^*+OH^* \qquad (11.6)$$

and that the initiation consists of

$$CH_4+O_2 \rightarrow CH_2O+H_2O$$

346

followed by (11.5) and 11.6). At high temperatures, he thinks that reaction (11.4) may occur. Hoare and Walsh [41,42] have examined the effect of surfaces on the rate of methane oxidation at about 500°C and suggest that the reactions of HO_2^* and H_2O_2 at the surface are important. On acid surfaces (e.g. silica with coatings of boric, silicic or phosphoric acids or TiO_2) they consider that $2H_2^* \xrightarrow{H^*} H_2O_2 + O_2$, while on many oxide surfaces, HO_2^* and H_2O_2 form water and oxygen. Thus the oxide surfaces slow the rate more markedly than the acid surfaces, and with them the effects of inert gases on the rate of oxidation are more marked because the gases hinder diffusion to the wall.

The addition of traces of other substances can accelerate oxidation. The action of oxides of nitrogen was studied by Bone and Gardner [11] and by Norrish and Wallace [43], and interest has been revived because the catalysis by these compounds is useful in the preparation of formaldehyde from methane. A detailed study by Karmilova, Enikolopyan and Nalbandjan [44] is interesting in relation to degenerate branching. They paid special attention to the rate of formation of formaldehyde in the oxidation in a flow system at 600° to 700°C, with 0·02 to 2 per cent nitric oxide as catalyst. Interpreting the growth

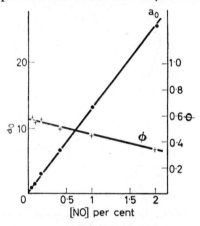

Figure 11.13. Effect of NO on production of formaldehyde from methane [44]

of formaldehyde as a branching reaction and treating formaldehyde as a chain centre, they assume

$$\frac{d[CH_2O]}{dt} = a_0 + \phi[CH_2O]$$

and hence

$$[CH_2O] = \frac{a_0}{\phi}(e^{\phi t} - 1)$$

They found $\phi \propto [O_2]$ and $a_0 \propto [O_2]$; ϕ decreases as [NO] increases, but a_0 increases linearly with [NO], as shown in *Figure 11.13*. They propose as initiating steps

$$\left. \begin{array}{l} NO + O_2 \rightarrow NO_2 + {}^*O^* \\ {}^*O^* + CH_4 \rightarrow CH_3^* + OH^* \end{array} \right\}$$

347

and as a branching step the reaction between CH_2O and O_2, which may be the same as (11.4). They also assume that NO can inactivate an intermediate radical (CH_3^* or $CH_3O_2^*$). They then derive

$$a_0 \propto [O_2][NO]/\{1+b[NO]\} \quad \text{and} \quad \phi \propto [O_2]/\{1+b[NO]\}$$

Many other studies of similar systems have been published [45].

At certain concentrations and temperatures, the $CH_4 + O_2$ system can ignite spontaneously. No regions of cool flames have been observed, however, but the P,T boundary of the ignitions shows a small low-pressure peninsula in oxygen-rich mixtures [46]. The ignitions are probably chain-thermal in origin; the peninsula may bound ignitions of CO. The addition of traces of nitrogen dioxide, nitric oxide, nitrosyl chloride or chlorine [47] lowers the P,T boundary, as shown in *Figure 11.14*, but little is known of the reactions involved.

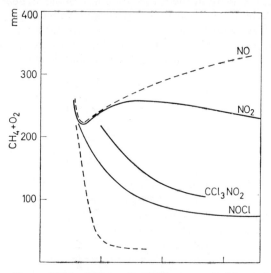

Figure 11.14. Effect of additives on ignition of $CH_4 + O_2$ at 490°C [47]

—— additives premixed - - - NO (upper) and NOCl (lower) placed in reaction vessel before admitting reactants

The oxidation of methane, like that of other hydrocarbons, is inhibited by lead tetraethyl. Hoare and Walsh [42] examined the inhibition of the slow reaction and concluded that it was due to reactions of chain centres with the surface of solid PbO particles formed as a fog by the oxidation of the lead tetraethyl. The relation of this behaviour to the phenomenon of knock in engines and the behaviour of metallic anti-knocks has been reviewed by Walsh and his collaborators [48,49].

11.3.2. *Ethane, propane and butane*

Some features of the oxidation of ethane, propane and butane have been mentioned earlier in this chapter. The only aspect of the mechanisms which will be discussed here is the acceleration of the rate of oxidation due to degenerate branching. The oxidations between 250 and 500°C proceed with a pressure rise which is a convenient measure of the extent of reaction, being approximately twice the pressure of oxygen consumed. Thus the equation (9.11, p. 265) becomes

$$\Delta p = \frac{A'}{\phi^2}\, e^{\phi t}$$

so that

$$\frac{d\Delta p}{dt} = \frac{A'}{\phi}\, e^{\phi t} = \phi \Delta p$$

Thus ϕ can be obtained by plotting $(d\Delta p)/(dt)$ against Δp. Knox[16] has used this method to relate ϕ to reactant concentrations and so to test reaction mechanisms. A typical plot obtained during the oxidation of propane is shown in *Figure 11.15*. It will be noticed that ϕ increases considerably during the acceleration until it reaches a constant value; Knox considers that this occurs

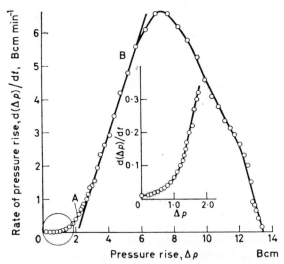

Figure 11.15. Rate against pressure rise in propane oxidation at 318°C[16]

Inset: enlargement of circled part of curve [1 Bourdon cm (Bcm)=0·215 cm Hg]

because (a) the branching intermediate, or its precursor, are destroyed at the walls in the early stages, but the walls become 'poisoned' as the reaction proceeds, and (b) some of the intermediates (such as propylene in the oxidation of propane) provide branching intermediates more readily than do the original hydrocarbons. He also shows that his reaction mechanism is consistent with the experimental finding that ϕ is a linear function of the hydrocarbon concentration (*Figure 11.16*). From these plots, it is possible to derive the 'lifetime' of the intermediate causing branching and the net number of branches per chain for each reaction under the conditions of the experiments. Knox showed that the lifetime is the reciprocal of the intercept of the line on the ϕ axis; it can be seen to be about 110 sec for ethane and 65 sec for propane at 318°C.

Knox has used this information to show that the intermediate is not likely to be an organic peroxide or hydroperoxide, at temperatures above 300°C. As shown in *Table 9.1*, taken from his work with Kirk[15], the hydroperoxides decompose far too quickly at such temperatures, their lifetimes at 318° being a few seconds. However, at lower temperatures, it is clearly possible for them to become effective branching agents. The dialkyl peroxides decompose even more rapidly than the hydroperoxides; from the figures in *Table 9.1* it can be shown that the lifetime of di-n-propyl peroxide is about 10^{-2} sec at 318°C.

This seems very strong support for the view held by Semenov and by Norrish that the intermediates responsible for degenerate branching, and hence for the slow auto-catalysis in the oxidation of hydrocarbons at temperatures

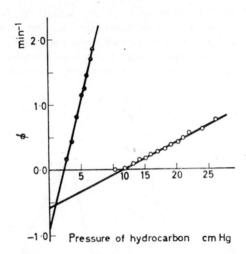

Figure 11.16. The acceleration constant, ϕ, in the oxidation of propane (○) and ethane (●) at 318°C[16]

above 300°C, are not organic hydroperoxides or peroxides but some more stable compounds such as aldehydes. However, there is also a strong possibility that hydrogen peroxide may play some part[49]; as indicated earlier, it has been detected in the oxidations, and it is rather surprisingly stable in the vapour phase in the absence of surfaces[50].

11.3.3. Higher hydrocarbons

With the higher hydrocarbons the number of intermediates is very large. Various schemes of degradative oxidation have been proposed from time to time[20], based on the formation of alcohols or aldehydes or, more recently, of alkoxy radicals. There is more similarity between the low- and high-temperature oxidations for the higher hydrocarbons than for the lower members of any series. In the low-temperature oxidations of the higher members, experiments with isotopically labelled ^{14}C molecules[51] have shown that all carbons are attacked by oxygen, although with different velocities, the order of reactivity being tertiary > secondary > primary[52]. As explained before, the attack produces peroxy radicals, which form hydroperoxides. These decompose to alkoxy or similar radicals. It is possible that the high-temperature oxidation starts in the same way. Thus iso-octane, $Me_3C \cdot CH_2 \cdot CHMe_2$, may form the radical $Me_3C \cdot CH_2 \cdot CMe_2O$, and this decomposes to acetone and the radical $Me_3C \cdot CH_2$ which in turn forms an alkoxyl radical, to continue the degradative oxidation–decomposition process.

Investigations of the rate of oxidation of the higher hydrocarbons have naturally been linked with their value as fuels in internal combustion engines or at burners. Kinetic studies of the slow oxidations led to the recognition of 'cool flames' which are luminous (owing to the fluorescence of excited H_2CO molecules) but do not consume much of the reactant mixture. Most aliphatic hydrocarbons above C_2, and their derivatives, show this phenomenon, and the region of temperature and pressure in which it occurs is not very different for different hydrocarbons of the same type, as shown by *Figure 11.17* and

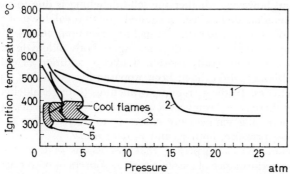

Figure 11.17. Cool flame regions for paraffin–air mixtures[53]
1 13 per cent methane; 2 10 per cent ethane; 3 5 per cent propane;
4 3·8 per cent n-butane; 5 2·7 per cent n-hexane

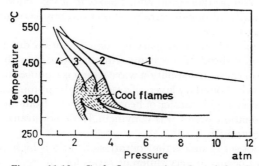

Figure 11.18. Cool flame region for olefin–air mixtures[54]
1 6 per cent ethylene; 2 4·5 per cent propylene; 3 3·6 per cent butylene; 4 2 per cent α-amylene

11.18. At higher pressures and temperatures, true ignitions occur, with considerable heat evolution. These hot ignitions are often preceded by cool flames, and investigation of the pressure rise or product formation before ignition shows two distinct auto-catalysis processes with distinct induction periods τ_1 and τ_2. During τ_1, peroxides and aldehydes build up and the rate increases auto-catalytically until a cool flame passes; pressure and aldehyde concentration are scarcely affected by this, but peroxide concentration falls considerably. As the second stage begins, the aldehyde concentration rises and the overall rate of oxidation increases auto-catalytically, until after the induction period τ_2 a violent explosion occurs. Outside the regions of ignition, the slow reactions

351

can show similar phases, the characteristics being more pronouncedly like the τ_1 regime at lower temperatures. Within the cool flame region, several cool flames may occur.

There is no satisfactory general mechanism which explains the facts known about the two-stage ignition. Although other views have been expressed, it is widely accepted[20,55] that the cool flames are near-isothermal ignitions due to branching of chains, for example by the reaction between intermediate peroxides and aldehydes

$$RO_2 + CH_3 \cdot CHO \rightarrow RO^* + CH_3CO^* + OH^*$$

It is uncertain, however, whether the self-quenching is due to some reaction product—formaldehyde has been suggested—or to breakdown of e.g. the RO_2 radical, before it can enter the branching reaction, to give less reactive products. The τ_1 regime thus depends upon both aldehyde and peroxide concentrations. It is generally shortened by the addition of either of these substances, although there have been apparently conflicting reports of the effect of aldehydes. In the τ_2 regime, branching through aldehydes is widely accepted, but there have been very few quantitative treatments. It is generally found that increasing temperature causes τ_1 to decrease but τ_2 to increase; with increasing pressure, both τ_1 and τ_2 decrease.

It is therefore hardly surprising that discussions of the reactions which determine the performance of gasoline fuels as sources of power are speculative rather than quantitative. Attention has concentrated on eliminating the undesirable features of the oxidations, such as knock in the internal combustion engines of high compression ratio and, thanks to a vast effort, this has been achieved empirically, although certain rationalizations were made at an early stage of the investigations.

The phenomenon of knock in spark ignition engines is due to auto-ignition of the unburnt gas ahead of the flame front moving from the spark source. This auto-ignition causes a detonation wave which is troublesome mechanically and also disturbs the boundary layers of gases near the piston head and cylinder walls, allowing very rapid transfer of heat to the metal from the hot gases. The presence of detonation waves was convincingly demonstrated by high-speed schlieren photography[56].

Knock does not set in unless the compression ratio is high, and for a given engine, the onset occurs at very different ratios for different fuels. It requires a very high ratio for the simpler hydrocarbons, for aromatics and for some naphthenes. With higher paraffin, it requires a higher ratio for the more branched isomers.

When knocking occurs, formaldehyde can be detected in the non-burning charge which is about to ignite. It can be found under non-knocking conditions, but knocking has not been observed without formaldehyde being present in experiments designed for this purpose. Formaldehyde has also been observed under conditions where knock has been suppressed by adding lead tetraethyl.

Knock can be lessened by engine design: a short travel for the flame is helpful, for this gives less time for auto-ignition to occur. With modern engines, the pressure and temperature lead to induction periods which are very short, around 1 msec.

Knock can also be lessened by certain additives and increased by other additives. It is reasonably well established that the harmful additives, such as organic peroxides or nitrites, ethers or higher aldehydes, shorten the induction period $\tau_1 + \tau_2$ in the reaction under milder conditions; and conversely, additives such as amines and some metallic compounds which lengthen the induction period, are effective as antiknocks[57]. Rogener[58] found that lead tetraethyl increased the induction period τ_2 but had little effect on τ_1 when various fuel–air mixtures were rapidly compressed to high pressures and temperatures.

It is interesting that the list of effective antiknocks known today is almost the same in extent and order as that assembled by Calingaert in 1938[59]. Only two other substances have proved effective, ferrocene and methyl cyclopentadienyl manganese tricarbonyl. In Calingaert's list, the most effective antiknocks were lead tetraethyl, iron carbonyl, nickel carbonyl, diethyl telluride and bismuth triethyl; of these, only lead tetraethyl has been extensively used, partly because it is far more effective than the other compounds and partly because its combustion products have less deleterious effects on the engine.

It was shown quite early that the metal alkyls are effective because of the metal, and only those metals that are easily oxidized are effective[60]. Egerton[61] also considered that the metal must be molecularly dispersed in the reaction mixture.

Another view, that the metals or their oxides are present as colloidal particles which act as heterogeneous inhibitors, advanced by Muraour[62], has been revived by Walsh and his collaborators[48,49]. Their views are based in part on experiments on the effects of lead tetraethyl on the slow oxidations of ether and of methane, and in part on direct observations on engines. They believe that the occurrence of fogs of metal oxide particles in each case, coupled with the observed inhibitory effect of oxide surfaces on the kinetics of the slow oxidations, indicate that the antiknock acts through surface reactions of radicals, such as HO_2^*, and other intermediates of the oxidation, such as H_2O_2.

On the other hand, Norrish and his collaborators[63,64] believe that Egerton's view is correct, i.e. the antiknocks are molecularly dispersed. This belief is based on a study by kinetic spectroscopy of ignition in mixtures of oxygen, heptane and amyl nitrite (which acts as a photo-initiator). The effective antiknocks delay the onset of ignition, as found under engine conditions. Smokes are sometimes formed, but there is no correlation between smoke formation and antiknock properties; in particular, lead tetraethyl does not produce a smoke, but the spectra of Pb and PbO were observed during the induction periods. In addition, they argue, the amount of lead dispersed under engine conditions gives insufficient surface area for effective inhibition, unless the particles are exceedingly small (about 10 Å diam.), and such particles would rapidly evaporate under these conditions of temperature (800–1,000 °C), whether they consist of Pb or PbO.

It is clear that the evidence for each of these views is drawn in part from experimental conditions which are not those of the engine cylinder. This evidence cannot be ignored; it is useful and indicative, provided that trends due to the effect of temperature and pressure changes are not ignored. But the nearer experimental conditions approach actual engine conditions the better. In this connection, it would appear that quantitative studies of the rate of formation and rate of evaporation of colloidal smokes of Pb and PbO, in relation to the actual ignition delays, would be very useful. Some calculations of these rates have recently been published [65].

11.4. SENSITIZED IGNITIONS OF HYDROGEN AND OXYGEN

Some interesting examples of catalysis and inhibition have been found to occur with the thermal reaction between hydrogen and oxygen. The homogeneous reaction is extremely slow at temperatures below 400°C, although heterogeneous reaction occurs on many surfaces at lower temperatures. Not far above 400°C, however, abrupt changes from slow reaction to ignitions have been found when slight changes are made in the temperature or pressure of suitable mixtures of hydrogen and oxygen, and there is a sharp boundary separating regions of slow reaction and ignition. This boundary, shown as a log P,T plot in *Figure 11.3*, consists of a low-pressure, low-temperature region bounded by the first and second pressure limits of ignition and another ignition region above a third pressure limit. The boundary varies somewhat in position with the size of the vessel and its shape, the nature of its walls and the composition of the gas mixture [18]. There is evidence that the reactions leading to ignition within the low-pressure low-temperature region are branched-chain reactions. In the first place, slow reactions and ignitions near the lower or first pressure boundary of ignition occur at the end of a short induction period, lasting a few tenths of a second, and the pressure change (which is proportional to the extent of reaction) increases exponentially at the end of the induction period [59]. As explained in section 9.4, this is characteristic of a branched-chain reaction. If the net branching factor is ϕ, then the pressure change is connected with time by the equations

$$\frac{d\Delta p}{dt} = \phi\Delta p \quad \text{and} \quad \ln \Delta p = \phi t + \text{constant}$$

The plots [67] in *Figure 11.19(a)* and *11.19(b)* show the ways in which p and $d\Delta p/dt$ vary with time during the induction periods, while those in *11.19(c)* show that $\ln \Delta p$ is a linear function of time during the period of acceleration. From these plots, ϕ can be determined, as was done for the auto-catalysis in the oxidation of hydrocarbons (p. 349).

Moreover, assuming that ignition occurs whenever $\phi > 0$, and selecting suitable reactions for branching and termination of chains, excellent descriptions of the first and second boundaries of ignition were obtained [18,68]. Thus the positive branching reaction is believed to be

$$H^* + O_2 \rightarrow OH^* + {}^*O^* \tag{11.7}$$

and the termination reaction at low pressures (where diffusion to the walls is fast) is

$$H^* \text{ or } OH^* + \text{wall} \rightarrow \text{end chains}$$

At high pressures, near the second boundary, the chain centres are removed as the relatively inert HO_2 formed in the reaction

$$H^* + O_2 + M \rightarrow HO_2^* + M \tag{11.8}$$

This reaction competes more effectively with reaction (11.7) at lower temperatures, as (11.7) has an activation energy of 15 to 17 kcal mole. Thus the second boundary falls as the temperature is lowered (*Figure 11.3*). A great deal of work has been done to check this basic scheme. Broadly speaking, it appears correct, and with the addition of certain reactions concerned with the fate of the

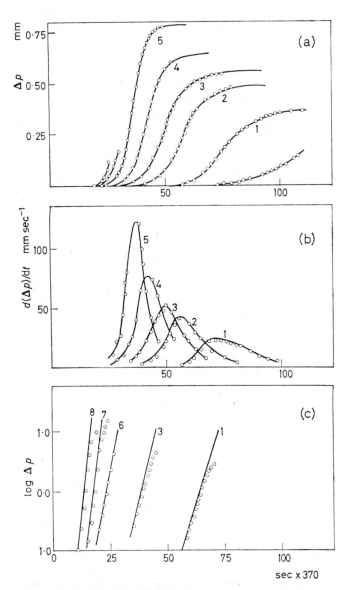

Figure 11.19. Exponential increase in pressure in low-pressure explosions of hydrogen–oxygen mixtures[67]
(*a*) and (*b*), 1–5: initial pressures, 6·1, 6·4, 6·8, 7·1, 7·5 mm; 485°C (*c*) 1,3,6 485°C; 7,8 520°C

HO_2^* radical and the proved existence of H_2O_2 in mixtures just above the second boundary[69], almost all the experimental details can be explained by it.

Evidently the walls are effective inhibitors of the reaction. The rate of the termination reaction can be controlled by diffusion or by the actual reaction with the wall. If the efficiency of reaction with the wall is very low (say only one collision in a thousand), branching will soon outstrip termination, and ignition occurs at low pressures. Thus in vessels of quartz or Pyrex (especially if coated with KCl or treated with HF) the limit is a few tenths of a mm Hg in vessels of 5 cm diam. for temperatures between 430 and 520°C. The limit P_1 is inversely proportional to the diameter and varies with temperature according to $P_1 \propto \exp(E_1/RT)$. With metal vessels, or some quartz vessels, lower limits are at pressures of 10 to 15 mm; the efficiency of reaction with the wall is high (say more than one in every hundred collisions) and the rate is controlled by diffusion to the wall. The addition of inert gas now slows the diffusion and so lowers the limit, whereas in vessels where the efficiency of the walls is low, addition of inert gases has little effect on the limit.

The second boundary is also altered by the nature of the wall, but to a minor degree. The effect of different gases as M in reaction (11.8) is very marked, however. Gases such as water vapour are more effective than hydrogen or oxygen, so the reaction is auto-inhibited, and the limit is lowered by added water vapour as well as by CO_2 and N_2O. Iodine also lowers the limit, not through reaction (11.8) but by removing hydrogen atoms to give inactive iodine atoms

$$H + I_2 \rightarrow HI + I$$

Hydrocarbons rather unexpectedly lower the second limit of ignition. Levy[70] and Baldwin and co-workers[71] have shown that the simple paraffins can all suppress the ignitions, although there are striking differences from one to another. With increasing pressures of ethane or propane the limit falls almost linearly. The rate of fall is different with different proportions of the reactants but does not change much with the vessel diameter nor with changes in the material of the walls. Baldwin et al. concluded that the ethane is itself the inhibitor and competes with the oxygen for hydrogen atoms

$$H + C_2H_6 \rightarrow H_2 + C_2H_5$$

the ethyl radicals reacting with oxygen to give 'inactive' HO_2

$$C_2H_5 + O_2 \rightarrow C_2H_4 + HO_2$$

The effect is the catalysis of the termination reaction (11.8) at the expense of the branching reaction (11.7). Propane probably behaves in a similar way.

Methane acts in a very different way, however. The limit is lowered slightly, and almost linearly, as the mole fraction of methane is increased, until at a critical fraction ignitions are suddenly suppressed. In addition, there is a pronounced effect of vessel diameter, though not of vessel surface, upon the critical fraction. Baldwin and co-workers[72] concluded that methane is not the cause of the abrupt suppression, but that this is due to the intermediate oxidation product, formaldehyde. They consider that, for each mixture, the hydrogen atom concentration passes through a maximum before the formaldehyde concentration reaches a steady state; if this maximum is high enough, a branched-chain thermal ignition occurs, but if it is too low, a short burst of reaction suppressed by further formation of formaldehyde. Thus the condition for ignition has some 'thermal' element and shows a dependence on vessel diameter. A similar condition is found in some sensitized ignitions.

Oxygen or hydrogen atoms injected into the hydrogen+oxygen mixtures widen the boundaries of explosion considerably. Other additives can have the same effect and have been called *sensitizers* of the reaction. NO_2, NOCl, N_2O, NH_3, C_2N_2, NO and Cl_2 have been found effective. The most thoroughly investigated[73] sensitizers are NO_2 and NOCl. When suitable pressures of the hydrogen and oxygen are mixed with traces of NO_2 and run into a heated vessel at 350–450°C, ignition occurs if the sensitizer pressures lie between a lower and an upper limit. In effect, the boundary of the unsensitized ignitions

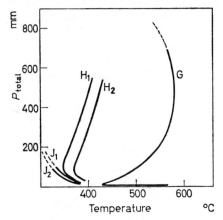

Figure 11.20.   Effect of NO_2 and NO on the ignition region of hydrogen–oxygen mixtures

is moved to the left, as shown schematically in *Figure 11.20*, from G to H, by addition of small proportions of NO_2, but retreats to the right with higher proportions. A mixture of $2H_2+O_2$ at 100 mm and 380°C will not react in the absence of NO_2, will ignite with 1 per cent of NO_2 but will react only very slowly with 2 per cent or more of it.

There is an induction period in which no pressure change occurs before slow reaction or ignition, and the induction periods change smoothly across the limits of ignition. They may be very short (for example at high hydrogen pressures or at higher temperatures) or, under other conditions, can last several tens of seconds. The variation of the sensitizer limits and of the induction periods with temperature, total pressure of reactants, addition of inert gases and the diameter of the vessel were thoroughly investigated between 1933 and 1940; this work has been reviewed by Dainton and Norrish[73]. During this period, attempts were made to explain these variations in terms of a net branching factor ϕ, characteristic of the initial composition and constant during the induction period. The sensitizer limits of ignition were supposed to correspond to some critical value of ϕ, just as the boundaries of the unsensitized ignition correspond to $\phi \geqslant 0$. The induction periods were then taken as the times for the concentration [X] of chain centres to reach a critical value $[X]_c$. From eqn. 9.8, it can then be shown that if ϕ is constant

$$\tau = \frac{1}{\phi} \ln \left(1 + \frac{\phi}{I}[X]_c \right)$$

It was hoped to relate ϕ to changes in the composition of mixtures, etc. by measurements of τ. However, for a variety of reasons which have been outlined elsewhere, this theory has been abandoned, and it is now believed that ϕ varies continuously throughout the induction period[74,75]. Initially, the NO_2 or $NOCl$ function as chain terminators, removing chain centres. As long as they are present in moderate concentrations, ϕ has large negative values, i.e. the reaction is not branched. Recent photometric studies of $H_2 + O_2 + NO$ mixtures[75-77] have amply confirmed that NO_2 is removed during the induction periods, and the lengths of these have been predicted for mixtures in which the rate law of the reaction between NO_2 and H_2 is known. These studies have also shown that the rate of removal of NO_2 accelerates markedly at the end of the induction period. With mixtures between, or close to, the sensitizer limits, a pressure pulse begins just *after* this acceleration, followed a little later by the fall of pressure associated with the slow reaction between hydrogen and oxygen or the sharp pressure drop after ignition. *Figure 11.21* shows[77] the accelerated removal of NO_2 (wide trace) and the pressure pulse (narrow trace) at the end of the induction periods, shown as oscilloscope traces. The upper curves show the end of the induction period before slow reaction, the lower before ignition.

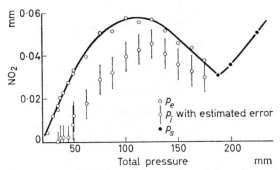

Figure 11.22. Variation of p_e, p_i and p_s with total pressure[76]

The pressure, p_e, of NO_2 at the end of the induction periods varies with the composition of the initial mixtures. As the initial concentration of nitrogen dioxide is increased, p_e rises sharply to a maximum within the ignition boundary and then falls as the upper limit of ignition is approached. The pressures, p_i, of nitrogen dioxide at the onset of ignition, after the accelerated removal, vary in a manner similar to p_e, always lying below p_e.

At pressures well above the sensitizer limit, the pressure of nitrogen dioxide falls to a stationary level, p_s, probably because the rate of removal of NO_2 by the reaction with H_2 is balanced by its formation in the termolecular reaction $2NO + O_2 \rightarrow 2NO_2$. There is thus a slow catalysed reaction between oxygen and hydrogen, with NO and NO_2 as intermediates[74,77]. Near the upper limit, however, other reactions appear to assist in the formation of NO_2, so raising

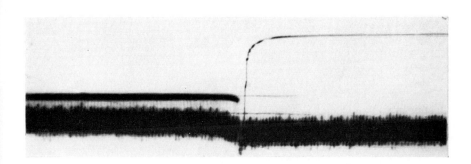

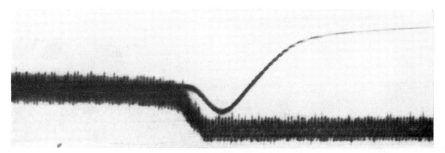

Figure 11.21. End of induction periods in NO₂-sensitized hydrogen–oxygen mix-tures[70]

Upper figure, before slow reaction; lower, before ignition. Wide trace: removal of NO₂; narrow trace: pressure

the value of p_s above the level expected from the balance of the reactions

$$NO + \tfrac{1}{2}O_2 \rightarrow NO_2$$
$$NO_2 + H_2 \rightarrow H_2O + NO$$

The upper sensitizer limit is almost certainly due to the fact that, as the initial pressure of NO_2 is increased, p_i eventually lies below p_s, and so cannot be reached. The upper limit of ignition found as the total pressure of a mixture of fixed composition is increased, appears to be due to a very similar crossing of p_i and p_s curves. This is very clearly shown in *Figure 11.22* and *11.23*.

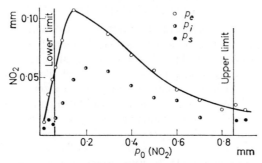

Figure 11.23. Variation of p_e, p_i and p_s with initial pressure of NO_2[70]

Below the lower limit, there again appears a stationary level of NO_2[77]. This is at first surprising, because it would be thought that the rate of the termolecular reaction would be negligible compared with that of removal of NO_2 by reaction with H_2; in the absence of oxygen this latter reaction is certainly fast. However, the oxygen slows this reaction, partly by acting as a third body in the reactions that terminate the chains in the $H_2 + NO_2$ reaction

$$OH^* + NO + O_2 \rightarrow HNO_2 + O_2$$
$$OH^* + NO_2 + O_2 \rightarrow HNO_3 + O_2$$

and partly because oxygen competes with NO_2 for hydrogen atoms

$$H^* + NO_2 \rightarrow OH^* + NO$$
$$H^* + O_2 + M \rightarrow HO_2^* + M \tag{11.8}$$

The last reaction becomes more successful as the concentration of NO_2 falls, and if followed by

$$HO_2^* + NO \rightarrow OH^* + NO_2 \tag{11.9}$$

it provides an alternative path for converting NO to NO_2, which may be the main cause of the stationary levels of NO_2 just outside the limits[77].

As the upper sensitizer limit almost certainly occurs because the necessary level of p_i falls below p_s, and as p_s occurs at almost the same absolute level below the lower limit, it is tempting to ascribe the lower limit to the same cause. This may be true in vessels of large diameter, but in those of smaller diameter the ignition region shrinks, and p_i, just inside the limits, seems to be much higher than p_s, just outside them. This effect is probably connected in some way with the behaviour of the system as NO_2 changes from p_e towards p_i. The pressure rises in *Figure 11.21* show that there is self-heating in this regime, and this has a bigger effect when p_i lies a considerable distance below p_e. If the ignitions were truly isothermal and due to branching under isothermal conditions, then the p_i, p_s condition might be sufficient; but if they are partly thermal, then the extra condition (such as p_i lying a sufficient distance below p_e) would be more severe in a vessel of small diameter.

It seems very likely that the system is isothermal, until the concentration of NO_2 falls to p_e and the net branching factor ϕ is less than zero. Any potential branching reactions, such as

$$H^* + O_2 \rightarrow HO^* + {}^*O^*$$
$$O^* + H_2 \rightarrow OH^* + H^*$$

are held in check by reactions of H^*, OH^* and $^*O^*$ with NO_2 as well as by reaction (11.8). As NO_2 is removed and NO formed, the restraints diminish, especially because reaction (11.9) becomes important. Thus ϕ moves towards zero. Analysis of a reaction scheme based on all likely reactions gives an expression for ϕ, and if it is assumed that ϕ reaches zero as p_{NO_2} reaches p_e, expressions can be derived relating p_e to variables such as the initial pressure of NO_2, the pressure of the reactants or inert gases added, and so on. These relationships are in very good agreement with the experimental findings[74].

The function of nitric oxide seems to be that of a catalyst, by reducing the termination due to reaction (11.8). Experimental support for this view comes from the use of nitric oxide itself as sensitizer and from the behaviour of other sensitizers that apparently yield nitric oxide[74]. When mixtures of hydrogen and oxygen are run into nitric oxide placed in the hot reaction vessel, ignitions occur almost instantaneously, provided the pressure of nitric oxide lies above a lower limit which is very similar in value to that with nitrogen dioxide. There may be an upper limit with nitric oxide; the full analysis of the proposed reaction scheme suggests this[77], but it is difficult to check because of the possible formation of nitrogen dioxide as the gases mix during entry. When sensitizers like nitrosyl chloride are used, the behaviour is very similar to that when NO_2 is added. There is an induction period which is shorter if the nitrosyl chloride is partially decomposed; there are sensitizer limits almost identical with those observed with NO_2; and it seems very likely that it is the same NO, NO_2 system which controls the limits[74]. Other nitrogenous gases used as sensitizers apparently behave in the same way. Chloropicrin certainly does. Recent work on the behaviour of ammonia as a sensitizer, coupled with the observation that traces of nitric oxide are formed in the thermal oxidation of ammonia, suggests that ammonia also yields nitric oxide as the effective catalyst. A difference from the other sensitizers is that the ammonia[78] is removed by oxidation rather than by reaction with hydrogen. It would be interesting to know whether a stationary level of nitrogen dioxide is reached in this system, too.

REFERENCES

[1] SEMENOV, N. N. *Some Problems of Chemical Kinetics and Reactivity* Vol. I (Trans. J. E. S. Bradley): Pergamon Press, London, 1958, pp. 85, 129, 262

[2] SEMENOV, N. N. *Some Problems of Chemical Kinetics and Reactivity* Vol. II (Trans. J. E. S. Bradley): Pergamon Press, London, 1958, p. 123 *et seq.*

[3] HAWKINS, E. G. E. *Organic Peroxides*: Spon, London, 1961

[4] WALLING, C. *Free Radicals in Solution*: Wiley, New York, 1957, Chapter 9

[5] KNOX, J. H. and NORRISH, R. G. W. *Proc. R. Soc. A* 1954, **221**, 151

[6] SHTERN, V. Y. *Zh. fiz. Khim.* 1954, **28**, 613; see Semenov[2], p. 99

REFERENCES

[7] FOK, N. V. and NALBANDJAN, A. B. *Dokl. Akad. Nauk. S.S.S.R.* 1953, **89**, 125

[8] ROBERTSON, A. and WATERS, W. A. *Trans. Faraday Soc.* 1946, **42**, 201

[9] GEORGE, P., RIDEAL, E. K. and ROBERTSON, A. *Proc. R. Soc. A* 1946, **185**, 288

[10] BONE, W. A. and HILL, S. G. *Proc. R. Soc. A* 1930, **129**, 434

[11] BONE, W. A. and GARDNER, J. B. *Proc. R. Soc. A* 1936, **154**, 297

[12] NORRISH, R. G. W. and FOORD, S. G. *Proc. R. Soc. A* 1936, **157**, 503

[13] KARMILOVA, L. V., ENIKOLOPYAN, N. S. and NALBANDYAN, A. B. *Zh. fiz. Khim.* 1957, **31**, 851

[14] ENIKOLOPYAN, N. S. *Seventh Symposium (International) on Combustion* (Ed. The Combustion Institute): Butterworth, 1959, p. 157

[15] KIRK, A. D. and KNOX, J. H. *Trans. Faraday Soc.* 1960, **56**, 1296

[16] KNOX, J. H. *Trans. Faraday Soc.* 1959, **55**, 1363

[17] SEMENOV, N. N. *Some Problems of Chemical Kinetics and Reactivity* Vol. I (Trans. J. E. S. Bradley): Pergamon Press, London, 1958, p. 95 *et seq.*

[18] LEWIS, B. and VON ELBE, G. *Combustion, Flames and Explosions of Gases*: Academic Press, New York, 1951, p. 27

[19] SEMENOV, N. N. *Some Problems of Chemical Kinetics and Reactivity* Vol. II (Trans. J. E. S. Bradley): Pergamon Press, London, 1958, pp. 27, 42

[20] LEWIS, B. and VON ELBE, G. *Combustion, Flames and Explosions of Gases*: Academic Press, New York, 1951, p. 139 *et seq.*

[21] SHU, N. W. and BARDWELL, J. *Canad. J. Chem.* 1955, **33**, 1415

[22] BOLLAND, J. L. *Quart. Rev. (Lond.)* 1949, **3**, 1

[23] BATEMAN, L. *Quart. Rev. (Lond.)* 1954, **8**, 147

[24] BAWN, C. E. H. *Disc. Faraday Soc.* 1953, **14**, 181

[25] COOPER, H. R. and MELVILLE, H. W. *J. chem. Soc.* 1951, pp. 1984, 1994

[26] VARTANYAN, L. S., MAIZUS, Z. K. and EMANUEL, N. M. *Zh. fiz. Khim.* 1956, **30**, 856, 862

[27] HAWKINS, E. G. E. *Organic Peroxides*: Spon, London, 1961, Chapter 12

[28] SEMENOV, N. N. *Some Problems of Chemical Kinetics and Reactivity* Vol. I (Trans. J. E. S. Bradley): Pergamon Press, London, 1958, p. 167

[29] BATEMAN, L., GEE, G., MORRIS, A. L. and WATSON, W. F. *Disc. Faraday Soc.* 1951, **10**, 250

[30] BATEMAN, L. and HUGHES, H. *J. chem. Soc.* 1952, p. 4594

[31] BAWN, C. E. H., PENNINGTON, A. A. and TIPPER, C. F. H. *Disc. Faraday Soc.* 1951, **10**, 282

[32] WEISS, J. *Rep. Progr. Chem.* 1947, **44**, 70
WATERS, W. A. *The Chemistry of Free Radicals*: Oxford University Press, London, 1948, p. 234

[33] TOBOLSKY, A. V., METZ, D. J. and MESROBIAN, R. B. *J. Amer. chem. Soc.* 1950, **72**, 1942

[34] BOLLAND, J. L. and GEE, G. *Trans. Faraday Soc.* 1946, **42**, 236, 244

[35] WOODWARD, A. E. and MESROBIAN, R. B. *J. Amer. chem. Soc.* 1953, **75**, 6189

[36] BROOK, J. H. T. and MATTHEWS, J. B. *Disc. Faraday Soc.* 1951, **10**, 298

[37] BOLLAND, J. L. and TEN HAVE, P. *Disc. Faraday Soc.* 1947, **2**, 252; *Trans. Faraday Soc.* 1947, **43**, 201

[38] HAMMOND, G. S. *et al.*, *J. Amer. chem. Soc.* 1954, **76**, 3861; 1955, **77**, 3233, 3238, 3380

[39] RUST, F. F. and VAUGHAN, W. E. *Industr. Engng Chem. (Industr.)* 1949, **41**, 2595

[40] NORRISH, R. G. W. *Disc. Faraday Soc.* 1951, **10**, 269

[41] HOARE, D. E. and WALSH, A. D. *Fifth (International) Symposium on Combustion*: Reinhold, New York, 1955, pp. 467, 474

[42] HOARE, D. E. and WALSH, A. D. *Proc. R. Soc. A* 1952, **215**, 454

[43] NORRISH, R. G. W. and WALLACE, J. *Proc. R. Soc. A* 1934, **145**, 307

[44] KARMILOVA, L. V., ENIKOLOPYAN, N. S. and NALBANDJAN, A. B. *Zh. fiz. Khim.* 1956, **30**, 798

[45] TOPCHIEV, A. V. *Nitration of Hydrocarbons* (Trans. C. Matthews): Pergamon Press, London, 1959, Chapter V

[46] NEUMANN, K. and SERBINOFF, A. *Zh. fiz. Khim.* 1933, **4**, 41

[47] ASHMORE, P. G.—unpublished results

[48] CHAMBERLAIN, G. H. N., HOARE, D. E. and WALSH, A. D. *Disc. Faraday Soc.* 1953, **14**, 89

[49] CHEANEY, D. E., DAVIES, D. A., DAVIS, A., HOARE, D. E., PROTHEROE, J. and WALSH, A. D. *Seventh Symposium (International) on Combustion*: Butterworth, London, 1959, p. 183

[50] HOARE, D. E., PROTHEROE, J. B. and WALSH, A. D. *Trans. Faraday Soc.* 1959, **55**, 548

[51] NEIMAN, M. B. *et al.*, *J. gen. Chem. U.S.S.R.* 1955, **25**, 1317

[52] WALSH, A. D. *Trans. Faraday Soc.* 1946, **42**, 269; 1947, **43**, 297

[53] See reference 20, p. 180

[54] See reference 20, p. 18

[55] SEMENOV, N. N. *Some Problems of Chemical Kinetics and Reactivity* Vol. II (Trans. J. E. S. Bradley): Pergamon Press, London, 1958, p. 101

[56] MALE, T. *Third Symposium on Combustion and Flame and Explosion Phenomena*: Williams & Wilkins, Baltimore, 1949, p. 721

[57] TAYLOR, C. F. *et al.*, *S.A.E. Quart. Trans.* 1950, **4**, 232

[58] Report by JOST, W. *Third Symposium on Combustion and Flame and Explosion Phenomena*: Williams & Wilkins, Baltimore, 1949, p. 424

[59] CALINGAERT, G. *Science of Petroleum* Vol. IV: Oxford University Press, London, 1938, p. 3024 *et seq.*

[60] EGERTON, A. and GATES, S. F. *J. Instn Petrol. Tech.* 1927, **13**, 284

[61] EGERTON, A. *Trans. Faraday Soc.* 1928, **24**, 697
EGERTON, A. and SMITH, F. L. *Phil. Trans. A* 1935, **234**, 507

[62] MURAOUR, H. *Chim. et Ind.* 1925, **14**, 851

[63] ERHARD, K. H. L. and NORRISH, R. G. W. *Proc. R. Soc. A* 1956, **234**, 178; 1960, **259**, 297

[64] CALLEAR, A. B. and NORRISH, R. G. W. *Proc. R. Soc. A* 1960, **259**, 304

[65] WRIGHT, P. G. *Combust. & Flame* 1961, **5**, 205

[66] KOVALSKII, A. A. *Phys. Z. Sowjet.* 1933, **4**, 723

[67] DAINTON, F. S. *Chain Reactions*: Methuen, London, 1956, p. 95

[68] SEMENOV, N. N. *Some Problems of Chemical Kinetics and Reactivity* Vol. II (Trans. J. E. S. Bradley): Pergamon Press, London, 1958, Chapter 3

[69] LEWIS, B. and VON ELBE, G. *Combustion, Flames and Explosions of Gases*: Academic Press, New York, 1951, p. 35; *Rep. Progr. Chem.* 1954, **51**, 183

[70] LEVY, A. *Fifth Symposium (International) on Combustion*: Reinhold, New York, 1955, p. 495

[71] BALDWIN, R. R., CORNEY, N. S. and SIMMONS, R. F. *Fifth Symposium (International) on Combustion*: Reinhold, New York, 1955, p. 502

[72] BALDWIN, R. R., CORNEY, N. S. and WALKER, R. W. *Trans. Faraday Soc.* 1960, **56**, 802

[73] DAINTON, F. S. and NORRISH, R. G. W. *Proc. R. Soc. A* 1941, **177**, 393, 411, 421

[74] ASHMORE, P. G. *Trans. Faraday Soc.* 1955, **51**, 1090

[75] ASHMORE, P. G. and LEVITT, B. P. *Advanc. Catalys.* 1957, **9**, 367

[76] ASHMORE, P. G. and LEVITT, B. P. *Seventh Symposium (International) on Combustion* (Ed. The Combustion Institute): Butterworth, London, 1959, p. 45

[77] TYLER, B. J. Thesis, University of Cambridge, 1961

[78] WALSH, A. D.—private communication

APPENDIX I: DERIVATION OF ADSORPTION ISOTHERMS FOR UNIFORM SURFACES

THE SIMPLEST derivation[1] of an isotherm which describes the adsorption of gas molecules on a set of uniform adsorption sites is based on the kinetic treatment of adsorption outlined in section 6.6. If the adsorption reaches a dynamic equilibrium, with a fraction θ_e of the sites occupied (or of the surface covered), it follows from equation (6.2) that:

$$\frac{\theta_{eq}}{1-\theta_{eq}} = \frac{\alpha p}{\beta(2\pi mkT)^{1/2}} \tag{A.I.1}$$

If α (the probability of sticking on the *bare* surface) and β ($\beta\theta$ is the rate of desorption) are assumed to be independent of θ, the coefficient of p in equation (A.I.1) is constant at constant temperature and so

$$\frac{\theta_{eq}}{1-\theta_{eq}} = Bp \quad \text{or} \quad \theta_{eq} = \frac{Bp}{1+Bp} \tag{A.I.2}$$

This is the simplest form of the Langmuir adsorption isotherm.

However, as shown in the later sections of Chapter 6, the measured rate of adsorption of gases does not fall off in proportion to $(1-\theta)$ as the surface fills up.

Fortunately, the equilibrium conditions can be derived by statistical mechanics, independently of the molecular mechanism of the adsorption. This method is able to take into account variations in the properties of the gas and the surface species and is potentially very powerful.

Let the system to be studied be regarded[2,3] as a gas G that can be adsorbed on a surface S to give the adsorbed species GS:

$$G+S \rightleftharpoons GS$$

This reaction will have an equilibrium constant $K = c_a/c_g c_s$ where c_g is the concentration of the gas molecules, c_s that of the vacant sites and c_a that of the occupied sites GS. If the whole surface has N_s identical sites available for adsorption, at equilibrium N_{eq} of these are occupied and the area of the surface is S cm^2, then

$$c_a = N_{eq}/S, \quad c_s = (N_s-N_{eq})/S \tag{A.I.3}$$

The equilibrium constant can also be evaluated[2,3] in terms of the partition functions of the reactants and products and the standard energy change of the reaction at absolute zero, ΔE_0°. For a reaction in the gas phase represented by the equation aA $\rightleftharpoons$ bB the equilibrium constant is

$$K = \frac{(f_B/V)^b}{(f_A/V)^a} e^{-\Delta E_0^\circ/RT} \tag{A.I.4}$$

In this expression, ΔE_0° is the internal energy change of the reaction at absolute zero, with reactants and products in the standard state of one molecule per cubic centimetre, V is the volume of the system (in cubic centimetres), and f_A, f_B are the total partition functions of one molecule of A and of B, respectively, in the volume V. K is in terms of concentrations of molecules per cubic centimetre.

Each partition function represents the number of energy states available to that molecule at temperature T relative to the number available at absolute zero, while the factor $e^{-\Delta E_0^\circ/RT}$ represents the ratio of states available to products and reactants at absolute zero. The total amount of matter present divides itself between products and reactants at equilibrium according to the number of states available.

Each total partition function is the product of several partition functions representing the number of states available for translational, rotational, vibrational and electronic energy. For most reactions at moderate temperatures, there is only one electronic state, and $f_{el} = 1$. The other partition functions depend upon the temperature T, the mass m of the molecule, the moments of inertia I_1, I_2, I_3 about the three axes, and the vibrations ν_1, ν_2, ν_3 of the

Table A.I.1. Partition functions

	In one dimension, length L:	In two dimensions, area A:	In three dimensions, volume V:
Translation	$\dfrac{(2\pi mkT)^{1/2}L}{h}$	$\dfrac{(2\pi mkT)A}{h^2}$	$\dfrac{(2\pi mkT)^{3/2}V}{h^3}$
Rotation	For an atom: 1	For a linear molecule: $\dfrac{8\pi^2 IkT}{h^2}$	For a non-linear molecule: $\dfrac{8\pi^2(8\pi^3 I_1 I_2 I_3)^{1/2}(kT)^{3/2}}{h^3}$
Vibration	For an atom: 1	For each vibration of frequency ν: $(1-e^{-h\nu/kT})^{-1}$	

molecule, and upon the fundamental constants k (Boltzmann) and h (Planck). The expressions for these partition functions are listed in Table A.I.1.

Generally speaking, the translational partition functions are very large, about 10^8 for a hydrogen atom in one dimension of 1 cm length. The rotational partition functions are much smaller, and the vibrational partition functions are close to unity unless the temperature is very high or the vibration very weak.

For the surface reaction equilibrium, in terms of partition functions

$$K = \frac{c_a}{c_g c_s} = \frac{f_{GS}}{(f/_G V) f_S} e^{-\Delta E_0^\circ/RT} \qquad (\text{A.I.5})$$

The standard states of the surface species are 1 molecule cm^{-2}. Considering first a monatomic gas and its reaction with the surface to give a firmly adsorbed species, $f_G = (2\pi mkT)^{3/2}V/h^3$ and f_{GS} and f_S can be taken as unity. Substituting these values, and also the values of c_s and c_a, from (A.I.3), equation (A.I.5) becomes

$$\frac{N_{eq}}{c_g(N_s - N_{eq})} = \frac{h^3 e^{-\Delta E_0^\circ/RT}}{(2\pi mkT)^{3/2}} \qquad (\text{A.I.6})$$

At a constant temperature, the expression on the right of this equation is constant, and c_g, equal to p/kT, is proportional to p. Therefore

$$\frac{N_{eq}}{N_s - N_{eq}} = (\text{constant}) \times p \qquad (\text{A.I.7})$$

But N_{eq}/N_S is equal to θ, the fraction of the surface covered at equilibrium

$$\therefore \theta = Bp/1+Bp \tag{A.I.8}$$

The constant B is given by $h^3 e^{-\Delta E_0^\circ/RT}/(2\pi m)^{3/2}(kT)^{5/2}$. The value of $(-\Delta E_0^\circ)$ cannot be evaluated exactly, and so it is usually put equal to q_0, the heat evolved upon adsorption on a nearly empty surface. Equation (A.I.8) is of the same form as equation (A.I.3).

The isotherm for the adsorption of a polyatomic gas on the surface, with one molecule per site, has precisely the same form as equation (A.I.8) but the constant B contains an additional factor f'_{GS}/f'_G. f'_G is the internal partition function of the gas, representing the rotational and vibrational states; f'_{GS} similarly represents the vibrations of the adsorbed species and any possible rotations about the bond connecting the molecule to the surface.

If the adsorbed gas has complete freedom in the surface, it can be looked upon as a two-dimensional gas, and the equilibrium is therefore between a two- and a three-dimensional gas, the surface not being regarded as a reactant. This treatment leads to an equation for the fraction θ of surface covered

$$\theta = p \frac{h}{(2\pi m)^{1/2}(kT)^{3/2}} \frac{f'_{GS}}{f'_G N'_S} e^{q/RT} \tag{A.I.9}$$

where f'_G and f'_{GS} are the *internal* partition functions of the molecule in the gas and on the surface, respectively, and N'_S is the maximum number of molecules which can be adsorbed on 1 cm² of the surface, either because the number of sites is limited or because of the packing of the adsorbed molecules on the surface. Such a mechanism of adsorption suggests one explanation for constant 'sticking factors', although there are others.

If a diatomic molecule is dissociated into atoms upon adsorption, or a polyatomic molecule into two radicals, and the adsorption is strongly localized, the equation becomes

$$\frac{\theta}{1-\theta} = p^{1/2} \frac{h^{3/2}}{(2\pi m)^{3/4}(kT)^{5/4}} \frac{f'_{GS}}{f'^{1/2}_G} e^{q/ET} \tag{A.I.10}$$

where m is the mass of the molecule and f'_G, f'_{GS} have the same significance as before.

In summary, the statistical mechanical and the kinetic treatments lead to equations of the same form, with more explicit expression for the constants of the equations in the former treatment.

REFERENCES

[1] LANGMUIR, I. *J. Amer. chem. Soc.* 1918, **40**, 1361
[2] TRAPNELL, B. M. W. *Chemisorption*: Butterworth, London, 1955, Chapter 5
[3] LAIDLER, K. J. *Catalysis* (Ed. P. H. Emmett) Vol. I: Reinhold, New York, 1954, Chapter 3

APPENDIX II: DEVIATION OF ADSORPTION ISOTHERMS FOR NON-UNIFORM SURFACES

LANGMUIR[1] suggested that most surfaces should be regarded as a collection of groups of sites with the activity (heat of adsorption, and so on) constant within each group but different from group to group. Within each group, with sites of type i, the fraction of sites occupied for an adsorption with one molecule per site is

$$\theta_i = B_i p / 1 + B_i p \tag{A.II.1}$$

The fraction of the whole surface covered at equilibrium is obtained by a suitable summation over all values of i. If there are N_i sites of type i among a total N_s, then

$$\theta = \sum N_i \theta_i / \sum N_i \tag{A.II.2}$$

Later treatments have developed from this suggestion, replacing the summations by integrations after assuming some plausible distribution of sites with energy. Thus the site group is to be identified by its heat of adsorption, q, and

$$\theta_q = \frac{1 + B_q p}{B_q p} = \frac{B_0 p e^{q/RT}}{1 + B_0 p e^{q/RT}}$$

and the fraction of surface covered is (with suitable limits for q)

$$\theta = \frac{\int \theta_q N_q dq}{\int N_q dq} \tag{A.II.3}$$

Various attempts have been made to establish the form of the expression for N_q from the isotherms found empirically, but the problem is formidable. More success has come by using distributions which give plausible fits for the q versus θ curves, and at the same time permit the integration of equation (A.II.3). Two of these distributions lead to useful isotherms.

Zeldovitch[2] suggested that a Boltzmann distribution of the sites, of the form $N_q = N_0 e^{-q/q_m}$, might be suitable. The heat of adsorption then depends logarithmically upon the coverage, and some experimental heats approximate to this except when θ approaches zero or unity. With this distribution, equation (A.II.3) can be integrated to give

$$\theta = C p^{RT/q_m} \tag{A.II.4}$$

where C is independent of θ and p. This is of the same form as the empirical Freundlich isotherm, $\theta = C' p^{1/n}$, where C' and n are constants for a particular system. The equation has the disadvantage of predicting continued adsorption as the pressure increases, although the theoretical equation is not valid under these circumstances. An empirical generalized equation which overcomes this difficulty

$$= \theta \, (p/C'' + p)^{1/n} \tag{A.II.5}$$

has been used[3,4]. The Freundlich isotherm holds for dissociative adsorption as well as for molecular adsorption. It appears to hold for the chemisorption of hydrogen on tungsten powder at high pressures, and the heat of adsorption varies with θ in the expected (logarithmic) manner[5].

The heat of adsorption often falls nearly linearly as the coverage increases, especially at low and medium coverages. Temkin and Pyzhev[6] showed that a linear fall, associated with a constant fraction of sites for each value of q, leads to the isotherm

$$\theta = \frac{RT}{\alpha} \ln B'p \qquad \text{(A.II.6)}$$

where α is the slope of the q versus θ plot and B' is independent of θ and p. The adsorption of nitrogen on iron films[7] and on promoted iron catalysts[8] often follows this equation.

REFERENCES

[1] LANGMUIR, I. *J. Amer. chem. Soc.* 1918, **40**, 1361
[2] ZELDOVITCH, J. *Acta phys.-chim. URSS* 1934, **1**, 961
[3] SIPS, R. *J. chem. Phys.* 1950, **18**, 1024
[4] TOMPKINS, F. C. *Trans. Faraday Soc.* 1950, **46**, 569
[5] FRANKENBURG, W. G. *J. Amer. chem. Soc.* 1944, **66**, 1827, 1838
[6] TEMKIN, M. and PYZHEV, V. *Acta phys.-chim. URSS* 1940, **12**, 327
[7] PORTER, A. S. and TOMPKINS, F. C. *Proc. R. Soc. A* 1953, **217**, 544
[8] BRUNAUER, S., LOVE, K. S. and KEENAN, R. G. *J. Amer. chem. Soc.* 1942, **64**, 751

INDEX

Italicized page numbers indicate that the subject is referred to on subsequent pages.

369

INDEX

Silver
  ions, 60–1, 64
  metal, in
    exchange reactions, 19, 108, 186, 199
    films, 136, 242
    oxidations, 175, 193, 238, *242*
  salts, 8, 108
Single crystals, 130, 132, 242
Sites for adsorptions (see Adsorption sites)
Specific
  acid catalysis, 27–8, 44
  base catalysis, 27–8, 42
Specificity of
  crystal faces, 130, 132, *134*
  enzymes, 74
Stabilizers, 289
Stannic chloride, as catalyst, 313, *317*
Stationary states,
  attainment, 68, 71, 263
  of
    chain centres, 17, *259*
    intermediates, 13, 68, 80
Stereoregular polymers, *321*
Sticking coefficients, 153, 155, 160
Sucrase, 77
Sulphides, inhibition by, 189, 192, 236
Sulphur dioxide, oxidation, 11, *235*
Surface of catalysts,
  area, 114, *116*
  heterogeneity, 148–9, 165, 240
  sites on, 129, *139*, 149–50, 165
  structure, with promoters, 212, *216*
Synthesis of
  alcohols, *220*
  ammonia, *210*
  methanol, *227*

Tantalum, chemisorptions on, *146*
Temkin–Pyzhev mechanisms, 112, 176, *213*

Termination, linear and mutual, 17, 259
Thermal decompositions (see Decompositions)
Thoria, 108, 141, 221
Titanium
  catalysts, *321*
  oxide, 107, 120, 221, 232
Transfer, chain, 258, *295*
Transition state, in chemisorption, *155, 180*
Trypsin, 83
Tungsten,
  chemisorptions on, 130, 143, *146*, 150–1, 197
  decomposition over, 177–8, 218
  in hydrogenations, 20, 107, 191, 197, *200*
Turnover number, 9, 75, 97

Uniform surfaces, *130*
  and adsorption, 152, 363
Urease, 75–7, 96, 98

Vanadium pentoxide, 108, *235, 241*

Wall effects, in chain reactions, 261, 266, 272, 276, 281, 347, 349, 353–6
Water
  as cocatalyst, 9, *317*
  inhibition by, 192, 212, 238

Ziegler catalysts, 6, *321*
Zinc oxide, 107, 149, 197
  chemisorption on, 128, 140, 146, 162–3
  methanol synthesis, *228*

MADE AND PRINTED IN GREAT BRITAIN BY WILLIAM CLOWES AND SONS, LIMITED
LONDON AND BECCLES